BOOK 1

HELEN R. PEARSON ▪ ANN G. DUFFY ▪ JOHN M. McCAFFERY

GINN AND COMPANY

DESIGN AND PRODUCTION COORDINATION
Dimensions & Directions, Ltd.

PHOTO RESEARCH Helena Frost

COVER ILLUSTRATION John Martucci Studios

TECHNICAL ILLUSTRATION Vantage Art, Inc.

CALCULATOR FEATURES David Turinese

CAREER FEATURES William H. Chernik

PHOTOGRAPHERS
x—Joel Gordon; 26, 74—Michal Heron; 124—Joan Ruggles; 135—J. R. Holland/Stock Boston; 152—Herb Randle; 190—Joan Menschenfreund; 232—Jim Anderson/Woodfin Camp & Assoc.; 249—Helena Frost; 272—Sybil Hackman/Monkmeyer Photo; 312—Bohdan Hrynewych/Stock Boston; 333—John Colwell/Grant Heilman; 358—Leif Skoogfors/Woodfin Camp & Assoc.; 381, 390—Michal Heron; 403, 446—Timothy Eagan/Woodfin Camp & Assoc.; 472—John Colwell/Grant Heilman; 496—Lou Jones/Image Specialists; 505—Joel Gordon; 524—Owen Franken/Stock Boston.

Home Office: Lexington, Massachusetts 02173
0-663-41935-2

Contents

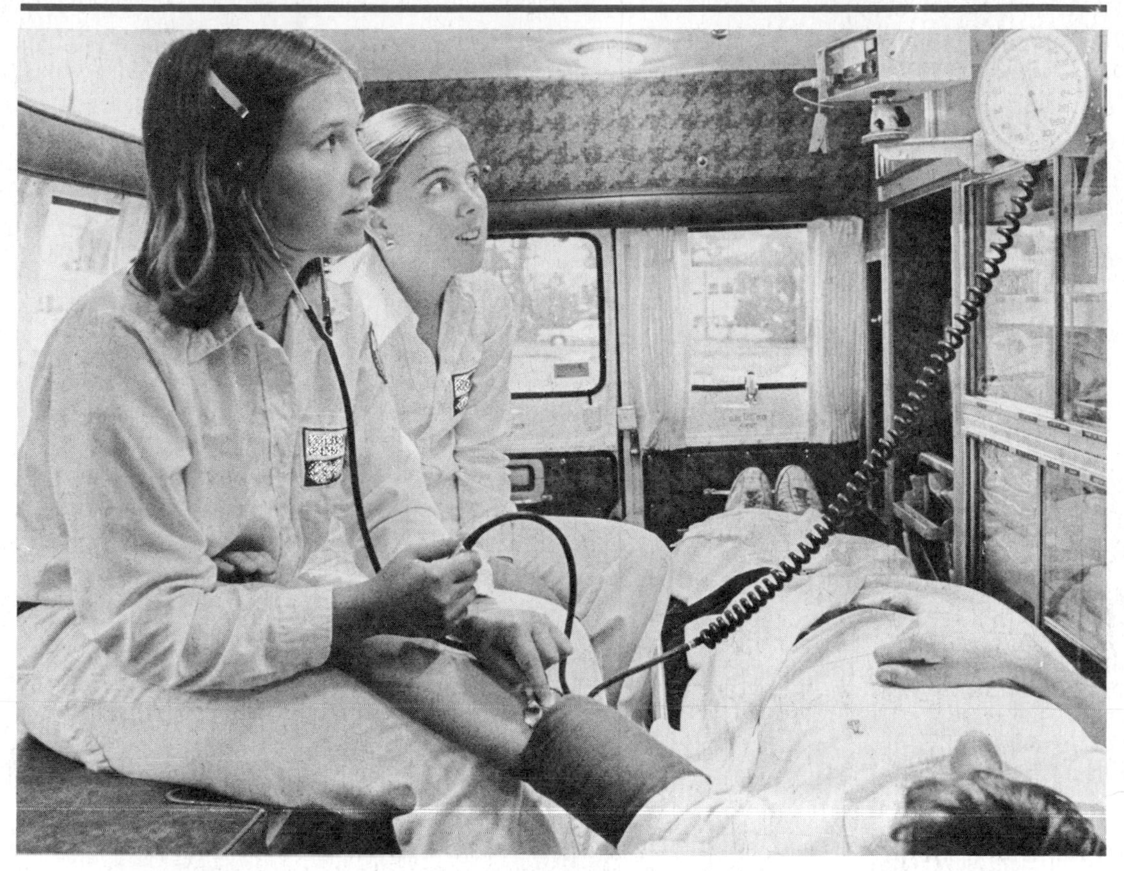

CHAPTER 2 ■ POSITIVE AND NEGATIVE NUMBERS 26

CHAPTER 3 ■ EQUATIONS AND INEQUALITIES 74

CHAPTER 4 ■ SPECIAL EQUATIONS CALLED FORMULAS 124

TO THE STUDENT

Our hope is that you may enjoy your study of algebra and attain a high degree of proficiency in the subject. To this end we offer the following suggestions:

1. Always have pencil and paper at hand when studying your lesson.
2. Have a definite time each day to study your algebra. Learn to concentrate on your assignment. Do not permit anything to distract you. Allow one hour for the preparation of each algebra assignment, even though you often may do it in less time.
3. Read the subject matter carefully. Be sure that you understand each sentence. Use the glossary or index in the back of the book, or look in a dictionary, for the meanings of any words you do not understand. If, however, you are unable to understand any part of your assignment, form a definite question about it and ask your teacher for an explanation.
4. Before you attempt to solve a set of exercises, study the examples that precede the exercises. While studying, use your pencil and paper to follow each step of the solution. After you have studied the solution, test your understanding of the example by solving it independently.
5. When working an exercise or solving a problem, work carefully. Make drawings for your problems whenever possible; they will aid you in your thinking. Form the habit of checking both your work and the reasonableness of your answers.
6. Form the habit of reviewing previous work to be sure that you are retaining the subject matter.

CHAPTER 1
Introduction To Algebra

What's your life like today? What will you be doing ten years from now? Who knows? Maybe you will be an artist, a farmer, a child-care worker, or an engineer. Women and men now can choose from many interesting careers. Whatever you choose, one thing is certain, it probably will involve mathematics. Therefore, it makes sense to prepare yourself with as much mathematics as you can.

OBJECTIVES: Define terms and identify symbols basic to algebra. Graph sets of numbers. Evaluate algebraic expressions.

1-1 NUMBERS AND THEIR GRAPHS

Each point of a line may be matched with a number. A line for which this has been done, as pictured here, is the **number line**.

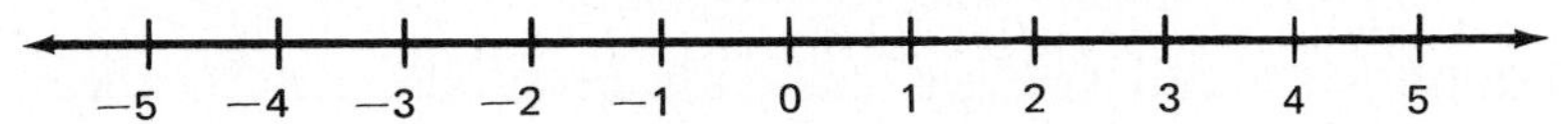

A point of the line is the **graph** of its matching number. A number is the **coordinate** of its matching point. When you draw the points for numbers, you *graph the numbers*. When you graph the numbers in a set, you *graph the set*.

EXAMPLE 1 Graph the **counting numbers**, 1, 2, 3, and so on.

Ⓜ SOLUTION

−2 −1 0 1 2 3 4 5

The arrowhead in color indicates that the graph continues in the pattern shown.

The counting numbers are are known as the natural numbers.

By including 0 with the counting numbers, we have the **whole numbers**, 0, 1, 2, 3, and so on. By also including a particular negative number for each counting number, we have the numbers known as the **integers**.

Zero is neither positive nor negative.

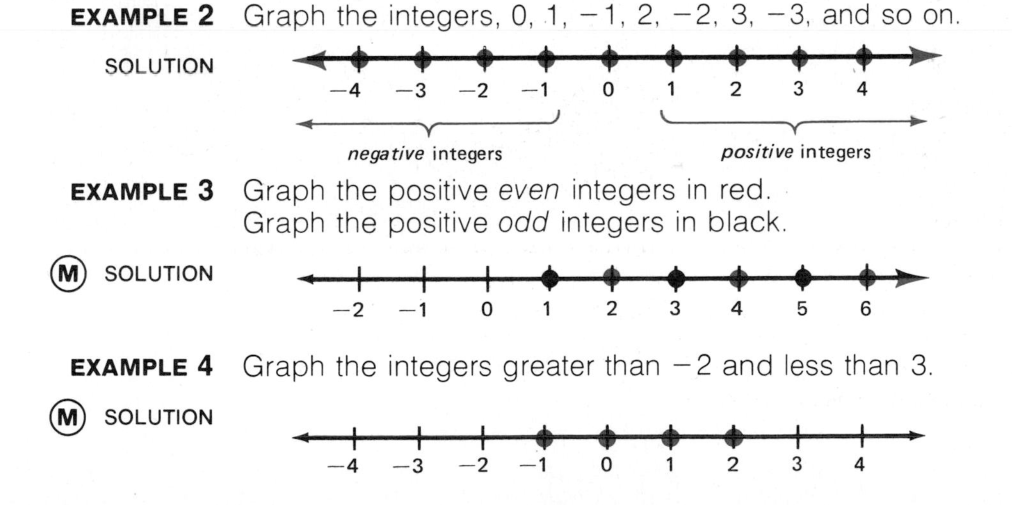

EXAMPLE 2 Graph the integers, 0, 1, −1, 2, −2, 3, −3, and so on.

SOLUTION

EXAMPLE 3 Graph the positive *even* integers in red. Graph the positive *odd* integers in black.

Ⓜ SOLUTION

An *even* integer is an integral multiple of 2. The *odd* integers are the other integers.

EXAMPLE 4 Graph the integers greater than −2 and less than 3.

Ⓜ SOLUTION

There are many ways to name a number. At times we shall refer to the *standard name*, meaning the name that seems to be most commonly used. If the names for a number include one having the form $\frac{a}{b}$ for which a and b are integers and b is not zero, the number is a **rational number**. The integers themselves are rational numbers since any integer, j, may also be named $\frac{j}{1}$.

EXAMPLE 5 Graph the rational numbers $-2\frac{3}{4}$, -1, 0, 2.4, and 4. Show each in $\frac{a}{b}$ form.

Ⓜ SOLUTION

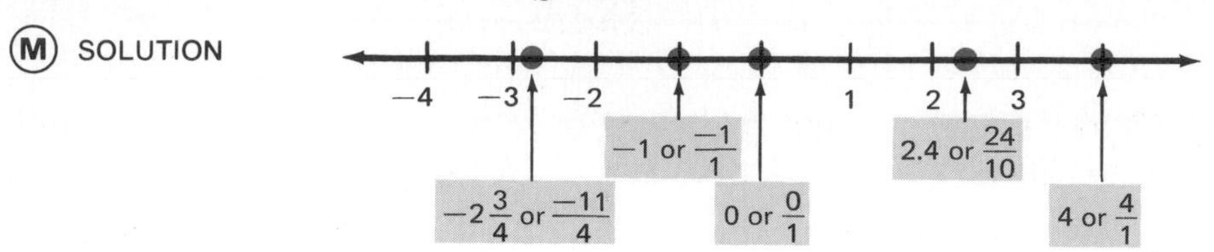

The numbers that match all the points of the number line are the **real numbers**. Here is the graph of the real numbers.

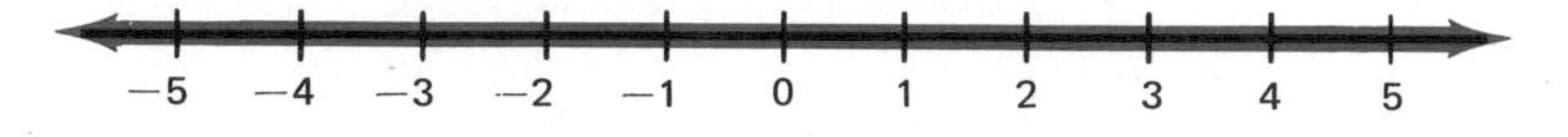

The real numbers greater than zero are the **positive real numbers**. Those less than zero are the **negative real numbers**.

EXAMPLE 6 Graph the positive real numbers.

Ⓜ SOLUTION

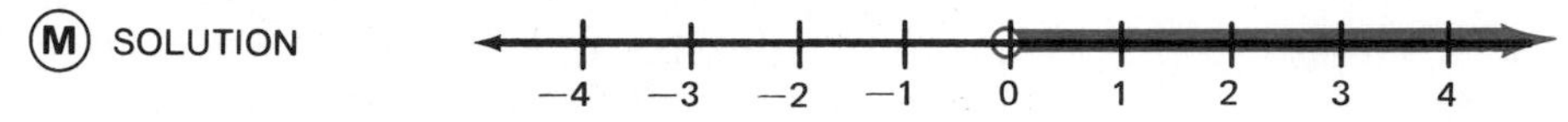

The ○ in Example 6 shows that the graph does not include the point for zero. Zero is neither a positive nor a negative real number. By filling in the ○ to include the point for zero, the graph would represent the *non-negative* real numbers.

EXAMPLE 7 Graph the real numbers greater than -2 and less than or equal to $3\frac{1}{2}$.

Ⓜ SOLUTION

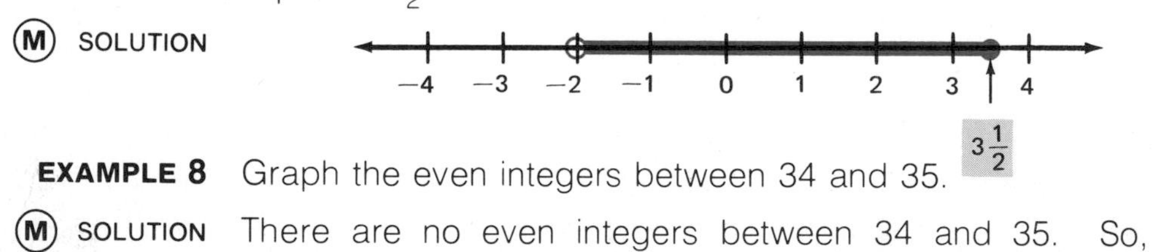

EXAMPLE 8 Graph the even integers between 34 and 35.

Ⓜ SOLUTION There are no even integers between 34 and 35. So, there are no points to show.

CLASSROOM EXERCISES

Graph these numbers. Use the number line.

1. 1, 3, 5, 7, and 9
2. -1, 0, and 1
3. -1.5, 0, and 3.7
4. even whole numbers
5. negative integers greater than -5
6. odd counting numbers less than 10
7. real numbers less than 1
8. positive integers
9. real numbers greater than -7

EXERCISES

A Graph these numbers. Use the number line.

1. 3, 6, 9, and 12
2. 0, 4, 9, and 15
3. whole numbers greater than 3
4. whole numbers greater than 4
5. negative integers greater than -10
6. negative integers less than 12
7. real numbers less than 2
8. real numbers greater than -1
9. -8, $-6\frac{1}{2}$, $-1\frac{3}{4}$, $\frac{1}{2}$, and 5
10. $-5\frac{3}{4}$, -3, $-1\frac{1}{2}$, 2, and $3\frac{3}{4}$
11. non-negative integers
12. non-positive integers
13. real numbers greater than 2 and less than 7
14. real numbers greater than -9 and less than -3
15. integers greater than or equal to -10 and less than -4
16. integers less than or equal to 12 and greater than 6

B

17. integers greater than or equal to -4 and less than or equal to 2
18. integers less than or equal to 8 and greater than or equal to -1
19. whole numbers greater than or equal to 3 and less than or equal to 12
20. whole numbers less than or equal to 8 and greater than or equal to 1
21. real numbers greater than or equal to $-5\frac{1}{2}$ and less than or equal to $3\frac{1}{4}$
22. integers greater than -6 and less than or equal to $-4\frac{1}{3}$
23. real numbers less than $2\frac{3}{4}$ and greater than or equal to $-1\frac{3}{4}$
24. integers less than or equal to -1 or greater than or equal to 2

C

25. integers greater than -2 or greater than 5
26. integers greater than -2 and greater than 5
27. real numbers greater than -5 and greater than or equal to -1
28. real numbers less than or equal to -4 or less than 2
29. integers less than or equal to 6 or greater than or equal to -3
30. integers greater than 7 and less than -4
31. real numbers greater than $4\frac{1}{2}$ or less than $4\frac{1}{2}$
32. rational numbers between 1 and 5

1-2 INDICATING OPERATIONS; VARIABLES, TERMS, AND EXPRESSIONS

A **variable**, usually a letter, is a symbol for a number. The **domain of a variable** is the set of numbers that are permitted to replace the variable.

A **term** is a numeral, a variable, or an indicated product or quotient involving numerals and variables. An **algebraic expression** is a numeral, a variable, a term, or a combination of these formed with the operation symbols so that the replacement of each variable by a member of its domain gives the name of a real number.

In a term involving a numeral and some variables, the numeral conventionally is shown first.

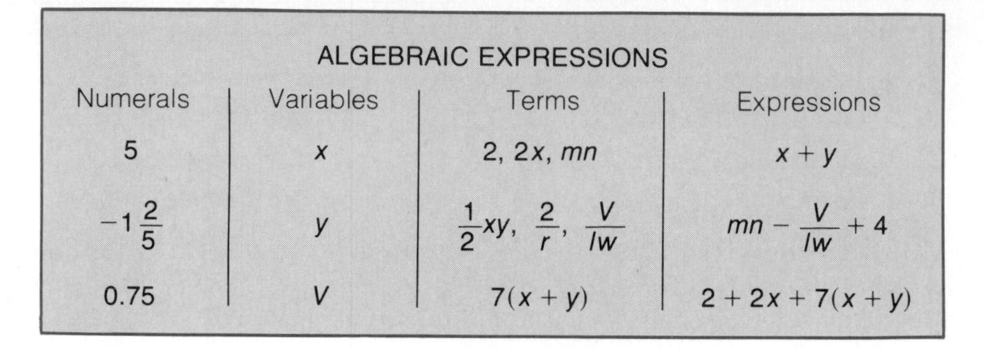

ALGEBRAIC EXPRESSIONS

Numerals	Variables	Terms	Expressions
5	x	$2,\ 2x,\ mn$	$x + y$
$-1\frac{2}{5}$	y	$\frac{1}{2}xy,\ \frac{2}{r},\ \frac{V}{lw}$	$mn - \frac{V}{lw} + 4$
0.75	V	$7(x + y)$	$2 + 2x + 7(x + y)$

The equals symbol, =, is used to show that two expressions name the same number.

EXAMPLE 1 Simplify the arithmetic expression $(22 - 7) + 6$.

(M) SOLUTION
$$(22 - 7) + 6 = 15 + 6$$
$$= 21$$

To *evaluate* an algebraic expression for a particular number for a variable, we replace the variable by that number. It is good practice to find the standard name for the real number that results.

EXAMPLE 2 Evaluate $3 + x$ for $x = 2$; for $x = 1.5$.

(M) SOLUTION

For $x = 2$,
$$3 + x = 3 + 2$$
$$= 5$$

For $x = 1.5$,
$$3 + x = 3 + 1.5$$
$$= 4.5$$

A raised dot between two terms indicates multiplication. Writing two terms next to each other can also indicate multiplication. However, parentheses sometimes are needed to avoid confusion.

INDICATING MULTIPLICATION				
$4 \times m$	$4 \cdot m$	$(4)(m)$	$4(m)$	$4m$
$x \times y$	$x \cdot y$	$(x)(y)$	$x(y)$	xy
3×6	$3 \cdot 6$	$(3)(6)$	$3(6)$	*not* 36
$7 \times (a + b)$	$7 \cdot (a + b)$	$(7)(a + b)$	$7(a + b)$	*not* $7a + b$

Parentheses in an expression also indicate that the operations enclosed are to be done first.

EXAMPLE 3 Evaluate $(5 \cdot n) + 7$ for $n = 4$; for $n = \frac{2}{5}$.

Ⓜ SOLUTION For $n = 4$,

$$\begin{aligned}(5 \cdot n) + 7 &= (5 \cdot 4) + 7\\ &= 20 + 7\\ &= 27\end{aligned}$$

For $n = \frac{2}{5}$,

$$\begin{aligned}(5 \cdot n) + 7 &= \left(5 \cdot \tfrac{2}{5}\right) + 7\\ &= 2 + 7\\ &= 9\end{aligned}$$

EXAMPLE 4 Evaluate $(3a) + (2b) + (4c)$ for $a = 2$, $b = 5$, and $c = \frac{3}{4}$.

Ⓜ SOLUTION

$$\begin{aligned}(3a) + (2b) + (4c) &= (3 \cdot 2) + (2 \cdot 5) + \left(4 \cdot \tfrac{3}{4}\right)\\ &= 6 + 10 + 3\\ &= 19\end{aligned}$$

The symbols $\div$, $\overline{)}$, and the fraction bar, —, can be used to indicate division.

INDICATING DIVISION		
$3 \div 4$	$4\overline{)3}$	$\frac{3}{4}$
$x \div y$	$y\overline{)x}$	$\frac{x}{y}$
$(s + t) \div r$	$r\overline{)s + t}$	$\frac{s + t}{r}$
$r \div (s + t)$	$(s + t)\overline{)r}$	$\frac{r}{s + t}$

Note that the fraction bar also may be used as a grouping symbol.

EXAMPLE 5 Evaluate $\frac{r}{s + t}$ for $r = 6$, $s = 1$, and $t = 0.5$.

Ⓜ SOLUTION

$$\begin{aligned}\frac{r}{s + t} &= \frac{6}{1 + 0.5}\\ &= \frac{6}{1.5}, \text{ or } 4\end{aligned}$$

EVALUATING AN ALGEBRAIC EXPRESSION

1. Replace each variable by a given number.
2. Perform the operations shown between parentheses first.
3. Perform the remaining operations.

CLASSROOM EXERCISES

Simplify.

1. $3 + (7 - 5)$ **2.** $(3 + 7) - 5$ **3.** $(19 - 8) + 6$ **4.** $8(6) - 4$

5. $8(6 - 4)$ **6.** $(8 \cdot 7) + (2 \cdot 5)$ **7.** $4 \div (4 + 2)$ **8.** $\frac{6 + 2}{4}$

Evaluate for $a = 7$, $b = 4$, $c = 2$, and $d = 0$.

9. $a - b$ **10.** $\frac{b + 6}{c}$ **11.** $a \cdot b$ **12.** $(4c) + (3d)$

EXERCISES

A Simplify.

1. $(4 \cdot 8) \cdot 2$ **2.** $4 \cdot (8 \cdot 2)$ **3.** $(2 + 3) + 7$ **4.** $2 + (3 + 7)$

5. $4 \cdot (5 + 7)$ **6.** $(4 \cdot 5) + 7$ **7.** $(8 - 4) - 3$ **8.** $8 - (4 - 3)$

9. $(24 \div 2) \div 3$ **10.** $(24 \div 3) \div 2$ **11.** $9 + (6 - 3)$ **12.** $(9 - 6) + 3$

13. $(14 + 6) \div 8$ **14.** $14 + (6 \div 8)$ **15.** $\frac{10 + 5}{5}$ **16.** $\frac{10}{5 + 5}$

17. $3.2(4.8 - 2.4)$ **18.** $(3.2)(4.8) - (3.2)(2.4)$ **19.** $\left(\frac{3}{4} + \frac{2}{3}\right) + \frac{5}{6}$ **20.** $\frac{3}{4} + \left(\frac{2}{3} + \frac{5}{6}\right)$

Evaluate for $s = 5$, $n = 3$, $r = 0$, $x = 6$, and $t = 9$.

21. $s - 2$ **22.** $x + s$ **23.** $(t + n) - r$ **24.** $t + (n - r)$ **25.** $(3r) + (2s)$

26. $(5x) + (9t)$ **27.** $(6r) + (6t)$ **28.** $(4n) + (sn)$ **29.** $x(n + t)$ **30.** $(xn) + (xt)$

31. $\frac{n + s}{t}$ **32.** $\frac{s}{x - n}$ **33.** $\frac{x \cdot n}{s}$ **34.** $\frac{r \cdot s}{x}$ **35.** $\frac{s + t}{2x}$

B **36.** $(x + n)(s + t)$ **37.** $x + (n(s + t))$ **38.** $(r + s)(t \div n)$ **39.** $((r + s)t) \div n$

40. $\frac{1}{x} + \frac{1}{n}$ **41.** $\frac{1}{x} \cdot \frac{1}{n}$ **42.** $\frac{1}{t} \div \frac{1}{s}$ **43.** $\frac{x}{4} - \frac{t}{x}$

C Evaluate for $x = 8$, $y = 6$, and $z = 4$.

44. $\left(\frac{x + y}{z} \div \frac{y + z}{x}\right) \div \frac{x + z}{y}$ **45.** $\frac{3x - 2y}{4z} \div \frac{5y - 2x}{3z}$ **46.** $\frac{4x + 7z}{5y - 3} \div \frac{6y - 3x}{8z - 2}$

1-3 FACTORS, COEFFICIENTS, AND EXPONENTS

When multiplication is indicated in a term, each constant or variable involved is a **factor** of the product.

$3 \cdot 2$ (factors: 3, 2) $\qquad 3 \cdot a$ (factors: 3, a) $\qquad ab$ (factors: a, b) $\qquad 7 \cdot x \cdot y$ (factors: 7, x, y)

Any factor of a product is the **coefficient** of the other factor or factors. Frequently, as is done in this book, the word *coefficient* is used to mean only the constant coefficient when a constant occurs with variables.

$3 \cdot a$: 3 is the coefficient of a; a is the coefficient of 3.
$(p \cdot q) \cdot r$: $(p \cdot q)$ is the coefficient of r; r is the coefficient of $p \cdot q$.
$9rs$: 9 is the constant coefficient.
$a = 1a$: 1 is the coefficient of a.

For a variable a, the constant coefficient is understood to be 1.

When a product has two or more equal factors, we may represent the product using an **exponent**—a number that tells how many times the factor, called the **base**, occurs in the product.

$7 \cdot 7 = 7^2$ (exponent 2, base 7) $\qquad a \cdot a \cdot a = a^3$ (exponent 3, base a) $\qquad \underbrace{xxx \cdots x}_{n \text{ factors}} = x^n$ (exponent n, base x)

$ayyy = ay^3 \qquad (a+b)(a+b) = (a+b)^2 \qquad ayayay = (ay)^3$, or a^3y^3

The number represented by a base and exponent is a **power** of the base. We use the base and exponent to name the power.

There is a distinction between *exponent* and *power*. Do not say "2 is the power of 5" for 5^2. The exponent merely indicates the number of factors. 2 is the exponent. 25 is the second power of 5.

> x or x^1 is the first power of x.
> 6^2 or 36 is the second power of 6.
> $(y+7)^5$ is the fifth power of $y+7$.

The *second power* of a number (the base) also is called the **square** of the number. The *first power* of any number is the number itself.

EXAMPLE 1 Find the standard name for 2^3; for 3^2; for $(3 \cdot 4)^2$.

SOLUTION

$$2^3 = 2 \cdot 2 \cdot 2 = 8 \qquad 3^2 = 3 \cdot 3 = 9 \qquad (3 \cdot 4)^2 = (12)^2 = 12 \cdot 12 = 144$$

EXAMPLE 2 Evaluate $7x^3$ for $x = 2$.

SOLUTION
$$7x^3 = 7 \cdot 2^3$$
$$= 7 \cdot 8$$
$$= 56$$

EXAMPLE 3 Find the fourth power of 3.

SOLUTION
$$3^4 = 3 \cdot 3 \cdot 3 \cdot 3$$
$$= 81$$

EXAMPLE 4 Find the square of $\frac{1}{2}$.

SOLUTION
$$\left(\frac{1}{2}\right)^2 = \frac{1}{2} \cdot \frac{1}{2}$$
$$= \frac{1}{4}$$

CLASSROOM EXERCISES

What is the constant coefficient in each term?

1. $7x$ **2.** $\frac{1}{4}xy$ **3.** $5a^3$ **4.** $-7(r + 2)$

Show these products using exponents.

5. $x \cdot x$ **6.** $(xy)(xy)$ **7.** $8 \cdot 8 \cdot 8 \cdot 8$

Show these without using exponents.

8. x^1 **9.** $4y^5$ **10.** $(m + n)^2$

Give the standard name for each.

11. 3^5 **12.** $(3 \cdot 4)^2$ **13.** $\left(\frac{1}{2}\right)^3$

Evaluate for $a = 2$; for $a = 7$.

14. a^3 **15.** $2a^2$ **16.** $3^2 \cdot a^2$

EXERCISES

A What is the constant coefficient in each term?

1. $2x^2y$ **2.** $3xz^3$ **3.** $\frac{1}{4}ab^2$ **4.** $\frac{2}{3}h^2k^3$

Show these products using exponents.

5. $z \cdot z \cdot z$ **6.** $m \cdot m$ **7.** $4 \cdot 4 \cdot 4 \cdot a \cdot a$ **8.** $5 \cdot 5 \cdot 5 \cdot 5 \cdot b \cdot b \cdot b$

9. $\frac{1}{3} \cdot \frac{1}{3} \cdot y \cdot y \cdot y$ **10.** $\frac{1}{2} \cdot \frac{1}{2} \cdot \frac{1}{2} \cdot t \cdot t$ **11.** $(s + 3)(s + 3)(s + 3)$ **12.** $(2r - t)(2r - t)$

Show these products without exponents.

13. a^2 **14.** $2b^2$ **15.** $(3y)^3$ **16.** $(4z)^2$ **17.** m^2n **18.** r^3p

Write the standard name for each.

19. 3^2 **20.** 5^3 **21.** $2 \cdot 9^2$ **22.** $9 \cdot 2^2$ **23.** $\left(\frac{2}{3}\right)^2$ **24.** $\left(\frac{1}{2}\right)^3$

Evaluate for $x = 3$; for $x = \frac{1}{2}$; for $x = 0.7$.

25. x^2 **26.** $2x^2$ **27.** $(2x)^3$ **28.** $(3x)^2$ **29.** $(2x)(3x)$ **30.** $x(0.5x)$

Evaluate for $a = 2$, $b = 1$, $c = 3$, $x = 0$, $y = 4$.

31. the fourth power of a
32. the third power of c
33. the fifth power of (xy)
34. the second power of (abc)
35. the square of $(c + c)$
36. the first power of $(2 + a)$

[B] Show these products using exponents.

37. $x \cdot y \cdot y \cdot x \cdot y \cdot x$
38. $a \cdot a \cdot b \cdot b \cdot b \cdot a \cdot b \cdot b \cdot a$
39. $\frac{1}{2} \cdot \frac{1}{2} \cdot c \cdot \frac{1}{2} \cdot \frac{1}{2} \cdot c \cdot c \cdot \frac{1}{2} \cdot c \cdot c$
40. $d \cdot d \cdot 5 \cdot 5 \cdot d \cdot 5 \cdot d \cdot 5 \cdot 5 \cdot d \cdot d$
41. $3 \cdot 3 \cdot z \cdot z \cdot 3 \cdot z \cdot z \cdot 3 \cdot 3$
42. $h \cdot h \cdot \frac{1}{3} \cdot \frac{1}{3} \cdot h \cdot \frac{1}{3} \cdot h \cdot h \cdot h \cdot \frac{1}{3}$

Write the standard name.

43. $\left(\frac{3}{5}\right)^2 \cdot \left(\frac{2}{3}\right)^2$
44. $\left(\frac{3}{5} \cdot \frac{2}{3}\right)^2$
45. $(2.4)^3 \cdot (0.9)^2$
46. $(0.9)^3 \cdot (2.4)^2$
47. $\left(1\frac{3}{4}\right)^3 \cdot \left(\frac{3}{7}\right)^3 \cdot \left(\frac{5}{8}\right)^2$
48. $\left(\frac{3}{7}\right)^2 \cdot \left(\frac{5}{8}\right)^3 \cdot \left(1\frac{3}{4}\right)^2$

Evaluate for $h = \frac{1}{5}$, $k = \frac{3}{4}$.

49. $200h^3k^2$ **50.** $128h^2k^3$ **51.** $0.75h^2k$ **52.** $0.6hk^2$ **53.** $\frac{2h^2}{3k^2}$ **54.** $\frac{3h^2}{2k^2}$

Evaluate for $a = 2$, $b = 1$, $c = 3$, $x = 0$, $y = 4$.

55. $\frac{(a+b)^2}{4}$ **56.** $(c^3)^2$ **57.** $(c + y)^{(x+a)}$ **58.** $\frac{a^2 + c^2}{y^2}$ **59.** $\frac{2^a + 2^c}{2^{(a+c)}}$

[C] Replace each of the following expressions by the simplest exponent form.

60. $\left(\frac{1}{2}x^3y^4\right)^3$ **61.** $\left(\frac{2}{3}a^4b^2\right)^3$ **62.** $(3z^5d^4)^4$ **63.** $(5h^3k^6)^4$ **64.** $(0.4x^7y^5)^2$

For *all* counting numbers a, b, and c, write *Yes* if the two expressions name the same number. Write *No* if they do not.

65. $a^b \stackrel{?}{=} b^a$
66. $a^ba^c \stackrel{?}{=} a^{b \cdot c}$
67. $(a + b)^c \stackrel{?}{=} a^c \cdot b^c$
68. $a^b \cdot a^c \stackrel{?}{=} a^{(b+c)}$
69. $(ab)^c \stackrel{?}{=} a(b^c)$
70. $a^{(b+c)} \stackrel{?}{=} a^b + a^c$
71. $(ab)^c \stackrel{?}{=} a^c \cdot b^c$
72. $(a^2)^b \stackrel{?}{=} (a^b)^2$
73. $(a^b)^c = a^{(bc)}$

For each pattern, tell how many terms you can simplify mentally; with pencil and paper; with a calculator.

74. 2^n for $n = 1, 2, 3, \ldots$
75. n^2 for $n = 1, 2, 3, \ldots$
76. n^n for $n = 1, 2, 3, \ldots$

1-4 GROUPING AND THE ORDER OF OPERATIONS

In arithmetic expressions, parentheses, ( ), brackets, [ ], and the fraction bar, —, say "do this first." These symbols are called *grouping symbols*. If one pair of grouping symbols is between another, always work between the innermost pair first.

EXAMPLE 1 Simplify $(3 + 4) \div 2$, $3 + (4 \div 2)$, $\frac{3+4}{2}$, and $[2(5 + 1)] \cdot 2$.

SOLUTION

Do this first. ↓ (on $3 + 4$)

$$(3 + 4) \div 2 = 7 \div 2 = 3\tfrac{1}{2}$$

Do this first. ↓ (on $4 \div 2$)

$$3 + (4 \div 2) = 3 + 2 = 5$$

Do this first. ↓ (on $3 + 4$)

$$\frac{3+4}{2} = \frac{7}{2} = 3\tfrac{1}{2}$$

Do this first. ↓ (on $5 + 1$) Do this next. ↓ (on $2 \cdot 6$)

$$[2(5 + 1)] \cdot 2 = [2 \cdot 6] \cdot 2 = 12 \cdot 2 = 24$$

When no grouping symbols are used in arithmetic expressions, the order of operations is as follows.

A. Simplify terms with exponents first.
B. Then do all the multiplications and divisions in the order in which they appear from left to right.
C. Finish by doing all the additions and subtractions in the order in which they appear from left to right.

EXAMPLE 2 Simplify $2(3)^2$.

Ⓜ SOLUTION $2(3)^2 = 2 \cdot 9 = 18$

EXAMPLE 3 Simplify $10 - 6 - 2$.

Ⓜ SOLUTION $10 - 6 - 2 = 4 - 2 = 2$

EXAMPLE 4 Simplify $12 \div 6 \cdot 3$.

Ⓜ SOLUTION $12 \div 6 \cdot 3 = 2 \cdot 3 = 6$

EXAMPLE 5 Simplify $7 - 5 \div 2$.

Ⓜ SOLUTION $7 - 5 \div 2 = 7 - 2\tfrac{1}{2} = 4\tfrac{1}{2}$

EXAMPLE 6 Evaluate $4x^3 - 2xy$ for $x = 3$ and $y = 5$.

Ⓜ SOLUTION

$$\begin{aligned} 4x^3 - 2xy &= 4 \cdot 3^3 - 2 \cdot 3 \cdot 5 \\ &= 4 \cdot 27 - 2 \cdot 3 \cdot 5 \\ &= 108 - 30 \\ &= 78 \end{aligned}$$

EXAMPLE 7 Evaluate $\frac{x^2 - x + 5}{2}$ for $x = 3$.

Ⓜ SOLUTION

$$\frac{x^2 - x + 5}{2} = \frac{3^2 - 3 + 5}{2}$$
$$= \frac{9 - 3 + 5}{2}$$
$$= \frac{11}{2}$$

> **EVALUATING AN ALGEBRAIC EXPRESSION**
>
> 1. Replace each variable by a given number.
> 2. Perform the operations shown between grouping symbols. Work between the innermost pair first.
> 3. Simplify terms with exponents.
> 4. Multiply and divide in the order in which the operations appear, from left to right.
> 5. Add and subtract in the order in which the operations appear, from left to right.

CLASSROOM EXERCISES

Simplify.

1. $(2 + 9) \cdot 9$ **2.** $(13 - 1) - 6$ **3.** $[3(4 + 2)](3)$ **4.** $3(5)^2$
5. $18 - 10 - 4$ **6.** $18 - (10 - 4)$ **7.** $6 \div 3 \cdot 2$ **8.** $3 + 6 \div 2$

Evaluate.

9. $5x^2y$ for $x = 4$ and $y = 5$
10. $y^2 + 10$ for $y = 7$
11. $2c^2 - cb$ for $b = 2$ and $c = 4$
12. $\frac{y^2 - 2y + 1}{9}$ for $y = 6$

EXERCISES

A Simplify.

1. $(7 + 8) \div 3$ **2.** $(15 + 9) \div 6$ **3.** $42 \div (4 + 10)$ **4.** $72 \div (11 + 7)$
5. $[3(2 + 5)](4)$ **6.** $[6(3 + 1)](3)$ **7.** $(5)[4(4 + 6)]$ **8.** $(8)[2(6 + 8)]$

9. $2 \cdot 6^2$ **10.** $4 \cdot 8^2$ **11.** $28 - 15 - 4$ **12.** $37 - 21 - 16$

13. $121 - (89 - 26)$ **14.** $150 - (75 - 25)$ **15.** $96 \div 8 \cdot 4$ **16.** $144 \div 18 \cdot 6$

17. $\frac{1}{2} \div 2 \cdot 5$ **18.** $\frac{3}{4} \div 5 \cdot 6$ **19.** $25 - 20 \div 4$ **20.** $56 - 28 \div 7$

21. $18 + [9(11 - 5)](2)$ **22.** $120 - [3(12 - 8)](8)$ **23.** $324 - [7(15 - 7)](4)$

Evaluate $6yz^2$ for the following.

24. $y = 2$ and $z = 4$ **25.** $y = 0.9$ and $z = 0.3$ **26.** $y = 0.6$ and $z = 0.8$

Evaluate $144 - a^2$ for the following.

27. $a = 4$ **28.** $a = 8$ **29.** $a = 0$ **30.** $a = 12$

Evaluate $6h^2 - 4hk$ for the following.

31. $h = 6$ and $k = 9$ **32.** $h = 5$ and $k = 4$ **33.** $h = 10$ and $k = 2$ **34.** $h = 7$ and $k = 7$

Evaluate $\frac{y^2 + 3y - 6}{4}$ for the following.

35. $y = 8$ **36.** $y = 3$ **37.** $y = 15$ **38.** $y = 10$

Evaluate $2z^3 - 4yz$ for the following.

39. $z = 4$ and $y = 2$ **40.** $z = 3$ and $y = 4$ **41.** $z = 5$ and $y = \frac{1}{2}$ **42.** $z = 2$ and $y = \frac{1}{3}$

B Simplify.

43. $5 \cdot 3^2 - (4 + 2)^2$ **44.** $\frac{(6 - 2)(6 + 2)}{4} + (6 \cdot 4) - 2$ **45.** $8 - [2 \times 3 - (4 + 1)]$

Evaluate for $x = 3$, $y = 4$, $z = 2$, $a = 5$, $b = 0$, and $c = 4$.

46. $(x + y)^2 \cdot a$ **47.** $(a + c)^x \cdot b$ **48.** $(x + y)[z \div (a - c)]$

49. $(c + b)[a \div (x + z)]$ **50.** $(x + c)^2(y - z)^2$ **51.** $\frac{b[x + y - (a - c)]}{3a^2}$

Evaluate for $x = \frac{1}{2}$, $y = \frac{1}{3}$, and $h = \frac{1}{4}$.

52. $\frac{2x^2 + xy}{3}$ **53.** $\frac{x^2 - hy}{9}$ **54.** $h(2x - y)$ **55.** $3x^2y - 5h^3$

C Evaluate for $x = 0.5$, $y = 0.2$, and $h = 0.1$.

56. $\frac{2xy}{h} + (hy)$ **57.** $\frac{2x^2}{3} + \frac{4y}{3}$ **58.** $\frac{1}{x} + \frac{1}{y} - \frac{1}{2h}$ **59.** $\frac{3x}{2} + \frac{2y}{3} + \frac{5h}{6}$

CHECKING YOUR UNDERSTANDING

WORDS AND SYMBOLS

algebraic expression
base, a^b (base a circled)
coefficient
coordinate
counting number
even integer
exponent, a^b (exponent b circled)
factor
graph
grouping symbols, ( ), [ ], —
integer
negative number
number line
odd integer
positive number
power of a number, a^b (whole expression circled)
rational number, $\frac{a}{b}$
real number
square of a number, a^2 (whole expression circled)
variable
whole number

CONCEPTS

- Each point of the number line can be matched with a real number and each real number can be matched with a point of the number line. [1-1]

- When an arithmetic expression involves more than one operation, there is a definite order in which the operations should be performed. [1-4]

PROCESSES

- Draw the graph of a given set of numbers. [1-1]

  1. the integers less than -3 **2.** the real numbers greater than 5

- Write an expression with or without exponents. [1-3]

  3. $3 \cdot 3 \cdot 3 \cdot x \cdot x$ **4.** $3x^3$

- Simplify or evaluate an expression. [1-2, 1-3, 1-4]

  5. $40 - [3(5 + 6)]$ **6.** 4^3 **7.** $15 \div 5 \times 2 - 4 + 1$

  8. $6x + 3y$ for $x = 3, y = 2$ **9.** $(4x)^2$ for $x = 3$ **10.** $5xy - y^2$ for $x = 2, y = 4$

DIVISORS

A **divisor** a of a whole number b is a whole number that gives a whole number quotient c. In such a case, we say that a divides b. For example, 3 is a divisor of 6 since $6 \div 3 = 2$.

Tell which whole numbers

1. have no divisors. **2.** have exactly 1 divisor. **3.** have exactly 2 divisors.

4. have infinitely many divisors. **5.** divide no other number.

6. divide every number. **7.** divide infinitely many numbers.

OBJECTIVE: Use operations and their properties to simplify algebraic expressions.

1-5 SOME PROPERTIES OF ADDITION AND MULTIPLICATION

Addition and multiplication of real numbers have similar properties. They are shown in the chart on the next page. Study the chart. An understanding of these properties is useful throughout algebra.

EXAMPLE 1 Use the Commutative Property of Multiplication. Complete the other expression. $y \cdot x + 2 \cdot y = ? \cdot ? + 2 \cdot y$

SOLUTION $y \cdot x + 2 \cdot y = x \cdot y + 2 \cdot y$

EXAMPLE 2 Use the Associative Property of Addition. Show the other expression. $(a + 2) + 3 = ?$

SOLUTION $(a + 2) + 3 = a + (2 + 3)$

An example of an application of the Distributive Property is shown in the chart. This Property also may be applied to more than two terms.

EXAMPLE 3 Use the Distributive Property.

Show this product as a sum. $6(y + z + 3)$	Show this sum as a product. $2a + 3a + 5a$
SOLUTION $6(y + z + 3)$ $= 6 \cdot y + 6 \cdot z + 6 \cdot 3$	$2a + 3a + 5a$ $= (2 + 3 + 5)a$

The Distributive Property also holds for subtraction.

> For any real numbers a, b, and c,
> $a(b - c) = ab - ac$ and $(b - c)a = ba - ca$.

From now on we shall use only "Distributive Property" to refer to this property for addition or subtraction.

EXAMPLE 4 Use the Multiplication Property of One and the Distributive Property. Show this difference as a product. $s - sr$.

SOLUTION $s - sr = s \cdot 1 - sr$
$= s(1 - r)$

PROPERTIES OF ADDITION AND MULTIPLICATION

Commutative Property of Addition

For any real numbers a and b,

$$a + b = b + a.$$

This means that two numbers can be added in either order with the same result.

$$12 + 5\tfrac{3}{8} = 5\tfrac{3}{8} + 12$$

Commutative Property of Multiplication

For any real numbers a and b,

$$a \cdot b = b \cdot a.$$

This means that two numbers can be multiplied in either order with the same result.

$$3 \times 18.7 = 18.7 \times 3$$

Associative Property of Addition

For any real numbers a, b, and c,

$$(a + b) + c = a + (b + c).$$

This means that two additions can occur in either order with the same result.

$$(9 + 6) + 8 = 9 + (6 + 8)$$

Associative Property of Multiplication

For any real numbers a, b, and c,

$$(a \cdot b) \cdot c = a \cdot (b \cdot c).$$

This means that two multiplications can occur in either order with the same result.

$$(7 \times 2) \times \tfrac{6}{11} = 7 \times \left(2 \times \tfrac{6}{11}\right)$$

Addition Property of Zero

For any real number a,

$$a + 0 = a \quad \text{and} \quad 0 + a = a.$$

This means that adding zero leaves values unchanged. That is, zero is the **identity element for addition.**

$$7.5 + 0 = 7.5$$

Multiplication Property of One

For any real number a,

$$1 \cdot a = a \quad \text{and} \quad a \cdot 1 = a.$$

This means that a factor of 1 leaves values unchanged. That is, one is the **identity element for multiplication.**

$$1 \times 83\tfrac{1}{2} = 83\tfrac{1}{2}$$

Distributive Property of Multiplication Over Addition

For any real numbers a, b, and c,

$$a(b + c) = ab + ac \quad \text{and} \quad (b + c)a = ba + ca.$$

This means that adding terms and then multiplying the sum by a number gives the same result as multiplying each term by the number and then adding.

$$6(3 + 4) = (6 \times 3) + (6 \times 4)$$

CLASSROOM EXERCISES

Use a property of Addition or Multiplication to complete each sentence.

1. $x + 9 = ? + ?$ **2.** $(c + d) + 7 = ? + ?$ **3.** $(4 \cdot e) \cdot f = ? \cdot ?$ **4.** $6 \cdot (h + 2) = ? + ?$

EXERCISES

A Complete the following exercises using the given property.

■ Commutative Property of Addition

1. $m + 6 = ? + ?$ **2.** $h + 15 = ? + ?$ **3.** $5x + 3y = ? + ?$

4. $20c + 8d = ? + ?$ **5.** $? + ? = 6h + 4k$ **6.** $? + ? = 4a + 0$

■ Commutative Property of Multiplication

7. $12 \cdot w = ? \cdot ?$ **8.** $8 \cdot z = ? \cdot ?$ **9.** $(7c) \cdot (9d) = ? \cdot ?$

10. $(15g) \cdot (5h) = ? \cdot ?$ **11.** $? \cdot ? = (4x) \cdot (10y)$ **12.** $? \cdot ? = (3m) \cdot (24n)$

■ Associative Property of Addition

13. $(a + b) + 6 = ? + ?$ **14.** $(x + y) + 10 = ? + ?$

15. $4m + (6n + 8p) = ? + ?$ **16.** $7x + (14y + 21z) = ? + ?$

17. $? + ? = (5a + 10b) + 15c$ **18.** $? + ? = (8y + 16h) + 24k$

■ Associative Property of Multiplication

19. $(8 \cdot a) \cdot b = ? \cdot ?$ **20.** $(12 \cdot x) \cdot y = ? \cdot ?$ **21.** $4c \cdot (8d \cdot 12f) = ? \cdot ?$

22. $6g \cdot (12h \cdot 18k) = ? \cdot ?$ **23.** $? \cdot ? = (9p \cdot 18q) \cdot 27r$ **24.** $? \cdot ? = (3x \cdot 5y) \cdot 7z$

■ Distributive Property

25. $3 \cdot (a + b) = ? + ?$ **26.** $9(m - n) = ? - ?$ **27.** $? + ? = 8(p + q)$

28. $(7 + w)z = ? + ?$ **29.** $(12 - c)d = ? - ?$ **30.** $? \cdot ? = 3z + 10z$

31. $? \cdot ? = 7h + 18h$ **32.** $4m - 4n = ? \cdot ?$ **33.** $7c + 7d = ? \cdot ?$

■ Addition Property of Zero

34. $12 + 0 = ?$ **35.** $25 + 0 = ?$ **36.** $0 + 40 = ?$ **37.** $0 + 32 = ?$

■ Multiplication Property of One (with other properties)

38. $1 \cdot 8 = ?$ **39.** $15 \cdot 1 = ?$ **40.** $1 \cdot z = ?$ **41.** $h \cdot 1 = ?$

42. $z + 9z = (1 + ?)?$ **43.** $0 \cdot x + x = (? + ?)?$ **44.** $p + \frac{1}{3}p = (? + ?)?$

B **45.** Is there a commutative property for subtraction? for division? Explain.

C **46.** For the four operations indicated by $+, -, \times, \div$, there are 16 possible "distributive properties". What are they? Which of the 16 hold true? Explain.

1-6 SIMPLIFYING POLYNOMIALS

A **monomial** is a numeral, a variable with a whole-number exponent, or an indicated product involving numerals and variables. A **polynomial** is a monomial or an indicated sum or difference of monomials. A polynomial of two terms is a **binomial**. A polynomial of three terms is a **trinomial**.

POLYNOMIALS

Monomials	Binomials	Trinomials	Other Polynomials
7	$x - y$	$4x^3 + 3y^2 - 2z$	$4x^3 + 2x^2 - 4x - 7$
x	$2x^2 + 3x$	$1 + y + y^2$	$3a + 4b - 5c + 6d$
$6x^3$	$2 + 3ab$	$a^2x - 2a + x$	$wx + xy + yz + zw$
$0.7x$	$0.5r + 3s$	$\frac{2}{3}m + \frac{1}{2}n - r$	$r^2 + s^2 + rs - 1 - s$
$-3xy$	$\frac{1}{2}t + at$	$-0.3d + 1.6k^3 - 1.5$	$y^5 - 3y^4 + \frac{1}{4}y^3 - y^2 + y + 4$

A polynomial does *not* have a variable in a denominator.

Terms of a polynomial that contain the same variables to the same powers are **like terms** or **similar terms**. All constants terms also are like terms.

$3x - 2y + 3y$ — $2y$ and $3y$: like terms

$x^2 + xy + 2xy - 7$ — xy and $2xy$: like terms

$x^2 - xy + 3 - z$ — no like terms

Like terms may be combined to *simplify* a polynomial.

EXAMPLE 1 Simplify $3x + 2x$.

(M) SOLUTION
$$3x + 2x = (3 + 2)x = 5x$$

EXAMPLE 2 Simplify $7a - 4a$.

(M) SOLUTION
$$7a - 4a = (7 - 4)a = 3a$$

EXAMPLE 3 Simplify $y^2 + 2y^2$.

(M) SOLUTION
$$y^2 + 2y^2 = 1y^2 + 2y^2 = (1 + 2)y^2 = 3y^2$$

EXAMPLE 4 Simplify $3x + 4x + 2y + 7y$.

(M) SOLUTION
$$3x + 4x + 2y + 7y = (3 + 4)x + (2 + 7)y = 7x + 9y$$

EXAMPLE 5 Simplify $7m + 4m - m$.

Here is another variation on the Distributive Property.

Ⓜ **SOLUTION**

$$\begin{aligned} 7m + 4m - m &= 7m + 4m - 1m \\ &= (7 + 4 - 1)m \\ &= 10m \end{aligned}$$

When combining like terms, it is helpful to group them together first.

EXAMPLE 6 Simplify $4r + 3r^2 + 7r - 2r^2 + 6$.

Ⓜ **SOLUTION**

$$\begin{aligned} 4r + 3r^2 + 7r - 2r^2 + 6 &= 4r + 7r + 3r^2 - 2r^2 + 6 \\ &= (4 + 7)r + (3 - 2)r^2 + 6 \\ &= 11r + r^2 + 6, \quad \text{or } r^2 + 11r + 6. \end{aligned}$$

CLASSROOM EXERCISES

Identify which of the following are polynomials.

1. $x + 1$ **2.** $17c + 4$ **3.** $\frac{y + 1}{y - 1}$ **4.** $2x^2 + 3x - 1$

Identify the like terms.

5. $3x + 2x^2 + 5x$ **6.** $2y + 4 + 3y$ **7.** $4x^2 - 3x + 2z^2 + 7z$

Simplify by combining like terms.

8. $7y + 3y$ **9.** $4x^2 + 3x^2$ **10.** $5a + 4a + 2b + 6b$
11. $3z + 5z + 2z^2$ **12.** $8n + 7n - 4n$ **13.** $4h + 5h + 2k + 9k + 17$

EXERCISES

A Simplify by combining like terms.

1. $8z + 15z$ **2.** $32a + 18a$ **3.** $\frac{1}{5}b + \frac{2}{3}b$ **4.** $\frac{3}{8}h + \frac{1}{4}h$
5. $36k - 18k$ **6.** $24c - 9c$ **7.** $12x^2 + 28x^2$ **8.** $3y^2 + 18y^2$
9. $64r^2 + 22r^2$ **10.** $50s^2 + 25s^2$ **11.** $5.4z^2 - 2.7z^2$ **12.** $0.40p^2 - 0.12p^2$
13. $8c + 10c + 5d + 9d$ **14.** $22y + 28y + 6z + 19z$ **15.** $45k + 18k + 16h + 22h$
16. $38a + 14a + 29b + 31b$ **17.** $41p - 15p + 28q - 10q$ **18.** $55m - 39m + 60n - 38n$
19. $9x + 6x + 4x^2$ **20.** $15z + 18z + 9z^2$ **21.** $38y^2 + 12y + 17y$
22. $64a^2 + 40a + 20a$ **23.** $39m - 14m + 20m^2$ **24.** $84n - 24n + 30n^2$
25. $15b + 8b + 3b$ **26.** $49c + 28c + 14c$ **27.** $6h + 18h + 30h$

28. $9k + 27k + 63k$ **29.** $48z - 30z - 4z$ **30.** $72x - 36x - 18x$

31. $85a - 50a + 25a$ **32.** $96y - 54y + 28y$ **33.** $27m + 18m - 9m$

34. $42n + 18n - 56n$ **35.** $17p + 9p + 14q + 6q + 18$

36. $29a + 13a + 16b + 24b + 14$ **37.** $23x + 49y + 17x - 11y + 50$

38. $35z + 27w + 18z - 15w + 18$ **39.** $32c - 12c + 46d - 28d - 30$

B Simplify.

40. $3.6h + 42.4h + 0.04h$ **41.** $3x + 7x^2 + 5 + 8x + 3x^2 + 6$

42. $d^2 + 9d + 2 - 4d + 3d^2$ **43.** $2c^2 + 5c + 9 - 2c + 4c^2$

C **44.** $2(m + 3n) + 4(3m + 2n)$ **45.** $2h(3h^2 + 5k) + k(4h + 3k^2)$

CHECKING YOUR UNDERSTANDING

WORDS

binomial
identity element
like terms
monomial
polynomial
trinomial

Properties of Addition:
- Commutative
- Associative
- Zero

Properties of Multiplication:
- Commutative
- Associative
- One

Distributive Property of Multiplication Over Addition

CONCEPTS

- Expressions having like terms may be simplified using the Properties of Addition and Multiplication. [1-5, 1-6]

PROCESSES

- Use the Properties of Addition and Multiplication as part of the process of simplifying polynomials. [1-5]

  1. $(x + 7) + 3 = ? + ?$ (Associative Property)

  2. $5x \cdot 4 = ? \cdot ?$ (Commutative Property)

- Use the Distributive Property and the Multiplication Property of One to write products as sums and sums as products. [1-5]

  3. $5(x + 3) = ? + ?$ **4.** $5y + y = ? \cdot ?$

- Simplify a polynomial. [1-6]

  5. $13a - 4a$ **6.** $3x - x + 5x^2$ **7.** $5a - 5b + 8a + 2$

OBJECTIVE: Represent ideas given in words by algebraic expressions.

1-7 PROBLEM SOLVING: WRITING ALGEBRAIC EXPRESSIONS

The format for symbol assignment that is introduced in this lesson will be maintained throughout the text.

In the language of algebra, we use algebraic symbols and expressions to represent ideas that are given in words.

Idea in Words	Symbol or Expression
the number	n
five more than the number the number increased by five	$n + 5$
five less than the number the number less five the number decreased by five	$n - 5$
five less the number	$5 - n$
five times the number	$5n$
one-fifth of the number	$\frac{1}{5}n$ or $\frac{n}{5}$

We call such an aid for memory a mnemonic aid.

For a variable, we often use a letter symbol that reminds us of the idea we wish to represent.

EXAMPLE 1 Lee has some quarters. Write a symbol for the number of quarters he has.

Ⓜ SOLUTION Use q for the number of quarters Lee has.

EXAMPLE 2 Represent the value in *cents* of q quarters.

SOLUTION The value of each quarter is 25 cents.

$\frac{¢}{\text{quarter}} \cdot \text{quarters} = ¢$

Ⓜ Use $25q$ for the value in cents of q quarters.

EXAMPLE 3 Represent the value in *dollars* of q quarters.

SOLUTION 1 The value of each quarter is one-fourth of a dollar.

$\frac{\$}{\text{quarter}} \cdot \text{quarters} = \$$

Ⓜ Use $\frac{1}{4}q$ for the value in dollars of q quarters.

Property of Addition or Multiplication to complete each sentence. [1-5]

6)(4z) = ? · ? **57.** $4m + (3n + 2k) = ? + ?$ **58.** $k \cdot 1 = ?$

+ 2y = ? · ? **60.** $? + ? = 4(2w + 5s)$ **61.** $0 + 3t = ?$

. [1-6]

+ 3x **63.** $18t - 2t$ **64.** $9q^2 - 4q^2$

z + 8z − 2z **66.** $5w^2 + 7w + 9w$ **67.** $2s + 7t + 7s - 2t$

− 3a + 3b + b **69.** $17x + 31z + 15x - 12$ **70.** $9v + 2w - 2v - w + 8$

n algebraic expression for each. [1-7]

e sum of two numbers is 38. Use l for the larger number. Represent smaller number.

is 2 years older than Jill. Use x for Jo's age. Represent Jill's age.

e d for a number. Represent another number that is 8 times as large.

E REVIEW

e letter of the best response.

ch is the graph of the counting numbers less than 3?

−3 −2 −1 0 1 2 3 **b.** −3 −2 −1 0 1 2 3

−3 −2 −1 0 1 2 3 **d.** −3 −2 −1 0 1 2 3

ch is equal to 3?

$\frac{8+4}{2}$ **b.** $8 + \frac{4}{2}$ **c.** $\frac{8+4}{2+2}$ **d.** $\frac{8}{2} + 4$ **e.** $\frac{8}{4+2}$

$3 \cdot x \cdot x \cdot x =$

$^3 \cdot x^3$ **b.** $3^2(3x)$ **c.** $2^3 3^x$ **d.** $3^2 x^3$ **e.** x^3

$=$

$r \cdot 2r \cdot 2r$ **b.** $2 \cdot r \cdot r \cdot r$ **c.** $2 \cdot r \cdot 3$ **d.** $2 \cdot 2 \cdot 2 \cdot r$ **e.** $2r + 2r + 2r$

$x = 4$ and $y = 3$, $3x^2 - 2xy =$

b. $x - y$ **c.** 34 **d.** 0 **e.** 24

$4k - 2m + 3k - 2 =$

$m + 5k$ **b.** $13mk - 2$ **c.** $4m + 7k$ **d.** $6m + 7k - 2$ **e.** $4m + 5k$

$x + x^2 =$

$x + x^2$ **b.** $9x$ **c.** $8 + x^2$ **d.** $8x$ **e.** $8 + x^2$

sum of two numbers is 17. When n is one of the numbers, the other is

$7 + n$ **b.** $n - 17$ **c.** $17 \div n$ **d.** $n + 17$ **e.** $17 - n$

Ⓜ SOLUTION 2 Use $\frac{q}{4}$ for the value in dollars of q quarters. $\frac{\text{quarters}}{\frac{\text{quarters}}{\$}} = \$$

Ⓜ SOLUTION 3 Use $0.25q$ for the value in dollars of q quarters. $\frac{\$}{\text{quarter}} \cdot \text{quarters} = \$$

EXAMPLE 4 Represent five-hundredths of n dollars.

Ⓜ SOLUTION 1 Use $0.05n$ for five hundredths of n dollars. (dimensionless) · \$ = \$

Ⓜ SOLUTION 2 Use $\frac{5}{100}n$ for five-hundredths of n dollars. (dimensionless) · \$ = \$

EXAMPLE 5 The sum of two numbers is 10, and n is used for one number. Represent the other number.

SOLUTION When n is subtracted from 10, the other number is the remainder.

Ⓜ Use $10 - n$ for the other number.

CHECK Is the sum of the two numbers 10?

$n + (10 - n) \stackrel{?}{=} 10$
$n + 10 - n \stackrel{?}{=} 10$
$10 = 10$ ✓

EXAMPLE 6 Represent two consecutive even integers.

Ⓜ SOLUTION Use n for an even integer.
$n + 2$ for the next larger even integer.

Two consecutive odd integers may be represented in similar fashion.

EXAMPLE 7 A sales clerk earns a commission of five cents on each dollar of sales for the week. Represent the number of dollars of sales for the week and the number of dollars of commission for the week.

Ⓜ SOLUTION Use s for the number of dollars of sales for the week.
$0.05s$ for the number of dollars of commission for the week.

$\frac{\$}{(\text{sales } \$)} \cdot (\text{sales } \$) = \$$

EXAMPLE 8 For the election of class officers, a roll of paper 5 meters long is to be cut to make a certain number of posters that are the same length. Represent the number of posters and the greatest length in meters that is possible for each.

Ⓜ SOLUTION Use n for the number of posters.
$\frac{5}{n}$ for the length in meters of each poster.

$\frac{(\text{m})}{(\text{poster})} = \frac{\text{m}}{\text{poster}}$

CLASSROOM EXERCISES

Write algebraic expressions for each of the following.

1. Joan has some half-dollars. Represent the number of half-dollars she has. Represent their value in cents. Represent their value in dollars.
2. Raul bought some baseball cards from a friend. Represent the number of cards he bought. Each card cost him 12 cents. Represent the cost of the cards in cents; in dollars.
3. The sum of two numbers is 15. One of them is y. Represent the other number.
4. Use c to represent an even integer. What may represent the next larger even integer?
5. Use w to represent a number of weeks. What may represent the same amount of time in days?
6. The difference of two numbers is 7. Use y for the smaller number. What may represent the larger number?
7. The difference of two numbers is 24. Use z for the smaller number. What may represent the larger number?
8. Use h to represent a length of time in hours. What may represent the time in minutes?
9. Use m to represent a number of minutes. What may represent the same amount of time in seconds?

EXERCISES

A Write algebraic expressions using only one variable for each exercise.

1. What is the value of n nickels in cents? in dollars?
2. What is the value of d dimes in cents? in dollars?
3. Use h to represent any counting number except 1. What may represent the next smaller counting number?
4. Rueben's age is represented by r. He is three years younger than Anna. What may represent Anna's age?
5. Use s for Susan's age. She is four years older than Joey. What may represent Joey's age?

B 10. Amy has some nickels and dimes. The number of dimes is four more than twice the number of nickels. Represent the number of nickels and the number of dimes.

11. A number is represented by z. Represent another number that is five less than three times the first number.

12. A car traveled for t hours at r kilometers per hour. Represent the distance that the car traveled.

C 13. A bag contains some red, blue, green, and yellow marbles. The number of green marbles is five more than three times the number of yellow marbles. The number of red marbles is one less than four times the number of yellow marbles. The number of blue marbles is three times the number of red marbles. Represent the number of each kind of marble.

14. Gunther has a four-digit numeral on his automobile license plate. The number of tens shown is five less than six times the number of ones. The number of hundreds is three more than four times the number of ones. The number of thousands is one-half the number of tens. Represent each of the four digits.

CHAPTER REVIEW

On a number line, draw the graph for each set. [1-1]

1. the counting numbers less than 10
2. the whole numbers less t
3. the even integers between 1 and 5
4. the real numbers greater
5. the real numbers greater than -1 and less than 3
6. the integers less than 4 a greater than -2

Simplify. [1-2]

7. $8 - (2 + 3)$
8. $2 \cdot (6 + 4)$
9. $(7 - 4) \cdot 6$
10. $12 \div (3 + 3)$
11. $(9 - 6) - 3$
12. $(6 \div 3) \cdot 2$

Evaluate for $x = 8$, $y = 4$, $z = 2$, and $w = 1$.

13. $w + (z \cdot y)$
14. $(x \div y) - z$
15. $6 - (z - w)$
16. $z + \frac{y}{w}$

Give the constant coefficient in each term. [1-3]

18. $7x$
19. $4x^2z$
20. $\frac{3}{4}h^3$

Write with exponents.

21. $m \cdot m \cdot m$
22. $3 \cdot 3 \cdot t \cdot t$
23. $x \cdot x \cdot x \cdot x \cdot x$
24. $\frac{2}{3} \cdot \frac{2}{3} \cdot \frac{2}{3} \cdot w \cdot w$
25. $(3 + s)(3 + s)$
26. $(a + b)(a + b$

Write without exponents.

27. b^4
28. $3m^2$
29. $2m^3$
30. $(3r)^2$
31. s^3t

Simplify.

33. 6^2
34. $3 \cdot 4^3$
35. $(2 \cdot 3)^4$
36. $\left(\frac{1}{2}\right)^3$
37. $(4 \cdot 1)^2$

Evaluate for $a = 4$, $b = 3$, $c = 2$, and $d = 0$.

39. a^4
40. b^2
41. $7c^3$
42. a^2c
43. $3cd^3$

Simplify. [1-4]

45. $45 \div 9 \cdot 7$
46. $12 - 7 + 5$
47. $20 - 13 - 3$
48. $4 +$
49. $9 + 12 \div 3$
50. $7 \times [10 - (28 \div 7)]$
51. $[(9 + 6) \div 5] - 2$
52. $56 \div$

Evaluate $\frac{a(b - 2)}{b}$ for

53. $a = 8$ and $b = 4$.
54. $a = 3$ and $b = 6$.
55. $a = 2$ and

CHAPTER TEST

1. Use the number line. Draw the graph for the counting numbers less than 5.
2. Draw the graph for the integers greater than -3 and less than 4.
3. Evaluate $\frac{a+b}{c}$ for $a = 6$, $b = 4$, and $c = 2$.
4. Evaluate ab for $a = 20$ and $b = 3$.
5. What is the constant coefficient in $4ab$?
6. What is the standard name for 5^2?
7. Simplify $3 + (4)(2)$.
8. Simplify $2 + (3)(4 + 5)$.
9. Use the Commutative Property of Multiplication to complete the statement, $a \cdot 12 = ? \cdot ?$.
10. Use the Distributive Property to write the product as a sum, $6 \cdot (x + 20) = ? + ?$.
11. Simplify $5x + 3y + y$.
12. Simplify $7x^2 - 2x^2 - x$.
13. Write an expression for the value in cents of x quarters.
14. Represent the next larger even number following the even number n.

Write the letter of the best response.

15. Which shows the *real* numbers less than 3?

a. −1 0 1 2 3 4

b. −1 0 1 2 3 4

c. −1 0 1 2 3 4

d. −1 0 1 2 3 4

16. For $n = 5$, $7n =$

a. 2 **b.** 12 **c.** 35 **d.** 55 **e.** 75

17. What exponent is in the expression $\frac{2 + 3^4 - 5}{6}$?

a. 2 **b.** 3 **c.** 4 **d.** 5 **e.** 6

18. $3 + 4 \cdot 5 - 6 =$

a. 6 **b.** 7 **c.** 12 **d.** 17 **e.** 29

19. What property allows us to write $(a + 9) + 3 = a + (9 + 3)$?

a. Commutative Property for Addition
b. Associative Property for Addition
c. Distributive Property
d. Multiplication Property of One

20. $3x^2 + 5x^2 + 2x - x =$

a. $9x^2$ **b.** $8x^4 + 2$ **c.** $10x^2 - x$ **d.** $8x^2 + 2$ **e.** $8x^2 + x$

21. When n is an odd integer, what is the next smaller odd integer?

a. $n - 2$ **b.** $n - 1$ **c.** n **d.** $n + 1$ **e.** $n + 2$

CHAPTER 2
Positive and Negative Numbers

Much is known about the lives and habits of creatures that live on land. Much remains to be learned about creatures that live in the sea. This is a task of marine scientists, such as the two who are engaged in fisheries research here. One of the most important goals they have is learning the effects that land creatures have on sea creatures and their environment.

OBJECTIVES: Identify positive and negative numbers. Match them with points on the number line. Match them with their opposites. Add and subtract positive and negative numbers. Simplify polynomials.

2-1 OPPOSITES

The numbers associated with all the points of the number line are the *real numbers*. The real numbers that are greater than zero are *positive*. Those that are less than zero are *negative*.

Zero is neither positive nor negative. Positive integers often are shown with the positive sign, +. However, since the positive integers "behave" exactly as counting numbers, we do not use the positive sign.

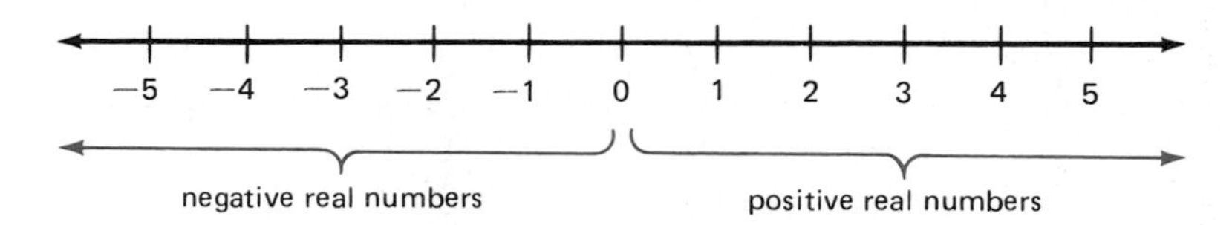

Each real number is associated with a real number called its **opposite**. If a number is positive, its opposite is negative. If a number is negative, its opposite is positive. The opposite of zero is zero itself. The graphs of two opposite numbers are the same distance from, but on *opposite* sides of, the point for zero.

Caution: For a variable, a, read "$-a$" as the "opposite of a" rather than "negative a." The latter reading may create the impression that "$-a$" represents a negative number. This is not always so.

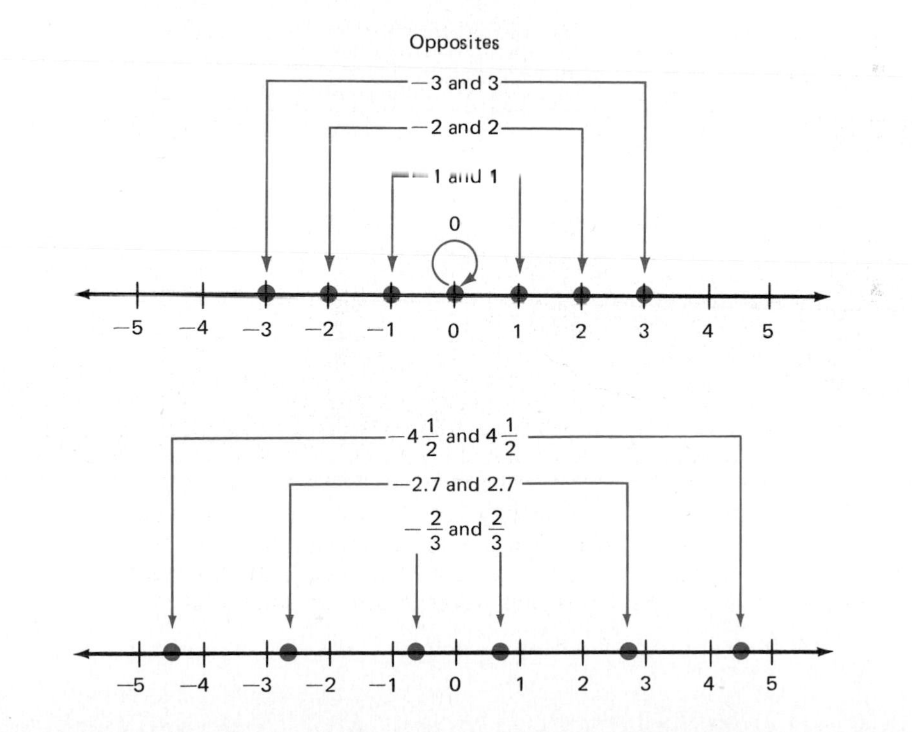

The symbol "−" is used to indicate the opposite of a number. The symbol "$-x$" can be read "the opposite of x". Remember, $-x$ represents a positive number whenever x represents a negative number.

EXAMPLE 1 What is the opposite of 4? of −4 (negative 4)?

SOLUTION 4 and −4 are opposites of each other. Another way to represent the opposite of −4 (negative 4) is $-(-4)$. Thus, $-(-4) = 4$.

EXAMPLE 2 What is $-x$ (the opposite of x) for $x = \frac{2}{3}$? for $x = -\frac{2}{3}$?

SOLUTION For $x = \frac{2}{3}$, $-x = -\frac{2}{3}$. | For $x = -\frac{2}{3}$, $-x = -\left(-\frac{2}{3}\right)$, or $\frac{2}{3}$.

The idea of opposite numbers is used to define the **absolute value** of a number. The absolute value of a positive number is the number itself. The absolute value of a negative number is its opposite. The absolute value of zero is zero. The absolute value of a number is *never* a negative number.

The absolute value of a number, x, is represented by $|x|$ which is read "the absolute value of x."

> If x is positive, $|x| = x$.
> If $x = 0$, $|x| = 0$.
> If x is negative, $|x| = -x$.

EXAMPLE 3 Simplify $|1.5|$. Simplify $|-1.5|$.

SOLUTION 1.5 is positive.
Thus, $|1.5| = 1.5$

−1.5 is negative.
Thus, $|-1.5| = -(-1.5)$
$= 1.5$

EXAMPLE 4 Evaluate $|x|$ for $x = 3\frac{1}{2}$; for $x = -3\frac{1}{2}$.

SOLUTION For $x = 3\frac{1}{2}$, $|x| = |3\frac{1}{2}|$
$= 3\frac{1}{2}$

For $x = -3\frac{1}{2}$, $|x| = |-3\frac{1}{2}|$
$= 3\frac{1}{2}$

CLASSROOM EXERCISES

Write the opposite.

1. -4 **2.** 7 **3.** -2.4 **4.** 7.1

5. 8°C below zero **6.** 1500 meters above sea level

7. a loss of \$6 **8.** 8 strokes above par

Find $|x|$.

9. $x = 7.3$ **10.** $x = -8.1$ **11.** $x = -42.3$ **12.** $x = 4\frac{1}{2}$

EXERCISES

A Write the opposite.

1. 4 m east **2.** A.D. 1870 **3.** 34 B.C.

4. 12° north **5.** $-7\frac{1}{3}$ **6.** $8\frac{2}{3}$

7. 80° east longitude **8.** 60° west longitude

9. 8 mm above average **10.** 2 stories below ground level

Simplify.

11. $|-5|$ **12.** $|7|$ **13.** $|\ \ 4.0|$ **14.** $|0.520|$ **15.** $|\ \ 8\frac{1}{4}|$

B **16.** $-(-2)$ **17.** $-(8 + 4)$ **18.** $-(-6) + 4$ **19.** $7 + [-(-3)]$

20. $-\left(-\frac{1}{3}\right) + \frac{1}{3}$ **21.** $-(3.4 + 6.5)$ **22.** $-|-2|$ **23.** $4|-3|$

24. $3|6| + |2|$ **25.** $2|-4| + |5|$ **26.** $3|-5| + |6|$ **27.** $5|-2| + 3|-1|$

C Tell whether each statement is *true* or *false*. If a statement is true for *every* situation, write "True." If it is false for *any* situation, write "False."

28. The absolute value of every real number is greater than zero.

29. Some real numbers do not have absolute values.

30. The absolute value of any integer equals the absolute value of the opposite of the integer.

31. There is a real number which equals the absolute value of its opposite.

32. $|a| = -a$ when $a < 0$. **33.** $|a| = a$ when $a > 0$.

2-2 ADDITION USING THE NUMBER LINE

The number line can help us add positive and negative numbers. A positive number will suggest a move in the positive direction (to the right) along the number line. A negative number will suggest a move in the negative direction (to the left).

Numbers to be added are called **addends**. The result of adding is a **sum**.

$$\underset{\text{addend}}{15\frac{3}{8}} + \underset{\text{addend}}{29} = \underset{\text{sum}}{44\frac{3}{8}}$$

Addends are represented by arrows above the number line. The first tail starts at the origin. The next tail starts at the head of the preceding arrow, and so on. The sum is represented by an arrow below the number line. The "sum arrow" begins at the origin and ends at the head of the *final* "addend arrow."

EXAMPLE 1 Show the sum of the addends 2 and 3 using the number line.

SOLUTION

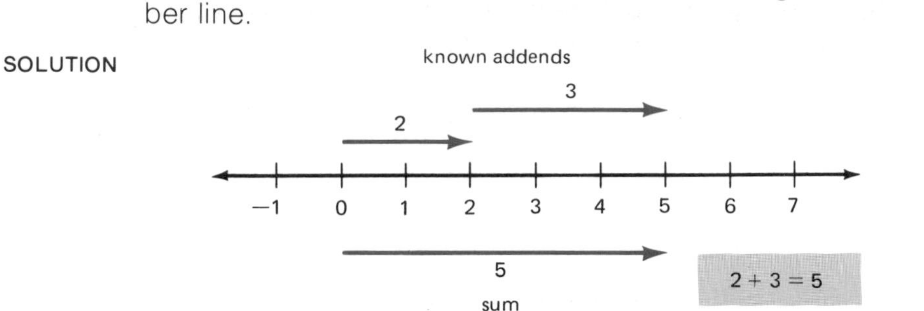

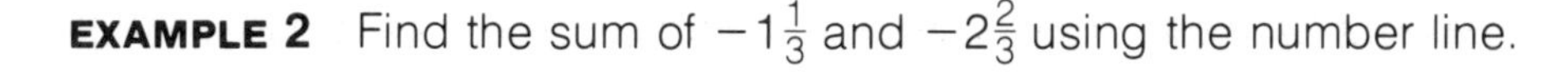

EXAMPLE 2 Find the sum of $-1\frac{1}{3}$ and $-2\frac{2}{3}$ using the number line.

SOLUTION

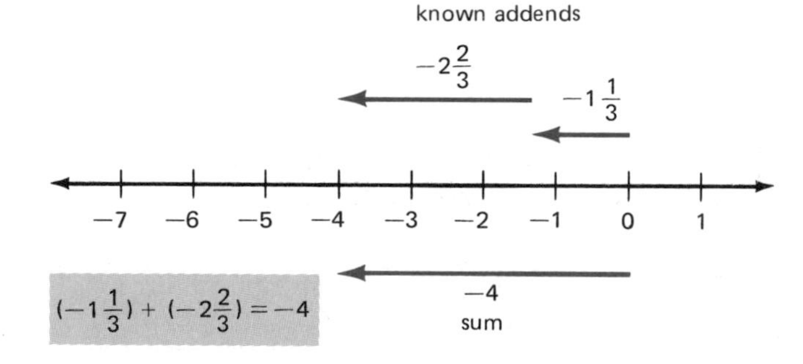

EXAMPLE 3 Find the sum of 3 and −7 using the number line.

SOLUTION

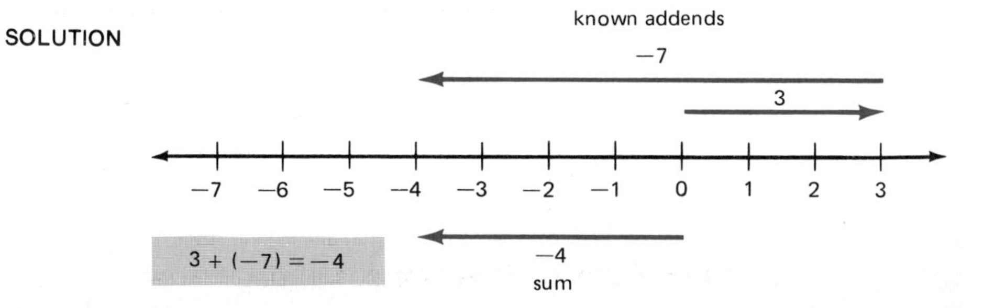

EXAMPLE 4 Find the sum of -7 and 3 using the number line.

SOLUTION

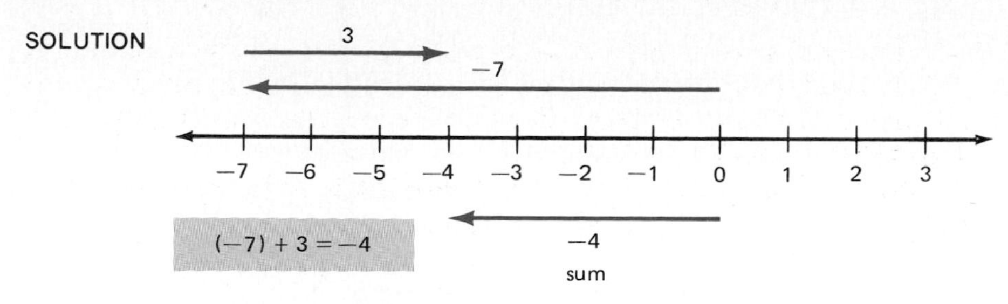

The Addition Property of Zero tells us that when zero is one of two addends, the sum is the other addend.

EXAMPLE 5 Find the sum of -2.3 and 0 using the number line.

SOLUTION

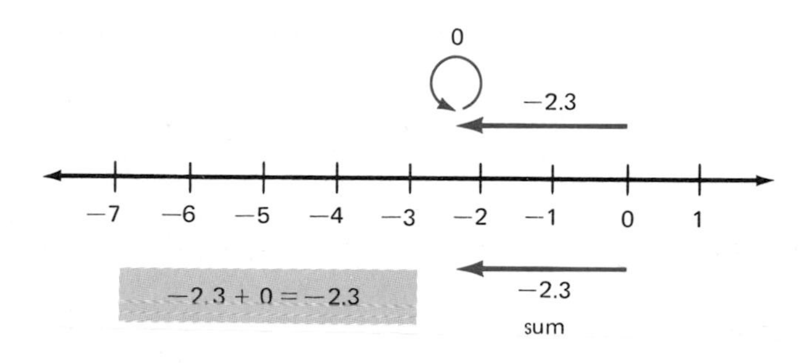

The sum of a number and its opposite is zero. A number and its opposite are **additive inverses** of each other.

"Additive inverse" is another way to say "opposite."

EXAMPLE 6 Find the sum of 7 and -7 using the number line.

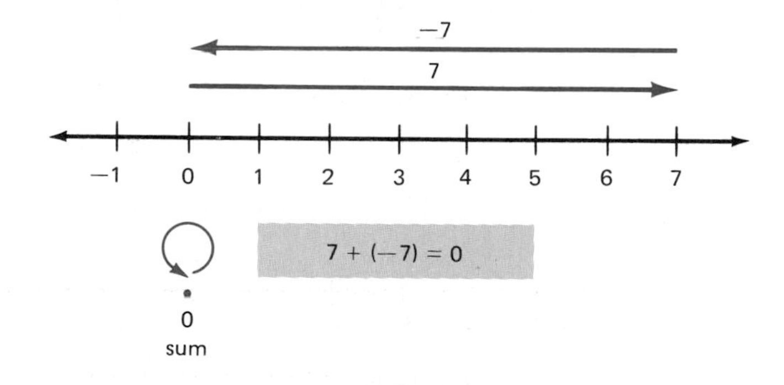

7 and -7 are additive inverses of each other.

The statements

"7 is the additive inverse (opposite) of -7,"

"-7 is the additive inverse (opposite) of 7,"

and

"7 and -7 are additive inverses (opposites),"

all say the same thing.

ADDING TWO REAL NUMBERS USING THE NUMBER LINE

1. Start at zero. Move to the right for positive numbers. Move to the left for negative numbers.
2. Start the second move where the first move ends.
3. Read the sum from zero to where the second move ends.

CLASSROOM EXERCISES

Give the addition sentence suggested by each diagram.

1. −4 −3 −2 −1 0 1 2 3

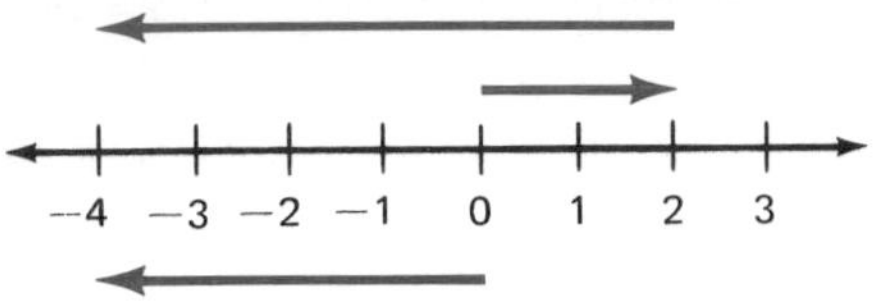

2. −3 −2 −1 0 1 2 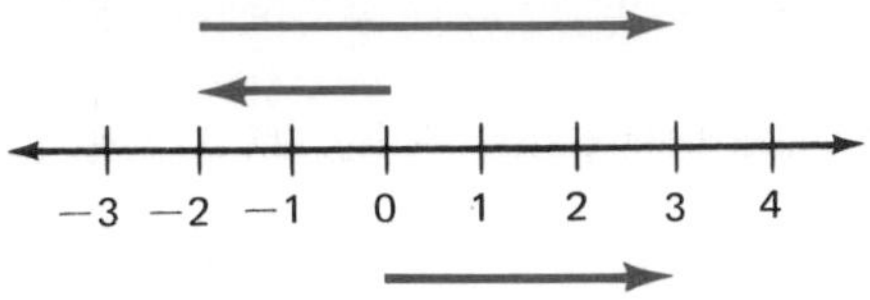 3 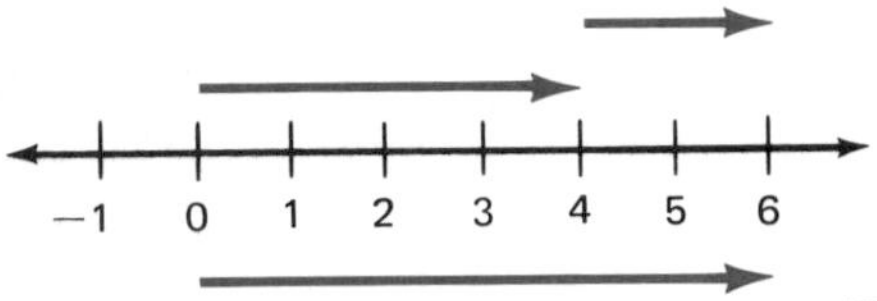 4

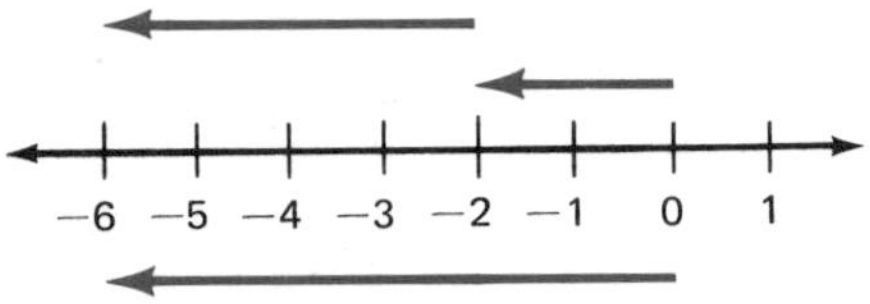

3. −1 0 1 2 3 4 5 6

4. −6 −5 −4 −3 −2 −1 0 1

EXERCISES

A Find each sum. Use the number line, if needed.

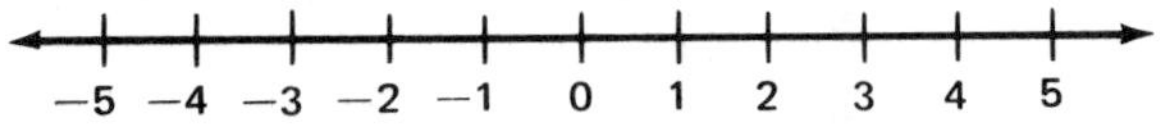

−5 −4 −3 −2 −1 0 1 2 3 4 5

1. $4 + (-6)$
2. $(-8) + (-3)$
3. $6 + 5$
4. $(-5) + (7)$
5. $8 + (-4)$
6. $(-6) + (-2)$
7. $(-20) + 10$
8. $8 + (-8)$
9. $(-20) + 20$
10. $-3\frac{1}{2} + \left(-1\frac{1}{2}\right)$
11. $4\frac{1}{2} + 3\frac{1}{2}$
12. $5\frac{2}{3} + 2\frac{2}{3}$
13. $\left(-4\frac{1}{2}\right) + 10\frac{1}{2}$
14. $10.5 + (-15.5)$
15. $(-4.7) + 10.2$

B

16. $\left(-4\frac{4}{5}\right) + 2\frac{2}{5}$
17. $\left(-6\frac{5}{7}\right) + \left(-3\frac{4}{7}\right)$
18. $6\frac{4}{9} + \left(-3\frac{2}{9}\right)$
19. $\left(-10\frac{1}{5}\right) + 4\frac{4}{5}$
20. $8\frac{2}{5} + \left(-10\frac{1}{5}\right)$
21. $\left(-4\frac{3}{4}\right) + \left(-4\frac{3}{4}\right)$
22. $\left(-7\frac{5}{6}\right) + 10\frac{4}{6}$
23. $\left(-6\frac{1}{4}\right) + \left(-3\frac{2}{4}\right) + 7\frac{1}{4}$
24. $\left(-5\frac{2}{3}\right) + \left(-6\frac{2}{3}\right) + 12\frac{1}{3}$

C

25. $\left(-2\frac{2}{3}\right) + 4\frac{1}{6} + \left(-2\frac{1}{3}\right)$
26. $\left(-5\frac{4}{5}\right) + 6\frac{7}{10} + 4\frac{3}{5}$
27. $\left(-2\frac{3}{4}\right) + 1\frac{1}{2} + \left(-3\frac{1}{4}\right)$

Simplify.

28. $-|-3| + 8$
29. $-|11| + |-3|$
30. $-|6\frac{2}{3}| + |-8\frac{1}{3}| + \left(-7\frac{5}{6}\right)$

2-3 ADDITION USING ABSOLUTE VALUES

It is important to know how to add positive and negative numbers without using a number line. Instead, you may use absolute values.

When both addends have the same sign, first add their absolute values. The sum has the same sign as the original addends.

EXAMPLE 1 Add 2 and 3.

SOLUTION $|2| + |3| = 5$

The sum is +.

Therefore, $2 + 3 = 5$.

EXAMPLE 2 Add $-1\frac{1}{2}$ and $-2\frac{3}{4}$.

SOLUTION $\left|-1\frac{1}{2}\right| + \left|-2\frac{3}{4}\right| = 4\frac{1}{4}$

The sum is −.

Therefore, $\left(-1\frac{1}{2}\right) + \left(-2\frac{3}{4}\right) = -4\frac{1}{4}$.

When the addends are additive inverses of each other, the sum is 0.

EXAMPLE 3 Add 1.5 and −1.5.

SOLUTION $1.5 + (-1.5) = 0$

When one addend is positive and the other is negative, use the following steps.

TO ADD A POSITIVE REAL NUMBER AND A NEGATIVE REAL NUMBER

1. Find the difference of their absolute values.
2. The result has the same sign as the addend having the greater absolute value.

EXAMPLE 4 Add 1 and −6.

SOLUTION $|-6| - |1| = 5$

The sum is −.

Therefore, $1 + (-6) = -5$.

EXAMPLE 5 Add $-5\frac{1}{3}$ and $2\frac{3}{4}$.

SOLUTION $|-5\frac{1}{3}| - |2\frac{3}{4}| = 2\frac{7}{12}$

The sum is −.

Therefore, $-5\frac{1}{3} + 2\frac{3}{4} = -2\frac{7}{12}$.

EXAMPLE 6 Add −2, −3, and 4.

SOLUTION

$$\begin{aligned}(-2) + (-3) + 4 &= (-5) \\ &= -1\end{aligned}$$

EXAMPLE 7 Add 5.6, −8.2, 4.7, and −5.3.

SOLUTION

$$\begin{aligned}5.6 + (-8.2) + 4.7 + (-5.3) &= (-2.6) + (-0.6) \\ &= -3.2\end{aligned}$$

ADDING TWO REAL NUMBERS

1. If both are positive, add them as you always have. The sum is positive.
2. If both are negative, add their absolute values. The sum is negative.
3. If one is positive and the other negative, but they are not additive inverses, find the difference of their absolute values. The result has the same sign as the addend having the greater absolute value.

CLASSROOM EXERCISES

Add.

1. -11 and 3
2. -20 and 20
3. -5 and -2
4. 13 and -14
5. $-\frac{1}{2}$ and $\frac{1}{2}$
6. 4.0 and -1.5

Simplify.

7. $-4.3 + (-2.7)$
8. $\frac{2}{5} + \left(-\frac{7}{5}\right)$
9. $\left(-\frac{1}{2}\right) + \left(-\frac{1}{4}\right)$
10. $(-30) + 20$
11. $56 + (-74)$
12. $6 + 5 + (-5)$
13. $(-8) + 6 + (-6)$
14. $(-3) + (-5) + 5$
15. $0.41 + (-0.12)$
16. $(-0.30) + (-0.47)$
17. $\left(-\frac{3}{5}\right) + \frac{3}{5} + \left(-\frac{1}{5}\right)$
18. $\left(-\frac{1}{8}\right) + \left(-\frac{3}{8}\right) + \frac{7}{8}$

EXERCISES

A Add.

1. -2 and -3
2. -5 and 2
3. 4 and -2
4. 5 and -4
5. $4\frac{1}{2}$ and $-6\frac{1}{2}$
6. -2.30 and 0.75

Simplify.

7. $7 + (-9)$
8. $6 + (-9)$
9. $(-8) + (-3)$
10. $(-12) + (-2)$
11. $(-11) + 2$
12. $(-9) + 3$
13. $\left(-\frac{2}{3}\right) + \frac{3}{4}$
14. $\left(-\frac{5}{8}\right) + \frac{8}{9}$
15. $\left(-\frac{3}{4}\right) + \frac{2}{3}$
16. $\left(-\frac{8}{9}\right) + \frac{5}{8}$
17. $(-8.6) + (-8.2)$
18. $(-4.7) + (-3.8)$
19. $8.6 + 8.2$
20. $4.7 + 3.8$
21. $(-5.4) + 0.63$
22. $8.7 + (-8.7)$
23. $6.4 + (-6.4)$
24. $(-3.0) + 4.7$
25. $(-4.3) + (-8.6)$
26. $(-6.34) + 0.003$
27. $6 + (-5) + (-2)$
28. $-8 + 7 + (-2)$
29. $-16 + (-21) + (-8) + 6$
30. $-21 + 4 + (-3) + (-8)$
31. $10 + (-5) + (-6) + (-4)$
32. $8 + (-2) + 6 + (-7)$

B

33. $32 + [-18 + (-16 + (-15))]$
34. $(-127) + 468 + (-621) + 524$
35. $385 + (-764) + (-897) + 429$
36. $[(-17 + (-16)) + 14] + 32$
37. $-[25 + (-3)] + [-(-2 + 5)]$
38. $-[21 + 4] + [-(6 + (-4))]$
39. $-2.7 + |3.4| + |-0.02| + (-0.005)$
40. $(4.7) + (-6.2) + (-1.03) + |8.124| + (-5.0)$

C Evaluate each expression for $w = 2.4$, $x = -3.5$, $y = 2\frac{1}{2}$, and $z = -5.75$.

41. $w + (-x) + (-z)$
42. $x + (-y) + z$
43. $(-x) + (-w) + y + (-z)$
44. $x + w + (-y) + (z)$
45. $x + (-w) + (-z) + y$
46. $(-w) + x + (-y) + z$
47. $(-x) + (2 + w) + (-z + 1)$
48. $x + z + [(-w) + y + (-8)]$

2-4 SUBTRACTING POSITIVE AND NEGATIVE NUMBERS

For the operation of addition, two numbers called *addends* are used to find another number called the *sum*.

addend		addend		sum
↓		↓		↓
9	+	8	=	17

For the operation of subtraction, a sum and a known addend are used to find an unknown addend, called the *difference*.

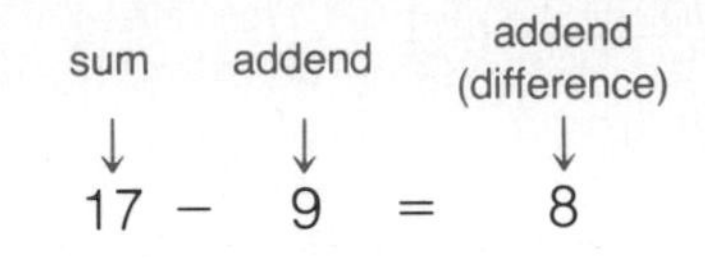

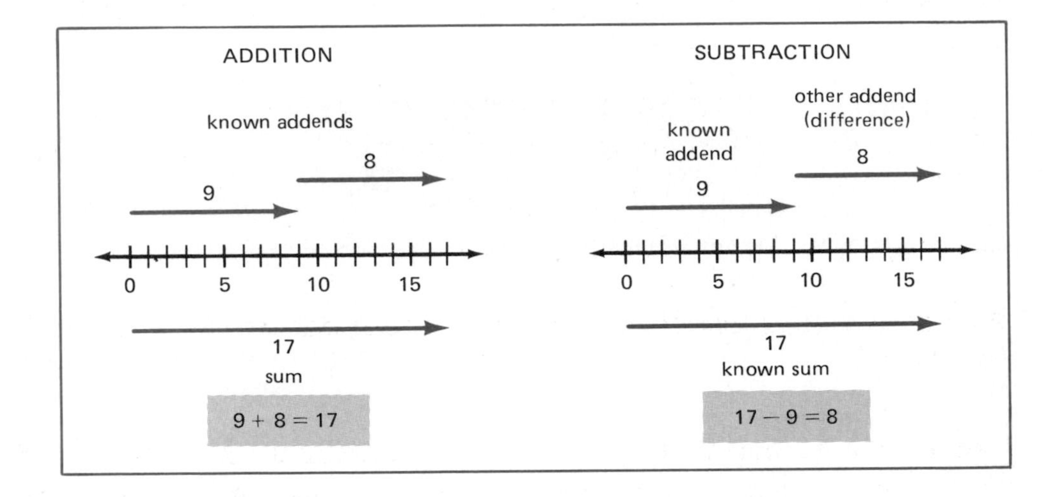

The difference may be found by adding *the opposite* of the known addend.

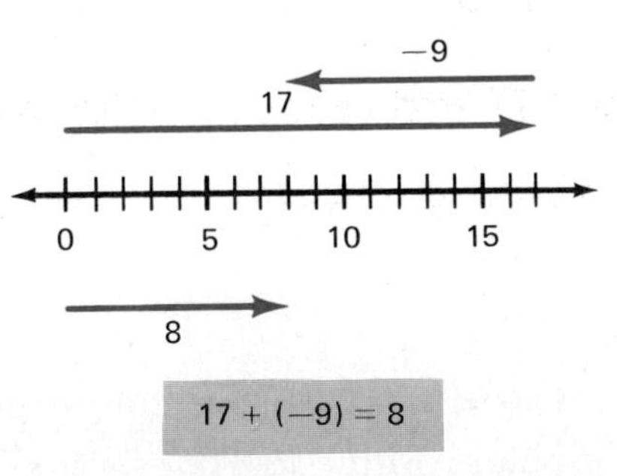

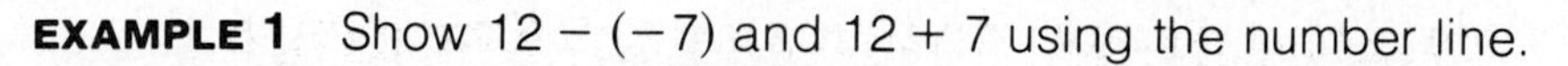

EXAMPLE 1 Show $12 - (-7)$ and $12 + 7$ using the number line.

SOLUTION

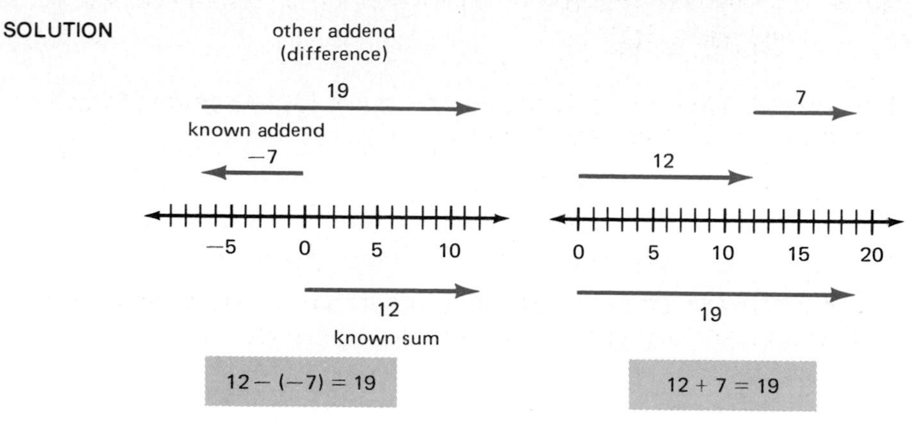

Subtracting a number and adding its opposite, or additive inverse, give the same result. This fact provides us with a method for finding the difference of any two numbers.

> For any real numbers a and b,
>
> $$a - b = a + (-b)$$

As a check, the difference, $a - b$, and the known addend, b, have a as their sum.

EXAMPLE 2 Subtract 6 from 8.

SOLUTION $8 - 6 = 8 + (-6)$
$= 2$

CHECK $2 + 6 \stackrel{?}{=} 8$
$8 = 8$ ✓

EXAMPLE 3 Subtract 8 from 6.

SOLUTION $6 - 8 = 6 + (-8)$
$= -2$

CHECK $-2 + 8 \stackrel{?}{=} 6$
$6 = 6$ ✓

EXAMPLE 4 Subtract $7\frac{3}{4}$ from -4.

SOLUTION $-4 - 7\frac{3}{4} = -4 + \left(-7\frac{3}{4}\right)$
$= -11\frac{3}{4}$

CHECK $-11\frac{3}{4} + 7\frac{3}{4} \stackrel{?}{=} -4$
$-4 = -4$ ✓

EXAMPLE 5 Subtract -6.2 from 3.

SOLUTION $3 - (-6.2) = 3 + 6.2$
$= 9.2$

CHECK $9.2 + (-6.2) \stackrel{?}{=} 3$
$3 = 3$ ✓

EXAMPLE 6 Subtract $-2\frac{1}{2}$ from -3.

SOLUTION $-3-\left(-2\frac{1}{2}\right)=-3+2\frac{1}{2}$
$=-\frac{1}{2}$

CHECK $-\frac{1}{2}+\left(-2\frac{1}{2}\right)\stackrel{?}{=}-3$
$-3=-3$ ✓

EXAMPLE 7 Subtract $-7\frac{5}{6}$ from $-2\frac{1}{3}$.

SOLUTION $-2\frac{1}{3}-\left(-7\frac{5}{6}\right)=-2\frac{1}{3}+7\frac{5}{6}$
$=5\frac{3}{6}$, or $5\frac{1}{2}$

CHECK $5\frac{1}{2}+\left(-7\frac{5}{6}\right)\stackrel{?}{=}-2\frac{1}{3}$
$-2\frac{1}{3}=-2\frac{1}{3}$ ✓

> SUBTRACTING POSITIVE AND NEGATIVE NUMBERS
>
> To subtract one real number from another, add its opposite, or additive inverse.

CLASSROOM EXERCISES

Complete the following.

1. $-6-(4)=\square$ because $4+\square=-6$.
2. $10-(-3)=\square$ because $-3+\square=10$.
3. $-20-(-4)=\square$ because $-4+\square=-20$.
4. $6-(9)=\square$ because $9+\square=6$.
5. $20-(6)=\square$ because $6+\square=20$.
6. $10-(6)=\square$ because $6+\square=10$.

Give each difference as a sum, then simplify.

7. $-6-10$
8. $-4-(5)$
9. $6-(-3)$
10. $8-(10)$
11. $-15-(-3)$
12. $-2.4-(-1.7)$
13. $8.2-(-3.04)$
14. $-6.52-(3.2)$
15. $6-(5)$
16. $2-(-5)$
17. $-3-(-7)$
18. $-2-(-4)$
19. $9-(3)$
20. $-8-(-5)$
21. $10-(10)$
22. $15-(-8)$

EXERCISES

A Write each difference as a sum, then simplify.

1. $5-9$
2. $(-5)-9$
3. $20-8$
4. $(-16)-7$
5. $5-(-7)$
6. $(-13)-(-13)$
7. $8-(-8)$
8. $(-3)-(-10)$
9. $(-10)-10$
10. $11-(-5)$
11. $(-30)-(-50)$
12. $27-32$
13. $(-15)-12$
14. $27-(-17)$
15. $3\frac{1}{2}-4$
16. $(-7.2)-6.5$
17. $6\frac{1}{4}-\left(-3\frac{3}{4}\right)$
18. $-5\frac{1}{16}-3\frac{3}{8}$
19. $(-17.3)-(5.86)$
20. $(-20)-\left(-6\frac{1}{2}\right)$
21. $13-(-16)$
22. $23-(-17)$
23. $-32-(-29)$
24. $-62-(-37)$

B Simplify.

25. $(4 - 3) - (6 - 10)$
26. $(2 - 6) - (7 - 8)$
27. $[(-2) + (-7)] - (-9)$
28. $4 - [(-5) - 6]$
29. $[(-5) - 8] - (-12)$
30. $(-6) - [(-10) + 3]$
31. $-4 - [(-6) - (-7)]$
32. $\left[\left(-\frac{9}{10}\right) + \left(-\frac{3}{100}\right)\right] - \left[-\frac{2}{25} - \left(-\frac{7}{25}\right)\right]$

C **33.** $\left[\left(\frac{3}{5}\right) - \left|\left(-\frac{7}{10}\right) - \left(-\frac{2}{5}\right)\right|\right] + \left[-\left(-\frac{4}{5}\right) - \left(-\frac{3}{10}\right)\right]$

34. $\left[\left|\left(-\frac{3}{4}\right) - \left(-\frac{1}{2}\right)\right| - \left(-\frac{1}{4}\right)\right] + \left[-\left(-\frac{3}{4}\right) - \frac{1}{2}\right]$

35. $[(-2.1) - (-6.4)] - [|(-3.4) - (-0.03)| - (-4.12)]$

36. $[7.5 - (-3.6)] - [-(-4.93) - |(-3.7) - 5.04|]$

CHECKING YOUR UNDERSTANDING

WORDS AND SYMBOLS

absolute value of a number, $|a|$
additive inverse, or opposite, of a number, $-a$

CONCEPTS

- Each real number is associated with a real number called its opposite. The opposite of a negative number is its absolute value. [2-1]

- For any two real numbers, there is a sum and a difference. Each may be either positive or negative. [2-2 to 2-4]

PROCESSES

- Find both the opposite and the absolute value of a real number. [2-1]

1. -3
2. 7.1
3. $-\frac{4}{5}$

- Add and subtract positive and negative numbers. [2-2 to 2-4]

4. $(-7) + (-1)$
5. $4 + (-6)$
6. $8 + (-3)$
7. $10 - 15$
8. $4 - (-7)$
9. $-11 - 4$

OBJECTIVES: Multiply and divide positive and negative numbers. Simplify polynomials. Evaluate expressions.

2-5 MULTIPLYING POSITIVE AND NEGATIVE NUMBERS

The numbers one, zero, and negative one have special properties when used as factors in multiplication.

Multiplication Property of One

For any real number a, $1 \cdot a = a$ and $a \cdot 1 = a$.

Multiplication Property of Zero

For any real number a, $0 \cdot a = 0$ and $a \cdot 0 = 0$.

Multiplication Property of Negative One

For any real number a, $(-1)a = -a$ and $a(-1) = -a$.

You have already studied the Multiplication Property of One. That is, the product of 1 and any number is that number. Because of the Multiplication Property of Zero, the product of 0 and any number is 0. Because of the Multiplication Property of Negative One, the product of -1 and any number is the opposite, or additive inverse, of that number.

EXAMPLE 1 Multiply 7 and 1; 3 and 0; 8 and -1.

SOLUTION

$$\begin{aligned} 7 \cdot 1 &= 1 \cdot 7 \\ &= 7 \end{aligned} \qquad \begin{aligned} 3 \cdot 0 &= 0 \cdot 3 \\ &= 0 \end{aligned} \qquad \begin{aligned} 8(-1) &= (-1)8 \\ &= -8 \end{aligned}$$

We can also use the Multiplication Property of Negative One to help us find products when negative factors are involved. In general, the product of a positive number and a negative number is negative.

EXAMPLE 2 Multiply 4 and -5.

SOLUTION

$$\begin{aligned} (4)(-5) &= (4)(-1)(5) \\ &= (-1)(4)(5) \\ &= (-1)(20) \\ &= -20 \end{aligned}$$

In general, the product of two negative numbers is positive.

EXAMPLE 3 Multiply -1 and -1.

SOLUTION
$$(-1)(-1)$$
$$= -(-1)$$
$$= 1$$

EXAMPLE 4 Multiply -3 and -2.

SOLUTION
$$(-3)(-2)$$
$$= (-1)(3)(-1)(2)$$
$$= (-1)(-1)(3)(2)$$
$$= (1)(6)$$
$$= 6$$

EXAMPLE 5 Simplify $(2)(-3)(4)$, $(-2)(-3)(4)$, and $(-2)(-3)(-4)$.

Ⓜ SOLUTION
$(2)(-3)(4) = (-6)(4) = -24$ | $(-2)(-3)(4) = (6)(4) = 24$ | $(-2)(-3)(-4) = (6)(-4) = -24$

In general, to multiply, first find if the product is positive or negative. Then multiply absolute values and use the result of the first step.

EXAMPLE 6 Simplify $\left(-\frac{1}{3}\right)\left(-\frac{2}{5}\right)$.

Ⓜ SOLUTION The product is positive. $\left(-\frac{1}{3}\right)\left(-\frac{2}{5}\right) = \left(\frac{1}{3}\right)\left(\frac{2}{5}\right) = \frac{2}{15}$

A consequence of the Properties of Zero and One are the following:

For all real numbers a and b,

$(-1)(-a) = a$
$a(-b) = -ab$
$-(-a) = a$
$(-a)(-b) = ab$
$(-a)b = -(ab)$

MULTIPLYING POSITIVE AND NEGATIVE NUMBERS

1. Find if the product is positive or negative using these rules:
   a. The product of two positive numbers or two negative numbers is a positive number.
   b. The product of a positive number and a negative number is a negative number.
2. Find the product of the absolute values and then use your findings from Step 1.

CLASSROOM EXERCISES

Simplify each product.

1. $4 \cdot 0$ **2.** $4 \cdot 6$ **3.** $3(-7)$ **4.** $(-1)(-4)$

5. $(-4)(4)$ **6.** $(-6)(4)(-3)$ **7.** $(-2)(-5)$ **8.** $(-3)(-4)$

9. $(-1)(4)$ **10.** $(-1)(6)$ **11.** $(-1)(-9)$ **12.** $1 \cdot 6$

13. $\frac{1}{2} \cdot \frac{1}{3}$ **14.** $-\frac{1}{4} \cdot -\frac{1}{5}$ **15.** $\left(-\frac{2}{3}\right)\left(\frac{3}{4}\right)$ **16.** $(0)\left(\frac{2}{3}\right)$

EXERCISES

A Simplify each product.

1. $3(-5)$ **2.** $6 \cdot 0$ **3.** $9(-1)$ **4.** $(-2)(10)$

5. $8(-10)$ **6.** $\frac{1}{2}(-4)$ **7.** $\frac{1}{3}(6)$ **8.** $-12\left(\frac{1}{4}\right)$

9. $25\left(-\frac{1}{5}\right)$ **10.** $\left(\frac{1}{2}\right)\left(-\frac{1}{3}\right)$ **11.** $-2(-8)$ **12.** $0.3(-0.4)$

13. $0.01(100)$ **14.** $-2(0.05)$ **15.** $-4(25)$ **16.** $\frac{3}{5}\left(-\frac{5}{3}\right)$

17. $\left(-\frac{7}{8}\right)\left(-\frac{16}{7}\right)$ **18.** $\left(-\frac{3}{8}\right)\left(-\frac{16}{3}\right)$ **19.** $\left(-\frac{1}{7}\right)\left(\frac{1}{4}\right)$ **20.** $\left(\frac{2}{5}\right)\left(-\frac{1}{9}\right)$

21. $-\frac{3}{4}(-6)$ **22.** $(-8)\left(-\frac{5}{2}\right)$ **23.** $-3\frac{1}{2}\left(-\frac{1}{5} \cdot \frac{10}{14}\right)$ **24.** $-\frac{4}{5}\left(-\frac{10}{3} \cdot -\frac{21}{28}\right)$

25. $-\frac{14}{10}\left(-\frac{5}{7} \cdot -\frac{10}{45}\right)$ **26.** $(-3.17)(1.2)$ **27.** $(81.4)(-3.6)$ **28.** $(-2.801)(-2.1)$

B Evaluate each expression for $a = 4$, $b = -5$, $c = \frac{1}{2}$, $d = 0.3$, $x = -1$, $y = 2$, and $z = 1$.

29. $a(b + c) - d$ **30.** $-a(y + z)$ **31.** $-x^4$ **32.** x^{76}

33. $(-x)^{94}$ **34.** $(a + b)^2$ **35.** $(y + z)^2$ **36.** $(a - b)^2$

37. $(-x)^4$ **38.** $(y - x)^2$ **39.** $b \cdot c \cdot x \cdot y \cdot z$ **40.** x^{57}

C Evaluate each expression for $x = -3$, $y = 2$, $a = -0.5$, and $b = -0.2$.

41. $-2(3a - 4)$ **42.** $-4(2x - 3)$ **43.** $-(a - b)$ **44.** $-(x - y)$

45. $6(2a - b) + 8[5a - 3(a - 2)]$ **46.** $4(2a - x) + 7[3y - 2(x + y)]$

AN ARITHMETIC CURIOSITY

		EXAMPLE
A.	Choose any positive number.	321
B.	Double it.	642
C.	Multiply by 1000.	642 000
D.	Add the original number.	642 321
E.	Divide by 3 times the original number (963).	667
F.	Your result is always 667.	

1. Try other examples. **2.** Can you explain this?

2-6 SIMPLIFYING POLYNOMIALS

Polynomials can often be simplified by using the Distributive Property, the Multiplication Properties of One and Negative One, and methods of adding and subtracting positive and negative numbers.

EXAMPLE 1 Simplify $7b - 9b$.

Ⓜ SOLUTION
$$\begin{aligned} 7b - 9b &= (7 - 9)b \\ &= [7 + (-9)]b \\ &= -2b \end{aligned}$$

EXAMPLE 2 Simplify $3x + 7x - x - 12x$.

Ⓜ SOLUTION
$$\begin{aligned} 3x + 7x - x - 12x &= 3x + 7x - 1x - 12x \\ &= (3 + 7 - 1 - 12)x \\ &= (10 - 1 - 12)x \\ &= (9 - 12)x \\ &= [9 + (-12)]x \\ &= -3x \end{aligned}$$

EXAMPLE 3 Simplify $5b - 6b$.

Ⓜ SOLUTION
$$\begin{aligned} 5b - 6b &= (5 - 6)b \\ &= [5 + (-6)]b \\ &= -1b \\ &= -b \end{aligned}$$

EXAMPLE 4 Simplify $-3x - x$.

Ⓜ SOLUTION
$$\begin{aligned} -3x - x &= -3x - 1x \\ &= (-3 - 1)x \\ &= [-3 + (-1)]x \\ &= -4x \end{aligned}$$

Remember, when you simplify a polynomial, you can combine only the *like* terms. If not all terms are alike, you may wish to group the like terms first.

EXAMPLE 5 Simplify $3a + 4b - 5a - 2b$.

Ⓜ SOLUTION
$$\begin{aligned} 3a + 4b - 5a - 2b &= 3a + 4b + (-5a) + (-2b) \\ &= 3a + (-5a) + 4b + (-2b) \\ &= [3 + (-5)]a + [4 + (-2)]b \\ &= -2a + 2b \end{aligned}$$

EXAMPLE 6 Simplify $3x - 2x^2 - 5x$.

(M) SOLUTION

$$\begin{aligned} 3x - 2x^2 - 5x &= 3x + (-2x^2) + (-5x) \\ &= 3x + (-5x) + (-2x^2) \\ &= [3 + (-5)]x + (-2x^2) \\ &= -2x - 2x^2 \end{aligned}$$

SIMPLIFYING A POLYNOMIAL

1. Find and group the like terms.
2. Combine like terms by using the Distributive Property.

CLASSROOM EXERCISES

Simplify by combining like terms.

1. $4h + 5h$
2. $2f + 3f$
3. $9k - 2k$
4. $6m - 2m$
5. $5c - c$
6. $4g + 5g - 6g$
7. $3xy + 6x^2 + 10x^2$
8. $x^2 + 7x^2 + 10$
9. $3b + 5p + 6b$
10. $a + b + c - b$
11. $2a + 5b - 2a + 5b$
12. $4x^3 + 5x^2 - 2x^2 + x^2$
13. $3x - 5x$
14. $6y - 8y$
15. $a - 4a + 2b$
16. $x - 2y + 5b$
17. $2a - 3b - 5a + b$
18. $3x - 5y - 8x + y$

EXERCISES

A Simplify.

1. $3x + 4x$
2. $2x + 5x$
3. $2a - 5a$
4. $4b - 7b$
5. $-3a - 4a$
6. $-4y - 7y$
7. $6x + x$
8. $2x + x$
9. $2y - y$
10. $6w - w$
11. $3b - 2b$
12. $9z - 8z$
13. $2a - 2b + 2a + 3b$
14. $4a - 4b + 3a + 2b$
15. $2a - b + 2a$
16. $5x - y + 3x$
17. $2x + 3x^2 - 5x^2$
18. $2x - 3x^2 + 6x^2$
19. $3a - 7b + 6a - 4b$
20. $3x - 8y + 2a - 5y$
21. $a^2 - 2b^2 + b^2$
22. $4x^2 - 3y^2 + y^2$
23. $4a^2 - 6b^2 - 4a^2$
24. $3x^2 - 2y^2 - 3x^2$
25. $6r + (-7t) + 12r + 9t$
26. $5a + 7b + (-1a) + 2b + 3a$
27. $12 + 19x^2 + 15x + (-6) + (-3x)$
28. $23 + 5a^2 + 8a + (-2a) + (-8)$
29. $16b + 38 + 13b + (-17)$
30. $12x + 19 + (-8x) + 5$

31. $6x^2 + 3x + 2x^2 - 4x + 3x^2$
32. $5x^2 - 2x + 3x^2 - 4x - 6x^2$
33. $3a - 2b + 3c - a - 3b - 4c$
34. $6m - 3n + 4p - 6n + 4m - 3p$
35. $-4p - 2q + 3r - 6r + 7q + 9p$
36. $8x - 3y + 2z - 4z + 6y - 2x$
37. $2a^2 - 3a + 6b - 4a + 9a^2$
38. $6b^2 - 21b + 4b^2 - 8a + (-5a)$
39. $-3x + 4y - 2x + 4z - 6y$
40. $10p - 6q + 4p - 3r + 7p + 6r$

B

41. $3(2x^2 + 4) + 2(6x^2 + 8)$
42. $2 + 3(b + 5)$
43. $(-5x) - 3(x + 4)$
44. $2(5a^2 + 3) + 3(4x^2 + 7)$
45. $2 + 6(x + 5)$
46. $-6x + 8(2x + 4)$
47. $8(x + 2) + 3[6x + 2(3x + 4)]$
48. $3(y + 1) + 4[7y + 2(2y + 3)]$
49. $4(a + 3b + 6) + 7(b + 2)$
50. $3(x + 2y + 4) + 5(2x + 3)$
51. $5(a + b) + 8(a + b) + 4a$
52. $2(x + y) + 3(x + y) + 4x$
53. $6(a + 2) + 5(3 + a)$
54. $4(b + 3) + 13(b + 5)$
55. $2(4a^2 + 6a + 3) + 9(8a^2 + 4a)$
56. $6(3m^2 + 6m + 5) + 8(7m^2 + 6m)$

C

57. $9[2(4a + 3b + 4) + 7(a + 14)] + 8(5a + 3b)$
58. $8(2x + y) + 13[2x + 3(4y + 2x + 6)]$

POSITIVE AND NEGATIVE SIGNS

The signs + and − began to appear in Holland in the fifteenth century as an aid to commerce. Goods were packaged so that each bale was about as heavy as some standard weight, and therefore about as heavy as each other. As each bale was weighed it was marked, for example, +4 if it was 4 units over the standard weight and −3 if it was 3 units under. The total then for *n* bales was *n* times the standard, adjusted by the sum for the markings on the bales.

This suggests a method for adding numbers that are almost equal.

EXAMPLE Add $3\frac{3}{4}$, $4\frac{1}{2}$, $4\frac{1}{4}$, 4, and $3\frac{7}{8}$.

SOLUTION

$$3\tfrac{3}{4} + 4\tfrac{1}{2} + 4\tfrac{1}{4} + 4 + 3\tfrac{7}{8}$$
$$\left(4 - \tfrac{2}{8}\right) + \left(4 + \tfrac{4}{8}\right) + \left(4 + \tfrac{2}{8}\right) + \left(4 + \tfrac{0}{8}\right) + \left(4 - \tfrac{1}{8}\right)$$

The sum is the same as $5(4) + \frac{3}{8}$. The sum is $20\frac{3}{8}$.

Use this method for the following exercises.

1. Add these scores: 76, 78, 78, 81, 82, 83, 85. Use 80 as a standard.
2. Larry worked $7\frac{3}{4}$ hours on Monday. On Tuesday through Friday he worked $6\frac{1}{2}$, $6\frac{3}{4}$, $7\frac{1}{4}$, and $7\frac{1}{4}$ hours. How many hours did Larry work?

2-7 DIVIDING POSITIVE AND NEGATIVE NUMBERS

In arithmetic you may have learned your basic division facts by relating them to the multiplication facts you knew.
For example, because $\boxed{5} \cdot 3 = 15$
you knew $15 \div \boxed{5} = 3$.

Later you used this same relationship between multiplication and division to help you check division. For example, you have some assurance that

The quotient is that number which, when multiplied by the divisor, gives the dividend. To check division, multiply the quotient and divisor. The result should be the dividend.

quotient ↓

divisor → $27\overline{)1026}$ with quotient 38 ← dividend (1026)   because $27 \cdot 38 = 1026$,

or $\frac{1026}{27} = 38$ because $27 \cdot 38 = 1026$.

Because we shall want this relationship to hold for division involving any real numbers, we base our definition on it.

Division by zero is undefined.

> For any real numbers a and b, with $b \neq 0$,
>
> $a \div b = c$ when $b \cdot c = a$
>
> or $\frac{a}{b} = c$ when $b \cdot c = a$

It follows from the definition that the quotient of two positive numbers is positive, the quotient of two negative numbers is positive, and the quotient of a positive and a negative number is negative.

EXAMPLE 1 Simplify $12 \div 4$.

SOLUTION Since $4 \cdot 3 = 12$,
$12 \div 4 = 3$.

EXAMPLE 2 Simplify $-12 \div 4$.

SOLUTION Since $4(-3) = -12$,
$-12 \div 4 = -3$.

In general, to divide, first determine whether the quotient is positive or negative. Then divide the absolute values and use the result of the first step.

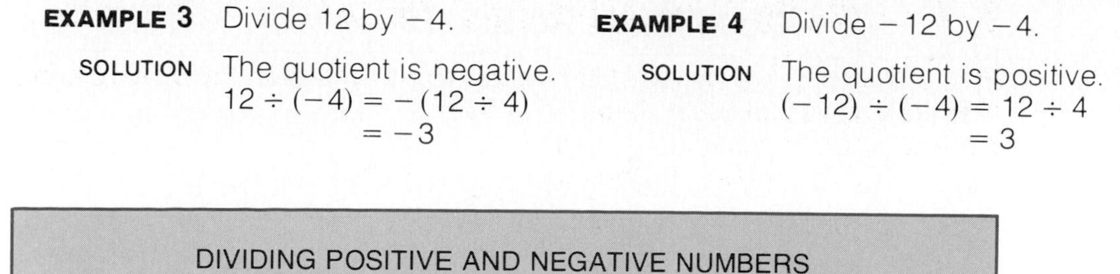

EXAMPLE 3 Divide 12 by -4.

SOLUTION The quotient is negative.

$$12 \div (-4) = -(12 \div 4)$$
$$= -3$$

EXAMPLE 4 Divide -12 by -4.

SOLUTION The quotient is positive.

$$(-12) \div (-4) = 12 \div 4$$
$$= 3$$

DIVIDING POSITIVE AND NEGATIVE NUMBERS

1. Find if the quotient is positive or negative using these rules:
   a. The quotient of two positive numbers or two negative numbers is a positive number.
   b. The quotient of a positive number and a negative number is a negative number.
2. Find the quotient of the absolute values and then use your findings from Step 1.

The fraction form may be used to indicate a division. The rules for dividing positive and negative numbers suggest the following properties for fractions.

$$\frac{-a}{b} = -\frac{a}{b}, \quad \frac{a}{-b} = -\frac{a}{b}, \quad \frac{-a}{-b} = \frac{a}{b}, \quad b \neq 0.$$

EXAMPLE 5 Divide 1 by -2.

(M) SOLUTION $\frac{1}{-2} = -\frac{1}{2}$

EXAMPLE 6 Divide -1.2 by 4.

(M) SOLUTION $\frac{-1.2}{4} = -0.3$

EXAMPLE 7 Divide -0.12 by -0.4.

(M) SOLUTION

$$\frac{-0.12}{-0.4} = \frac{0.12}{0.40}$$
$$= \frac{12}{40}$$
$$= \frac{3}{10}, \text{ or } 0.3$$

EXAMPLE 8 Divide 12 by -0.4.

(M) SOLUTION

$$\frac{12}{-0.4} = -\frac{12}{0.4}$$
$$= -\frac{120}{4}$$
$$= -30$$

CLASSROOM EXERCISES

Simplify each quotient.

1. $\frac{-12}{3}$ 2. $\frac{-10}{5}$ 3. $\frac{-30}{5}$ 4. $\frac{25}{-5}$ 5. $\frac{8}{-1}$

6. $\frac{-6}{6}$ 7. $\frac{0}{4}$ 8. $\frac{8}{-3}$ 9. $\frac{-15}{6}$ 10. $\frac{-15}{-1}$

11. $20 \div 5$ 12. $2.8 \div 7$ 13. $10 \div -0.2$ 14. $-0.4 \div 2$

15. $56 \div (-7)$ 16. $-16 \div 6$ 17. $6\frac{2}{3} \div -3\frac{1}{3}$ 18. $-1.75 \div (-0.25)$

EXERCISES

A Simplify each quotient.

1. $\frac{14}{-7}$ 2. $\frac{-10}{-2}$ 3. $\frac{12}{-2}$ 4. $\frac{-4}{-4}$ 5. $\frac{-18}{9}$

6. $\frac{-24}{9}$ 7. $\frac{-12}{3}$ 8. $\frac{-8}{-4}$ 9. $\frac{7}{1}$ 10. $\frac{-7}{-1}$

11. $\frac{0}{3}$ 12. $\frac{-0.04}{-2}$ 13. $\frac{-3.0}{6}$ 14. $\frac{-2.7}{0.9}$ 15. $\frac{80}{-16}$

16. $(-20) \div (-4)$ 17. $-63 \div 7$ 18. $-63 \div 9$ 19. $-51 \div 17$

20. $-84 \div -12$ 21. $-78 \div 13$ 22. $-120 \div -8$ 23. $-288 \div 72$

24. $-175 \div -25$ 25. $360 \div -45$ 26. $-144 \div 24$ 27. $-729 \div 9$

28. $392 \div -8$ 29. $-4900 \div -70$ 30. $8.4 \div -0.4$ 31. $-50 \div 2.5$

B 32. The product of two numbers is -32. One of the numbers is -16. Find the other.

33. A number divided by -3 equals 9. Find the number.

Evaluate for $x = 4$, $y = -6$ and $z = -8$.

34. $\frac{-xy}{-1}$ 35. $\frac{xz}{y}$ 36. $\frac{x^2}{y}$ 37. $\frac{-yz}{x}$ 38. $\frac{xy}{z}$ 39. $\frac{z}{xy}$

Evaluate for $a = -6$, $b = 3$ and $c = -2$.

40. $\frac{a+b}{2}$ 41. $abc \div (-9)$ 42. $bc \div a$ 43. $\frac{(a+1)^2 - b}{-(b+c)}$

C Evaluate C_t for $C_1 = 20$, $C_2 = 30$, and $C_3 = 40$.

44. $C_t = \frac{1}{\frac{1}{C_1} + \frac{1}{C_2} + \frac{1}{C_3}}$ 45. $C_t = \frac{C_1 C_2 C_3}{C_2 C_3 + C_1 C_3 + C_1 C_2}$

2-8 EVALUATING ALGEBRAIC EXPRESSIONS

To evaluate an algebraic expression, we replace the variables by numbers from their domains and perform the indicated operations.

EXAMPLE 1 Suppose $a = 2$ and $b = -3$.

Find the value for $\frac{2ab - 3b^2}{ab}$.

Ⓜ SOLUTION

$$\frac{2ab - 3b^2}{ab} = \frac{2(2)(-3) - 3(-3)^2}{2(-3)}$$
$$= \frac{2(2)(-3) - 3(9)}{2(-3)}$$
$$= \frac{-12 - 27}{-6}$$
$$= \frac{-39}{-6}$$
$$= 6\frac{1}{2}$$

EXAMPLE 2 Let $x = 2$.
Find the value for $(-x)^4$; for $-(x^4)$.

Ⓜ SOLUTION

$$(-x)^4 = (-2)^4$$
$$= (-2)(-2)(-2)(-2)$$
$$= 16$$
$$-(x^4) = -(2^4)$$
$$= -(2 \cdot 2 \cdot 2 \cdot 2)$$
$$= -16$$

EXAMPLE 3 Let $x = -2$.
Find the value for $(-x)^4$; for $-(x^4)$.

Ⓜ SOLUTION

$$(-x)^4 = [-(-2)]^4$$
$$= (2)^4$$
$$= (2)(2)(2)(2)$$
$$= 16$$
$$-(x^4) = -[(-2)^4]$$
$$= -(-2^4)$$
$$= -(-2)(-2)(-2)(-2)$$
$$= -(16)$$
$$= -16$$

EXAMPLE 4 Evaluate $2[x^2 + 3(y - 4z)]$ for $x = 5$ $y = 3$, and $z = 6$.

Simplify between the innermost grouping symbols first.

Ⓜ **SOLUTION**

$$\begin{aligned} 2[x^2 + 3(y - 4z)] &= 2[5^2 + 3(3 - 4 \cdot 6)] \\ &= 2[5^2 + 3(3 - 24)] \\ &= 2[5^2 + 3(-21)] \\ &= 2[25 - 63] \\ &= 2(-38) \\ &= -76 \end{aligned}$$

> EVALUATING AN ALGEBRAIC EXPRESSION
>
> 1. Replace each variable by a number from its domain.
> 2. Perform the operations shown between parentheses. Work between the innermost parentheses first.
> 3. Perform the remaining operations. Remember, between parentheses or when there are no parentheses, operations are performed in the following order:
>   a. Simplify terms with exponents.
>   b. Multiply and divide from left to right.
>   c. Add and subtract from left to right.

CLASSROOM EXERCISES

Evaluate each expression for $a = -3$ and $b = -2$.

1. $2a + b$ **2.** $3a - 2b$ **3.** $-2a - 2b$
4. $-2(a + b)$ **5.** $2a^2 + b^2$ **6.** $a^2 - b^2$
7. $(-a)^3$ **8.** $(-b)^2$ **9.** $2[a^2 + 3(a - 4b)]$

EXERCISES

A Evaluate each expression for $x = 2$, $y = -3$, $z = -4$, and $w = 0$.

1. $2x + 3y$ **2.** $3x + 5y$ **3.** $3x - 2y$ **4.** $6x - 4y$
5. $5x + z$ **6.** $2x + 3z$ **7.** $x^2 + y^2$ **8.** $2y^2 + x^2$
9. $x^2 - y^2$ **10.** $2x^2 - 3y^2$ **11.** $x - 2z$ **12.** $y - z$
13. $12w^4$ **14.** $-6w^5$ **15.** $-(z^3)$ **16.** y^6

17. $(-z)^3$
18. $(-y)^6$
19. $-2y^2 + 4xy + 2x^2$
20. $2x^2 - 3xy + 2y^2$
21. $-4x^2 + 6xy + 8y^2$
22. $x^2 + 2y^2 + 3xy$
23. $z^2 + 2yz + y^2$
24. $w^2 + zw + 3z^2$
25. $3[y^2 - 2(x^2 + 3)]$
26. $5[x^2 + 4(y^2 + 2)]$
27. $6[z^2 + 3(w + x)]$
28. $2[y^2 + 4(x + y + z)]$

B **29.** $\dfrac{4y - x^2}{z^2}$
30. $\dfrac{x^2 - y^2}{y - x}$
31. $\dfrac{-3w^5 + 6x}{3x - 2y}$
32. $\dfrac{x^2 + 2x + 1}{3x + 5y}$
33. $\dfrac{z^2 + 3z - 4}{x^2 + y^2}$
34. $\dfrac{y^2 - 3y + 5}{x + y}$

C **35.** Evaluate $\dfrac{3(x - 2)^2 + 6y}{x + (y - 2)^2}$ for $x = 4$ and $y = 5$.

36. Evaluate $\dfrac{2[a + 2(a + b)^2]}{a^2 + 2ab + 5b^2}$ for $a = 8$ and $b = 2$.

37. Evaluate $b^3 - 3b^2 - a$ for $a = -0.2$ and $b = 0.1$

CHECKING YOUR UNDERSTANDING

WORDS

Multiplication Property of Zero; of Negative One

CONCEPTS

- Any two real numbers may be multiplied. The product may be either positive or negative. [2-5]

- Any real number may be divided by any non-zero real number. The product may be either positive or negative. Division by zero is undefined. [2-7]

PROCESSES

- Multiply and divide positive and negative numbers. [2-5, 2-7]

1. $(3)(-5)$
2. $(-7)(-4)(2)$
3. $\dfrac{-18}{6}$
4. $\dfrac{-42}{-7}$

- Simplify a polynomial. [2-6]

5. $-7x - 2x$
6. $2y - 3x - 5y + 7x$
7. $-8x^2 + x - 5x^2$

- Evaluate an algebraic expression for positive or negative replacements. [2-8]

- **8.** $-7xy^2$ for $x = -2$, $y = -3$

9. $(-a)^3 - b^3 + ab$ for $a = 3$, $b = -1$

GETTING TO KNOW YOUR CALCULATOR

The electronic calculator can be a useful tool in mathematics. Since it is a tool, first you must understand how to use it. Remember every calculator model is different. For particular questions you should refer to the manual that comes with your calculator.

Before you try any of the following exercises, be sure to locate on your calculator the keys that are described here.

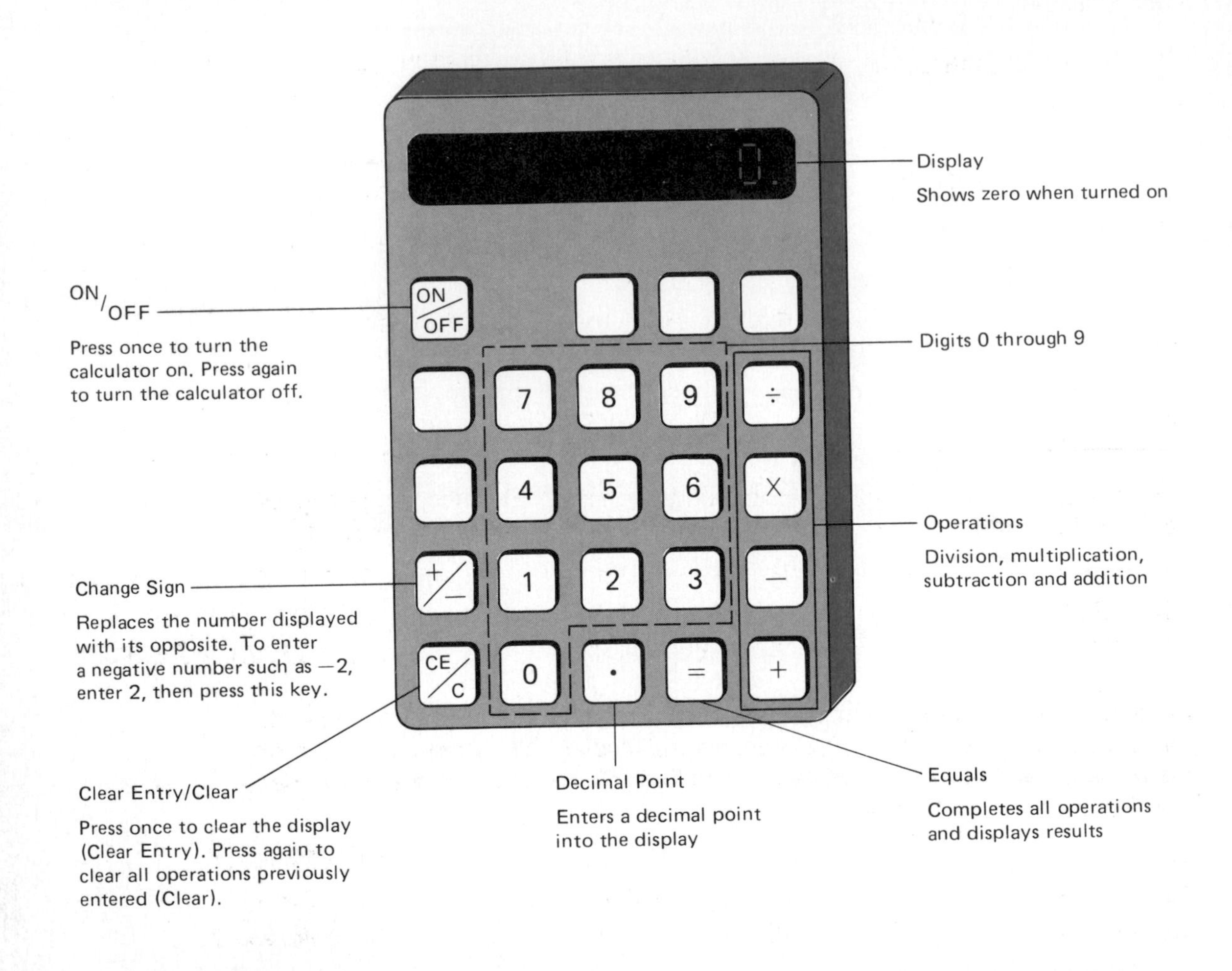

EXAMPLE 1 Use the calculator to add 7 and -9.

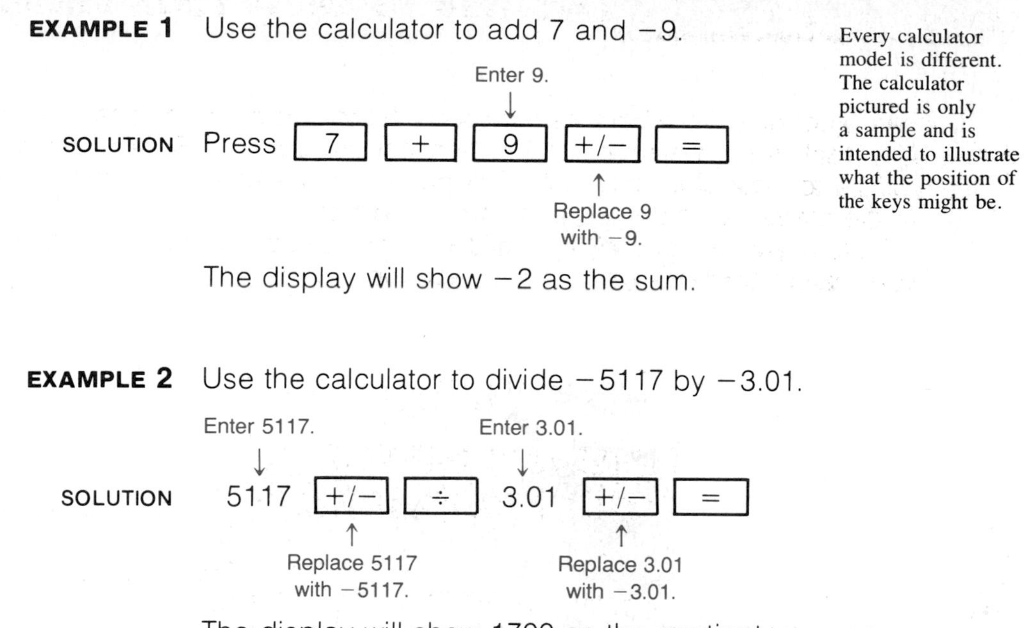

SOLUTION Press [7] [+] [9] [+/−] [=]

The display will show -2 as the sum.

Every calculator model is different. The calculator pictured is only a sample and is intended to illustrate what the position of the keys might be.

EXAMPLE 2 Use the calculator to divide -5117 by -3.01.

SOLUTION 5117 [+/−] [÷] 3.01 [+/−] [=]

The display will show 1700 as the quotient.

EXERCISES

Use your calculator to perform the indicated operation. Record your results on paper. They should give you a clue as to whether you made any mistakes.

1. $541 + 458$ **2.** $2573 - 2018$ **3.** 18×37

4. $76\,923 \div 231$ **5.** $0.83 + 1.39$ **6.** $562.1 - 473.3$

7. $24.864 \div 56$ **8.** $1.3653 \div 0.123$ **9.** $0.001554 \div 0.00002$

Do each of the following mentally. Record your results on paper. Then do each using your calculator. If a result on the display differs from the result on paper, you have made a mistake. Try both methods again to see if you can find the reason for your mistake.

10. $8 + (-3)$ **11.** $-6 + 14$ **12.** $-21 + (-11)$

13. $13 - (-4)$ **14.** $-15 - (-23)$ **15.** -8×12

16. $-7 \times (-9)$ **17.** $-44 \div 4$ **18.** $-56 \div (-7)$

OBJECTIVES: Multiply and divide monomials. Simplify fractions. Add, subtract, multiply, and divide with fractions.

2-9 MULTIPLYING MONOMIALS

A counting number used as an exponent shows how many times another number, the base, is used as a factor.

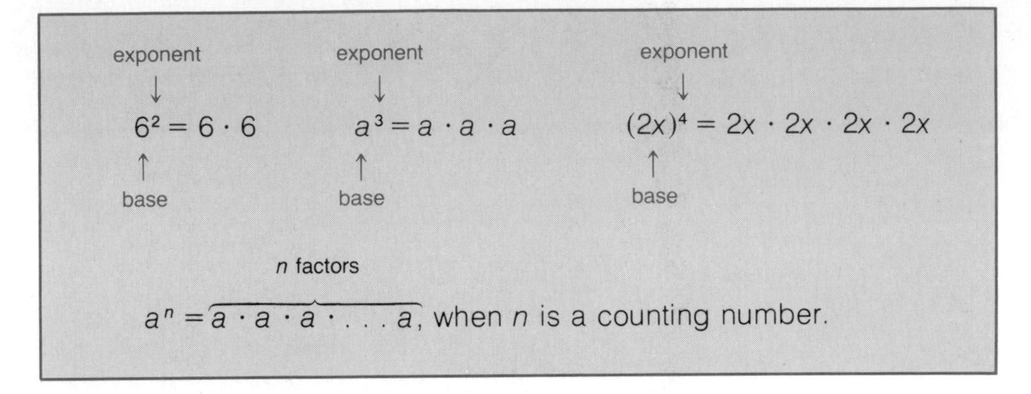

When two terms have the same base, you may use exponents and the properties of multiplication to simplify their product.

EXAMPLE 1 Multiply x^3 and x^2.

SOLUTION
$$\begin{aligned} x^3 \cdot x^2 &= (x \cdot x \cdot x)(x \cdot x) \\ &= x \cdot x \cdot x \cdot x \cdot x \\ &= x^5 \end{aligned}$$

In Example 1, note that the exponent of the product, x^5, is the sum of the exponents of the factors, x^3 and x^2. In general, when two terms have the same base, you may add their exponents to find their product.

EXAMPLE 2 Multiply $4x^3$ and $5x^4$.

SOLUTION
$$\begin{aligned} (4x^3)(5x^4) &= 4 \cdot x^3 \cdot 5 \cdot x^4 \\ &= 4 \cdot 5 \cdot x^3 \cdot x^4 \\ &= 20x^{3+4} \\ &= 20x^7 \end{aligned}$$

EXAMPLE 3 Multiply $3a^2$ and $-5a$.

SOLUTION
$$\begin{aligned} (3a^2)(-5a) &= 3 \cdot a^2 \cdot (-5) \cdot a^1 \\ &= 3 \cdot (-5) \cdot a^2 \cdot a^1 \\ &= -15a^3 \end{aligned}$$

EXAMPLE 4 Multiply $-6a$ and $3b$.

SOLUTION
$$(-6a)(3b) = -6 \cdot a \cdot 3 \cdot b$$
$$= -6 \cdot 3 \cdot a \cdot b$$
$$= -18ab$$

MULTIPLYING MONOMIALS

1. Find the product for the coefficients, making sure that the product is correctly shown as positive or negative.
2. Find the product for the variables, adding the exponents for terms that have the same base.

$$x^a \cdot x^b = x^{a+b}$$

For this rule, the base x may be any real number but exponents a and b are restricted to the positive integers.

CLASSROOM EXERCISES

Simplify each product.

1. $4x \cdot 3$ **2.** $(3m)(-2)$ **3.** $-5a \cdot 4$ **4.** $(-7x)(5x)$
5. $(3a)(4a)$ **6.** $(6m)(-2m)$ **7.** $(6h)(-k)$ **8.** $(2xy)(-2)$
9. $(-2bc)(-5)$ **10.** $(-x)(-x)$ **11.** $-\frac{2}{5}h\left(-\frac{1}{2}h\right)$ **12.** $(1.2w)(6w)$
13. $(-r^2t^5)(rt^2)$ **14.** $(3x^4)(-2x^4y^3)$ **15.** $(5ab^2)(25ac)$ **16.** $(a^2b^5)(a^3b^6)$

EXERCISES

A Simplify each product.

1. $(-6x)(-5)$ **2.** $-3c \cdot 4$ **3.** $-4y \cdot b$ **4.** $(-8c)(-d)$
5. $(4r)(s)$ **6.** $(3p)(-6)$ **7.** $(3ab)(-4)$ **8.** $(-xy)(z)$
9. $(4hk)(g)$ **10.** $(-4c)(-5c)$ **11.** $(-2h)(-3h)$ **12.** $-\frac{1}{2}k\left(\frac{1}{3}k\right)$
13. $\frac{2}{3}c\left(\frac{1}{2}c\right)$ **14.** $\frac{3}{5}s\left(\frac{2}{3}s\right)$ **15.** $(0.2x)(5x)$ **16.** $(1.3x)(10x)$
17. $(0.02p)(5p)$ **18.** $(1.5c)\left(\frac{1}{3}c\right)$ **19.** $(4a^2)(-7a)$ **20.** $(-5x^2)(3x^5)$
21. $8(-10m)$ **22.** $(3a^2)(2a^3)$ **23.** $x^4 \cdot x^6$ **24.** $-6b^2 \cdot 5b^4$
25. $(-5a^2)(-5b^4)$ **26.** $(-4x^3)(5a^3)$ **27.** $6b^4(-7b^3)$ **28.** $-14(2x)$
29. $-15x^3\left(\frac{2}{3}x\right)$ **30.** $(3m^2)(-4mn)$ **31.** $(-3c^2x)(-3c^2d)$ **32.** $(4h)(5h^2)$
33. $(0.2x^4)(4x^5)$ **34.** $4^3 \cdot 4^2$ **35.** $10^2 \cdot 10^5$ **36.** $\left(1\frac{1}{4}m\right)(4m^7)$
37. $5^2 \cdot 5^3$ **38.** $10^7 \cdot 10^3$ **39.** $9 \cdot 9^2$ **40.** $2 \cdot 2^3$

B

41. $(-3x^2y^2z)(-3x^2y^2z)(-3x^2y^2z)$

42. $(-4a^2b)(-3ab^2)(a^2b^4)$

43. $(0.2a)(5a^2b)(-abc^2)$

44. $(-0.5xy^2z^3)(0.5xy^2z^3)(-0.5x^2y^2)$

45. $(2xyz)(x^2y)(0.3xz^2)$

46. $(-4ax)(-0.8bx)(2a^2b^2)$

47. $(-0.4xy^2)(-1.5xz^3)$

48. $(1.3xz^2)(3xy^4)$

49. $(-4a)(a^2)(-a^3) + (3a^2)(a^4)$

50. $(-2m)(mn^2)(-5mp^2) + (-m^2)(2mn)(4np^2)$

51. $(-3ab^2c)(-2ab)^2$

52. $(4xy^3)^4$

53. $(-x)^5(-2y)^4$

54. $(0.3a^2b)^2$

55. $\left(\frac{x}{3}\right)^2$

56. $\left(-\frac{1}{2}ab^2\right)^3$

C

57. $(x^{n+1})(x^n)$

58. $(y^{2n})(y^{3n})$

59. $(y^{n+2})(y)$

60. $(x^n)^2$

61. $(x^n)^{10}$

62. $(x^2)^n$

63. $x^{(3^2)}$

64. $(xy)^2$

65. $(x^ny)^2$

66. $(x^ny^m)^2$

67. $(xy)^n$

68. $(x^2y^3)^n$

69. $(x^m)^n$

70. $(x^ny^m)^k$

71. $x^{(nm)}$

A MENTAL ARITHMETIC CHALLENGE

a	1	2	3	4	5	6	7	8	...
$a \cdot a$	1	4	9	16	25	36	49	64	...

Use the table above.

EXAMPLE

1. Find the sum of any two consecutive numbers in the top row. — Add 3 and 4.
2. Find the difference of two corresponding numbers in the bottom row. — Subtract 9 from 16.
3. Compare your results. Repeat Steps 1 and 2 for other pairs of consecutive numbers. What appears to be true?

Suppose you know two consecutive entries in the top row, and one of the two entries in the bottom row.

know	know
know one but not both	

4. Tell how you could find the other bottom-row entry.

Use the procedure from Exercise 4. Mentally simplify each.

5. 21^2 **6.** 19^2 **7.** 31^2 **8.** 29^2 **9.** 51^2 **10.** 39^2

11. 61^2 **12.** 49^2 **13.** 101^2 **14.** 99^2 **15.** 42^2 **16.** 78^2

2-10 MULTIPLYING WITH FRACTIONS; SIMPLIFYING FRACTIONS

In arithmetic you learned to multiply using fractions by multiplying numerators and multiplying denominators.

$$\frac{a}{b} \cdot \frac{c}{d} = \frac{a \cdot c}{b \cdot d}, \; b \neq 0, \; d \neq 0$$

EXAMPLE 1 Multiply $\frac{3}{4}$ and $\frac{7}{8}$

SOLUTION
$$\frac{3}{4} \cdot \frac{7}{8} = \frac{3 \cdot 7}{4 \cdot 8}$$
$$= \frac{21}{32}$$

A fraction is in **lowest terms** when the numerator and the denominator have no common factor involving a variable and no common integral factor, except 1 and -1. To *simplify a fraction* $\frac{a}{b}$ means to find a fraction $\frac{c}{d}$ in lowest terms such that $\frac{a}{b} = \frac{c}{d}$. We simplify fractions by first finding the common factors of the numerator and denominator. Then we use the Multiplication Property of One ($a \cdot 1 = a$ for any number a) to eliminate those common factors.

Simplifying a fraction is the same activity as *reducing* it to lowest terms.

EXAMPLE 2 Simplify $\frac{21}{28}$

SOLUTION
$$\frac{21}{28} = \frac{7 \cdot 3}{7 \cdot 4}$$
$$= \frac{7}{7} \cdot \frac{3}{4}$$
$$= 1 \cdot \frac{3}{4}$$
$$= \frac{3}{4}$$

EXAMPLE 3 Simplify $\frac{5x}{15x^2}$

SOLUTION
$$\frac{5x}{15x^2} = \frac{5x \cdot 1}{5x \cdot 3x}$$
$$= \frac{5x}{5x} \cdot \frac{1}{3x}$$
$$= 1 \cdot \frac{1}{3x}$$
$$= \frac{1}{3x}$$

Once you understand how the Multiplication Property of One lets you eliminate common factors from the numerator and denominator, you may use a shorter method to simplify a fraction. Example 4 shows how.

EXAMPLE 4 Multiply $\frac{3}{4}$ and $\frac{7}{9}$. Simplify the product.

SOLUTION

$$\frac{3}{4} \cdot \frac{7}{9} = \frac{3 \cdot 7}{4 \cdot 9} = \frac{21}{36} = \frac{3}{3} \cdot \frac{7}{12} = 1 \cdot \frac{7}{12} = \frac{7}{12}$$

Shorter Method

$$\frac{3}{4} \cdot \frac{7}{9} = \frac{\overset{1}{\cancel{3}} \cdot 7}{4 \cdot 3 \cdot \underset{1}{\cancel{3}}} = \frac{7}{12}$$

Shortest Method

Ⓜ $$\frac{\overset{1}{\cancel{3}}}{4} \cdot \frac{7}{\underset{3}{\cancel{9}}} = \frac{7}{12}$$

EXAMPLE 5 Multiply $\frac{8x}{15y}$ and $\frac{-9y}{14x}$.

Ⓜ SOLUTION

$$\frac{\overset{4 \cdot 1}{\cancel{8x}}}{\underset{5 \cdot 1}{\cancel{15y}}} \cdot \frac{\overset{-3 \cdot 1}{\cancel{-9y}}}{\underset{7 \cdot 1}{\cancel{14x}}} = \frac{-12}{35} = -\frac{12}{35}$$

EXAMPLE 6 Multiply $\frac{3x^2}{4}$ and $\frac{6}{x}$.

Ⓜ SOLUTION

$$\frac{3\overset{x}{\cancel{x^2}}}{\underset{2}{\cancel{4}}} \cdot \frac{\overset{3}{\cancel{6}}}{\underset{1}{\cancel{x}}} = \frac{9x}{2}$$

MULTIPLYING WITH FRACTIONS

Multiply numerators; multiply denominators.

$$\frac{a}{b} \cdot \frac{c}{d} = \frac{ac}{bd},\ b \neq 0,\ d \neq 0.$$

SIMPLIFYING FRACTIONS

Use the Multiplication Property of One. Eliminate common factors from the numerator and denominator to obtain a fraction in lowest terms.

$$\frac{ac}{bc} = \frac{a}{b} \cdot \frac{\overset{1}{\cancel{c}}}{\underset{1}{\cancel{c}}} \quad \text{or} \quad \frac{a\overset{1}{\cancel{c}}}{b\underset{1}{\cancel{c}}} = \frac{a}{b}$$

CLASSROOM EXERCISES

Simplify.

1. $\frac{4}{8}$
2. $\frac{-7}{21}$
3. $\frac{30}{42}$
4. $\frac{4a}{5a}$
5. $\frac{a}{a^3}$
6. $\frac{x^4}{x^3}$
7. $\frac{xy^2}{x^2y}$
8. $\frac{8a^2}{12a}$
9. $\frac{5a^2}{-10a}$
10. $\frac{4b^2}{-8b}$

Simplify each product.

11. $\frac{3}{4} \cdot \frac{8}{11}$
12. $\frac{5}{6} \cdot \frac{3}{8}$
13. $\frac{4}{-5} \cdot \frac{5}{11}$
14. $\frac{2x}{y} \cdot \frac{3}{z}$
15. $\frac{3x}{-2y} \cdot \frac{-3}{x}$
16. $\frac{2y}{3} \cdot \frac{4x}{5y}$
17. $\frac{3}{5} \cdot \frac{2y}{7x}$
18. $\frac{2x}{5y} \cdot \frac{10y}{1}$

EXERCISES

A Simplify.

1. $\frac{4a}{20a^3}$
2. $\frac{2x}{10x^2}$
3. $\frac{a^3b^2}{a^2b^3}$
4. $\frac{3a^2}{9a}$

Simplify each product.

5. $\frac{3x}{y} \cdot \frac{4}{z}$
6. $\frac{2a}{b} \cdot \frac{5}{d}$
7. $\frac{4a}{3b} \cdot \frac{5a}{7b}$
8. $\frac{3a}{4b} \cdot \frac{5a}{11b}$
9. $\frac{2}{3} \cdot \frac{6}{7}$
10. $\frac{3}{4} \cdot \frac{8}{11}$
11. $\frac{-7m}{5} \cdot 3$
12. $\frac{5x}{-7} \cdot 5$
13. $b^2 \cdot \frac{b}{a}$
14. $x^3 \cdot \frac{x}{y}$
15. $\frac{-c}{d} \cdot \frac{3}{4}$
16. $\frac{-a}{b} \cdot \frac{7}{8}$
17. $\frac{2y}{3} \cdot \frac{6}{y}$
18. $\frac{3x}{-4} \cdot \frac{8}{x}$
19. $\frac{4x^2}{1} \cdot \frac{1}{x}$
20. $\frac{3r^2}{1} \cdot \frac{1}{r}$
21. $\frac{121x^2}{5} \cdot \frac{15}{11x}$
22. $\frac{72}{10y} \cdot \frac{130y^2}{24}$
23. $\frac{66z^3}{-105} \cdot \frac{21z}{-198}$
24. $\frac{14y^2}{19} \cdot \frac{76y^2}{84}$
25. $\frac{75x^4}{2} \cdot \frac{38}{300x}$
26. $\frac{64}{15x^2} \cdot \frac{120x^5}{256}$

B

27. $\frac{3a^2}{4b} \cdot \frac{-2b^3}{3a} \cdot \frac{2z}{-9}$
28. $\left(\frac{3x}{y}\right)^2 \cdot \frac{(-2x^2)}{3y^2}$
29. $\frac{(-2a)^3}{3x^2} \cdot \frac{6x^3}{-2a^2}$
30. $\left(\frac{3x}{y}\right)^3 \cdot \frac{3y}{-x}$
31. $\frac{6m^3n}{10a^2} \cdot \frac{4a^2m}{9n^2}$
32. $\frac{7xy^3}{11z^2} \cdot \frac{44z^3}{21x^2y}$

C

33. $\frac{25x^2}{36y} \cdot \frac{18y^2}{125x^3} \cdot \frac{5z^2}{8y^3} \cdot \frac{6y^2}{5z^2}$
34. $\frac{155xy}{63z} \cdot 36z^2 \cdot \frac{16xyz}{105x^2y^2} \cdot \frac{xy}{48xy^2}$

2-11 DIVIDING MONOMIALS

The Multiplication Property of One can help you simplify the quotient of two monomials that have some factors in common.

EXAMPLE 1 Divide xyz by $2xz$, $x \neq 0$, $z \neq 0$.

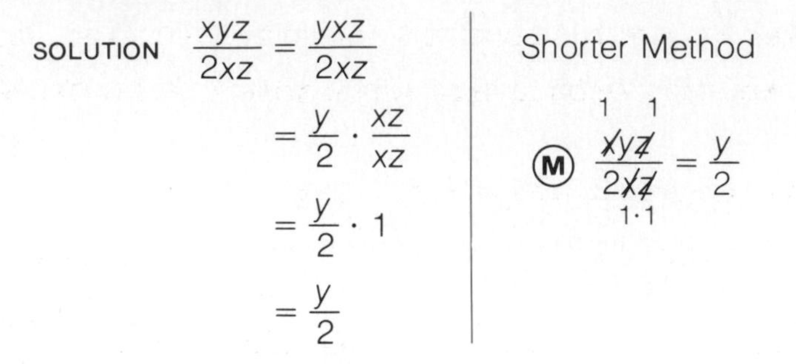

SOLUTION $\frac{xyz}{2xz} = \frac{yxz}{2xz}$

$= \frac{y}{2} \cdot \frac{xz}{xz}$

$= \frac{y}{2} \cdot 1$

$= \frac{y}{2}$

Shorter Method

Ⓜ $\frac{\not{x}y\not{z}}{2\not{x}\not{z}} = \frac{y}{2}$

When two terms have the same base, you may use exponents to help you simplify their quotient.

EXAMPLE 2 Divide a^7 by a^2.

SOLUTION 1

$\frac{a^7}{a^2} = \frac{aaaaa\not{a}\not{a}}{\not{a}\not{a}}$

$= a^5$

SOLUTION 2

Ⓜ $\frac{a^7}{a^2} = \frac{a^5\not{a^2}}{\not{a^2}}$

$= a^5$

In Example 2, note that the exponent of the quotient, a^5, is the difference of the exponents of the terms a^7 and a^2. In general, when two terms have the same base, you may subtract the smaller exponent from the larger exponent to help you find their quotient.

EXAMPLE 3 Divide $12x^5$ by $-4x$.

SOLUTION 1

Ⓜ $\frac{12x^5}{-4x} = \frac{\not{12}\not{x} \cdot x^4}{\not{-4}\not{x}}$

$= -3x^4$

SOLUTION 2

Ⓜ $\frac{12x^5}{-4x} = (-3)x^{5-1}$

$= -3x^4$

EXAMPLE 4 Divide a^2 by a^5.

SOLUTION 1

Ⓜ $\frac{a^2}{a^5} = \frac{\cancel{a^2}^{1}}{\cancel{a^2}_{1} \cdot a^3}$, or $\frac{1}{a^3}$

SOLUTION 2

Ⓜ $\frac{a^2}{a^5} = \frac{1}{a^{5-2}}$, or $\frac{1}{a^3}$

An expression like $\frac{x^2}{x^2}$, $x \neq 0$, is equal to 1. If we subtract exponents, we get x^{2-2}, or x^0. For this reason, a term with exponent zero is defined to be 1.

EXAMPLE 5 Divide $-24x^7y^3z^2$ by $4x^2y^5z^2$.

SOLUTION 1

Ⓜ $$\frac{-24x^7y^3z^2}{4x^2y^5z^2} = \frac{-6x^{7-2}z^{2-2}}{y^{5-3}}$$
$$= \frac{-6x^5z^0}{y^2}$$
$$= \frac{-6x^5}{y^2}$$

SOLUTION 2

Ⓜ $$\frac{\overset{-6 \cdot x^5 \cdot 1 \cdot 1}{\cancel{-24}\cancel{x^7}\cancel{y^3}\cancel{z^2}}}{\underset{1 \cdot 1 \cdot y^2 \cdot 1}{\cancel{4}\cancel{x^2}\cancel{y^5}\cancel{z^2}}} = \frac{-6x^5}{y^2}, \text{ or } -\frac{6x^5}{y^2}$$

DIVIDING MONOMIALS

1. Find the quotient for the coefficients, making sure that the quotient is correctly shown as positive or negative.
2. Find the quotient for the variables, subtracting the exponents for terms that have the same base.

$\frac{x^a}{x^b} = x^{a-b}$ if $a > b$ $\quad \frac{x^a}{x^b} = \frac{1}{x^{b-a}}$ if $a < b$ $\quad \frac{x^a}{x^a} = 1$ $\quad x^0 = 1$

CLASSROOM EXERCISES

Simplify each quotient.

1. $n^5 \div n$ **2.** $x^4 \div x^4$ **3.** $18a^2 \div 6$ **4.** $-6x \div 3$ **5.** $(4ab) \div (-1)$

6. $\frac{x^3}{x}$ **7.** $\frac{a}{a^3}$ **8.** $\frac{-15a^5b^8}{5a^5b^2}$ **9.** $\frac{-27x^5y^7}{-3x^3y^2}$ **10.** $\frac{8a^3b^6c}{48a^2b^4c^3}$

EXERCISES

A Simplify each quotient.

1. $c^3 \div c$
2. $b^4 \div b$
3. $\frac{10m^2}{-5}$
4. $\frac{6x}{-2}$
5. $-14x \div (-7)$
6. $-x^7 \div (-x^2)$
7. $(4x^2) \div (-4x^2)$
8. $\frac{(-2a^2)}{(-8a^2)}$
9. $\frac{3y}{15x^2y}$
10. $\frac{-1}{-3m^4}$
11. $2a^4b^4 \div ab^2$
12. $-5pq^2 \div 5pq$
13. $\frac{50c^4d^3}{-5c^3d}$
14. $\frac{6xyz^2}{12x^3yz}$
15. $\frac{22a^3b^3c^3}{11a^3b^4c^2}$
16. $\frac{48a^2c^3}{16a^3c}$
17. $\frac{-2}{-8x^2}$
18. $\frac{16m}{8}$
19. $\frac{-14m^3}{-2}$
20. $\frac{-24x}{-2x}$
21. $\frac{16m^5}{4m}$
22. $\frac{-30a}{-15}$
23. $\frac{8y^6}{y^6}$
24. $\frac{-2ab}{2a}$

B

25. $\frac{-x^5}{(-x)^2}$
26. $\frac{-4x^6}{(2x)^3}$
27. $\frac{x-y}{-(x-y)}$
28. $\frac{2x-y}{-(2x-y)}$
29. $\frac{16x^5y^2}{(2xy)^3}$
30. $\frac{(4x^5y^2)^2}{(-2x^2y^2)^3}$
31. $\frac{-(3a^3b^2)^3}{6(a^2b^3)^3}$
32. $\frac{(-3r^3t^6)^2}{-6(r^2t^4)^3}$

C

33. $\frac{3x^2}{x} + \frac{12x^4}{6x^3}$
34. $\frac{70x^5}{10x^2} - \frac{36x^4}{6x}$
35. $\frac{45a^3b^2}{9ab} - \frac{52a^2b^5}{4b^4}$

EXPANDING OUR LANGUAGE

Prefixes and suffixes are used to expand our language capabilities without requiring that we learn a vast number of new words. Consider the words unicycle, bicycle, and tricycle.

1. How are the words alike?
2. How are the objects alike?
3. How are the words different?
4. How are the objects different?

You have begun to study polynomials. Consider the words monomial, binomial, trinomial, and polynomial.

5. How are the words alike and different?
6. How are the mathematical expressions alike and different?
7. Make a list of at least seven words that use the prefix "tri".

2-12 DIVIDING WITH FRACTIONS

If the product of two numbers is 1, each number is the **reciprocal** or **multiplicative inverse** of the other.

RECIPROCALS

$\frac{3}{4}$ and $\frac{4}{3}$ $\left(\frac{3}{4} \cdot \frac{4}{3} = 1\right)$ a and $\frac{1}{a}$, $a \neq 0$ $\left(a \cdot \frac{1}{a} = 1\right)$

$\frac{5}{x}$ and $\frac{x}{5}$, $x \neq 0$ $\left(\frac{5}{x} \cdot \frac{x}{5} = 1\right)$ $\frac{p}{q}$ and $\frac{q}{p}$, $p \neq 0$, $q \neq 0$ $\left(\frac{p}{q} \cdot \frac{q}{p} = 1\right)$

Remember that $a = \frac{a}{1}$.

You have found that instead of subtracting one number from another, you may add its opposite, or additive inverse.

$$a - b = a + (-b)$$

Similarly, instead of dividing by a non-zero number, you may multiply by its reciprocal, or multiplicative inverse.

$$a \div b = a \cdot \frac{1}{b},\ b \neq 0$$

To check division you may multiply the quotient and divisor. The result should be the dividend.

Just as subtraction amounts to finding an unknown addend given a sum and one addend, division amounts to finding an unknown factor given a product and one factor.

EXAMPLE 1 Divide $\frac{3}{4}$ by $\frac{7}{9}$.

Ⓜ SOLUTION $\frac{3}{4} \div \frac{7}{9} = \frac{3}{4} \cdot \frac{9}{7}$

$= \frac{27}{28}$

CHECK $\frac{\overset{3}{\cancel{27}}}{\underset{4}{\cancel{28}}} \cdot \frac{\overset{1}{\cancel{7}}}{\underset{1}{\cancel{9}}} \stackrel{?}{=} \frac{3}{4}$

$\frac{3}{4} = \frac{3}{4}$ ✓

EXAMPLE 2 Divide $8x$ by $\frac{1}{4}$.

Ⓜ SOLUTION $8x \div \frac{1}{4} = 8x \cdot \frac{4}{1}$

$= 32x$

CHECK $32x \cdot \frac{1}{4} \stackrel{?}{=} 8x$

$8x = 8x$ ✓

EXAMPLE 3 Divide $\frac{x}{3}$ by $\frac{-x}{2}$, $-x \neq 0$.

Ⓜ SOLUTION $\frac{x}{3} \div \frac{-x}{2} = \frac{\overset{1}{\cancel{x}}}{3} \cdot \frac{2}{\underset{-1}{-\cancel{x}}}$

$= \frac{2}{-3}$, or $-\frac{2}{3}$

CHECK $-\frac{\overset{1}{\cancel{2}}}{3} \cdot \frac{-x}{\underset{1}{\cancel{2}}} \stackrel{?}{=} \frac{x}{3}$

$-\frac{-x}{3} \stackrel{?}{=} \frac{x}{3}$

$\frac{x}{3} = \frac{x}{3}$ ✓

EXAMPLE 4 Divide $\frac{4a^3}{21}$ by $\frac{2a}{7}$, $a \neq 0$.

Ⓜ SOLUTION $\frac{4a^3}{21} \div \frac{2a}{7} = \frac{\overset{2a^2}{\cancel{4a^3}}}{\underset{3}{\cancel{21}}} \cdot \frac{\overset{1}{\cancel{7}}}{\underset{1 \cdot 1}{\cancel{2a}}}$

$= \frac{2a^2}{3}$

CHECK $\frac{2a^2}{3} \cdot \frac{2a}{7} \stackrel{?}{=} \frac{4a^3}{21}$

$\frac{4a^3}{21} = \frac{4a^3}{21}$ ✓

> DIVIDING WITH FRACTIONS
>
> 1. To divide by a number, multiply by its reciprocal, or multiplicative inverse.
>
> $$\frac{a}{b} \div \frac{c}{d} = \frac{a}{b} \cdot \frac{d}{c}$$
>
> $$= \frac{ad}{bc},\ b, c, d \neq 0$$
>
> 2. Simplify the quotient to lowest terms.

CLASSROOM EXERCISES

Simplify each quotient.

1. $6 \div \frac{1}{3}$ **2.** $\frac{x}{3} \div \frac{x}{2}$ **3.** $\frac{c}{5} \div \frac{c}{3}$ **4.** $2\frac{3}{4} \div \frac{1}{4}$

5. $10 \div \frac{1}{5}$ **6.** $b^2 \div \frac{b}{a}$ **7.** $\frac{-ab}{3} \div \frac{b}{4}$ **8.** $15 \div \frac{2}{3}$

9. $\frac{15}{a} \div \frac{2}{3a}$ **10.** $\frac{4xy}{1} \div \frac{2x^2}{3}$ **11.** $\frac{1}{10} \div \frac{a}{50}$ **12.** $\frac{c}{d} \div \frac{a}{b}$

EXERCISES

A Simplify each quotient.

1. $12 \div \frac{1}{4}$ **2.** $10 \div \frac{1}{5}$ **3.** $\frac{x}{4} \div \frac{x}{3}$ **4.** $\frac{y}{3} \div \frac{y}{2}$

5. $\frac{a}{5} \div \frac{a}{4}$ **6.** $\frac{b}{14} \div \frac{b}{11}$ **7.** $\frac{x^2}{\frac{x}{y}}$ **8.** $\frac{a^3}{\frac{a}{b}}$

9. $\frac{ax}{3} \div \frac{x}{2}$ **10.** $\frac{2x}{3} \div \frac{4}{9}$ **11.** $\frac{2xy}{3} \div \frac{2x^2}{3}$ **12.** $\frac{3ab}{4} \div \frac{6a^2}{4}$

13. $\frac{-\frac{a}{b}}{\frac{c}{a}}$ **14.** $\frac{-\frac{x}{y}}{\frac{z}{x}}$ **15.** $\frac{\frac{a}{b}}{\frac{b}{a}}$ **16.** $\frac{\frac{x}{y}}{\frac{y}{x}}$

17. $\frac{y^2}{x^2} \div \frac{a^2}{x^3}$ **18.** $\frac{p^3}{2q} \div \frac{-p^2}{4q}$ **19.** $19x^2 \div \frac{3x}{38}$ **20.** $25m \div \frac{2}{m^2}$

B Perform the indicated operations.

21. $\left(\frac{2}{3} \div \frac{3}{4}\right) \div \frac{7}{8}$ **22.** $\frac{3}{4} \div \left(\frac{7}{8} \div \frac{5}{6}\right)$ **23.** $\frac{2}{3} \div \left(\frac{3}{4} \div \frac{7}{8}\right)$

24. $\frac{2}{x^2} \cdot \frac{x}{6} \div \frac{y}{9}$ **25.** $\frac{a^3}{8} \cdot \frac{2}{a^2} \div \frac{a}{6}$ **26.** $\frac{ab^2}{c} \cdot \frac{bc^2}{a} \div abc$

C **27.** $\frac{(-4a)^2}{(6ab)^3} \div \frac{(-4a^2b)^2}{(3ab^2)^2}$ **28.** $\frac{(2a^2b)^3}{(-5ac)^2} \div \frac{(8ab^2)^2}{(-10a^2c^2)^2}$

29. $\frac{(-1.5x^2y)^2}{(0.2y^2z)^2} \div \frac{(0.5xy^2)^2}{(0.1z^2)^3}$ **30.** $\frac{(0.3xy)^3}{(0.2xy^2z)^3} \div \frac{(0.6yz)^2}{(0.4xy^2)^3}$

ARITHMETIC MIND READING

Find the columns in which your age appears. Add the numbers at the top of those columns.

1. What is special about the sum you obtain?
2. Have a friend name the columns in which his or her age appears. Add the numbers at the top of those columns and "guess" his or her age. (If an age does not appear on this chart, the person is 32 or older.)
3. Can you modify the above procedure so that this chart works for ages greater than 31?
4. Can you extend this chart so that it works for ages greater than 31?

A	B	C	D	E
16	8	4	2	1
17	9	5	3	3
18	10	6	6	5
19	11	7	7	7
20	12	12	10	9
21	13	13	11	11
22	14	14	14	13
23	15	15	15	15
24	24	20	18	17
25	25	21	19	19
26	26	22	22	21
27	27	23	23	23
28	28	28	26	25
29	29	29	27	27
30	30	30	30	29
31	31	31	31	31

THE METRIC SYSTEM

The metric system of measurement was first proposed in 1670. Today over 90% of the world's population lives in countries that have adopted or are changing to the metric system. It has become the international language of measurement for scientists and business people, and is rapidly gaining in use for everyday purposes of home, school, and work.

The meter (m) is a unit of *length*. It originally was defined to be one ten-millionth of the distance from the equator to the north pole. Today, the meter is defined in terms of the wavelength of a certain kind of radiation. In practical terms, one meter is about half the height of an ordinary door. A tennis court covers an *area* of approximately 250 square meters (m^2). A medium-sized refrigerator requires a packing crate whose *volume* is about 1 cubic meter (m^3).

The liter (L) is a metric unit for measuring *capacity*. The gram (g) and the degree Celsius (°C) are metric units used for measuring, respectively, *mass* and *temperature*.

The metric system is related to our system of decimal numeration. Units are related by factors that are powers of ten. The names of units are formed by using prefixes which indicate these factors.

Prefix	Meaning	Units of Mass
kilo (k)	one thousand	1 kilogram (kg) equals 1000 g
hecto (h)	one hundred	1 hectogram (hg) equals 100 g
deka (da)	ten	1 dekagram (dag) equals 10 g
deci (d)	one-tenth	1 decigram (dg) equals 0.1 g
centi (c)	one-hundredth	1 centigram (cg) equals 0.01 g
milli (m)	one-thousandth	1 milligram (mg) equals 0.001 g

Complete a chart, similar to the above, for each of these.

1. Units of Distance

2. Units of Capacity

3. Extend the charts for units of mass, distance and capacity to include prefixes meaning "one million" and "one-millionth". Use your school library if necessary.

Collect examples of objects having the following.

4. mass 1 g

5. mass 1 kg

6. length 1 m

7. length 1 cm

8. length 1 mm

9. area 1 cm^2

10. volume 1 cm^3

11. capacity 1 mL

12. capacity 1 L

2-13 ADDING AND SUBTRACTING WITH FRACTIONS

When addition or subtraction involves fractions, the denominators may be the same. To find the sum or difference, add or subtract the numerators. Show the result as a new numerator over the common denominator.

EXAMPLE 1 Add $\frac{2}{3}$ and $\frac{5}{3}$.

Ⓜ SOLUTION $\frac{2}{3} + \frac{5}{3} = \frac{2 + 5}{3}$

$= \frac{7}{3}$

EXAMPLE 2 Subtract $\frac{3}{b}$ from $\frac{a}{b}$.

Ⓜ SOLUTION $\frac{a}{b} - \frac{3}{b} = \frac{a - 3}{b}$

When denominators are different, replace fractions by other fractions for the same numbers so that all denominators are the same. Then work as in Examples 1 and 2.

EXAMPLE 3 Subtract $\frac{x}{6}$ from $\frac{5x}{12}$.

Ⓜ SOLUTION $\frac{5x}{12} - \frac{x}{6} = \frac{5x}{12} - \left(\frac{2}{2} \cdot \frac{x}{6}\right)$

$= \frac{5x}{12} - \frac{2x}{12}$

$= \frac{5x - 2x}{12}$

$= \frac{3x}{12}$, or $\frac{x}{4}$

EXAMPLE 4 Add $\frac{2x^2}{3}$ and $\frac{3x^2}{4}$.

Ⓜ SOLUTION $\frac{2x^2}{3} + \frac{3x^2}{4} = \frac{4}{4} \cdot \frac{2x^2}{3} + \frac{3}{3} \cdot \frac{3x^2}{4}$

$= \frac{8x^2}{12} + \frac{9x^2}{12}$

$= \frac{8x^2 + 9x^2}{12}$

$= \frac{17x^2}{12}$

It may be necessary for you to review methods for finding common denominators; also, for replacing a fraction by another fraction for the number so that there are common denominators.

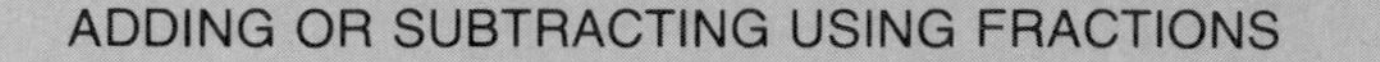

ADDING OR SUBTRACTING USING FRACTIONS

1. Find a common denominator.
2. If necessary, replace fractions with other fractions for the same number so that all denominators are the same.
3. Add or subtract the numerators. Show the new numerator over the common denominator.
4. Simplify the sum or difference to lowest terms.

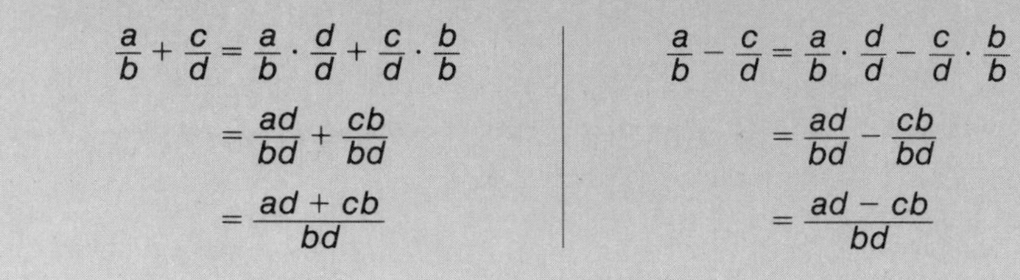

$$\frac{a}{b}+\frac{c}{d}=\frac{a}{b}\cdot\frac{d}{d}+\frac{c}{d}\cdot\frac{b}{b}=\frac{ad}{bd}+\frac{cb}{bd}=\frac{ad+cb}{bd}$$

$$\frac{a}{b}-\frac{c}{d}=\frac{a}{b}\cdot\frac{d}{d}-\frac{c}{d}\cdot\frac{b}{b}=\frac{ad}{bd}-\frac{cb}{bd}=\frac{ad-cb}{bd}$$

CLASSROOM EXERCISES

Perform the indicated operation.

1. $\frac{3}{4}+\frac{2}{4}$
2. $\frac{5}{13}+\frac{6}{13}$
3. $\frac{4}{9}-\frac{2}{9}$
4. $\frac{7}{11}-\frac{4}{11}$
5. $\frac{5}{a}+\frac{6}{a}$
6. $\frac{5}{z}+\frac{-7}{z}$
7. $\frac{-4k}{t}+\frac{6k}{t}$
8. $\frac{2n}{m^2}+\frac{3n}{m^2}$
9. $\frac{7}{a}-\frac{4}{a}$
10. $\frac{4}{x}-\frac{6}{x}$
11. $\frac{2}{3}+\frac{5}{6}$
12. $\frac{x}{2}+\frac{3x}{4}$
13. $\frac{m}{4}+\frac{m}{6}$
14. $\frac{h}{5}-\frac{h}{2}$
15. $\frac{x}{10}-\frac{3x}{5}$
16. $-\frac{1}{3}-\frac{1}{2}$

EXERCISES

A Perform the indicated operation.

1. $\frac{2}{3}+\frac{1}{3}$
2. $\frac{4}{3}-\frac{2}{3}$
3. $\frac{a}{6}+\frac{3a}{6}$
4. $\frac{x}{4}+\frac{3x}{4}$
5. $\frac{a}{c}+\frac{b}{c}$
6. $\frac{2}{a}+\frac{3}{a}$
7. $\frac{1}{c}+\frac{1}{c}$
8. $\frac{3}{x}-\frac{4}{x}$
9. $\frac{4}{xy}-\frac{3}{xy}$
10. $\frac{-4}{m}-\frac{3}{m}$
11. $\frac{7}{10}-\frac{3}{20}$
12. $-\frac{1}{4}-\frac{1}{8}$
13. $\frac{t}{3}+\frac{2t}{7}$
14. $\frac{x}{7}-\frac{4x}{5}$
15. $\frac{2b}{5}-\frac{3b}{4}$
16. $\frac{3x^2}{4}+\frac{x^2}{8}$

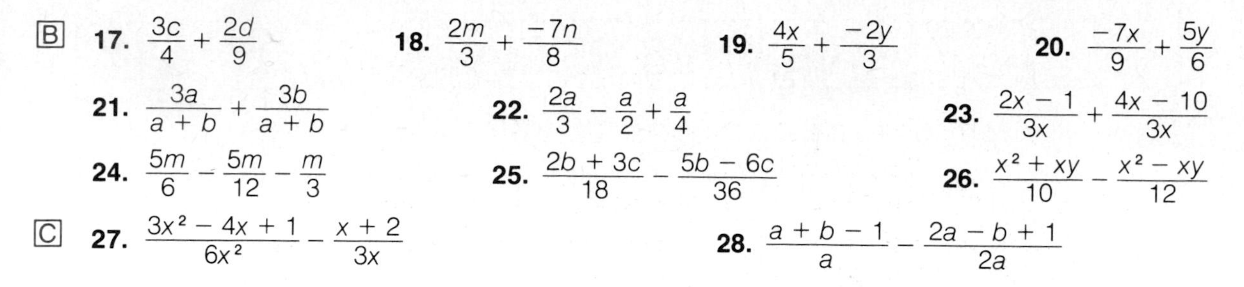

B

17. $\frac{3c}{4} + \frac{2d}{9}$ **18.** $\frac{2m}{3} + \frac{-7n}{8}$ **19.** $\frac{4x}{5} + \frac{-2y}{3}$ **20.** $\frac{-7x}{9} + \frac{5y}{6}$

21. $\frac{3a}{a+b} + \frac{3b}{a+b}$ **22.** $\frac{2a}{3} - \frac{a}{2} + \frac{a}{4}$ **23.** $\frac{2x-1}{3x} + \frac{4x-10}{3x}$

24. $\frac{5m}{6} - \frac{5m}{12} - \frac{m}{3}$ **25.** $\frac{2b+3c}{18} - \frac{5b-6c}{36}$ **26.** $\frac{x^2+xy}{10} - \frac{x^2-xy}{12}$

C

27. $\frac{3x^2-4x+1}{6x^2} - \frac{x+2}{3x}$ **28.** $\frac{a+b-1}{a} - \frac{2a-b+1}{2a}$

CHECKING YOUR UNDERSTANDING

WORDS AND SYMBOLS

lowest terms multiplicative inverse reciprocal of a number, $\frac{1}{a}$

CONCEPTS

- When terms in a product or quotient have the same base, their exponents may be added or subtracted to simplify the expression containing them. [2-9, 2-11]
- The rules for adding, subtracting, multiplying, and dividing fractions containing variables are the same as for arithmetic fractions. [2-10, 2-12, 2-13]
- A fraction whose numerator and denominator contain common factors other than 1 and −1 may be simplified using the Multiplication Property of One. [2-10]

PROCESSES

- Multiply and divide monomials. [2-9, 2-11]

1. $(3x^2)(-2x^3)$ **2.** $(-4a)(-5b)$ **3.** $16x \div (-2x)$ **4.** $\frac{36x^3y}{-9xy}$

- Add, subtract, multiply, divide, and simplify fractions that involve variables. [2-10, 2-12, 2-13]

5. $\frac{3x}{9x^2}$ **6.** $\frac{9x^2}{5} \cdot \frac{10}{3x}$ **7.** $\frac{5x^3}{21} \div \frac{3x}{7}$

8. $\frac{2x}{5} + \frac{3x}{5}$ **9.** $\frac{x}{6} - \frac{3x}{4}$ **10.** $\frac{5x^2}{2} + \frac{2x^2}{3}$

CHAPTER REVIEW

Write the opposite of each number. [2-1]

1. 33 **2.** $\frac{1}{2}$ **3.** -1.1

For each x, find $-x$.

4. $x = 1066$ **5.** $x = -8\frac{1}{3}$ **6.** $x = 0$

Simplify.

7. $|1492|$ **8.** $|-3\frac{1}{2}|$ **9.** $|-10^2|$

For each x, find $|x|$.

10. $x = 1776$ **11.** $x = -\frac{7}{3}$ **12.** $x = -0.51$

Simplify each sum. Use the number line if needed. [2-2]

−3 −2 −1 0 1 2 3

13. $-1.5 + 3$ **14.** $-2 + \left(-\frac{2}{3}\right)$ **15.** $\left(-\frac{1}{2}\right) + \left(-\frac{1}{2}\right)$

Add. [2-3]

16. $-2\frac{1}{4}$ and $4\frac{1}{2}$ **17.** -0.58 and -5.8 **18.** 1.1, -2.02, and 3.003

Subtract. [2-4]

19. 1789 from 1776 **20.** 1.1 from -3.3 **21.** $-\frac{1}{2}$ from $6\frac{1}{2}$

22. -28 from -208 **23.** 12 from 0 **24.** $-7\frac{1}{2}$ from 0

Simplify. [2-5, 2-6]

25. $\frac{1}{2}(-0.5)$ **26.** $\left(-1\frac{1}{2}\right)\left(-2\frac{1}{2}\right)$ **27.** $(-3)(4)(-5)$

28. $(-1)(2)(-3)(-4)$ **29.** $-1(2001)$ **30.** $(-5)(-6)(-7)(0)$

31. $-270a + 225a$ **32.** $5x - 5x^2 - 5x$ **33.** $x - 2x + 3x - 4x$

34. $3m^2 - 10m - 1 + 7 - m$ **35.** $x^2 - 2x + 6 - x^2 - x - 1$ **36.** $2a + 5b - c - a - 7b$

Divide. [2-7]

37. 135 by -3 **38.** -225 by -5 **39.** -315 by 7

Evaluate each expression for $x = -2$, $a = 3\frac{1}{2}$, and $b = 5$. [2-8]

40. $2a + x$ **41.** $2(3a + x)$ **42.** $\frac{5x}{b} - 1$

43. $\frac{2x + b}{3x - a}$ **44.** $\frac{2(x - b)}{4(x + b)}$ **45.** $2[x^2 + 3(b - 2a)]$

Simplify. [2-9 to 2-13]

46. $(5w)(3w)$ **47.** $\frac{5}{2}x^3 \cdot x^4$ **48.** $-\frac{3}{4}x(4x^2)$

49. $10(-0.4x)$ **50.** $-4c^2(-3c^3)$ **51.** $-2a(-3b)(4c)(-5a)$

52. $\frac{a}{b} \cdot \frac{b^2}{a}$ **53.** $x \cdot \frac{5}{x}$ **54.** $3\left(\frac{17m}{51}\right)$

55. $-\frac{a}{2}\left(\frac{3}{2a}\right)$ **56.** $\frac{0.2ax^2}{3} \cdot \frac{4}{0.5a^2x}$ **57.** $\left(\frac{5x}{3}\right)\left(\frac{12}{4x}\right)(-8)$

58. $\frac{4xy}{4}$ **59.** $6x^2y \div (-2y)$ **60.** $\frac{z}{xyz}$

61. $40x \div 8x$ **62.** $\frac{-48a^4}{16a^3b}$ **63.** $-18x^2ya \div 81xy^2$

64. $\frac{-2x}{5} \div 2$ **65.** $\frac{5}{8}x \div \frac{-x}{2}$ **66.** $\frac{2x}{3y} \div \frac{x}{y}$

67. $\frac{2a}{b} \div b$ **68.** $\frac{a^3}{2} \div \frac{2}{3a}$ **69.** $\frac{-18m^3}{15x} \div \frac{-4m^2x}{3}$

70. $\frac{7x}{5} - \frac{3x}{5}$ **71.** $\frac{b}{7} - \frac{5}{7}$ **72.** $\frac{3x}{15} + \frac{x}{5}$ **73.** $\frac{2t}{3} + \frac{3t}{4}$

CAPSULE REVIEW

Write the letter of the best response.

1. Subtracting 6 from a number gives the same result as

a. adding 6. **b.** adding -6. **c.** subtracting -6. **d.** adding 6 or subtracting -6.

2. Subtracting -3 from a number gives the same result as

a. subtracting 3. **b.** adding 3. **c.** adding -3. **d.** subtracting 3 or adding -3.

3. Which is the largest number?

a. $|-2|$ **b.** $|-1|$ **c.** $\left|\frac{1}{2}\right|$ **d.** $\left|-\frac{1}{2}\right|$ **e.** 0

4. Steps [1] and [2] in the diagram show which sum?

2

1

−2 −1 0 1 2 3 4

a. $2 - 2$ **b.** $-2 + 2$ **c.** $-2 - 4$ **d.** $-2 + 4$ **e.** $2 - 4$

5. $-T - (-T) =$

a. $2T$ **b.** $-2T$ **c.** T **d.** 0 **e.** $-T$

6. For $x = 3$, and $y = -1$, $\frac{2(y - x)}{4y - x} =$

a. $-1\frac{1}{7}$ **b.** $\frac{8}{13}$ **c.** $\frac{1}{2}$ **d.** $\frac{8}{7}$ **e.** $-\frac{8}{7}$

7. For $x = -\frac{1}{3}$, which expression gives the greatest value?

a. $\frac{1}{x}$ **b.** $\frac{1}{\frac{1}{x}}$ **c.** $\left|\frac{1}{x}\right|$ **d.** x^2 **e.** $\frac{1}{x^2}$

8. $\frac{5}{x} \div \frac{8}{x} =$

a. $\frac{40}{x^2}$ **b.** $40x^2$ **c.** $\frac{5}{8}$ **d.** $\frac{8}{5}$ **e.** $\frac{5x^2}{8}$

9. $\frac{2}{3} + \frac{2x}{3x} =$

a. 0 **b.** $\frac{4x}{9x}$ **c.** $\frac{4x}{6x}$ **d.** $\frac{4}{6}$ **e.** $\frac{4}{3}$

10. For $x = \frac{1}{2}$, $2[x^2 - 3(x - 4x)] =$

a. $-\frac{17}{2}$ **b.** $-\frac{17}{4}$ **c.** $-\frac{19}{4}$ **d.** $\frac{19}{4}$ **e.** $\frac{19}{2}$

CHAPTER TEST

1. Write the *opposite* of 1.5.

2. Simplify $|-2|$.

Simplify each sum. Use the number line if needed.

−5 −4 −3 −2 −1 0 1 2 3 4 5

3. $(-3) + (-2)$

4. $1 + (-4)$

5. $(-5) + (-3)$

6. $(-4) + 6$

7. Subtract 8 from 5.

8. Subtract 7 from -3.

9. Simplify $7x - x^2 - 6x - 3x^2$.

10. Simplify $5a - 4b + 3a - 4b$.

11. Multiply -10 and -2.

12. Multiply 17 and -1.

13. Simplify the product $(6)(0)(-8)$.

14. Simplify the product $(-2)(-2)(-2)$.

15. Divide 50 by -5.

16. Divide -8 by -4.

17. Multiply $3a$ and $-2a$.

18. Multiply n^2 and n^3.

19. Divide x^{10} by x^2.

20. Divide $-18x^2$ by $-2x$.

21. For $a = -2$ and $b = 3$, find the value of $a^2 + b$.

22. For $x = 5$ and $y = 2$, find the value of $15 - xy$.

23. Simplify $\frac{15x^6}{3x^2}$.

24. Multiply $\frac{3x}{4}$ and $\frac{2x}{3}$.

25. Write the reciprocal of $\frac{a}{b}$.

26. Divide $\frac{2x}{3}$ by $\frac{5}{6}$.

27. Add $\frac{2}{3}$ and $\frac{3}{4}$.

28. Add $\frac{x}{2}$ and $\frac{x}{4}$.

Write the letter of the best response.

29. The opposite of $\frac{3}{4}$ is

a. $-\frac{4}{3}$ **b.** $-\frac{3}{4}$ **c.** 0 **d.** $\frac{3}{4}$ **e.** $\frac{4}{3}$

30. Where on the number line is the sum of -2 and 1?

A B C D E

-3 -2 -1 0 1 2 3

a. *A* **b.** *B* **c.** *C* **d.** *D* **e.** *E*

31. The sum of -30 and 10 is

a. -40 **b.** -20 **c.** 0 **d.** 20 **e.** 40

32. The sum of -100 and -80 is

a. -180 **b.** -20 **c.** 20 **d.** 180 **e.** 800

33. $5x^2 + x - 6x^2 + 3x =$

a. $3x$ **b.** $-x^2 + 3x$ **c.** $-x^2 + 4x$ **d.** $x^2 + 4x$ **e.** $-x^2 - 2x$

34. $(-2)(-3)(4) =$

a. -24 **b.** -1 **c.** 1 **d.** 10 **e.** 24

35. $(5)(1)(-1) =$

a. -5 **b.** -4 **c.** 4 **d.** 5 **e.** 7

36. -12 divided by 4 is

a. -16 **b.** -8 **c.** -3 **d.** 3 **e.** 8

37. The product of $2x^2$ and $-3x$ is

a. $-6x^3$ **b.** $-5x^3$ **c.** $-6x^2$ **d.** $5x$ **e.** $2x^2 - 3x$

38. $15x^6$ divided by $-3x^2$ is

a. $-5x^3$ **b.** $-5x^4$ **c.** $12x^2$ **d.** $12x^3$ **e.** $12x^4$

39. For $a = 2$ and $b = -3$, the value of $5a + b^2$ is

a. -1 **b.** 4 **c.** 7 **d.** 19 **e.** 49

40. The product of $\frac{2}{3}$ and $\frac{1}{4}$ is

a. $\frac{2}{7}$ **b.** $\frac{3}{7}$ **c.** $\frac{8}{3}$ **d.** $\frac{3}{8}$ **e.** $\frac{1}{6}$

41. $\frac{3}{8}$ divided by $\frac{2}{3}$ is

a. $\frac{1}{4}$ **b.** $\frac{5}{24}$ **c.** $\frac{25}{24}$ **d.** $\frac{16}{9}$ **e.** $\frac{9}{16}$

42. $\frac{1}{4} + \frac{2}{3} -$

a. $\frac{3}{4}$ **b.** $\frac{11}{12}$ **c.** $\frac{1}{6}$ **d.** $\frac{2}{7}$ **e.** $\frac{3}{7}$

CHAPTER 3
Equations and Inequalities

It's basic. People employed in public service and the people they serve have to know how to communicate. Particularly challenging and rewarding is teaching or learning a new language. This is true whether the language is a native-American dialect, a European tongue, English as a second language, or a special language used in some school subject area—such as mathematics.

OBJECTIVES: Identify equations and inequalities.
Identify solutions of equations and inequalities.

3-1 NUMBER SENTENCES

A true number sentence gives information that agrees with fact. A false number sentence gives information that does not agree with fact. A sentence that contains one or more variables is an **open number sentence**. It does not give enough information for you to decide if it is true or false.

True Sentences	False Sentences	Open Sentences
$1 + 2 = 3$	$2^3 \neq 8$	$x + 3 < 5$
$12 > 7$	$10 - (-2) = 8$	$2(y + 4) = y + 2$

A number sentence showing that two expressions represent the same number is an **equation**. A number sentence showing that two expressions represent different numbers is an **inequality**. The expressions are the **members** of the equation or inequality.

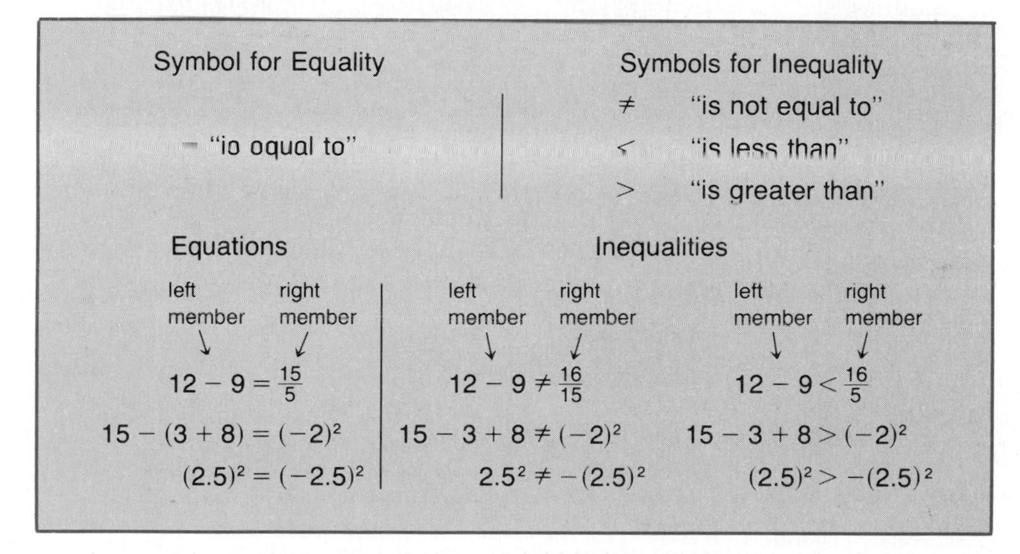

To decide whether to use = or ≠ between two arithmetic expressions, first simplify each expression. If the expressions name the same number, use =. If the expressions do not name the same number, use ≠.

EXAMPLE 1 Would you use $=$ or $\neq$ to make a true sentence?

a. $(4 \cdot 2) \cdot 3 \boxed{?} 4 \cdot (2 \cdot 3)$

b. $5^2 \boxed{?} 5 \cdot 2$

SOLUTION

a.
$$(4 \cdot 2) \cdot 3 \boxed{?} 4 \cdot (2 \cdot 3)$$
$$8 \cdot 3 \boxed{?} 4 \cdot 6$$
$$24 = 24$$
Thus, $(4 \cdot 2) \cdot 3 \boxed{=} 4 \cdot (2 \cdot 3)$

b.
$$5^2 \boxed{?} 5 \cdot 2$$
$$25 \neq 10$$
Thus, $5^2 \boxed{\neq} 5 \cdot 2$

To decide whether to use $=$, $<$, or $>$ between two arithmetic expressions, first simplify each expression. If the expressions name the same number, use $=$. If the expressions name different numbers, use $<$ or $>$ so that the symbol points to the expression for the smaller number.

EXAMPLE 2 Would you use $=$, $<$, or $>$ to make a true sentence?

$0.8 \boxed{?} \frac{7}{8}$

SOLUTION Since $\frac{7}{8} = 7 \div 8$, or 0.875,

$0.8 \boxed{<} \frac{7}{8}$.

EXAMPLE 3 Would you use $=$, $<$, or $>$?

a. $(-4)^2 \boxed{?} 4^2$

b. $-9\left(\frac{1}{4}\right) \boxed{?} -9\frac{1}{4}$

SOLUTION

a.
$$(-4)^2 \boxed{?} 4^2$$
$$16 = 16$$
Thus, $(-4)^2 \boxed{=} 4^2$

b.
$$-9\left(\tfrac{1}{4}\right) \boxed{?} -9\tfrac{1}{4}$$
$$-\tfrac{9}{4} \boxed{?} -9\tfrac{1}{4}$$
$$-2\tfrac{1}{4} > -9\tfrac{1}{4}$$
Thus, $-9\left(\frac{1}{4}\right) \boxed{>} -9\frac{1}{4}$

When a number is used for the variable in an open sentence, we get a true sentence or a false sentence. A number that gives a true sentence is a **solution** of the equation or inequality. The set of all solutions is the **solution set** of the equation or inequality.

EXAMPLE 4 Is 5 a solution of $2x + 1 = 11$?

SOLUTION
$$2x + 1 = 11$$
$$2 \cdot 5 + 1 \stackrel{?}{=} 11$$
$$11 = 11$$

CONCLUSION 5 is a solution of $2x + 1 = 11$.

EXAMPLE 5 Is 2 a solution of $x^2 > 6$?

SOLUTION
$$x^2 > 6$$
$$2^2 \stackrel{?}{>} 6$$
4 is not greater than 6.

CONCLUSION 2 is not a solution of $x^2 > 6$.

CLASSROOM EXERCISES

Replace each ? with = or ≠ to make a true sentence.

1. $(6 \cdot 4) \cdot 5 \; ? \; 6 \cdot (4 \cdot 5)$ **2.** $7^2 \; ? \; 7 \cdot 2$ **3.** $-9\left(\frac{1}{3}\right) \; ? \; -9\frac{1}{3}$ **4.** $3 \cdot (8 - 4) \; ? \; 3(8) - 3(4)$

Replace each ? with <, >, or = to make a true sentence.

5. $\frac{3}{4} \; ? \; 0.75$ **6.** $9^2 \; ? \; 85$ **7.** $-12\left(\frac{1}{4}\right) \; ? \; -12\frac{1}{4}$ **8.** $(-6)^2 \; ? \; 6^2$

9. Is 4 a solution of $3x - 2 = 10$? **10.** Is -3 a solution of $y^2 < 12$?

EXERCISES

A Replace each ? with = or ≠ to make a true sentence.

1. $7 \cdot (9 \cdot 12) \; ? \; (7 \cdot 9) \cdot 12$ **2.** $(20 \cdot 5) \cdot 2 \; ? \; 20 \cdot (5 \cdot 2)$ **3.** $8^2 \; ? \; 2 \cdot 8$ **4.** $12^2 \; ? \; 2 \cdot 12$

5. $13 + 17 \; ? \; 17 + 13$ **6.** $28 + 32 \; ? \; 32 + 28$ **7.** $18(4) + 7(4) \; ? \; (18 + 7)4$

Replace each ? with <, >, or = to make a true sentence.

8. $\frac{3}{8} \; ? \; 0.37$ **9.** $\frac{4}{5} \; ? \; 0.85$ **10.** $\frac{7}{12} \; ? \; \frac{5}{18}$ **11.** $\frac{7}{15} \; ? \; \frac{3}{7}$

12. $(-3)^2 \; ? \; 3^2$ **13.** $(-8)^2 \; ? \; 8^2$ **14.** $\left(\frac{1}{3}\right)^2 \; ? \; \left(-\frac{1}{3}\right)^2$ **15.** $\left(-\frac{1}{5}\right)^2 \; ? \; \left(\frac{1}{5}\right)^2$

Tell whether -9 is a solution.

16. $2x + 4 = 14$ **17.** $p^2 > 180$

Tell whether 6.2 is a solution.

18. $2z - 18.4 = -6$ **19.** $x^2 < 37.4$

B Replace each ? with <, >, or = to make a true sentence.

20. $\left(-2\frac{7}{9}\right)\left(4\frac{1}{5}\right) \; ? \; -11$ **21.** $\left(15\frac{3}{4}\right) \div \left(-3\frac{3}{8}\right) \; ? \; -4\frac{2}{3}$ **22.** $(0.08)^2 \; ? \; (0.075)^2$

23. $3\left(\frac{1}{4}\right) \; ? \; \left(\frac{1}{4}\right)^3$ **24.** $(14)^5 \; ? \; (-14)^5$ **25.** $1.296 \times 10^7 \; ? \; 1.296 \times 10^6$

C Replace each ? with <, >, or = to make a true sentence (x and y are counting numbers). If a suitable replacement is not possible, briefly explain why.

26. $\frac{1}{x} \; ? \; x$ **27.** $-(x^6) \; ? \; (-x)^6$ **28.** $(y)^9 \; ? \; (-y)^9$ **29.** $x^y \; ? \; y^x$

30. If $y = -5c$, is $\frac{y - 3c}{c} = -8c$ true? **31.** If $y = -2d$, is $\frac{3y + 2d}{-2} = 3y + 4d$ true?

SIMPLIFYING ARITHMETIC EXPRESSIONS

To use your calculator correctly you must find the order in which it performs operations. Try the following for $7 + 5 \times 2$.

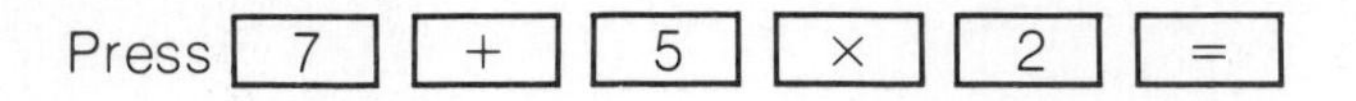

If your calculator displays 17, it follows the order of operations that we have agreed upon. That is, it performs the multiplication 5×2 first and then adds 7.

If your calculator displays 24 instead of 17, it performs operations in the order in which they are entered. That is, it performs the addition $7 + 5$ first and then multiplies by 2. To obtain the correct result for $7 + 5 \times 2$,.you must change the order in which you enter the operations.

Press [5] [×] [2] [+] [7] [=]

The display will show the correct result, 17.

EXAMPLE 1 Use your calculator to simplify $272 + 153 \div 34$.

SOLUTION The order of operations requires that the division $153 \div 34$ be completed before the addition. Whether or not your calculator follows the order of operations we have agreed upon, the following steps will give the correct result.

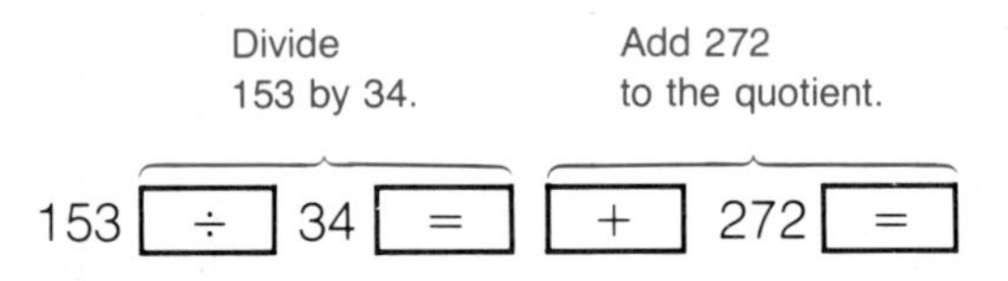

The display will show 276.5.

When using your calculator, you sometimes have to save intermediate results and re-enter them in the display later. If you can find ways to avoid recording an intermediate result, you will be using your calculator more efficiently.

EXAMPLE 2 Use your calculator to simplify $24 \times 15 + 38 \times 15$.

SOLUTION 1 Press 24 [×] 15 [=]

Save 360 as an intermediate result. Clear the display.

Re-enter 360. ↓

Press 38 [×] 15 [=] [+] 360 [=]

SOLUTION 2 Using the Distributive Property,
$24 \times 15 + 38 \times 15 = (24 + 38) \times 15$.

Press 24 [+] 38 [=] [×] 15 [=]

For either procedure, the display will show 930.

EXERCISES

Simplify with your calculator. Consecutive pairs of results will give you a clue as to whether your work is correct.

1. $43 \times 7 + 15$

2. $(-14) \times (-47) - 45$

3. $(-36)[(-23) + 82)]$

4. $(-9)(26)(18)$

5. $(-93) + 83.2 - 2.6$

6. $2.99 + 3.4 \times 11 - 44.6$

7. $-391 + \dfrac{(-57) + (-215)}{16}$

8. $\dfrac{892 + 8 \times 391}{-5}$

Use the calculator to simplify each of these *without* using the Distributive Property. Remember to save and re-enter the intermediate result. Then simplify again using the Distributive Property. Record and compare your results for each method.

9. $32 \cdot 8 + 25 \cdot 8$

10. $(202)(6) - (93)(6)$

11. $27 \cdot 73 - 27 \cdot 56$

12. $(-18)(-97) + (-18)(44)$

13. $(-9) \cdot 110 - (-9) \cdot 21$

14. $(-10.3)(270) + (9.9)(270)$

OBJECTIVE: Use addition, subtraction, multiplication, and division to solve equations.

3-2 USING SUBTRACTION OR ADDITION TO SOLVE EQUATIONS

The process of finding the solution or solutions of an equation is called **solving the equation**. Certain properties of the equality of numbers may be used in a step-by-step method to solve equations. The first property we study, The Subtraction Property, allows us to subtract the same number from both members of an equation.

This property also says: if $a = b$ and $c = d$, then $a - c = b - d$.

THE SUBTRACTION PROPERTY OF EQUALITY

If a, b, and c are expressions for real numbers, and $a = b$, then

$$a - c = b - c.$$

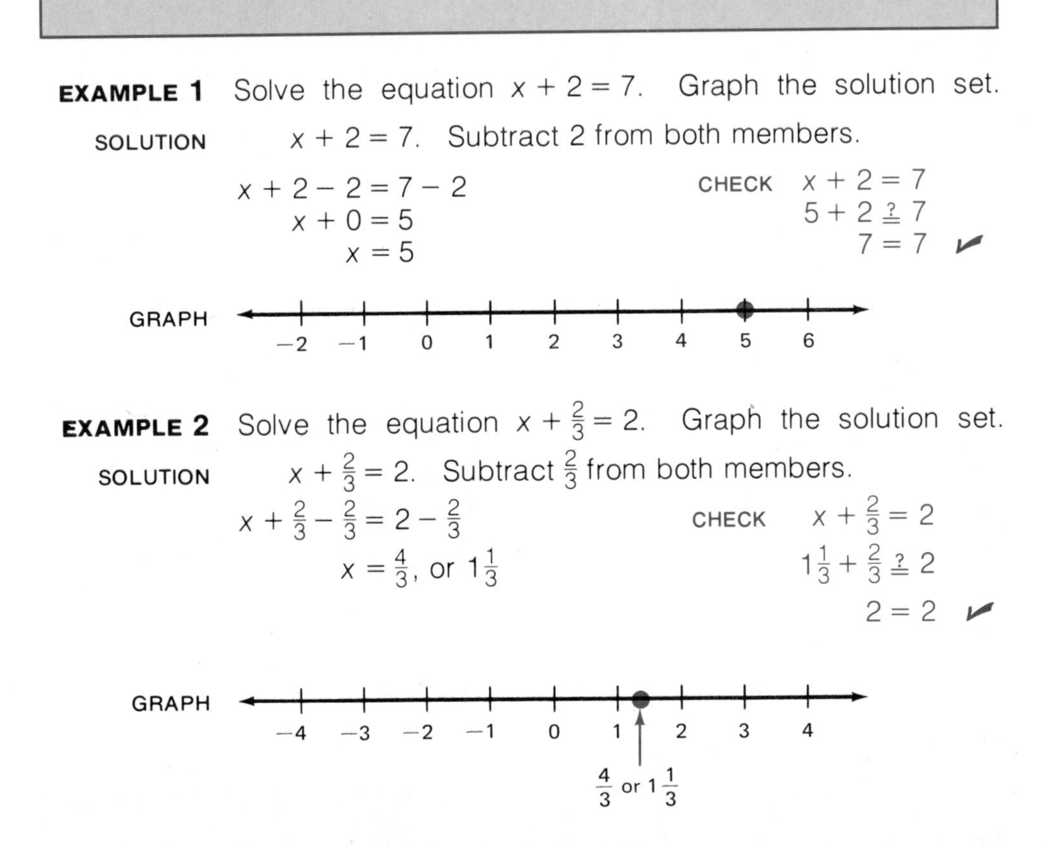

EXAMPLE 1 Solve the equation $x + 2 = 7$. Graph the solution set.

SOLUTION $x + 2 = 7$. Subtract 2 from both members.

$$x + 2 - 2 = 7 - 2$$
$$x + 0 = 5$$
$$x = 5$$

CHECK
$$x + 2 = 7$$
$$5 + 2 \stackrel{?}{=} 7$$
$$7 = 7 \checkmark$$

GRAPH

EXAMPLE 2 Solve the equation $x + \frac{2}{3} = 2$. Graph the solution set.

SOLUTION $x + \frac{2}{3} = 2$. Subtract $\frac{2}{3}$ from both members.

$$x + \frac{2}{3} - \frac{2}{3} = 2 - \frac{2}{3}$$
$$x = \frac{4}{3}, \text{ or } 1\frac{1}{3}$$

CHECK
$$x + \frac{2}{3} = 2$$
$$1\frac{1}{3} + \frac{2}{3} \stackrel{?}{=} 2$$
$$2 = 2 \checkmark$$

GRAPH

EXAMPLE 3 Solve $b + 1.25 = 0.75$. Graph the solution set.

Ⓜ SOLUTION

$$b + 1.25 = 0.75$$
$$S_{1.25} \qquad b + 1.25 - 1.25 = 0.75 - 1.25$$
$$b = -0.50$$

The "S" notation indicates an application of the Subtraction Property of Equality.

CHECK

$$b + 1.25 = 0.75$$
$$-0.50 + 1.25 \stackrel{?}{=} 0.75$$
$$0.75 = 0.75 \checkmark$$

GRAPH

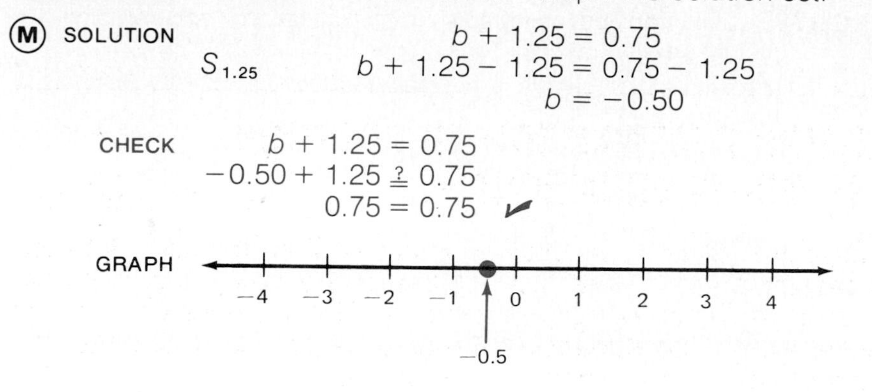

The process of solving an equation may produce a sentence like $a = x$. We may write $x = a$ in its place since the two equations have the same solution.

EXAMPLE 4 Solve $25 = y + 17$.

Ⓜ SOLUTION

$$25 = y + 17$$
$$S_{17} \qquad 25 - 17 = y + 17 - 17$$
$$8 = y$$
$$\text{or } y = 8$$

CHECK

$$25 = y + 17$$
$$25 \stackrel{?}{=} 8 + 17$$
$$25 = 25 \checkmark$$

The Addition Property of Equality allows us to add the same number to both members of an equation.

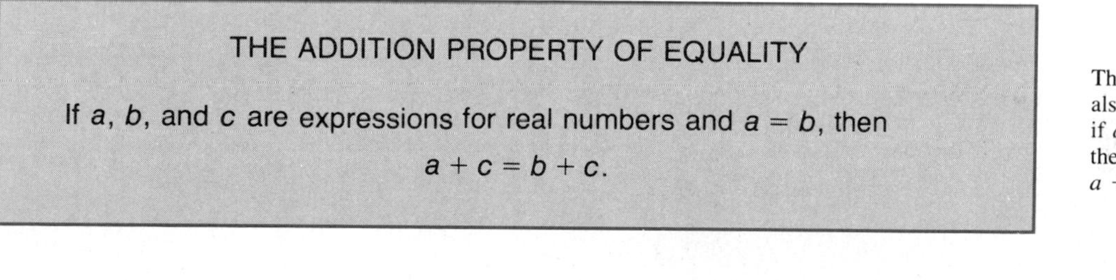

THE ADDITION PROPERTY OF EQUALITY

If a, b, and c are expressions for real numbers and $a = b$, then

$$a + c = b + c.$$

This property also says: if $a = b$ and $c = d$, then $a + c = b + d$.

EXAMPLE 5 Solve $a - 8 = 13$.

SOLUTION

$$a - 8 = 13. \quad \text{Add 8 to both members.}$$
$$a - 8 + 8 = 13 + 8$$
$$a = 21$$

CHECK

$$a - 8 = 13$$
$$21 - 8 \stackrel{?}{=} 13$$
$$13 = 13 \checkmark$$

EXAMPLE 6 Solve $-\frac{3}{4} = x - \frac{7}{8}$.

(M) SOLUTION

$$-\frac{3}{4} = x - \frac{7}{8}$$

$A_{\frac{7}{8}}$ $$-\frac{3}{4} + \frac{7}{8} = x - \frac{7}{8} + \frac{7}{8}$$

$$-\frac{6}{8} + \frac{7}{8} = x$$

$$\frac{1}{8} = x, \text{ or } x = \frac{1}{8}$$

CHECK

$$-\frac{3}{4} = x - \frac{7}{8}$$

$$-\frac{3}{4} \stackrel{?}{=} \frac{1}{8} - \frac{7}{8}$$

$$-\frac{3}{4} \stackrel{?}{=} -\frac{6}{8}$$

$$-\frac{3}{4} = -\frac{3}{4} \checkmark$$

The "A" notation indicates an application of the Addition Property of Equality.

EXAMPLE 7 Solve $-1.2 = -0.08 - x$.

(M) SOLUTION

$$-1.2 = -0.08 - x$$

A_x $$-1.2 + x = -0.08 - x + x$$

$$-1.2 + x = -0.08$$

$A_{1.2}$ $$-1.2 + x + 1.2 = -0.08 + 1.2$$

$$x = 1.12$$

CHECK

$$-1.2 = -0.08 - x$$

$$-1.2 \stackrel{?}{=} -0.08 - 1.12$$

$$-1.2 = -1.2 \checkmark$$

> Solving an Equation of the Form $x + a = b$
>
> Use the Subtraction Property of Equality and subtract a from both members of the equation.
>
> Solving an Equation of the Form $x - a = b$
>
> Use the Addition Property of Equality and add a to both members of the equation.

CLASSROOM EXERCISES

Solve each equation. Graph its solution set.

1. $x + 6 = 10$

2. $y + \frac{2}{5} = \frac{9}{10}$

3. $z + \frac{1}{3} = -\frac{1}{4}$

4. $k - 4 = -8$

5. $-2\frac{1}{2} = x - 3\frac{1}{4}$

6. $4\frac{1}{3} = h - 6\frac{1}{2}$

Solve each equation.

7. $a + 3.6 = 9.1$

8. $c + 2.5 = -3.2$

9. $x + 53 = -125$

10. $17 = y + 16$

11. $-12 = s + 3$

12. $m - 6 = 10$

13. $-2.05 = x - 1.6$

14. $4.82 = y - 3.9$

15. $7 = 23 - x$

EXERCISES

A Solve each equation. Graph its solution set.

1. $k + 75 = 50$ **2.** $w + \frac{3}{4} = \frac{4}{5}$ **3.** $b + 2\frac{1}{3} = 3\frac{3}{4}$

4. $h - 147 = -45$ **5.** $-\frac{1}{2} = b - \frac{5}{6}$ **6.** $-1\frac{3}{5} = d - 2\frac{1}{2}$

Solve each equation.

7. $y + 30 = 50$ **8.** $z + 56 = 72$ **9.** $n + \frac{5}{6} = \frac{1}{3}$

10. $a + 5\frac{3}{8} = 3\frac{5}{12}$ **11.** $d + \frac{2}{5} = -\frac{9}{10}$ **12.** $n + \frac{7}{9} = -\frac{2}{15}$

13. $c + 1.75 = 2.25$ **14.** $t + 3.24 = 4.88$ **15.** $z + 1.96 = -3.2$

16. $y + 7.68 = -10.3$ **17.** $x + 65 = -35$ **18.** $g + 156 = -64$

19. $58 = y + 39$ **20.** $100 = n + 57$ **21.** $-25 = w + 22$

22. $-181 = f + 154$ **23.** $x - 33 = 17$ **24.** $p - 25 = 36$

25. $y - 49 = -60$ **26.** $n - 82 = -107$ **27.** $-4\frac{2}{3} = z - 3\frac{5}{6}$

28. $-5\frac{7}{9} = n - 4\frac{5}{12}$ **29.** $\frac{2}{3} = h - \frac{1}{2}$ **30.** $\frac{11}{15} = w - \frac{5}{9}$

31. $-2.75 = a - 1.6$ **32.** $-5.08 = s - 3.9$ **33.** $-3.2 = c - 4.88$

34. $-12.9 = m - 17.76$ **35.** $7.4 = y - 4.24$ **36.** $18.3 = r - 5.05$

37. $2.4 = c - 8.68$ **38.** $-5.2 = -2.95 - x$ **39.** $-8.3 = -5.76 - y$

B **40.** $x + 9 = -21 + 13$ **41.** $x + 10 = (-2)(7)$ **42.** $r + 16 = \frac{(-3)(10)}{5}$

43. $w + 4\frac{1}{3} = \frac{-9 + 3}{24}$ **44.** $k + 3(-4 + 7) = -5$ **45.** $y + (-8)^2 = (5)^2$

46. $x - 12 = 8 + (-15)$ **47.** $z - 15 = (-5)8$ **48.** $y - 8 = \frac{10 \cdot 12}{6}$

49. $m - 25 = \frac{(-9)\,10}{5}$ **50.** $h - 7\frac{1}{2} = \frac{-8 + 2}{10}$ **51.** $t - 36 = \frac{4(-14)}{7}$

52. $x - 4\frac{3}{4} = \frac{-21 + 9}{18}$ **53.** $z - (-11)^2 = (8)^2$ **54.** $(-6)^3 = x - (-6)^2$

C Solve each equation for a.

55. $a + b = c$ **56.** $a - b = c$ **57.** $a + (-b) = c$

58. $a - (-b) = c$ **59.** $a + b + c = d$ **60.** $a + b - c = d$

61. $a - (-b) - (-c) = d$ **62.** $a + (-b) + (-c) = d$ **63.** $a + (-b) - (-c) = d$

3-3 USING DIVISION OR MULTIPLICATION TO SOLVE EQUATIONS

The Division Property of Equality allows us to divide both members of an equation by the same number, provided the number is not zero.

This property also says: if $a = b$ and $c = d$, $(c \neq 0,\ d \neq 0)$ then $\frac{a}{c} = \frac{b}{d}$.

THE DIVISION PROPERTY OF EQUALITY

If a, b, and c are expressions for real numbers with $a = b$ and $c \neq 0$, then

$$\frac{a}{c} = \frac{b}{c}$$

EXAMPLE 1 Solve $3x = 18$.

SOLUTION $3x = 18$

Divide both members by 3.

$$\frac{3x}{3} = \frac{18}{3}$$

$$x = 6$$

CHECK

$$3x = 18$$
$$3 \cdot 6 \stackrel{?}{=} 18$$
$$18 = 18 \checkmark$$

EXAMPLE 2 Solve $-5y = 1.5$.

Ⓜ SOLUTION

$$-5y = 1.5$$
$$D_{-5} \quad \frac{-5y}{-5} = \frac{1.5}{-5}$$
$$y = -0.3$$

The "D" notation indicates an application of the Division Property of Equality.

CHECK

$$-5y = 1.5$$
$$-5(-0.3) \stackrel{?}{=} 1.5$$
$$1.5 = 1.5 \checkmark$$

EXAMPLE 3 Solve $-12a = -\frac{1}{3}$.

Ⓜ SOLUTION

$$-12a = -\frac{1}{3}$$
$$D_{-12} \quad \frac{-12a}{-12} = \frac{-\frac{1}{3}}{-12}$$
$$a = -\frac{1}{3}\left(-\frac{1}{12}\right)$$
$$a = \frac{1}{36}$$

CHECK

$$-12a = -\frac{1}{3}$$
$$-12\left(\frac{1}{36}\right) \stackrel{?}{=} -\frac{1}{3}$$
$$-\frac{1}{3} = -\frac{1}{3} \checkmark$$

EXAMPLE 4 Solve $-0.3k = 10$.

Ⓜ **SOLUTION**

$$-0.3k = 10$$

$$D_{-0.3} \quad \frac{-0.3k}{-0.3} = \frac{10}{-0.3}$$

$$k = -\frac{100}{3}$$

CHECK

$$-0.3k = 10$$

$$-0.3\left(-\frac{100}{3}\right) = 10$$

$$\left(-\frac{3}{10}\right)\left(-\frac{100}{3}\right) \stackrel{?}{=} 10$$

$$10 = 10 \quad ✓$$

Improper fractions may by preferred to standard forms for fractions (e.g., mixed form in Example 4) for computational purposes.

The Multiplication Property of Equality allows us to multiply both members of an equation by the same number.

> **THE MULTIPLICATION PROPERTY OF EQUALITY**
>
> If a, b, and c are expressions for real numbers and $a = b$, then
>
> $a \cdot c = b \cdot c$ and $c \cdot a = c \cdot b$.

This property also says: if $a = b$ and $c = d$, then $a \cdot c = b \cdot d$. Also, by the Commutative Property of Multiplication, $a \cdot c = c \cdot b$.

EXAMPLE 5 Solve $\frac{1}{4}w = 12$.

SOLUTION

$$\frac{1}{4}w = 12$$

Multiply both members by 4.

$$4 \cdot \frac{1}{4}w = 4 \cdot 12$$

$$w = 48$$

CHECK

$$\frac{1}{4}w = 12$$

$$\frac{1}{4}(48) \stackrel{?}{=} 12$$

$$12 = 12 \quad ✓$$

EXAMPLE 6 Solve $\frac{x}{-6} = 7$.

Ⓜ **SOLUTION**

$$\frac{x}{-6} = 7$$

$$M_{-6} \quad -6\left(\frac{x}{-6}\right) = -6 \cdot 7$$

$$x = -42$$

CHECK

$$\frac{x}{-6} = 7$$

$$\frac{-42}{-6} \stackrel{?}{=} 7$$

$$7 = 7 \quad ✓$$

The "M" notation indicates an application of the Multiplication Property of Equality.

The process of solving an equation may produce a sentence like $-x = a$. Multiplying both members by -1 gives the equation $x = -a$.

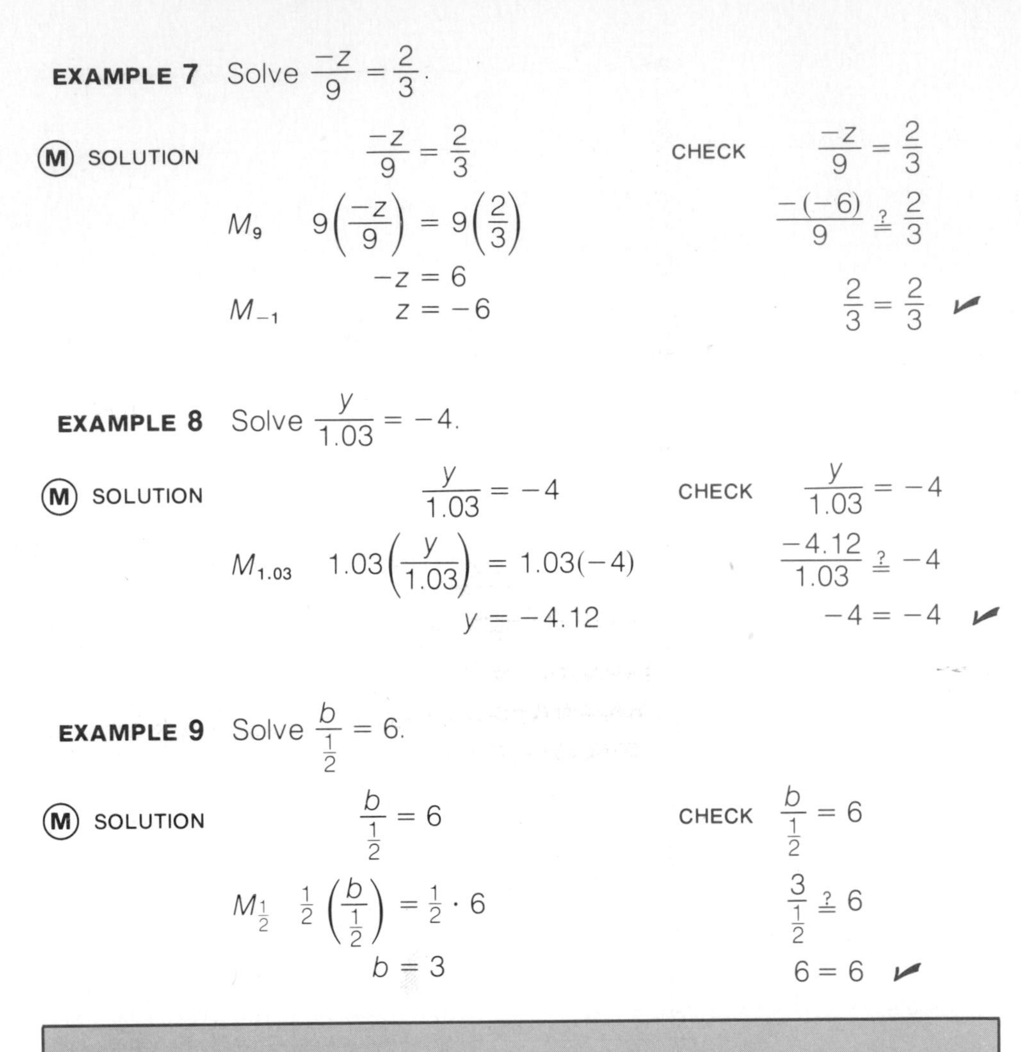

EXAMPLE 7 Solve $\frac{-z}{9} = \frac{2}{3}$.

Ⓜ SOLUTION

$$\frac{-z}{9} = \frac{2}{3}$$

$$M_9 \quad 9\left(\frac{-z}{9}\right) = 9\left(\frac{2}{3}\right)$$

$$-z = 6$$

$$M_{-1} \quad z = -6$$

CHECK

$$\frac{-z}{9} = \frac{2}{3}$$

$$\frac{-(-6)}{9} \stackrel{?}{=} \frac{2}{3}$$

$$\frac{2}{3} = \frac{2}{3} \checkmark$$

EXAMPLE 8 Solve $\frac{y}{1.03} = -4$.

Ⓜ SOLUTION

$$\frac{y}{1.03} = -4$$

$$M_{1.03} \quad 1.03\left(\frac{y}{1.03}\right) = 1.03(-4)$$

$$y = -4.12$$

CHECK

$$\frac{y}{1.03} = -4$$

$$\frac{-4.12}{1.03} \stackrel{?}{=} -4$$

$$-4 = -4 \checkmark$$

EXAMPLE 9 Solve $\frac{b}{\frac{1}{2}} = 6$.

Ⓜ SOLUTION

$$\frac{b}{\frac{1}{2}} = 6$$

$$M_{\frac{1}{2}} \quad \frac{1}{2}\left(\frac{b}{\frac{1}{2}}\right) = \frac{1}{2} \cdot 6$$

$$b = 3$$

CHECK

$$\frac{b}{\frac{1}{2}} = 6$$

$$\frac{3}{\frac{1}{2}} \stackrel{?}{=} 6$$

$$6 = 6 \checkmark$$

Solving an Equation of the Form $ax = b$

Use the Division Property of Equality and divide both members of the equation by a, $a \neq 0$.

Solving an Equation of the Form $\frac{x}{a} = b$

Use the Multiplication Property of Equality and multiply both members of the equation by a.

CLASSROOM EXERCISES

Solve.

1. $3x = 81$ **2.** $-4y = 1.2$ **3.** $-6z = -\frac{2}{3}$ **4.** $-0.5k = 8$

5. $\frac{x}{-4} = 9$ **6.** $\frac{-y}{7} = \frac{2}{3}$ **7.** $\frac{c}{0.04} = 100$ **8.** $\frac{r}{\frac{1}{2}} = 12$

EXERCISES

A Solve.

1. $5x = 30$ **2.** $9x = 72$ **3.** $-6y = 48$ **4.** $-7z = 84$

5. $6a = 4.2$ **6.** $12c = 1.56$ **7.** $-7k = 5.6$ **8.** $-16r = 8.0$

9. $3y = \frac{1}{5}$ **10.** $4z = \frac{4}{3}$ **11.** $-5x = \frac{10}{17}$ **12.** $-8w = \frac{20}{21}$

13. $0.5z = 8$ **14.** $1.2x = 96$ **15.** $-0.4g = 22$ **16.** $-2.5h = 30$

17. $\frac{1}{8}k = 6$ **18.** $\frac{1}{12}s = 14$ **19.** $-\frac{1}{3}x = 17$ **20.** $-\frac{1}{15}w = 8$

21. $\frac{x}{2} = 45$ **22.** $\frac{x}{8} = 4$ **23.** $\frac{z}{-10} = 5$ **24.** $\frac{a}{-6} = 7$

25. $\frac{t}{8} = \frac{1}{4}$ **26.** $\frac{p}{6} = \frac{5}{9}$ **27.** $\frac{-a}{10} = \frac{1}{15}$ **28.** $\frac{-d}{5} = \frac{8}{5}$

29. $\frac{y}{0.8} = 25$ **30.** $\frac{z}{0.4} = 18$ **31.** $\frac{x}{-0.6} = 14$ **32.** $\frac{r}{-0.5} = 32$

33. $\frac{x}{\frac{1}{8}} = 6$ **34.** $\frac{w}{\frac{1}{12}} = 36$ **35.** $\frac{z}{-\frac{1}{5}} = 25$ **36.** $\frac{y}{-\frac{1}{6}} = 15$

B **37.** $2^3x = 8$ **38.** $1\frac{1}{4}x = -0.08$ **39.** $(-8 + 20)x = -\frac{2}{3}$

40. $\frac{x}{-3\frac{1}{2}} = -2\frac{2}{7}$ **41.** $\left(\frac{2}{3} + \frac{-3}{4}\right)x = 14.75$ **42.** $\frac{x}{(-3)^3} = (-3)^2 \cdot 4$

C Solve for x.

43. $\left(\frac{a}{b}\right)x = \left(\frac{c}{d}\right)$ **44.** $\left(-\frac{b}{c}\right)x = \left(\frac{d}{a}\right)$ **45.** $\left(\frac{c}{a}\right)x = \left(-\frac{b}{d}\right)$

46. $\left(-\frac{a}{d}\right)x = \left(-\frac{c}{b}\right)$ **47.** $\frac{x}{\left(\frac{c}{d}\right)} = \left(\frac{a}{b}\right)$ **48.** $\frac{-x}{\left(\frac{d}{a}\right)} = \left(\frac{b}{c}\right)$

3-4 COMBINING TERMS IN EQUATIONS

Complicated equations may often be replaced by simpler ones by combining like terms in either member.

EXAMPLE 1 Simplify $5x - 2x = 18 - 3$.

SOLUTION

$$5x - 2x = 18 - 3$$

Combine terms. $$3x = 15$$

EXAMPLE 2 Simplify $3x + 4x + 2y + 7y = 5$.

SOLUTION

$$3x + 4x + 2y + 7y = 5$$

Combine terms. $$7x + 9y = 5$$

EXAMPLE 3 Simplify $30 = 0.5b + 5b - b$.

Ⓜ SOLUTION

$$30 = 0.5b + 5b - b$$

C.T. $$30 = 0.5b + 4b$$

C.T. $$30 = 4.5b$$

The "*C.T.*" notation indicates "combining terms."

EXAMPLE 4 Solve $5x - 2x = 18 - 3$.

Ⓜ SOLUTION

$$5x - 2x = 18 - 3$$

C.T. $$3x = 15$$

D_3 $$\frac{3x}{3} = \frac{15}{3}$$

$$x = 5$$

CHECK

$$5x - 2x = 18 - 3$$

$$5(5) - 2(5) \stackrel{?}{=} 15$$

$$25 - 10 \stackrel{?}{=} 15$$

$$15 = 15 \checkmark$$

EXAMPLE 5 Solve $30 = 0.5b + 5b - b$.

Ⓜ SOLUTION

$$30 = 0.5b + 5b - b$$

C.T. $$30 = 4.5b$$

$D_{4.5}$ $$\frac{30}{4.5} = b$$

$$\frac{300}{45} = b$$

$$\frac{20}{3} = b$$

$$b = \frac{20}{3}$$

CHECK The check is left for the student.

EXAMPLE 6 Solve $\frac{1}{2}d - \frac{1}{3}d = \frac{3(4-5)}{8}$.

SOLUTION

$$\frac{1}{2}d - \frac{1}{3}d = \frac{3(4-5)}{8}$$
$$\frac{3}{6}d - \frac{2}{6}d = \frac{3(-1)}{8}$$
$$\frac{1}{6}d = -\frac{3}{8}$$
$$M_6 \qquad 6\left(\frac{1}{6}d\right) = 6\left(-\frac{3}{8}\right)$$
$$d = -\frac{18}{8}$$
$$d = -\frac{9}{4}$$

CHECK The check is left for the student.

CLASSROOM EXERCISES

Solve each equation.

1. $2x + 3x = 15$
2. $5x + x = 24$
3. $3y + 4y = 35 - 7$
4. $0.5m + 0.5m = 1$
5. $\frac{1}{3}m - \frac{1}{4}m = \frac{2(3-5)}{6}$
6. $0.08a + 0.04a + 0.03a = 3$

EXERCISES

A Solve.

1. $7x - x = 26 - 2$
2. $5z + 3z = 17 + 7$
3. $-5a + a = 28 - 4$
4. $-9k + 4k = 16 + 9$
5. $12x + 3x = 6 - 36$
6. $6r + 4r = -52 + 12$
7. $-11w + 4w = 4 - 32$
8. $8s - 17s = -61 + 7$
9. $39 = 0.5x + 9x - 3x$
10. $76 = 12b - 4b + 1.5b$
11. $-85 = 2.5p + 11p - 5p$
12. $-93 = 17m - 5m + 3.5m$
13. $-152 = 4.5x + 7x - 21x$
14. $-250 = 16c - 31c + 2.5c$
15. $\frac{1}{2}y - \frac{1}{4}y = \frac{4(2-5)}{6}$
16. $\frac{1}{5}z - \frac{1}{6}z = \frac{3(4-5)}{2}$
17. $\frac{1}{4}x - \frac{1}{3}x = \frac{5(6-10)}{3}$
18. $\frac{1}{8}d - \frac{1}{7}d = \frac{7(9-15)}{8}$
19. $\frac{1}{9}k - \frac{1}{10}k = \frac{-8(4-9)}{6}$
20. $\frac{1}{3}n - \frac{1}{6}n = \frac{-7(5-11)}{9}$
21. $\frac{1}{2}v - \frac{3}{4}v = \frac{-12(6-14)}{16}$

B

22. $x + 7x - 5x = (45)(0.09)$
23. $12x + (-17x) = 8(11 - 21)$
24. $-\frac{1}{2}x + \frac{1}{3}x + \frac{1}{4}x = \frac{108}{-9}$
25. $-\frac{3}{4}x + \frac{5}{6}x + \left(-\frac{1}{9}x\right) = \frac{-51}{3}$

C Solve for x.

26. $ax + bx = c$
27. $r(gx) + s(kx) = p$
28. $\frac{x}{a} + \frac{x}{b} = c$

3-5 USING MORE THAN ONE PROPERTY TO SOLVE EQUATIONS

Sometimes two or more properties of equality may be needed to solve an equation.

EXAMPLE 1 Solve $4x + 5 = 37$.

SOLUTION $4x + 5 = 37$

First, use the Subtraction Property.

S_5 $\quad 4x + 5 - 5 = 37 - 5$

$4x = 32$

Then, use the Division Property.

D_4 $\quad \frac{4x}{4} = \frac{32}{4}$

$x = 8$

CHECK

$4x + 5 = 37$

$4(8) + 5 \stackrel{?}{=} 37$

$32 + 5 \stackrel{?}{=} 37$

$37 = 37$ ✓

EXAMPLE 2 Solve $\frac{x}{5} - 3 = 10$.

Ⓜ SOLUTION $\frac{x}{5} - 3 = 10$

A_3 $\quad \frac{x}{5} - 3 + 3 = 10 + 3$

$\frac{x}{5} = 13$

M_5 $\quad 5\left(\frac{x}{5}\right) = 5 \cdot 13$

$x = 65$

CHECK

$\frac{x}{5} - 3 = 10$

$\frac{65}{5} - 3 \stackrel{?}{=} 10$

$13 - 3 \stackrel{?}{=} 10$

$10 = 10$ ✓

When terms can be combined, it is best to do so *before* applying the properties of equality for solving the equation.

EXAMPLE 3 Solve $4x - 5x + 1 = 26 - 2$.

Ⓜ SOLUTION

$$
\begin{array}{ll}
 & 4x - 5x + 1 = 26 - 2 \\
C.T. & -x + 1 = 24 \\
S_1 & -x + 1 - 1 = 24 - 1 \\
 & -x = 23 \\
M_{-1} & x = -23
\end{array}
$$

CHECK

$$
\begin{aligned}
4x - 5x + 1 &= 26 - 2 \\
4(-23) - 5(-23) + 1 &\stackrel{?}{=} 24 \\
-92 + 115 + 1 &\stackrel{?}{=} 24 \\
24 &= 24 \checkmark
\end{aligned}
$$

EXAMPLE 4 Solve $\frac{1}{2}x - \frac{2}{3}x + \frac{3}{4}x = 5$.

Ⓜ SOLUTION

$$
\begin{array}{ll}
 & \frac{1}{2}x - \frac{2}{3}x + \frac{3}{4}x = 5 \\
 & \frac{6}{12}x - \frac{8}{12}x + \frac{9}{12}x = 5 \\
C.T. & \frac{7}{12}x = 5 \\
M_{12} & 12\left(\frac{7}{12}x\right) = 12(5) \\
 & 7x = 60 \\
D_7 & x = \frac{60}{7}
\end{array}
$$

CHECK The check is left for the student.

EXAMPLE 5 Solve $\frac{5x}{6} - 28 = 72$.

Ⓜ SOLUTION

$$
\begin{array}{ll}
 & \frac{5x}{6} - 28 = 72 \\
A_{28} & \frac{5x}{6} - 28 + 28 = 72 + 28 \\
 & \frac{5x}{6} = 100 \\
M_6 & 6\left(\frac{5x}{6}\right) = 6(100) \\
 & 5x = 600 \\
D_5 & \frac{5x}{5} = \frac{600}{5} \\
 & x = 120
\end{array}
$$

CHECK The check is left for the student.

EXAMPLE 6 Solve $\frac{x+2}{3} = 4$.

(M) SOLUTION

$$\frac{x+2}{3} = 4$$

$$M_3 \quad 3\left(\frac{x+2}{3}\right) = 3(4)$$

$$x + 2 = 12$$

$$S_2 \quad x + 2 - 2 = 12 - 2$$

$$x = 10$$

CHECK The check is left for the student.

CLASSROOM EXERCISES

Solve each equation.

1. $6y + 3 = 21$
2. $x + 4x = 20$
3. $4(y - 2) = 20$
4. $\frac{2b}{3} + 2 = 16$
5. $\frac{c+4}{5} = 6$
6. $\frac{a}{3} - 7 = 4$
7. $3w - 5w + 2 = 17 - 5$
8. $\frac{1}{3}k + \frac{1}{2}k + \frac{5}{9}k = 10$

EXERCISES

A Solve each equation.

1. $3a + 1 = 10$
2. $4y - 5 = 19$
3. $4x + 11 = -21$
4. $7z + 9 = -19$
5. $-8y + 3 = 59$
6. $-5f + 21 = 46$
7. $-6g + 15 = -27$
8. $-9d + 13 = 68$
9. $\frac{1}{7}x - 6 = 4$
10. $\frac{z}{5} - 8 = 4$
11. $\frac{m}{6} - 10 = -18$
12. $\frac{n}{3} - 15 = -20$
13. $\frac{-k}{4} - 18 = -2$
14. $\frac{-d}{9} - 12 = -3$
15. $\frac{r}{-8} - 6 = -13$
16. $6t - 9t + 4 = 26 - 7$
17. $-10x + 8x + 7 = 31 - 8$
18. $12y - 7y + 11 = 54 - 13$
19. $19w - 7w + 18 = 91 - 25$
20. $21a - 15a + 53 = 19 - 8$
21. $-17k + 25k + 39 = 38 - 15$
22. $15d - 30d + 62 = 50 - 33$
23. $-36p + 29p + 90 = 43 - 37$

24. $\frac{3}{4}s + \frac{2}{3}s - \frac{5}{6}s = 14$

25. $\frac{5}{9}r + \frac{1}{6}r - \frac{1}{2}r = 32$

26. $\frac{-3}{8}q + \frac{7}{12}q - \frac{5}{9}q = 15$

27. $\frac{-3}{4}g + \frac{2}{5}g - \frac{11}{15}g = 39$

28. $\frac{5}{6}r - \frac{3}{8}r + \frac{2}{9}r = -35$

29. $\frac{1}{2}q + \frac{4}{5}q - \frac{3}{10}q = -14$

30. $-\frac{2}{3}y + \frac{1}{4}y - \frac{4}{9}y = -8$

31. $-\frac{7}{10}x + \frac{5}{12}x - \frac{8}{15}x = -56$

32. $\frac{3}{4}x - 16 = 11$

33. $\frac{4z}{7} - 20 = 8$

34. $\frac{7d}{12} - 9 = -16$

35. $\frac{5r}{9} - 18 = -33$

36. $\frac{-2k}{3} - 24 = 18$

37. $\frac{-9t}{10} - 54 = 54$

38. $\frac{5w}{-6} - 36 = -46$

39. $\frac{8y}{-15} - 28 = -76$

40. $\frac{r + 5}{3} = 7$

41. $\frac{t + 7}{9} = 4$

42. $\frac{x + 6}{-5} = 6$

43. $\frac{y + 3}{-7} = 5$

44. $\frac{a + 8}{5} = -3$

45. $\frac{z + 9}{6} = -8$

46. $\frac{-x + 2}{4} = -5$

47. $\frac{-y + 12}{8} = -9$

48. $5(b - 4) = 10$

49. $8(t - 2) = 24$

50. $6(k - 7) = -66$

51. $3(n - 9) = -54$

52. $-4(q - 3) = 60$

53. $-7(v - 5) = 84$

54. $-9(y - 8) = -63$

55. $-12(c - 12) = -96$

56. $-(w + 5) = 5$

B

57. $\frac{-4x}{3} - 1 = -\frac{1}{6}$

58. $\frac{2y - 5}{4} = 20$

59. $1.2z + 1.24 = 4.6$

60. $0.06x + 0.8x - 0.22x = -1\frac{3}{5}$

61. $\frac{-4y - (-2)^3}{3^2 - 1} = 8$

62. $\frac{6w + (-3)^5}{4^2 - 4} = -20$

C Solve for x.

63. $ax + b = c$

64. $a(x - b) = c$

65. $\left(\frac{c}{d}\right)x + \left(\frac{e}{f}\right) = \left(\frac{a}{b}\right)$

66. $\left(\frac{a}{b}\right)x + \left(\frac{c}{d}\right)x + \left(\frac{e}{f}\right)x = g$

-0.

$-(-x) = x$

The Change Sign key [+/−] on your calculator replaces the number displayed by its opposite. Predict what should happen if you enter any non-zero number into the display and then press the Change Sign key several times. Try it and test your prediction.

3-6 EQUATIONS HAVING THE VARIABLE IN BOTH MEMBERS

Often the variable will appear in both members of an equation. To solve such an equation, we use the properties of equality to get all terms containing the variable in one member, usually the left member. Terms that do not contain the variable are collected in the other member.

EXAMPLE 1 Solve $6x = 2 + 4x$.

(M) SOLUTION

$$\begin{array}{ll} & 6x = 2 + 4x \\ S_{4x} & 6x - 4x = 2 + 4x - 4x \\ C.T. & 2x = 2 \\ D_2 & \frac{2x}{2} = \frac{2}{2} \\ & x = 1 \end{array}$$

CHECK

$$\begin{aligned} 6x &= 2 + 4x \\ 6(1) &\stackrel{?}{=} 2 + 4(1) \\ 6 &= 6 \checkmark \end{aligned}$$

EXAMPLE 2 Solve $4c + 10 = -c - 30$.

(M) SOLUTION

$$\begin{array}{ll} & 4c + 10 = -c - 30 \\ A_c & 4c + 10 + c = -c - 30 + c \\ C.T. & 5c + 10 = -30 \\ S_{10} & 5c + 10 - 10 = -30 - 10 \\ C.T. & 5c = -40 \\ D_5 & \frac{5c}{5} = \frac{-40}{5} \\ & c = -8 \end{array}$$

CHECK

$$\begin{aligned} 4c + 10 &= -c - 30 \\ 4(-8) + 10 &\stackrel{?}{=} -(-8) - 30 \\ -32 + 10 &\stackrel{?}{=} 8 - 30 \\ -22 &= -22 \checkmark \end{aligned}$$

EXAMPLE 3 Solve $\frac{1}{2}y - 1 + \frac{1}{4}y = \frac{3}{2}y - 2 + \frac{1}{2}$.

(M) SOLUTION

$$\begin{array}{ll} & \frac{1}{2}y - 1 + \frac{1}{4}y = \frac{3}{2}y - 2 + \frac{1}{2} \\ C.T. & \frac{3}{4}y - 1 = \frac{3}{2}y - \frac{3}{2} \\ S_{\frac{3}{2}y} & \frac{3}{4}y - 1 - \frac{3}{2}y = \frac{3}{2}y - \frac{3}{2} - \frac{3}{2}y \\ C.T. & -\frac{3}{4}y - 1 = -\frac{3}{2} \\ A_1 & -\frac{3}{4}y - 1 + 1 = -\frac{3}{2} + 1 \\ C.T. & -\frac{3}{4}y = -\frac{1}{2} \\ M_4 & 4\left(-\frac{3}{4}y\right) = 4\left(-\frac{1}{2}\right) \\ & -3y = -2 \\ D_{-3} & y = \frac{2}{3} \end{array}$$

CHECK The check is left for the student.

CLASSROOM EXERCISES

Solve.

1. $3x = x + 4$

2. $7x + 28 = 5x + 6$

3. $\frac{1}{2}x + 1 = \frac{1}{4}x - 2$

4. $2x = -7x + 18$

EXERCISES

A Solve and check.

1. $6x = x + 20$

2. $3x = 10 - 2x$

3. $3x = 5x - 8$

4. $2x = -7x + 18$

5. $4x = -25 - 6x$

6. $-5x = 12 + x$

7. $-6x = 30 - 4x$

8. $-10x = -4x - 54$

9. $5x = 7x + 10$

10. $8x = 5x - 12$

11. $8 - 5x = x - 4$

12. $6x - 15 = 84 - 3x$

13. $7x + 15 = 5x + 51$

14. $2x + 18 = 36 - 4x$

15. $15x - 13 = 2x + 7$

16. $11x + 17 = -3x - 11$

17. $-8x - 3 = 5x + 62$

18. $18 - 10x = 46 + 4x$

19. $-17x + 81 = -3x - 3$

20. $19x - 32 = 8x - 109$

21. $\frac{1}{3}x + 7 = \frac{1}{4}x - 2$

22. $\frac{1}{2}x + 2 = \frac{1}{3}x - 2$

23. $\frac{2}{3}x - \frac{4}{5} = \frac{3}{4}x - 1$

24. $1 - \frac{2}{5}x = \frac{7}{10}x - 5$

25. $\frac{5}{4}x - 1 = x + 2$

26. $6 - \frac{0}{3}x = 2x - 10$

27. $\frac{1}{3}x - 2 + \frac{1}{2}x = \frac{3}{4}x - 5 + 1\frac{1}{2}$

28. $\frac{7}{8}x - 10 - \frac{2}{3}x = \frac{5}{2}x - 9 + 4\frac{3}{4}$

29. $\frac{7}{2}x + 5\frac{1}{2} - 4 = \frac{-11}{12}x - 9 + \frac{3}{8}x$

30. $\frac{5}{3}x - 9\frac{1}{3} + 7 = \frac{7}{9}x - 14 + \frac{1}{6}x$

B

31. $0.4x = -3.2x + 72$

32. $0.1x = 0.3x - 7$

33. $0.3x + 0.4x + x = 2x + 0.15$

34. $7x + 1 + 0.5x = 3.5x + 2.2 - 2x + 6$

35. $0.6x - 1.5 = 8.4 - 0.3x$

36. $0.1 + 0.2x - 0.3 = 0.3x - 0.4$

37. $5x + 10 - x = 12 - x + 3$

38. $x - 8x + 3 = 5x + 12x + 45$

39. $x + 2x - 3x + 4x - 7 = 5x - 6x + 7x - 1$

40. $5x + 12 - 3x - 9x = -2x - 13 - x + 10x$

C Solve for x.

41. $ax + bc = cx - df$

42. $\left(\frac{a}{b}\right)x + \frac{c}{d} = \frac{e}{f} - \left(\frac{g}{h}\right)x$

CHECKING YOUR UNDERSTANDING

WORDS AND SYMBOLS

equation, $=$
inequality, $\neq$, $<$, $>$
open number sentence
solution set
solution of an equation or inequality

Properties of Equality:

Addition Subtraction Multiplication Division

CONCEPTS

- An equation containing one variable may be solved by using the Properties of Equality to replace the equation with a form for which the solution is clear. [3-2 to 3-6]

PROCESSES

- Given two arithmetic expressions, use $=$, $\neq$, $<$, or $>$ to make a true sentence. [3-1]

1. $78 \cdot 24 \ ? \ 24 \cdot 78$ **2.** $\frac{5}{9} \ ? \ \frac{5}{8}$ **3.** $2\left(\frac{1}{3}\right) \ ? \ \left(\frac{1}{3}\right)^2$

- Given an open sentence, determine whether a given number is a solution. [3-1]

4. Is 4 a solution of $4x - 3 = 12$? **5.** Is -8 a solution of $x^2 > 16$?

- Solve equations that have the form $x + a = b$, $x - a = b$, $ax = b$, or $\frac{x}{a} = b$. Check each solution. Graph each solution set. [3-2 to 3-6]

6. $\frac{1}{2}x - 2 = 1$ **7.** $5x - 2x + 7 = 13 - 4$ **8.** $2x + 8 = x + 3$

TWENTY INEQUALITY QUESTIONS

Jon is thinking of a whole number less than 1000. Mikki can ask questions that can be answered only "yes" or "no."

Is the number greater than 500? yes → Is it greater than 750? yes
Is it greater than 850? yes → Is it greater than 950? yes
Is it greater than 975? no → Is it greater than 965? no
Is it greater than 960? yes → Is it greater than 963? no
Is it 962? no → Is it 961? yes

Play this game with a classmate. Find out who can guess the other's number with the fewest guesses.

OBJECTIVE: Solve problems using equations.

3-7 PROBLEM SOLVING: WRITING EQUATIONS

In the statement of a problem, a mathematical relationship may be given by a *word sentence*. In solving the problem, we may use algebraic symbols and expressions for the ideas given in words. A result is a *number sentence*, such as an equation, that describes the mathematical relationship.

EXAMPLE 1 Replace each word sentence by an equation.

a. A number 5 times as great as n equals 80.

Ⓜ SOLUTION Use $5n$ for a number 5 times as great as n.

$5n = 80$

b. A number 5 greater than k is -26.

Ⓜ SOLUTION Use $k + 5$ for a number 5 greater than k.

$k + 5 = -26$

c. A number 4 less than w is 8.5.

Ⓜ SOLUTION Use $w - 4$ for a number 4 less than w.

$w - 4 = 8.5$

d. Seven-hundredths of d is 4.

Ⓜ SOLUTION 1

Use $0.07d$ for 0.07 of d.

$0.07d = 4$

Ⓜ SOLUTION 2

Use $\frac{7}{100}d$ for $\frac{7}{100}$ of d.

$\frac{7}{100}d = 4$

EXAMPLE 2 Replace each word sentence by an equation.

a. A number increased by 8 equals 11.

Ⓜ SOLUTION Use n for the number.

$n + 8 = 11$

b. A number decreased by $\frac{1}{4}$ equals 9.

Ⓜ SOLUTION Use n for the number.

$n - \frac{1}{4} = 9$

c. A number $\frac{3}{4}$ greater than twice another number is 42.

Ⓜ SOLUTION Use t for the other number.

$2t + \frac{3}{4} = 42$

d. Twice a number, less 4, equals 18 less than the number.

Ⓜ SOLUTION Use n for the number.

$$2n - 4 = n - 18$$

EXAMPLE 3 Write an equation for this relationship.

The sum of two consecutive even integers is 26.

n could be chosen to represent the larger number.

Ⓜ SOLUTION Use $\left[\begin{array}{ll} n & \text{for the smaller even integer.} \\ n + 2 & \text{for the next larger even integer.} \end{array}\right.$

$$n + n + 2 = 26$$

EXAMPLE 4 Write an equation for this relationship.

A number increased by 0.08 of the number equals 6800.

Ⓜ SOLUTION Use $\left[\begin{array}{ll} n & \text{for the number.} \\ 0.08n & \text{for eight-hundredths of the number.} \end{array}\right.$

$$n + 0.08n = 6800$$

EXAMPLE 5 Write an equation using one variable.

The mass of the cereal in two boxes is 1000 grams. One box contains 300 grams more than the other.

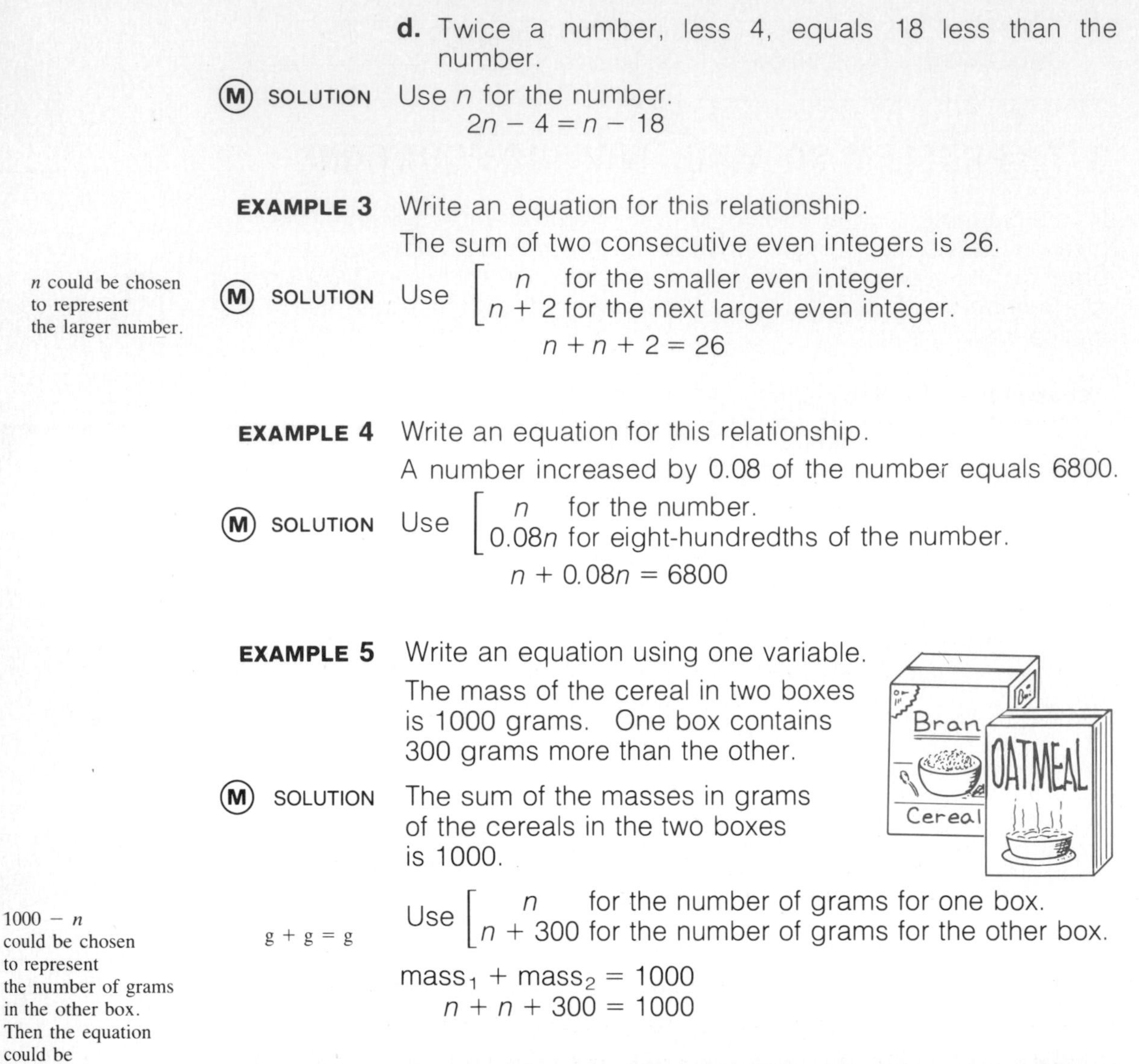

Ⓜ SOLUTION The sum of the masses in grams of the cereals in the two boxes is 1000.

$g + g = g$

Use $\left[\begin{array}{ll} n & \text{for the number of grams for one box.} \\ n + 300 & \text{for the number of grams for the other box.} \end{array}\right.$

$$\text{mass}_1 + \text{mass}_2 = 1000$$
$$n + n + 300 = 1000$$

$1000 - n$ could be chosen to represent the number of grams in the other box. Then the equation could be $n = 1000 - n + 300$, or $1000 - n = n + 300$ based on one box containing 300 grams more than the other.

WRITING AN EQUATION FOR A PROBLEM

1. Find a word sentence that describes a mathematical relationship.
2. Represent the ideas given in words by algebraic symbols and expressions.
3. Replace the words in the word sentence by their corresponding symbols and expressions.

CLASSROOM EXERCISES

For each exercise, use one variable and write an equation.

1. A number increased by 9 equals 28.
2. A number decreased by 7 equals 48.
3. 3000 is 75 times a number.
4. Five-eighths of a number is 40.
5. A number less $\frac{1}{2}$ the number equals 5.
6. Two containers have a mass of 35 kg. The mass of one is 3 kg more than the mass of the other.
7. One number is 3 larger than another. Four times their sum is 10 larger than their product.

EXERCISES

A For each exercise, use one variable and write an equation.

1. Eight times a number equals 48.
2. Four times a number equals 72.
3. A number increased by 43 equals 74.
4. A number increased by 175 equals 200.
5. A number decreased by $\frac{2}{3}$ equals $\frac{1}{2}$.
6. A number decreased by $\frac{3}{4}$ equals $\frac{1}{3}$.
7. 6 is 10 less than twice a number.
8. 14 is 13 less than 3 times a number.
9. The sum of two consecutive integers is 43.
10. The sum of two consecutive integers is 89.
11. Two boxes contain 85 items. One box contains 15 more than the other.
12. Two buses carry 93 passengers. One bus carries 9 more than the other.
13. One number is 5 larger than another. Twice their sum is 4 larger than their product.

B

14. A number increased by 28-hundredths of the number equals 25.6.
15. A number increased by $\frac{1}{2}$ the number equals 8.
16. When 76 is subtracted from 7 times a number, the difference is 71.
17. A number decreased by $33\frac{1}{3}\%$ of the number equals 48.

C

18. The numbers b and c differ by 9. Write three equations that state this fact.
19. The square of the sum of a and b exceeds the sum of the squares of a and b by $2ab$.

3-8 PROBLEM SOLVING: USING EQUATIONS

When solving a problem, we sometimes are able to describe a mathematical relationship with an equation using one variable. The solution of the equation often enables us to make a statement that settles the problem. However, we always should check the truth of this conclusion against the information given for the problem. If we find the conclusion is not true, we should check our work carefully for mistakes.

The *problem* is to find the number.

EXAMPLE 1 A number increased by 6 equals 95. Find the number.

Ⓜ SOLUTION Use n for the number.

$$n + 6 = 95$$

S_6 $\quad n = 95 - 6$

$$n = 89$$

CONCLUSION The number is 89.

CHECK 89 increased by 6 equals 95. ✔

Checking is a necessary part of the solution.

EXAMPLE 2 A number decreased by $\frac{1}{3}$ of the number equals 800. Find the number.

Ⓜ SOLUTION Use n for the number.

$$n - \tfrac{1}{3}n = 800$$

$$\tfrac{2}{3}n = 800$$

M_3 $\quad 2n = 3(800)$

D_2 $\quad n = \frac{2400}{2}$

$$n = 1200$$

CONCLUSION The number is 1200.

CHECK 1200 decreased by $\frac{1}{3}$ of 1200, or 400, equals 800. ✔

EXAMPLE 3 The sum of two consecutive integers is 397. Find the integers.

Ⓜ SOLUTION Use $\left[\begin{array}{ll} n & \text{for the smaller integer.} \\ n+1 & \text{for the larger integer.} \end{array}\right.$

$$n + n + 1 = 397$$

$$2n + 1 = 397$$

S_1 $\quad 2n = 396$

D_2 $\quad n = 198$. Also, $n + 1 = 199$.

CONCLUSION The two consecutive integers are 198 and 199.

CHECK The sum of 198 and 199 is 397. ✔

EXAMPLE 4 The mass of the cereal in two boxes is 1000 grams. One box contains 300 grams more than the other. Find the number of grams of cereal in each box.

Ⓜ **SOLUTION** The sum of the masses in grams is 1000.

Use n for the number of grams for one box.
$n + 300$ for the number of grams for the other box.

$\text{mass}_1 + \text{mass}_2 = 1000$

$n + n + 300 = 1000$

$2n + 300 = 1000$

S_{300} $2n = 700$

D_2 $n = 350$. Also, $n + 300 = 650$.

g + g = g

Sometimes it is quite helpful to have an intermediate equation between the sentence in English and the sentence that uses the variables.

CONCLUSION There are 350 g of cereal in one box and 650 g in the other.

CHECK $350 + 650 \stackrel{?}{=} 1000$
$1000 = 1000$ ✓

EXAMPLE 5 The length of a rectangle is 5 times its width. The perimeter of the rectangle is 24. Find the length and width.

5w
w w
5w

Ⓜ **SOLUTION** $2 \cdot \text{length} + 2 \cdot \text{width} = 24$

Use w for the width of the rectangle.
$5w$ for the length of the rectangle.

$2(5w) + 2w = 24$

$10w + 2w = 24$

$12w = 24$

D_{12} $w = 2$. Also, $5w = 10$.

CONCLUSION The length is 10 and the width is 2.

CHECK The check is left for the student.

USING EQUATIONS TO SOLVE PROBLEMS

1. Read the problem. Determine what number(s) must be found.
2. Find a word sentence to suggest an equation for the number(s).
3. Represent the unknown numbers by algebraic expressions.
4. Use the expressions to replace the word sentence by an equation.
5. Solve the equation.
6. Use the solution of the equation to write a statement (the conclusion) that settles the problem.
7. Check that the conclusion agrees with the problem situation.

If the conclusion does not "check," it is good advice to rework the problem.

CLASSROOM EXERCISES

Solve for the unknown numbers.

1. A number increased by 24 equals 75.

2. A number increased by 5 times itself equals 72.

3. The sum of two consecutive integers is -5.

4. The sum of two numbers is 32. One number is three times the other.

5. The difference of two numbers is 16. One number is 6 larger than two times the other.

6. The length of a rectangle is three times the width. The perimeter is 48. Find the length and width.

EXERCISES

Solve for the unknown numbers.

A

1. A number increased by 43 equals 97.

2. A number increased by -19 equals -6.

3. A number decreased by 31 equals 96.

4. A number decreased by -12 equals -28.

5. A number decreased by 5 times the number is 36.

6. A number decreased by 3 times the number is -18.

7. A number increased by 9 times the number is 80.

8. A number increased by 6 times the number is -35.

9. The sum of two consecutive integers is -31.

10. The sum of two consecutive integers is -119.

11. The sum of two numbers is 63. One number is 27 larger than the other.

12. The sum of two numbers is 60. One number is 3 times the other.

13. One number is 5 times as large as another. The sum of the numbers is 54.

14. One number is 39 smaller than another. The sum of the numbers is 111.

15. One number is 8 times another. Their difference is 56.

16. One number is 12 times another. Their difference is 165.

17. The length of a rectangle is 15 larger than its width. Its perimeter is 58. Find the length and width.

18. The length of a rectangle is 24 larger than its width. Its perimeter is 200. Find the length and width.

B **19.** Three-fourths of a number is 27.

20. Two-thirds of a number is 16.

21. Twice a number is one less than 3 times the number.

22. Three times a number is one less than two times the number.

23. The sum of 3 consecutive integers is -117.

24. The sum of 3 consecutive even integers is -96.

C **25.** The sum of 3 consecutive even integers is 50 more than the smallest one.

26. The sum of 3 consecutive odd integers is -5 less than the sum of the larger two integers.

27. The sum of three numbers is 3450. The second number is twice as large as the first number. The third number is 3 times as large as the first.

28. The sum of three numbers is 5. The second number is one-half the first number. The third number is one-third the first number.

CHECKING YOUR UNDERSTANDING

CONCEPTS

- A problem may be solved by replacing a word sentence with an equation and then solving the equation. Any conclusion provided by the solution of the equation should be checked against the information given for the problem. [3-7, 3-8]

PROCESSES

- Write a number sentence for a given word sentence. [3-7]

1. A number 3 greater than twice t is 9.

2. The sum of two consecutive odd integers is 56.

- Write and solve an equation that provides a solution for a problem. Check each conclusion. [3-8]

3. A number increased by 6 times the number is 98. Find the number.

4. The width of a rectangle is 4 less than the length. The perimeter of the rectangle is 68. Find the width and length.

THE MEMORY AND RECIPROCAL KEYS ON YOUR CALCULATOR

The keys shown here can make it easier to simplify mathematical expressions. Locate them on your calculator.

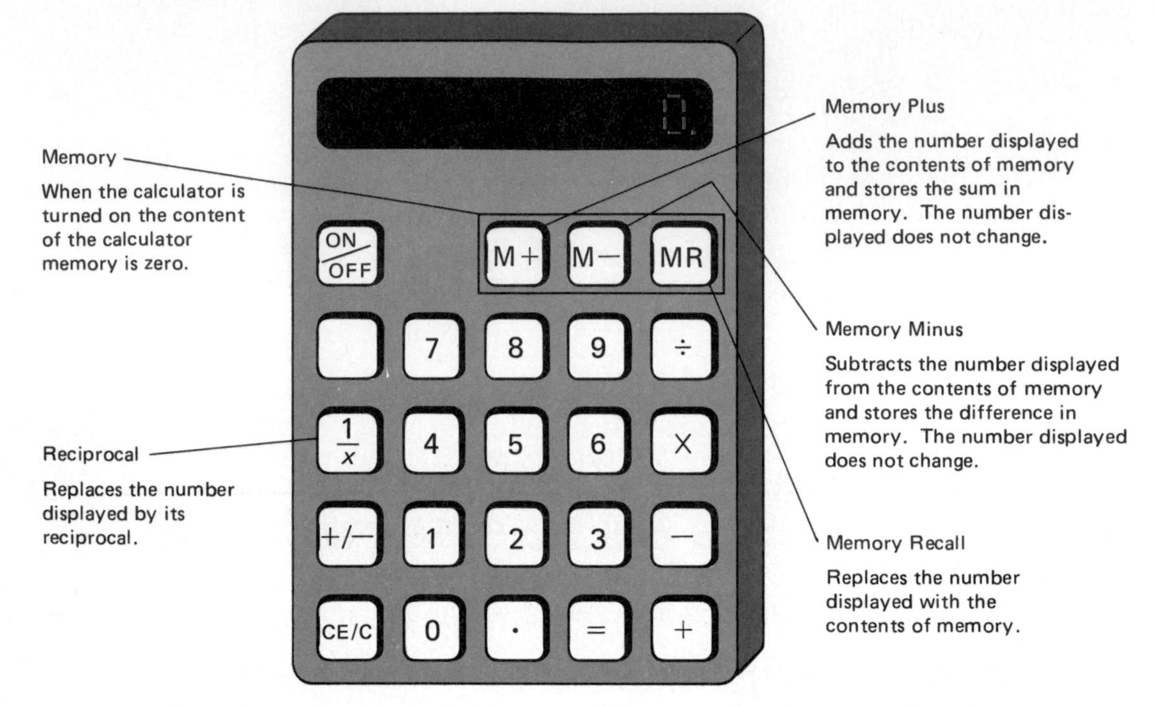

The Memory keys allow us to save intermediate results without recording them on paper.

EXAMPLE 1 Use your calculator to simplify $15 \times 37 + 19 \times 32$.

SOLUTION

Press	15	×	37	=	M+ (Add 555 to contents of memory.)	19	×	32	=	M+ (Add 608 to contents of memory.)	MR (Display contents of memory)
Display	15	15	37	555	555	19	19	32	608	608	1163
Memory	0	0	0	0	555	555	555	555	555	1163	1163

CONCLUSION $15 \times 37 + 19 \times 32 = 1163$

The Reciprocal key and the Change Sign ([+/−]) key perform similar tasks. The Change Sign key can be used to *add* the *additive inverse* of a number. The Reciprocal key can be used to *multiply* by the *multiplicative inverse* of a number.

EXAMPLE 2 Use your calculator to simplify $476 \div (57 - 29)$.

SOLUTION Recall that $476 \div (57 - 29) = 476 \cdot \left(\frac{1}{57 - 29}\right)$. Thus, we may use the reciprocal key.

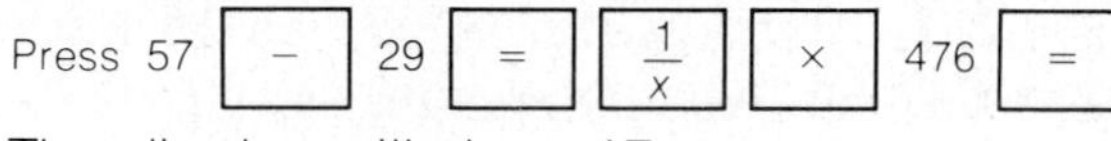

The display will show 17.

EXAMPLE 3 Use your calculator to simplify $381 - 12 \times 19$.

SOLUTION Recall that $381 - 12 \times 19 = 381 + [-(12 \times 19)]$. Thus, we may use the Change Sign key.

Press 12 [×] 19 [=] [+/−] [+] 381 [=]

The display will show 153.

EXERCISES

Simplify using your calculator. Use the memory of the calculator to avoid writing down intermediate results.

1. $4 \times 31 + (-7) \times 18$ **2.** $(-12) \times (-14) - 315 \div 21$ **3.** $28(17 - 23) + 31 \times (-8)$

4. $\frac{635 - 123}{(-18) + 58}$ **5.** $\frac{34.16 - 79.5}{0.147 + 0.103}$ **6.** $(-14) \times 9 + (-11) \times (-18) + 31 \times (-2)$

Simplify using your calculator. Use the Reciprocal and Change Sign keys, *not* the calculator memory, to avoid recording intermediate results.

7. $8.7 - 2.03 \times 9$ **8.** $-7 \div (215 - 183)$ **9.** $142 - 26 \times 7 - 9$

10. $\frac{1}{45 - 61}$ **11.** $\frac{-7}{199 - 9 \times 15}$ **12.** $\frac{12}{893 - 6(453 - 181) + 339}$

Simplify using your calculator. Use the memory, or the Reciprocal and Change Sign keys to avoid recording intermediate results.

13. $-15 \times 61 + 13 \times 4$ **14.** $1.3 \times 1.02 - 68 \div (19 - 83)$ **15.** $51 \div 136 - 209 \div 152$

16. $\frac{4}{14 + 66}$ **17.** $\frac{1}{8 - 24 \times 3}$ **18.** $\frac{412 - 21 \times 11}{153 - 73}$

OBJECTIVES: Use addition, subtraction, multiplication, and division to solve inequalities.

3-9 USING ADDITION OR SUBTRACTION TO SOLVE INEQUALITIES

We have been using the Addition and Subtraction Properties of Equality to solve equations. There are similar properties for inequalities. The Addition Property of Inequality allows us to add the same number to both members of an inequality. The Subtraction Property of Inequality allows us to subtract the same number from both members of an inequality.

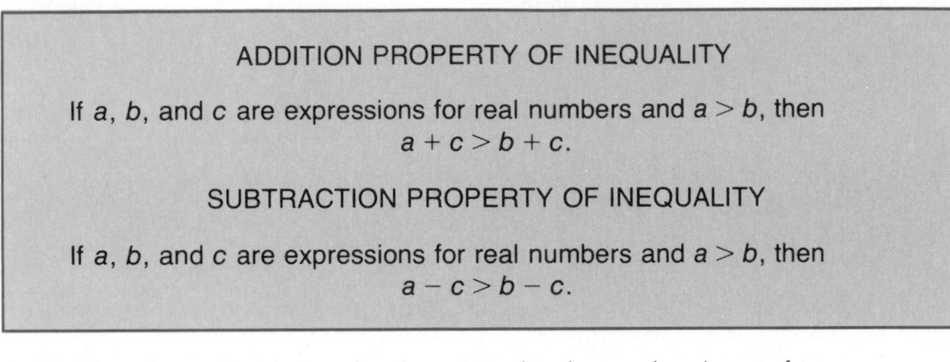

ADDITION PROPERTY OF INEQUALITY

If a, b, and c are expressions for real numbers and $a > b$, then
$$a + c > b + c.$$

SUBTRACTION PROPERTY OF INEQUALITY

If a, b, and c are expressions for real numbers and $a > b$, then
$$a - c > b - c.$$

These properties may also be stated using $<$ in place of $>$.

EXAMPLE 1 Solve $x + 2 > 7$. Graph the solution set.

Ⓜ SOLUTION

$$x + 2 > 7$$
S_2 $$x > 7 - 2$$
$$x > 5$$

The *ASMD* notation used to indicate applications of the Properties of Equality is used in similar fashion for applications of the Properties of Inequality.

CHECK Replace x by 6. Try other numbers for x if you wish.

$$x + 2 > 7$$
$$6 + 2 \overset{?}{>} 7$$
$$8 > 7 \checkmark$$

GRAPH

0 1 2 3 4 5 6 7 8

The ○━━▶ shows there are infinitely many solutions for $x + 2 > 7$. The ○ shows that the point for 5 is not included in the graph.

EXAMPLE 2 Solve $x - 2 < -\frac{9}{4}$. Graph the solution set.

Ⓜ **SOLUTION**

$$x - 2 < -\frac{9}{4}$$

A_2 $$x < -\frac{9}{4} + 2$$

$$x < -\frac{1}{4}$$

CHECK Use -1 for x.

Try other numbers for x if you wish.

$$x - 2 < -\frac{9}{4}$$

$$-1 - 2 \overset{?}{<} -2\frac{1}{4}$$

$$-3 < -2\frac{1}{4} \checkmark$$

In checking the result of solving an inequality, you should try some numbers that may be expected to not "work" as solutions.

GRAPH

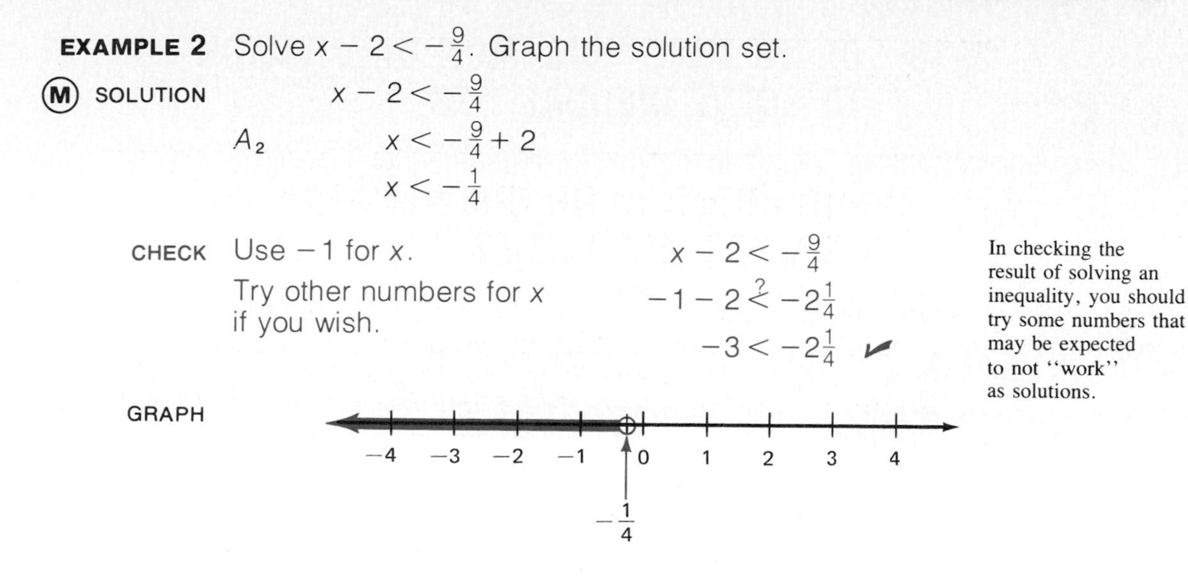

CLASSROOM EXERCISES

Solve each inequality. Graph its solution set. Check.

1. $x + 2 > 8$ **2.** $y + 6 < 15$ **3.** $a - 3 < -3\frac{1}{4}$ **4.** $p + 4\frac{1}{2} > 3$

EXERCISES

Solve each inequality. Graph its solution set. Check.

A

1. $x + 2 > 6$ **2.** $z + 2 > 5$ **3.** $r + 3 < 6$ **4.** $v + 5 < 9$

5. $x + 18 > 14$ **6.** $y + 25 > 15$ **7.** $w + 32 < 20$ **8.** $t + 9 < 3$

9. $f - 2 > 5$ **10.** $g - 3 > 2$ **11.** $m - 9 < 14$ **12.** $n - 12 < 6$

13. $x - 8 > -3$ **14.** $d - 7 > -4$ **15.** $h - 15 > -20$ **16.** $b - 22 > -30$

17. $r - 5 > -8\frac{1}{2}$ **18.** $a + \frac{1}{3} > 4$ **19.** $x + \frac{3}{4} < 6$ **20.** $y + \frac{5}{6} < 8$

B

21. $y - 4.1 > -2.2$ **22.** $w - 5.3 > -3.6$ **23.** $t + (-3) < 5$

24. $d + (-4) < 7$ **25.** $g - 2(-7) < 12$ **26.** $b - 3(-8) < 18$

27. $5x - 13 > 4x$ **28.** $3s + 4 < 2s - 1$ **29.** $2m + 30 > m + 5$

30. $2n + 3 < n - 1$ **31.** $3g + 50 > 2g + 15$ **32.** $x + 12 < 3(3.75)$

Solve each inequality for x.

C

33. $x + a > b$ **34.** $x + c < d$ **35.** $5x - 2c < n + 4x$

36. $-9x - 3m > r + (-10x)$ **37.** $-p + (-x) > q$ **38.** $u + (-x) < -v$

3-10 USING MULTIPLICATION OR DIVISION TO SOLVE INEQUALITIES

The Multiplication and Division Properties of Inequality are not quite the same as the Multiplication and Division Properties of Equality. The Properties of Inequality allow us to multiply or divide both members of an inequality by the same number. However, sometimes the order of the inequality is preserved and sometimes it is reversed.

Inequality	Multiply by	New Inequality	The Order of the Inequality is
$8 > 3$	2	$16 > 6$	preserved
$8 > 3$	-2	$-16 < -6$	reversed

Inequality	Divide by	New Inequality	The Order of the Inequality is
$3 < 8$	5	$\frac{3}{5} < \frac{8}{5}$	preserved
$3 < 8$	-5	$-\frac{3}{5} > -\frac{8}{5}$	reversed

The order of an inequality is preserved when we multiply or divide by a positive number. It is reversed when we multiply or divide by a negative number.

MULTIPLICATION PROPERTY OF INEQUALITY

If a, b, and c are expressions for real numbers and $a > b$, then $ac > bc$ if c is positive, and $ac < bc$ if c is negative.

DIVISION PROPERTY OF INEQUALITY

If a, b, and c are expressions for real numbers and $a > b$, then $\frac{a}{c} > \frac{b}{c}$ if c is positive, and $\frac{a}{c} < \frac{b}{c}$ if c is negative.

These properties may also be stated using $<$ in place of each $>$ and $>$ in place of each $<$.

EXAMPLE 1 Solve $8x < 16$. Graph the solution set.

Ⓜ SOLUTION

$$8x < 16$$

$$D_8 \qquad x < \frac{16}{8}$$

$$x < 2$$

CHECK Use 1 for x. Try other numbers for x if you wish.

$$8x < 16$$

$$8(1) \overset{?}{<} 16$$

$$8 < 16 \checkmark$$

GRAPH

−4 −3 −2 −1 0 1 2 3 4

EXAMPLE 2 Solve $\frac{x}{-3} > 1$. Graph the solution set.

Ⓜ SOLUTION

$$\frac{x}{-3} > 1$$

$$M_{-3} \qquad x < -3(1)$$

$$x < -3$$

Note that multiplying by −3 reverses the order of inequality for multiplication and division and *only* for those operations.

CHECK Use −4 for x. Try other numbers for x if you wish.

$$\frac{x}{-3} > 1$$

$$\frac{-4}{-3} \overset{?}{>} 1$$

$$\frac{4}{3} > 1 \checkmark$$

GRAPH

−5 −4 −3 −2 −1 0 1 2 3

EXAMPLE 3 Solve $\frac{-x}{2} < 5$. Graph the solution set.

Ⓜ SOLUTION

$$\frac{-x}{2} < 5$$

$$M_2 \qquad -x < 10$$

$$M_{-1} \qquad x > -10$$

This step could also be D_{-1}.

CHECK Use −9 for x.

$$\frac{-x}{2} < 5$$

$$\frac{-(-9)}{2} \overset{?}{<} 5$$

$$\frac{9}{2} < 5 \checkmark$$

GRAPH

−12 −11 −10 −9 −8 −7 −6 −5 −4

EXAMPLE 4 Solve $-0.6x > 1.38$. Graph the solution set.

Ⓜ SOLUTION

$$-0.6x > 1.38$$

$D_{-0.6}$ $$x < \frac{1.38}{-0.6}$$

$$x < -2.3$$

CHECK Use -3 for x.

$$-0.6x > 1.38$$
$$-0.6(-3) \overset{?}{>} 1.38$$
$$1.8 > 1.38 \checkmark$$

GRAPH

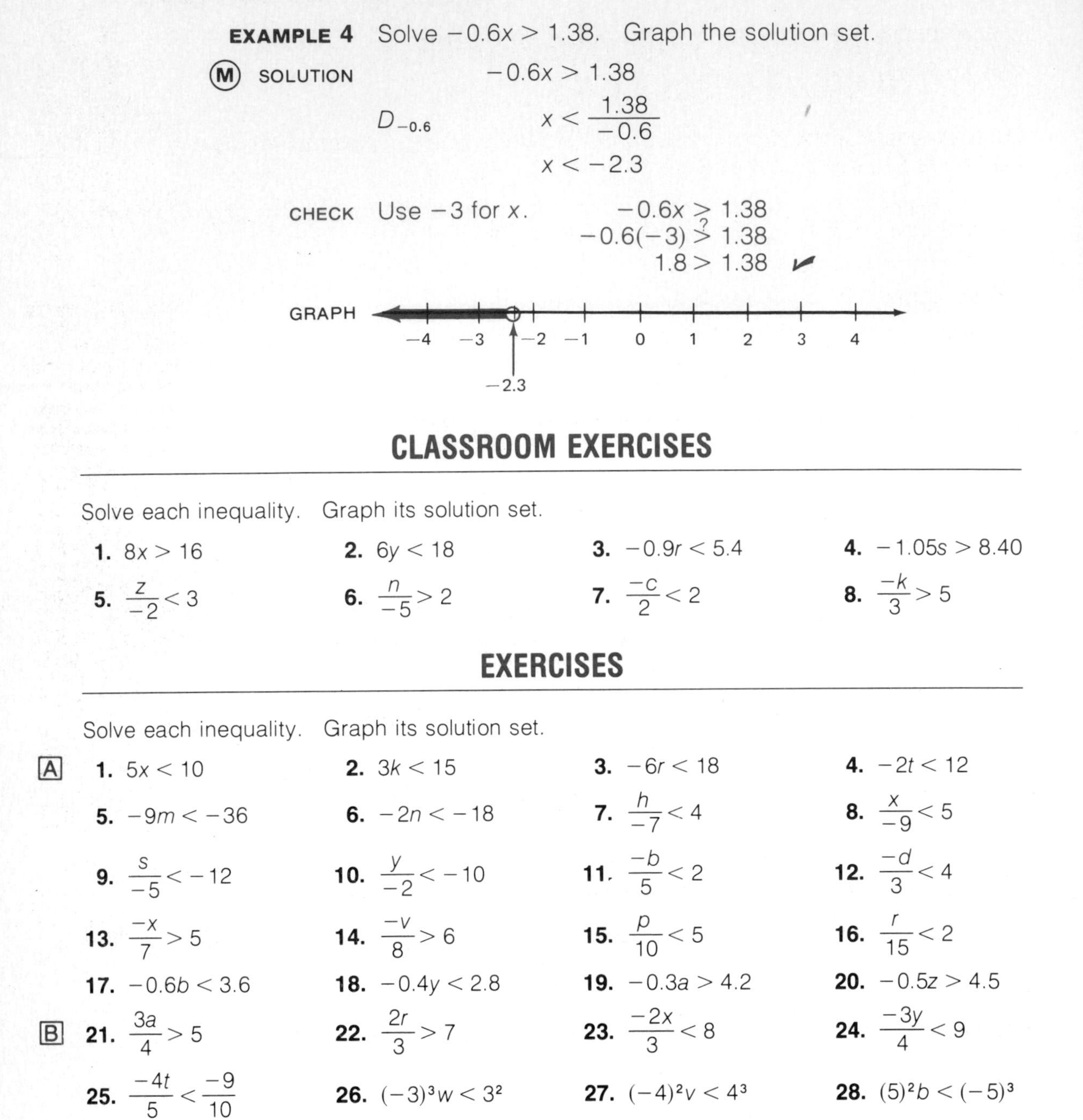

CLASSROOM EXERCISES

Solve each inequality. Graph its solution set.

1. $8x > 16$
2. $6y < 18$
3. $-0.9r < 5.4$
4. $-1.05s > 8.40$
5. $\frac{z}{-2} < 3$
6. $\frac{n}{-5} > 2$
7. $\frac{-c}{2} < 2$
8. $\frac{-k}{3} > 5$

EXERCISES

Solve each inequality. Graph its solution set.

A

1. $5x < 10$
2. $3k < 15$
3. $-6r < 18$
4. $-2t < 12$
5. $-9m < -36$
6. $-2n < -18$
7. $\frac{h}{-7} < 4$
8. $\frac{x}{-9} < 5$
9. $\frac{s}{-5} < -12$
10. $\frac{y}{-2} < -10$
11. $\frac{-b}{5} < 2$
12. $\frac{-d}{3} < 4$
13. $\frac{-x}{7} > 5$
14. $\frac{-v}{8} > 6$
15. $\frac{p}{10} < 5$
16. $\frac{r}{15} < 2$
17. $-0.6b < 3.6$
18. $-0.4y < 2.8$
19. $-0.3a > 4.2$
20. $-0.5z > 4.5$

B

21. $\frac{3a}{4} > 5$
22. $\frac{2r}{3} > 7$
23. $\frac{-2x}{3} < 8$
24. $\frac{-3y}{4} < 9$
25. $\frac{-4t}{5} < \frac{-9}{10}$
26. $(-3)^3w < 3^2$
27. $(-4)^2v < 4^3$
28. $(5)^2b < (-5)^3$

Solve for x.

C

29. $\frac{-ax}{-b} < -c$
30. $\frac{-ax}{b} < ab$
31. $\frac{-cx}{-d} > -de$

3-11 USING MORE THAN ONE PROPERTY TO SOLVE INEQUALITIES

Just as was true for solving an equation, more than one property may be needed to solve an inequality.

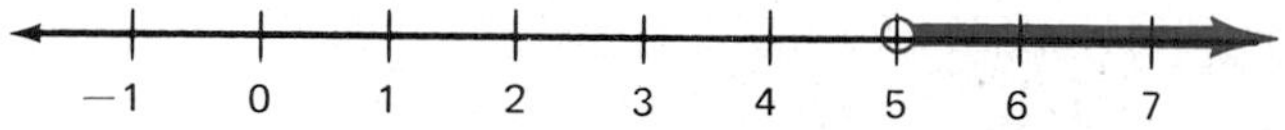

The order of steps in solving an equation or an inequality may be prescribed by "undoing" the operations and their order as indicated in the given sentence.

EXAMPLE 1 Solve $\frac{x-3}{2} > 1$. Graph the solution set.

Ⓜ SOLUTION

$$\frac{x-3}{2} > 1$$

M_2 $\quad x - 3 > 2$

A_3 $\quad x > 5$

GRAPH

EXAMPLE 2 Solve $-2x + 3 < 9$. Graph the solution set.

Ⓜ SOLUTION

$$-2x + 3 < 9$$

S_3 $\quad -2x < 6$

D_{-2} $\quad x > -3$

GRAPH

EXAMPLE 3 Solve $3x + x < -1 + x$. Graph the solution set.

Ⓜ SOLUTION

$$3x + x < -1 + x$$

$$4x < -1 + x$$

S_x $\quad 3x < -1$

D_3 $\quad x < -\frac{1}{3}$

GRAPH

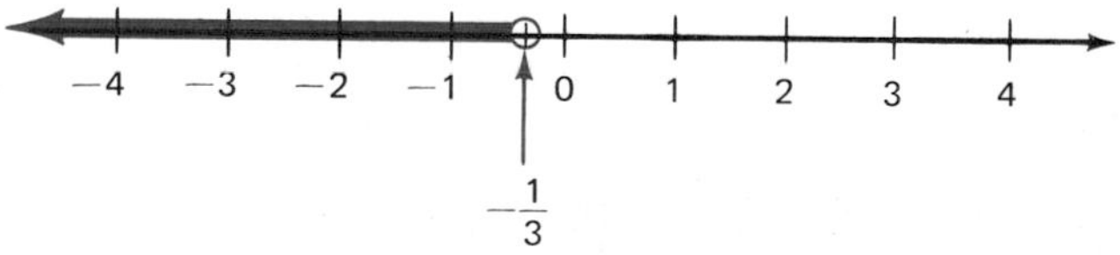

EXAMPLE 4 Solve $4 - 2x < -x - 5$. Graph the solution set.

Ⓜ SOLUTION

$$4 - 2x < -x - 5$$

S_4 $\quad -2x < -x - 9$

A_x $\quad -x < -9$

M_{-1} $\quad x > 9$

GRAPH

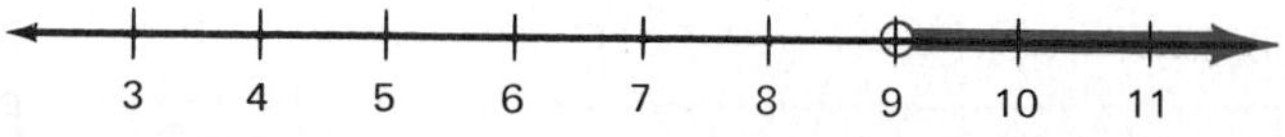

CLASSROOM EXERCISES

Solve each inequality. Graph its solution set.

1. $\frac{x-4}{3} > 4$
2. $-3y + 2 < 20$
3. $3z + 2z > z + 3$
4. $6 - 3w < -2w - 4$

EXERCISES

A Solve each inequality. Graph its solution set.

1. $\frac{x+2}{3} > 4$
2. $\frac{x+3}{4} > 5$
3. $\frac{d-2}{5} > -2$
4. $\frac{k-4}{3} > -8$
5. $-4r + 1 < 17$
6. $-6s + 5 < 41$
7. $-7n + 4 > 46$
8. $-3p + 10 > 31$
9. $2q + q > q + 4$
10. $5t + 3t > 2t + 6$
11. $3y + 4y < 2y + 20$
12. $6x + 2x < 4x + 32$
13. $2d + 3d < -d + 12$
14. $4b + 5b < -b + 40$
15. $-10 - 6k < -5k + 6$
16. $-9 - 10b < -9b + 16$
17. $-15 - 4a > -3a + 5$

B

18. $-\frac{2}{3}w < -20$
19. $-\frac{4}{5}z < -64$
20. $s + 0.25 > 3s - 0.75$
21. $-y - \frac{1}{2} > 5y + \frac{1}{2}$
22. $-6p - 45 < -8p + 25$
23. $\frac{1}{4}s + \frac{1}{2} < \frac{2}{3}s - \frac{3}{5}$

C Solve each inequality for x.

24. $x - a < b$
25. $ax + b > c$
26. $\frac{ax+b}{c} < d$

DIVISION RULES

By knowing a few divisibility rules, you may avoid much trial-and-error arithmetic. Two useful rules are

Numbers are divisible by 8 when 8 divides the last three digits.
Numbers are divisible by 9 when 9 divides the sum of the digits.

Find divisibility rules for division by each of these

1. 2
2. 3
3. 4
4. 5
5. 6
6. 10

Without dividing, tell which numbers from 1 to 10 divide each.

7. 48 765
8. 3060
9. 50 544
10. 645
11. 1260

3-12 COMPOUND SENTENCES AND THEIR GRAPHS

A sentence such as "$x = 2$ *and* $x < 6$" is a *compound* sentence. As with simpler open sentences, a number for the variable that gives a true sentence is a solution. A compound sentence using "and" is true only if *both* parts of the sentence are true.

A sentence such as "$x = 1$ *or* $x < -2$" is a compound sentence using "or". A compound sentence using "or" is true if *at least one* of the parts is true.

Compound Sentences	Solutions
$x = 2$ and $x < 6$	2
$x = 2$ and $x > 6$	There is no solution.
$x = 2$ or $x < 6$	all real numbers less than 6
$x = 2$ or $x > 6$	2 and all real numbers greater than 6

Some compound sentences can be shown in special ways. "$\geq$" can be used for "is greater than *or* equal to." "$\leq$" can be used for "is less than *or* equal to." A sentence like this, $a < x < b$, says "a is less than x *and* x is less than b," or that "x is greater than a *and* less than b."

Compound Sentences	Meaning	Solutions
$x \leq 5$	x is less than *or* equal to 5	5 and all real numbers less than 5
$x \geq -3$	x is greater than *or* equal to -3	-3 and all real numbers greater than -3
$-3 < x < 7$	x is greater than -3 *and* less than 7	all real numbers between -3 and 7
$-1 > x > -4$	x is less than -1 *and* greater than -4	all real numbers between -4 and -1
$3 < x \leq 6$	x is greater than 3 *and* less than or equal to 6	all real numbers between 3 and 6, and 6

EXAMPLE 1 Graph the solution set for $x \geq -3$.

SOLUTION

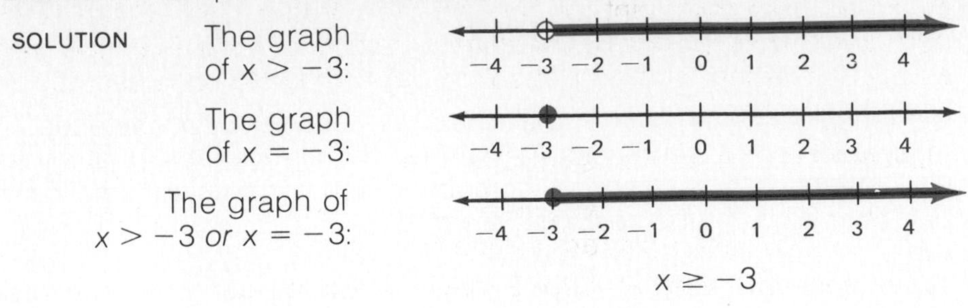

EXAMPLE 2 Graph the solution set for $-2 \leq x < 4$.

SOLUTION

$-2 \leq x$:

−4 −3 −2 −1 0 1 2 3 4

$x < 4$:

−4 −3 −2 −1 0 1 2 3 4

Note that numbers less than -2 satisfy one condition but not the other. A similar statement holds for numbers ≥ 4.

(M) $-2 \leq x$ *and* $x < 4$:

−4 −3 −2 −1 0 1 2 3 4

$-2 \leq x < 4$

EXAMPLE 3 Graph the solution set for "$x \leq 1$ *or* $x > 2$".

SOLUTION

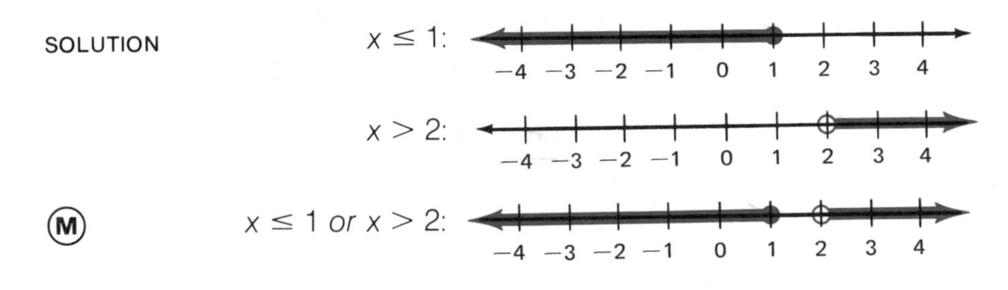

The solution set for "$x < 3$ *or* $x > 2$" is the set of real numbers. Therefore, its graph is the entire number line. For "$x < 2$ *and* $x > 3$" there are no solutions. Its graph shows no points.

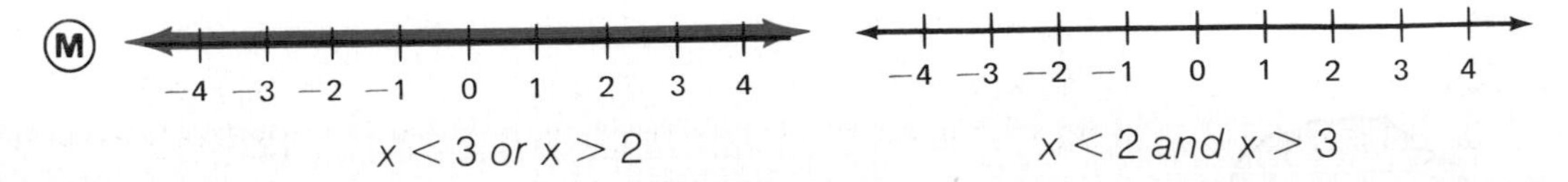

$x < 3$ *or* $x > 2$ $\qquad$ $x < 2$ *and* $x > 3$

We may think of the absolute value of a number as the distance of its graph from the point for zero on the number line. Since "distance from zero" may be found in *either* of two directions from the point for zero, a sentence involving absolute value may be replaced by a compound sentence.

EXAMPLE 4 Graph the solution set for $|x| > 2$; for $|x| < 2$.

SOLUTION Numbers whose graphs are more than 2 units from the zero point are solutions of $|x| > 2$.

Therefore, $|x| > 2$ may be restated as

Ⓜ $x < -2$ *or* $x > 2$.

−4 −3 −2 −1 0 1 2 3 4

Numbers whose graphs are less than 2 units from the zero point are solutions of $|x| < 2$.

Therefore, $|x| < 2$ may be restated as

Ⓜ $x > -2$ *and* $x < 2$,
or
$-2 < x < 2$.

−4 −3 −2 −1 0 1 2 3 4

DRAWING THE GRAPH FOR A SENTENCE INVOLVING ABSOLUTE VALUE

1. Interpret $|x| > a$ as $x > a$ *or* $x < -a$.
2. Interpret $|x| < a$ as $x < a$ *and* $x > -a$, or as $-a < x < a$.

CLASSROOM EXERCISES

Graph the solution set for each.

1. $-4 < x < 5$ **2.** $x \geq -2$ **3.** $x \leq 7$ **4.** $-1 \leq x < 3$
5. $x \leq 3$ or $x > 5$ **6.** $x < 1$ and $x > 6$ **7.** $|x| > 1$ **8.** $|x| < 3$

EXERCISES

A Graph the solution set for each.

1. $-3 < x < 2$ **2.** $-1 < x < 6$ **3.** $-8 < x < 7$ **4.** $-10 < x < 3$
5. $x \geq -8$ **6.** $x \geq -1$ **7.** $x \leq 3$ **8.** $x \leq 5$
9. $-4 \leq x < 6$ **10.** $-3 \leq x < 3$ **11.** $-5 < x \leq 2$ **12.** $-10 < x \leq 9$

13. $x \leq 2$ or $x > 5$
14. $x \leq 5$ or $x > 8$
15. $x < -2$ or $x \geq 7$
16. $x \leq -8$ or $x \geq 8$
17. $x < 5$ or $x > 2$
18. $x < 3$ and $x > 7$
19. $x < 4$ and $x > 9$
20. $|x| > 4$
21. $|x| > 8$

B **22.** $-\frac{1}{2} < x < 2\frac{1}{4}$
23. $-2.75 < x < 3.5$
24. $-8\frac{1}{2} \leq x < 6.8$
25. $|x| > 2.8$
26. $|x| \leq 4.44$
27. $x \leq 9$ and $x \geq -6$
28. $2x > x - 4$ or $3x < x + 6$
29. $|x - 1| < 5$
30. $|x + 6| \geq 8$

C **31.** $|4x - 3| > 3$
32. $|2x + 7| < 11$
33. $a \leq x < b, b > a$

CHECKING YOUR UNDERSTANDING

WORDS AND SYMBOLS

compound sentence, $\leq$, $\geq$

Properties of Inequality:

Addition   Subtraction   Multiplication   Division

CONCEPTS

- An inequality with one variable may be solved using Properties of Inequality to replace the inequality with a form for which the solution is clear. [3-9 to 3-11]

- A compound sentence using "and" is true only if both parts of the sentence are true. A compound sentence using "or" is true if at least one of the parts is true. [3-12]

- A sentence involving absolute value may be restated as a compound sentence. It may be based on the idea that the absolute value of a number is the distance of its graph from the point for zero in the number line. [3-12]

PROCESSES

- Solve inequalities using the Addition, Subtraction, Multiplication and Division Properties of Inequality. Graph each solution set. [3-9 to 3-11]

1. $x - 7 > 1$
2. $\frac{-4x}{7} < 3$
3. $-5x + 2 < x + 4$
4. $\frac{2x - 4}{-3} > -2x$

- Graph the solution set of a compound sentence or a sentence involving absolute value. [3-12]

5. $-3 < x < 5$
6. $x < 2$ or $x \geq 5$
7. $|x| < 5$

OBJECTIVE: Solve problems using inequalities.

3-13 PROBLEM SOLVING: WRITING AND USING INEQUALITIES

When we read an equation, we read "=" as "is," or "is equal to," or "equals." For inequalities, each of the symbols <, >, ≤, ≥ may be read in several ways.

Writing the Inequality	Reading the Inequality
$x < a$	*x is less than a.*
$x > a$	*x is greater than a.*
$x \leq a$	*x is less than or equal to a.* *x is not greater than a.* ($x \ngtr a$) *x is at most a.*
$x \geq a$	*x is greater than or equal to a.* *x is not less than a.* ($x \nless a$) *x is at least a.*
$a < x < b$	*x is between a and b.*

You may read inequalities from right to left as well as from left to right; $x < a$ may be read as "*a* is greater than *x*" as well as "*x* is less than *a*."

EXAMPLE 1 Replace each word sentence by an inequality.

a. A number divided by 2 is less than 5.

Ⓜ SOLUTION Use x for the number.

$\frac{x}{2} < 5$

b. 5 times a number is not greater than −8.

Ⓜ SOLUTION Use t for the number.

$5t \leq -8$

c. 3 more than twice a number is no less than 4.

Ⓜ SOLUTION Use w for the number.

$2w + 3 \geq 4$

d. A number is at least 5 more than one-half of the number.

Ⓜ SOLUTION Use n for the number.

$n \geq \frac{1}{2}n + 5$

EXAMPLE 2 Write an inequality for this information.

The trailer can carry 1000 kg safely.
Bags that are 40 kg each are being loaded on the trailer.
The trailer should not be overloaded.

Ⓜ SOLUTION The load should be no more than 1000 kg.

Use $\left[\begin{array}{l} n \text{ for the number of bags to be loaded.} \\ 40n \text{ for the mass of the bags in kilograms.} \end{array}\right.$

$40n \leq 1000$

$\frac{\text{kg}}{\text{bag}} \cdot \text{bags} = \text{kg}$

"No more than" and "at most" are equivalent to "less than or equal to."

Solving inequalities can help us solve problems.

EXAMPLE 3 The sum of two consecutive positive integers is at most 7. Find the integers.

Ⓜ SOLUTION Use $\left[\begin{array}{l} n \quad \text{for the smaller positive integer.} \\ n+1 \text{ for the larger positive integer.} \end{array}\right.$

$$n + n + 1 \leq 7$$
$$2n + 1 \leq 7$$
S_1 $$2n \leq 6$$
D_2 $$n \leq 3$$

n is positive. Therefore $n = 1$, 2, or 3, and $n + 1 = 2$, 3, or 4.

CONCLUSION The integers are 1 and 2, 2 and 3, or 3 and 4.

CHECK The sums of the positive integers 1 and 2, 2 and 3, and 3 and 4 are at most 7. ✓

EXAMPLE 4 Several pipe sections are to be joined to form a pipe that is at least 75 m long. Each section is 8 m long. How many sections are needed?

"At least" is equivalent to "greater than or equal to."

Ⓜ SOLUTION The total length of the sections must be at least 75 meters.

Use $\left[\begin{array}{l} s \text{ for the number of sections needed.} \\ 8s \text{ for the total length of the sections in meters.} \end{array}\right.$

$\frac{\text{m}}{\text{section}} \cdot \text{sections} = \text{m}$

$$8s \geq 75$$
D_8 $$s \geq \frac{75}{8}, \text{ or } 9\frac{3}{8}$$

CONCLUSION At least 10 sections of pipe are needed.

CHECK 8 times 10 is greater than 75. ✓

CLASSROOM EXERCISES

Replace each sentence by an inequality.

1. A number divided by 7 is less than 10.
2. 3 times a number is no less than -9.
3. A number is at least 2 greater than one-fourth the number.

What numbers are possible as solutions?

4. Four less than a number is no more than 12. Find the number.
5. The sum of 2 consecutive integers is no less than 19. Find the integers.

EXERCISES

A Replace each sentence by an inequality.

1. A number is less than 7.
2. A number is greater than 4.
3. $5n$ is no greater than 32.
4. $2m$ is no greater than 12.
5. The sum of two consecutive positive integers is at least 21.
6. The sum of two consecutive integers is no greater than -31.

What numbers are possible as solutions?

7. One less than a number is no greater than one more than twice the number. Find the number.
8. One more than a number is at most one less than three times the number. Find the number.
9. Sam is 5 years older than Tom. The sum of their ages is less than 33 years. Find each boy's age.
10. Carol is 10 kilograms heavier than Sue. Together, they are less than 100 kilograms. How heavy is each girl?
11. On July 15, Mrs. Lopez deposited $96.75 in her savings account. After she had deposited this money, she still had less than $185 in her account. How much money did she have in her account before she deposited the $96.75?
12. The club members agreed to buy no more than 250 tickets for a theater party. If they agreed to buy at least 80 orchestra tickets, how many balcony tickets would they buy?
13. After Mrs. Brennan had bought 114.5 hectares of land, she still owned less than 350 hectares. How many hectares of land did she own before she bought the 114.5 hectares?
14. Mr. Andrés bought 12.75 meters of copper wire. After he had used some of the wire, he still had more than 7.5 meters left. How much wire did he use?

B

15. The cashier in a movie box office sold 200 more adult admission tickets at $2 each than children's admission tickets at $0.75 each. Find the minimum number of each type of ticket sold for the total receipts to be at least $620.
16. In a school, the number of girls is 50 more than twice the number of boys. If the school has at most 650 pupils, find the greatest possible number of boys and girls.

C

17. Find integer values for n such that the reciprocal of n is less than one one-millionth.
18. Find integer values for n such that the reciprocal of n^2 is less than one one-millionth.

CHAPTER REVIEW

Replace ? by =, <, or > to make a true sentence. [3-1]

1. $\frac{4}{5} ? \frac{7}{8}$
2. $(-3)^2 ? -3^2$
3. $\frac{1}{3} - \frac{1}{6} ? \frac{1}{6} - \frac{1}{3}$

Solve. [3-2 to 3-6]

4. $x + 0.36 = 1.00$
5. $4\frac{2}{3} = 2\frac{1}{3} + x$
6. $x - \frac{1}{5} = -\frac{2}{5}$
7. $x - 3\frac{1}{3} = \frac{3(4)}{6}$
8. $x + 3\frac{1}{4} = 2(-3 + 4)$
9. $x - (-4)^2 = 5^2$
10. $3x = 1.5$
11. $2x = \frac{3}{5}$
12. $-0.02x = 0.08$
13. $\frac{x}{-1.5} = 12$
14. $\frac{x}{\frac{2}{3}} = -4$
15. $3x + 4x - 15x = 6 + 2$
16. $\frac{1}{2}x - \frac{1}{3}x = \frac{9 - 5}{2}$
17. $3.6x - 2.4x = \frac{2}{3}(36)$
18. $5n + 2n - 5 = 30$
19. $\frac{9}{5}C + 32 = -4$
20. $\frac{x + 3}{7} = 3$
21. $7(x - 5) = 98$
22. $\frac{1}{5}x + \frac{1}{2}x - 4 = 6$
23. $\frac{3x - 4}{5} = \frac{6(7 + 8)}{9}$
24. $5x + 13 - 2x = x + 1$
25. $0.5t - 30 = 1.1t$
26. $\frac{2}{3}m - 11 = 64 - 4\frac{1}{3}m$

Write an equation for each. Use only one variable. [3-7]

27. 12 more than 4 times a number is 28.
28. A number decreased by 0.1 of the number is 35.20.
29. One number is 4 greater than another. Twice their sum is 5 less than their product.

Solve. [3-8]

30. Three-tenths of a number is 45. Find the number.
31. A number increased by $\frac{1}{5}$ of the number equals 180. Find the number.
32. The sum of two consecutive integers is 65. Find the integers.
33. The larger of two numbers is 2 more than 3 times the smaller. Three times the larger is 48 greater than twice the smaller. Find the numbers.
34. The length of a rectangle is 3 times its width. The perimeter of the rectangle is 60. Find the length and the width.

Solve each inequality and graph its solution set. [3-9 to 3-10]

35. $x - (-5) < 15$
36. $x + 1\frac{3}{4} < 5\frac{1}{4}$
37. $x - 0.5 > -3$
38. $3x < 10$
39. $-\frac{x}{5} < 1.3$
40. $\frac{2x}{-4} > -6$

Solve. [3-11]

41. $3x - 2 < 8x + 5$

42. $8.3 - 2a > a + 1.7$

43. $\frac{4n - 3}{2} < 5n$

Graph the solution set for each inequality. [3-12]

44. $0 \leq x < 3$

45. $x \leq 1$ or $x > 3$

46. $|x| < 2$

Write an inequality for each. [3-13]

47. One-half of a number is no greater than 5.

48. The pencils I buy at 12¢ each must cost no more than one dollar in all.

Solve.

49. The sum of two consecutive positive integers is no greater than 10. Find the integers.

50. A student has scores of 85 and 71 for two tests. Find the score needed for a third test to give an average of at least 82 for the 3 tests.

CAPSULE REVIEW

Write the letter of the best response.

1. The solution for $\frac{1}{3}x + 7 = -\frac{1}{3}x + 3$ is

a. no solution **b.** -6 **c.** 15 **d.** 6 **e.** $\frac{-8}{3}$

2. 4 less than twice x may be written

a. $4 - 2x$ **b.** $2(x - 4)$ **c.** $2x - 4$ **d.** $\frac{2x}{4}$ **e.** $x^2 - 4$

3. Which symbol represents 45-hundredths of n?

a. $0.45n$ **b.** $45n$ **c.** $\frac{n}{45}$ **d.** $\frac{n}{0.45}$ **e.** $1.45n$

4. Which is the graph of the solution set for $\frac{1}{2}x < -4$?

a.  -8 **b.**  -8 **c.**  -2 **d.**  -2

5. Which is the graph of the solution set for $x > -3$ and $x < 4$?

a. -3 4 **b.**  -3 4 **c.**  -3 4 **d.**  -3 4

6. Which inequality says x is at most -4?

a. $x \geq -4$ **b.** $x \leq -4$ **c.** $x > -4$ **d.** $x < -4$ **e.** $x > 4$

7. The solutions for $\frac{-x}{3} < 4$ are the same as the solutions for

a. $x > 12$ **b.** $x > -12$ **c.** $x < 12$ **d.** $x < -12$ **e.** $x = 12$

8. Which equation will help find 3 consecutive even integers with sum 46?

a. $x + (x + 2) + (x + 4) = 46$ **b.** $(x - 4) + (x - 2) + x = 46$

c. $(x - 2) + x + (x + 2) = 46$ **d.** all of these

9. Which equation may be used to find two numbers whose sum is 84 when 3 times the smaller number is 2 less than twice the larger?

a. $3n = 2 - 2(84 - n)$ **b.** $3(84 - n) = 2 - 2(3n)$
c. $3n = 2(n - 84) - 2$ **d.** $3(84 - n) = 2n - 2$

CHAPTER TEST

Complete statements 1-4 by supplying the proper words. Use *equation*, *inequality*, *equals*, *is greater than*, or *is less than*.

1. $4 + 2$ __?__ 3×2
2. "<" is the symbol for __?__.
3. $7 \neq 2$ is an __?__.
4. $3 \cdot 17 = 51$ is an __?__.

Solve.

5. $x - 7 = 10$ **6.** $15 + x = 10$ **7.** $3x = 21$
8. $\frac{x}{5} = 30$ **9.** $3x + 2x = 30$ **10.** $12x - 2x = 46$
11. $4x + 3 = 27$ **12.** $4x + 2x = 20 + 4$ **13.** $7x = 12 + 4x$
14. $5x = 24 - x$ **15.** $0.3x - 0.2x = 30$ **16.** $\frac{1}{5}x - \frac{1}{2}x + 4 = -(-6)$

Graph the solution set for each equation.

17. $x + 3 = -2$ **18.** $x + \frac{2}{3} = 1$

Rewrite each word sentence as an equation.

19. A number increased by 17.5 equals 20.
20. *a* less *b* is 5.

Solve.

21. A number increased by 5 equals 15. Find the number.
22. Four times a number is 28. Find the number.

Graph the solution set for each inequality.

23. $x + 3 > 5$ **24.** $3x > 6$ **25.** $2x + 1 < -5$
26. $x - 2 < 3$ **27.** $\frac{x}{2} < 3$ **28.** $4x + 1 < 3x - 2$

Graph the solution set for each compound inequality.

29. $x > -2$ and $x < 4$ **30.** $a < 2$ and $a > 3$

Rewrite each word sentence as an inequality.

31. Three times a number is less than 12.
32. A number decreased by 4 is greater than 8.5.

Write the letter of the best response.

33. > is a symbol for

a. equals **b.** does not equal **c.** is less than **d.** is greater than

34. $2 + 3 \underline{\ \ ?\ \ } 7 - 4$

a. $=$ **b.** $<$ **c.** $>$ **d.** $\leq$ **e.** $\ngtr$

35. The solution for $15 - x = 10$ is

a. -10 **b.** -5 **c.** 0 **d.** 5 **e.** 10

36. The solution for $0.8x = 32$ is

a. 4 **b.** 25.6 **c.** 400 **d.** 2.56 **e.** 40

37. The solution for $5x - 3x = 1.20$ is

a. 2.40 **b.** 0.60 **c.** 6 **d.** 0.240 **e.** 60

38. The solution for $3x + 0.6 = 1.8$ is

a. 4 **b.** 0.8 **c.** 0.4 **d.** 8 **e.** 40

39. The solution for $\frac{1}{3}x + \frac{1}{2}x + 5 = 30$ is

a. 42 **b.** -150 **c.** 150 **d.** 210 **e.** 30

40. The graph of the solution set for $x - 3 = 10$ is

a. 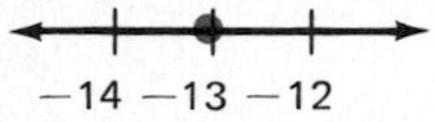 -14 -13 -12 **b.** 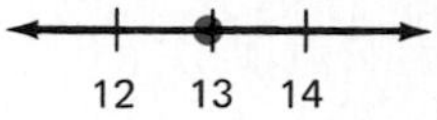 12 13 14 **c.** 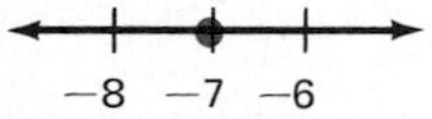 -8 -7 -6 **d.**  6 7 8

41. Which equation says *a number decreased by* 5 *equals* 100?

a. $5 - x = 100$ **b.** $x - 5 = 100$ **c.** $100 - x = 5$ **d.** $x + 5 = 100$

42. A number increased by $\frac{1}{2}$ gives $4\frac{1}{2}$. The number is

a. 2 **b.** 3 **c.** 4 **d.** 5 **e.** $6\frac{3}{4}$

43. The graph of the solution set for $2x > 1$ is

a. 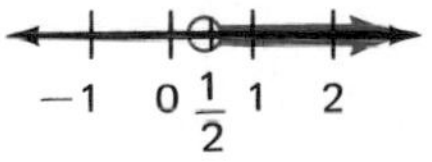 -1 0 $\frac{1}{2}$ 1 2 **b.** 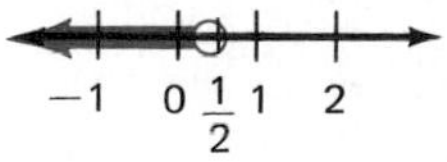 -1 0 $\frac{1}{2}$ 1 2 **c.** 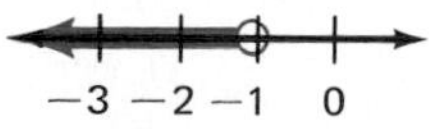 -3 -2 -1 0 **d.** 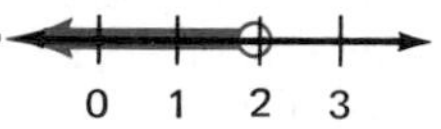 0 1 2 3

44. The graph of the solution set for $3x + 0.1 > x - 0.5$ is

a.  -1 0 **b.** 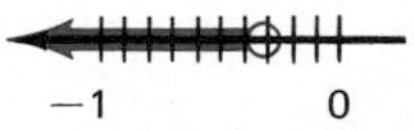 -1 0 **c.**  -1 0 **d.** 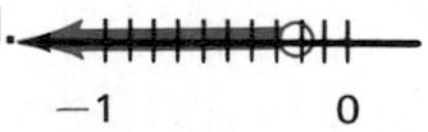 -1 0

45. Which is the graph of the solution set for the compound inequality $x < 2$ and $x > -1$?

a. 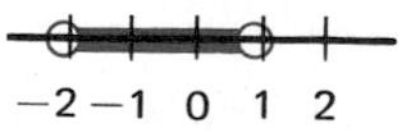 -2 -1 0 1 2 **b.** 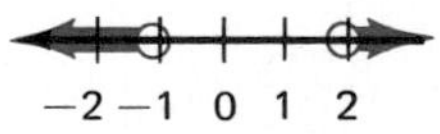 -2 -1 0 1 2 **c.** 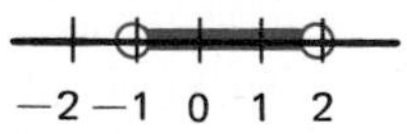 -2 -1 0 1 2 **d.** 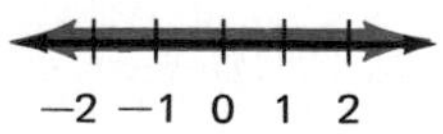 -2 -1 0 1 2

46. A wire must be more than 15 cm long and less than 20 cm long. Which compound inequality describes the possible lengths?

a. $15 < x > 20$ **b.** $15 > x < 20$ **c.** $15 > x > 20$ **d.** $15 < x < 20$

CHAPTER 4
Special Equations Called Formulas

Television, newspapers, and radio are main sources of information for many people. They accept much of the information received through these media as being correct. They form conclusions from this information. Thus, it is the responsibility and obligation of media reporters to be accurate, sensitive, and objective in presenting their stories.

OBJECTIVES: Find values using formulas. Solve problems using formulas.

4-1 EVALUATING FORMULAS

A **formula** is an equation which expresses a relationship in concise form. To use a formula, we must know the meaning for each symbol in the formula.

Formula	Meaning	Use
$A = s^2$	area = length of one side squared The area of a square equals the square of the length of one side.	mathematics
$d = rt$	distance = rate × time The distance traveled at a constant rate equals the product of the rate and the time spent traveling at that rate.	science
$i = prt$	interest = principal × rate × time The interest earned equals the amount of money invested (the principal) times the interest rate times the length of time the money is invested.	business

As shown in the chart, a formula usually is given with a single variable for its left member. We find a number for the left member by using numbers to replace the variables in the right member.

If you know numbers for all but one of the variables, no matter where that one variable is located in the formula, you may still use the formula.

EXAMPLE 1 Geri earns \$3 an hour for mowing lawns. The formula $E = 3h$ shows how much she earns (E) for the number of hours (h) that she works. Complete this table to show how much she earns using different numbers for h.

h	0	1	2	3	5	10
E	?	?	?	?	?	?

The unit equation for $E = 3h$ is $\$ = \frac{\$}{h} \cdot h$.

SOLUTION

h	0	1	2	3	5	10
E	0	3	6	9	15	30

EXAMPLE 2 The appliance sales clerk is paid a salary and a commission that depends on the amount of sales. Using w for wages for a week and s for the amount sold in dollars, this is the formula used: $w = 125 + 0.05s$
How much will the clerk earn for $3750 in sales?

$\$ = \$ + \frac{\$}{(\text{sales }\$)} \cdot (\text{sales }\$)$

When a solution involves replacing the variables in a formula, it is good practice to write the formula as the first step. Space does not always permit us to do so in the text.

Ⓜ **SOLUTION**

$$\begin{aligned} w &= 125 + 0.05s \\ &= 125 + 0.05(3750) \\ &= 125 + 187.5 \\ &= 312.5 \end{aligned}$$

CONCLUSION The clerk will earn $312.50 for $3750 in sales.

EXAMPLE 3 Use the formula $d = rt$. Find how far a car will travel at 50 km/h for 4 hours; at 75 km/h for 2 hours 15 minutes.

$\text{km} = \frac{\text{km}}{\text{h}} \cdot \text{h}$

Ⓜ **SOLUTION**

$$\begin{aligned} d &= rt \\ &= 50 \cdot 4 \\ &= 200 \end{aligned}$$

$$\begin{aligned} d &= rt \\ &= 75 \cdot 2.25 \\ &= 168.75 \end{aligned}$$

CONCLUSION At 50 km/h for 4 hours, a car travels 200 km. At 75 km/h for 2 hours 15 minutes, it travels 168.75 km.

EXAMPLE 4 The formula $S = R - \frac{1}{4}W$ may be used to find scores (S) on a multiple-choice test. Find the score for each student.

These are scores from a 50-item test in which there is no penalty for skipping an exercise, but there is a penalty for a wrong answer. Discuss whether or not subtracting one-fourth the number wrong is a fair penalty.

Number \ Student	Andy	Carrie	Lucy	Tim	Larry	Alana
Right (R)	28	40	47	10	40	39
Wrong (W)	12	10	0	40	7	3
(Not Completed)	10	0	3	0	3	8

Ⓜ **SOLUTION**

Andy:

$$\begin{aligned} S &= 28 - \tfrac{1}{4}(12) \\ &= 28 - 3 \\ &= 25 \end{aligned}$$

Carrie:

$$\begin{aligned} S &= 40 - \tfrac{1}{4}(10) \\ &= 40 - 2\tfrac{1}{2} \\ &= 37\tfrac{1}{2} \end{aligned}$$

Lucy:

$$\begin{aligned} S &= 47 - \tfrac{1}{4}(0) \\ &= 47 \end{aligned}$$

Tim:

$$\begin{aligned} S &= 10 - \tfrac{1}{4}(40) \\ &= 10 - 10 \\ &= 0 \end{aligned}$$

Larry:

$$\begin{aligned} S &= 40 - \tfrac{1}{4}(7) \\ &= 40 - 1\tfrac{3}{4} \\ &= 38\tfrac{1}{4} \end{aligned}$$

Alana:

$$\begin{aligned} S &= 39 - \tfrac{1}{4}(3) \\ &= 39 - \tfrac{3}{4} \\ &= 38\tfrac{1}{4} \end{aligned}$$

CLASSROOM EXERCISES

1. Evaluate the formula $V = 4w + 3$ for V when $w = 25$.
2. Complete the table of values for the formula $K = 3M - N$.

M	6	11	15	24	45
N	4	7	30	36	10
K	?	?	?	?	?

EXERCISES

A Evaluate each formula using the given numbers. Show the results in a table.

1. $p = 3s$, $s = 1, 2, 5, 8, 15$
2. $s = 6e$, $e = 1, 2, 4, 5, 10$
3. $A = s^2$, $s = 1, 2, 3, 5, 11$
4. $V = e^3$, $e = 1, 2, 3, 5, 8$
5. $C = \pi d$, $\pi = 3.14$, $d = 1, 2, 3, 6, 9$
6. $A = \pi r^2$, $\pi = 3.14$, $r = 1, 2, 3, 4, 5$
7. Evaluate the formula $B = \frac{1}{2}F + 8$ for B when $F = 6, 22, 54, 92$.
8. Evaluate the formula $J = 64 - 0.24K$ for J when $K = 40, 12, 240, 178$.

B 9. Evaluate the formula $s = \frac{1}{2}at^2$ for s using $a = 9.80$ and $t = 1, 2, 3, 5, 10$. Show the results in a table.

10. Evaluate the formula $E = \frac{1}{2}mv^2$ for E using $m = 2.2$ and $v = 1, 2, 3, 5, 10$. Show the results in a table.

C 11. Explain the meaning of the formula $A = \dfrac{a_1 + a_2 + a_3 + \cdots + a_n}{n}$.

THE PAYOFF

Kara is an artist. One August, while awaiting payment for a delivery of jewelry, Kara found herself unable to pay the rent. She did have a piece of silver chain with 31 links and agreed to "pay" one link a day for each day's rent. Each day Kara "paid" one link. On the thirty-first day, Kara received payment for the jewelry, recovered the thirty-one links, repaired three links, and the silver chain was intact. How was this possible?

4-2 PROBLEM SOLVING: USING FORMULAS

When we use a formula to solve a problem, it is not necessary to find a relationship among the variables. The formula shows us that relationship. To solve the problem, simply replace variables by known values. Then find the value for the remaining variable.

EXAMPLE 1 A sandbag is dropped from a balloon. It reaches earth in 12 seconds. How high is the balloon? Use the formula $s = 4.9t^2$ for the distance, s, of the fall in meters, when time, t, is in seconds.

You may not be able to check units in all formulas. Often, the constant contains implicit units that are not shown.

Ⓜ SOLUTION $s = 4.9t^2$. Replace t by 12. Find s.

$$s = 4.9(12)^2$$
$$= 705.6$$

CONCLUSION The sandbag fell 705.6 meters. The balloon is 705.6 meters above the ground.

EXAMPLE 2 A student had scores of 75, 85, and 83 on 3 tests. Find the average test score. Use the formula $A = \frac{a + b + c}{3}$.

Ⓜ SOLUTION $A = \frac{a + b + c}{3}$ Replace a by 75, b by 85, and c by 83. Find A.

$$\text{score/test} = \frac{\text{score} + \text{score} + \text{score}}{\text{tests}}$$

$$A = \frac{75 + 85 + 83}{3}$$
$$= \frac{243}{3}$$
$$= 81$$

CONCLUSION The average of the three test scores is 81.

EXAMPLE 3 The distance from Memphis to Atlanta is 585 km. How long would it take to drive the distance at the constant rate of 88 km/h? Use $d = rt$.

Ⓜ SOLUTION $d = rt$ Replace d by 585. Replace r by 88. Find t.

$$\text{km} = \frac{\text{km}}{\text{h}} \cdot \text{h}$$

$$585 = 88t$$
$$\frac{585}{88} = t$$
$$6.6 \doteq t$$

CONCLUSION It would take about 6.6 hours to drive from Memphis to Atlanta at 88 km/h.

A formula may use something other than a single letter to represent a variable.

EXAMPLE 4 For the softball season, Amy had 37 hits in 91 times at bat. Amy's softball rule book says that the formula $BA = \frac{h}{AB}$ gives a player's batting average. Find Amy's batting average.

Batting Average = $\frac{\text{number of hits}}{\text{number of times At Bat}}$

Ⓜ SOLUTION $BA = \frac{h}{AB}$ Replace h by 37 and AB by 91. Find BA.

$$BA = \frac{37}{91}$$

$$\doteq 0.407$$

It is common practice to omit the zero in the ones place when a decimal represents batting average.

CONCLUSION Amy's batting average was .407.

SOLVING A PROBLEM USING A FORMULA

1. Write the correct formula.
2. Replace variables by known values.
3. Perform the indicated operations to find the value for the other variable.
4. Make a concluding statement.

CLASSROOM EXERCISES

Solve

1. Find the average score for the six quiz scores 6, 9, 7, 4, 8, 5.
2. Find the batting average for a baseball player who has 45 hits in 135 times at bat.
3. Find the number of kilometers that a car can travel in $2\frac{1}{2}$ hours at 60 km/h.
4. Find the constant rate required for a car to travel a distance of 175 km in 3.5 hours.
5. It is 675 km from Omaha to Chicago. The McMurdos think they can drive the distance at 90 km/h. At this rate, how many hours would the trip take?

EXERCISES

A Solve.

1. In five basketball games, a forward scored 18, 24, 17, 25, 26 points. Find the average number of points per game.

2. In seven basketball games, a guard had 17, 13, 8, 14, 10, 13, 16 rebounds. Find the average number of rebounds per game.

3. Use the formula $s = 4.9t^2$. Find the number of meters a parachutist falls before pulling the rip cord 4 seconds after jumping.

4. The formula $r = 9.8t$ gives the rate (r) at which an object is traveling in meters per second after falling for t seconds. How fast will the parachutist in Exercise 3 be falling after 2 seconds? after 3? when the rip cord is pulled?

5. How far will a bus go in 26 hours at the average rate of 75 kilometers per hour?

6. How far will Marta bicycle in 3 minutes traveling 8 meters per second?

7. The formula $r = \frac{d}{t}$ gives the rate for a known distance and time. What is the average rate in kilometers per hour for traveling 350 kilometers in 2.5 hours?

8. The formula $t = \frac{d}{r}$ gives the time for a known distance and rate. In how many hours will an airplane go 1368 kilometers at 304 kilometers per hour?

9. Lestan rolls heavy barrels from the ground up an incline to a platform. The formula $F = 9.8b \times \frac{H}{L}$ tells how many newtons of force (F) are needed to do this. L means the length of the incline in meters, H the height of the platform in meters, and b the mass of the barrel in kilograms. How many newtons of force will be needed to roll a 150-kilogram barrel up an incline 5 meters long to a platform 1.5 meters high?

10. A designer of machinery wants to know how many newtons of force will be needed to roll a 250-kilogram cylinder of metal up an incline 6 meters long to a platform 2 meters high. What is the answer? (See Ex. 9.)

B 11. A formula for finding the normal mass of an adult who is at least 1.6 meters tall is $m = 0.98(h - 102)$. m represents the normal mass of the adult in kilograms. h represents the height in centimeters. If a person is 1.6 meters tall, $m = 0.98(160 - 102)$. Then, $m = 0.98(58)$, or 56.84. The person's normal mass is 56.84 kilograms. Copy and complete the table below.

Height	Actual Mass	Normal Mass	Mass Under (−) Mass Over (+)
1.65 m	65.2 kg	?	?
1.78 m	69.5 kg	?	?
1.83 m	79.4 kg	?	?

12. The formula $d = 0.008v^2$ gives the stopping distance (d) in meters for a car after the brakes have been applied under average conditions. How far back from a railroad crossing should a highway warning sign be placed to give drivers going 90 kilometers per hour (v) a chance to stop without driving onto the tracks?

C 13. Find the time needed to run a 40-kilometer marathon course maintaining a rate of 4 meters per second.

14. A supersonic transport airplane (SST) flies 4500 km from Paris to New York City in 2 hours 45 minutes. Find its speed in meters per second.

4-3 PROBLEM SOLVING: USING FORMULAS FROM GEOMETRY

The diagrams on this page and the next show basic geometric figures and related formulas that we should understand and remember. The figures shown below that are formed from line segments are called *polygons*. The line segments are the *sides* of the polygons.

Perimeter and Circumference

The **perimeter** of a polygon is the sum of the lengths of its sides. It may be thought of as the distance around the polygon. The distance around a circle is the **circumference** of the circle.

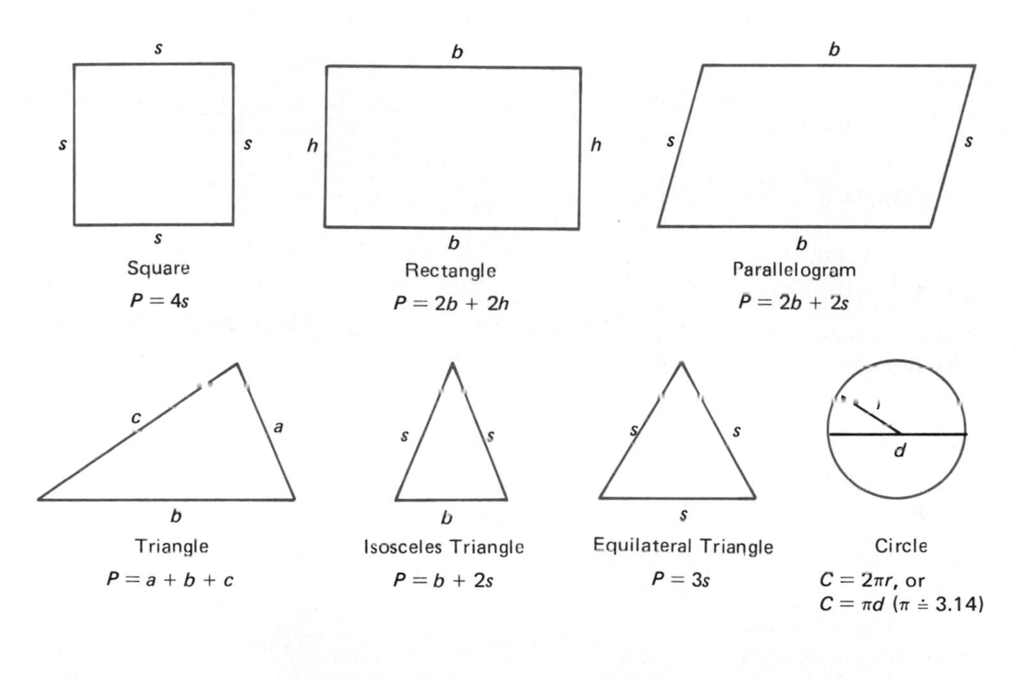

EXAMPLE 1 Find the perimeter of an isosceles triangle whose sides measure 6, 9, and 9.

6 9 9

Ⓜ SOLUTION Use $P = b + 2s$.

$$P = 6 + 2(9)$$
$$= 24$$

CONCLUSION The perimeter of the triangle is 24.

Area

The **area** of a plane figure is the number of square units it encloses.

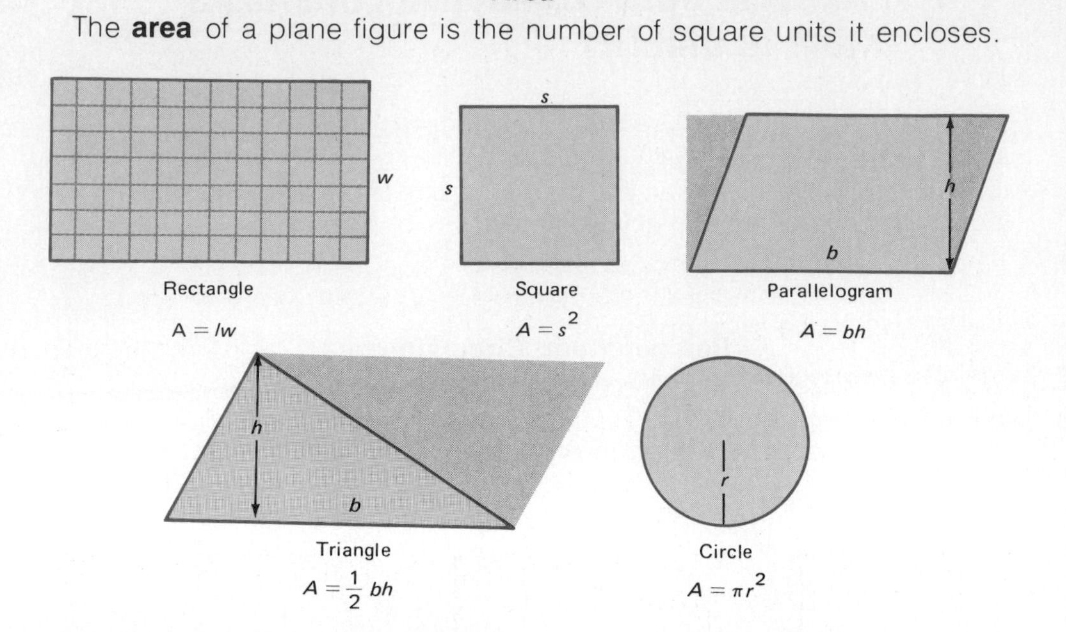

EXAMPLE 2 The top of a table for table tennis is 2.75 meters long and 1.52 meters wide. Find its area.

Ⓜ SOLUTION Use $A = lw$

$m^2 = m \cdot m$

$$A = 2.75\ (1.52)$$
$$\doteq 4.18$$

2.75 m

CONCLUSION The area of the table top is about 4.18 square meters.

1.52 m

Volume

The **volume** of a solid is the number of cubic units it encloses.

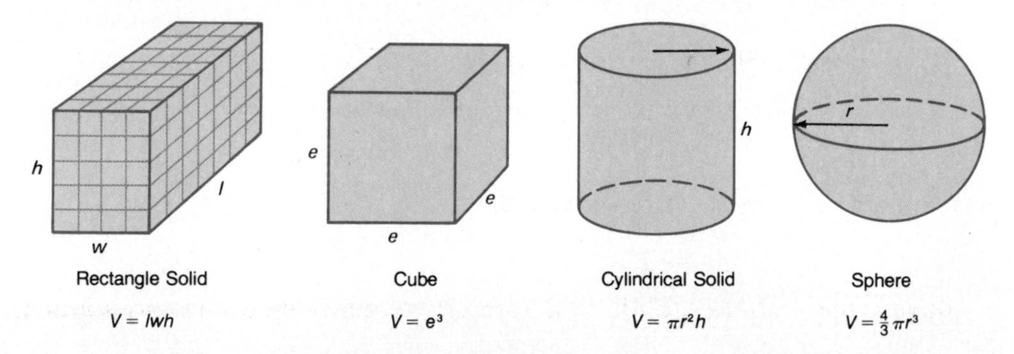

EXAMPLE 3 The diameter of a stereo record is 30.2 centimeters. Find its circumference.

A constant, such as π, is "dimensionless." It does not affect the units.

SOLUTION (M) The circumference is the distance around a circle.
Use $C = \pi d$.

$$C \doteq (3.14)(30.2)$$
$$\doteq 94.8$$

cm = (dimensionless) · cm

CONCLUSION The circumference of the record is about 94.8 cm.

EXAMPLE 4 Part of a spacecraft has the shape of a cylinder. Its diameter is 2.8 meters. Its length is 6.4 meters. Find its volume.

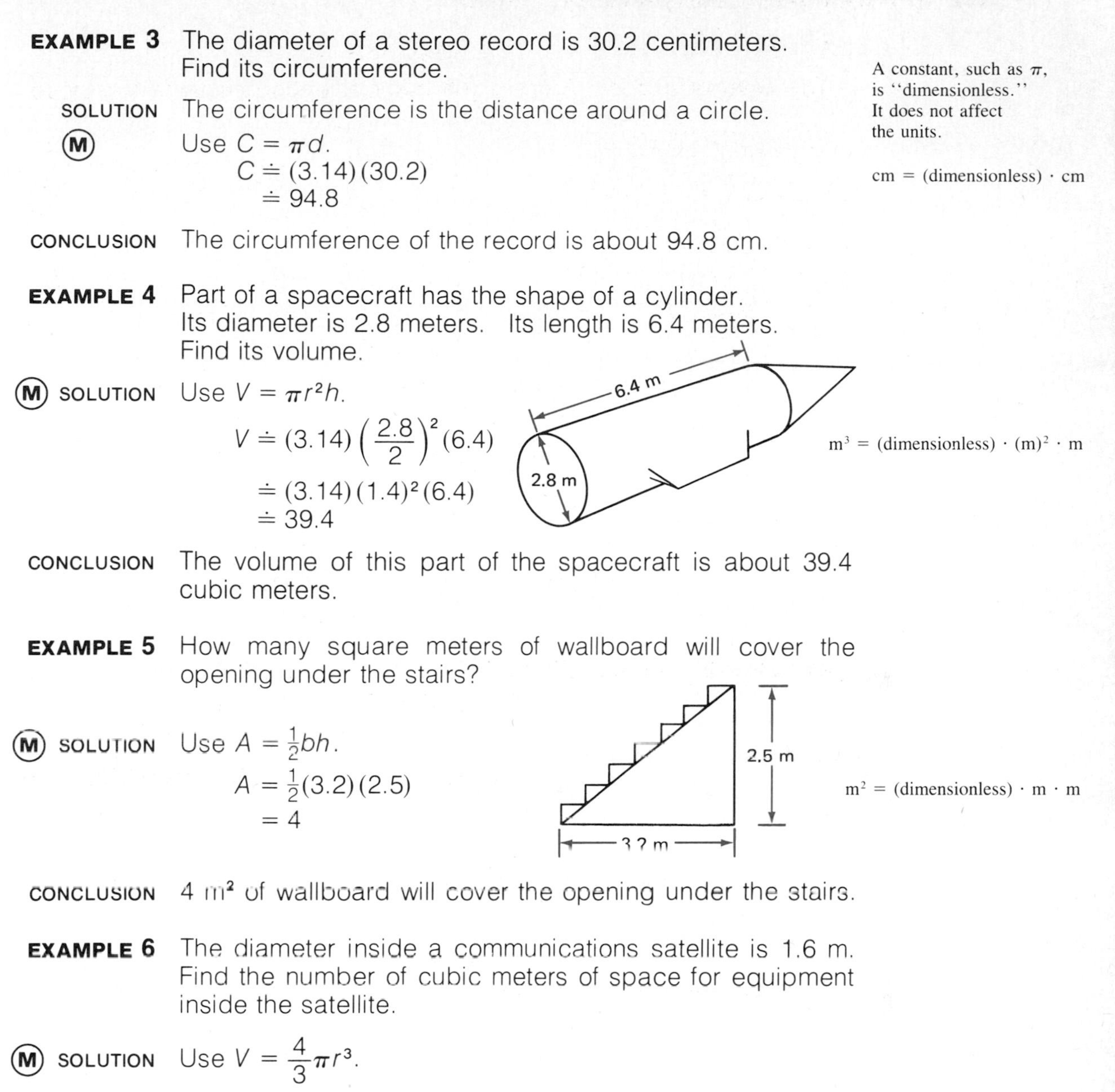

(M) **SOLUTION** Use $V = \pi r^2 h$.

$$V \doteq (3.14)\left(\frac{2.8}{2}\right)^2(6.4)$$
$$\doteq (3.14)(1.4)^2(6.4)$$
$$\doteq 39.4$$

m³ = (dimensionless) · (m)² · m

CONCLUSION The volume of this part of the spacecraft is about 39.4 cubic meters.

EXAMPLE 5 How many square meters of wallboard will cover the opening under the stairs?

(M) **SOLUTION** Use $A = \frac{1}{2}bh$.

$$A = \tfrac{1}{2}(3.2)(2.5)$$
$$= 4$$

m² = (dimensionless) · m · m

CONCLUSION 4 m² of wallboard will cover the opening under the stairs.

EXAMPLE 6 The diameter inside a communications satellite is 1.6 m. Find the number of cubic meters of space for equipment inside the satellite.

(M) **SOLUTION** Use $V = \frac{4}{3}\pi r^3$.

$$V \doteq \frac{4}{3}(3.14)\left(\frac{1.6}{2}\right)^3$$
$$\doteq \frac{4}{3}(3.14)(0.8)^3$$
$$\doteq 2.1$$

m³ = (dimensionless) · (m)³

CONCLUSION There are about 2.1 cubic meters of space for equipment.

CLASSROOM EXERCISES

Solve. Use 3.14 for π.

1. Find the perimeter of a rectangle with length 5 cm and width 7 cm.
2. Find the area of a triangle with base length 24 cm and height 9 cm.
3. Find the number of square meters of plastic needed to cover a circular swimming pool that has diameter length 6 m.
4. Find the volume of a gasoline storage cylinder that has diameter length 10 m and height 10 m.

Find each volume.

13. cube with edge length 4 cm
14. rectangular solid 3 cm by 5 cm by 4 cm
15. cylindrical solid with radius length 5 cm and height 4 cm
16. cylindrical solid with radius length 5 cm and height 8 cm
17. sphere with radius 3 cm
18. sphere with radius 6 cm

EXERCISES

A Find the area of a rectangle with base length b and height h.

1. $b = 10, h = 8$
2. $b = 20, h = 16$

Find the area of a triangle with base length b and height h.

3. $b = 12, h = 8$
4. $b = 24, h = 16$

Find the area of a circle with radius length r.

5. $r = 8$
6. $r = 3$

Find each perimeter.

7. equilateral triangle with side 6.1 cm
8. triangle with sides of lengths 7.4 km, 13.26 km, 0.88 km
9. square with sides of length 4.2 m
10. rectangle 10.7 cm by 3.05 cm

Find the circumference of each circle. Use 3.14 for π.

11. radius length 5
12. radius length 10

B Use a diagram and a formula to solve each problem.

19. A drum of driveway-sealer surfaces 60 m². Will one drum give one coat on a rectangular driveway 24.5 m by 2.5 m?
20. The radius of a circular patio is 3.5 m. One bag of concrete mix will surface 25 m². Is that enough mix for the job?
21. Find the circumference of Earth at the equator, where the radius is 2400 km.
22. How many cubic meters of water will fill a rectangular pool 20 m by 7 m by 3.5 m?

C

23. How many kiloliters of oil can be stored in a cylindrical tank having radius 15 m and height 12 m? (1 kiloliter = 1 m³)
24. An automobile wheel has a 35-centimeter diameter. How many revolutions will the wheel make as the car travels 100 km?
25. The diameter of the sun is about 100 times the diameter of Earth. The volume of the sun is how many times the volume of Earth?

MARKETING AND DISTRIBUTION

Marketing and Distribution careers involve goods and services that may be purchased, and their distribution. Career examples include persons who draw conclusions from statistics as to what goods and services should be produced, persons who transport the goods to markets, and persons who actually interact with customers.

Since competition is keen and the cost of raw materials high, business decisions are keyed to information obtained from Marketing Research Personnel, such as a *Market Research Analyst*. Marketing Research Personnel gather data from numerous sources, such as company files, experts, other companies in the field, published works, and customer surveys.

These data are collected, the statistics are analyzed, and conclusions are drawn. By this procedure, a company learns the likes and dislikes of potential customers, how best to package a product, and the "ideal" price for the product.

High school courses that help prepare students for these occupations include algebra, statistics, speech, English (grammar, in particular), journalism, sociology, and psychology.

MATHEMATICAL SAMPLER

1. You are a Market Research Analyst. You survey 25 potential consumers to help determine an average cost that consumers may expect to pay for an item. Here are the responses from your survey. $76, $82, $73, $60, $75, $92, $87, $82, $65, $101, $98, $99, $82, $75, $68, $73, $84, $86, $89, $57, $83, $79, $68, $79, $78.

The *mean*, *median*, and *mode* of these data are three numbers which represent the "average" of the responses. Use some reference books and find the meanings of these terms. Then find the mean, median, and mode for the above data.

OBJECTIVES: Write a formula to match information given by a rule, or suggested by a diagram or table.

4-4 WRITING FORMULAS FOR RULES, DIAGRAMS

A formula is an efficient and useful way to express a mathematical relationship or rule that is likely to be applied many times. When a rule is given as a word sentence, we may create a formula for it just as we sometimes create an equation to help us solve a problem.

EXAMPLE 1 One-half the sum of two numbers is an *average* of the numbers. Write a formula for this rule.

Ⓜ SOLUTION Use [a and b for the two numbers. h for the average.

$$h = \frac{1}{2}(a + b) \text{ or } \frac{a + b}{2}$$

EXAMPLE 2 A taxi fare is 30 cents for the first one-tenth kilometer plus 10 cents for each one-tenth kilometer after that. Write a formula for this rule.

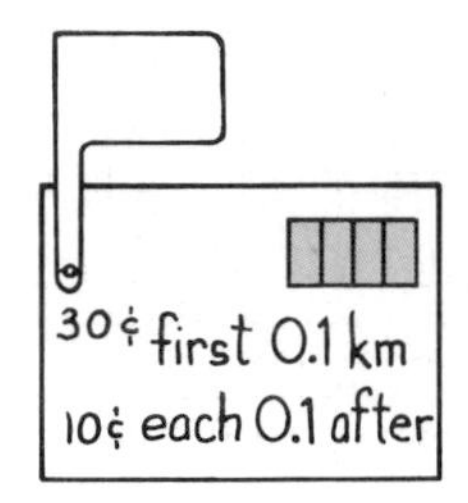

Ⓜ SOLUTION 1 Use [F for the fare in cents. n for the number of one-tenth kilometers traveled.

$¢ = ¢ + \frac{¢}{0.1 \text{ km}} \cdot (0.1 \text{ km})$

$$F = 30 + 10(n - 1)$$

This formula gives the taxi fare in cents for n one-tenth kilometers traveled.

Ⓜ SOLUTION 2 Use [F for the fare in cents. n for the number of one-tenth kilometers traveled after the first one-tenth kilometer.

$¢ = ¢ + \frac{¢}{0.1 \text{ km}} \cdot (0.1 \text{ km})$

$$F = 30 + 10n$$

This formula gives the taxi fare in cents when n represents the number of one-tenth kilometers traveled after the first.

Sometimes we may use formulas we already know to give us a new formula for a special case. In so doing, we may be able to simplify the formula by combining terms.

EXAMPLE 3 Each card in a set of rectangular cards has length 2 cm greater than its width. Write a formula for the perimeter of a card.

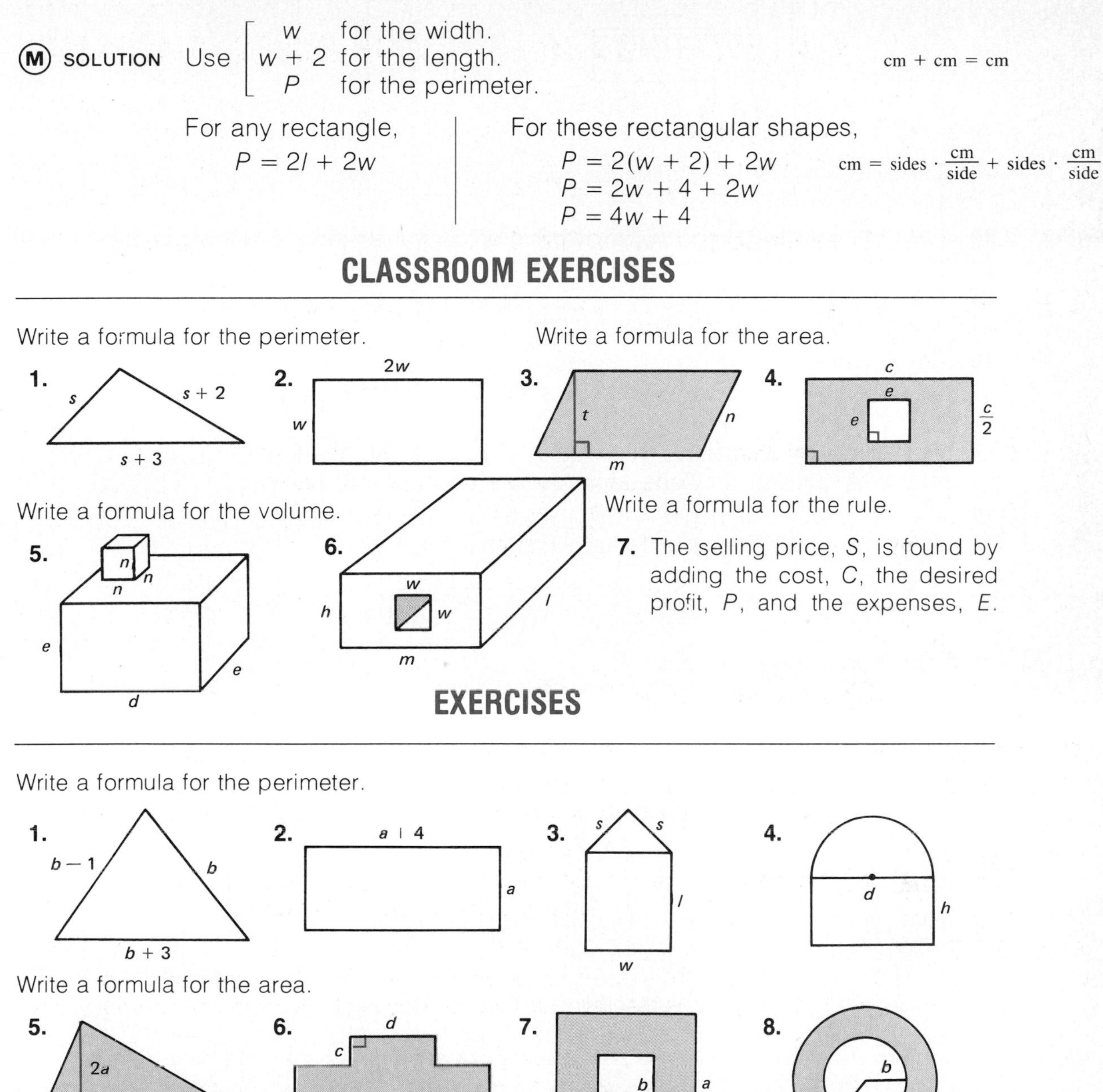

Ⓜ **SOLUTION** Use $\left[\begin{array}{ll} w & \text{for the width.} \\ w + 2 & \text{for the length.} \\ P & \text{for the perimeter.} \end{array}\right.$ cm + cm = cm

For any rectangle,

$$P = 2l + 2w$$

For these rectangular shapes,

$$P = 2(w + 2) + 2w \qquad \text{cm} = \text{sides} \cdot \frac{\text{cm}}{\text{side}} + \text{sides} \cdot \frac{\text{cm}}{\text{side}}$$

$$P = 2w + 4 + 2w$$

$$P = 4w + 4$$

CLASSROOM EXERCISES

Write a formula for the perimeter.

1. **2.**

Write a formula for the area.

3. **4.**

Write a formula for the volume.

5. **6.**

Write a formula for the rule.

7. The selling price, S, is found by adding the cost, C, the desired profit, P, and the expenses, E.

EXERCISES

A Write a formula for the perimeter.

1. **2.** **3.** **4.**

Write a formula for the area.

5. **6.** **7.** **8.**

Write a formula for the volume.

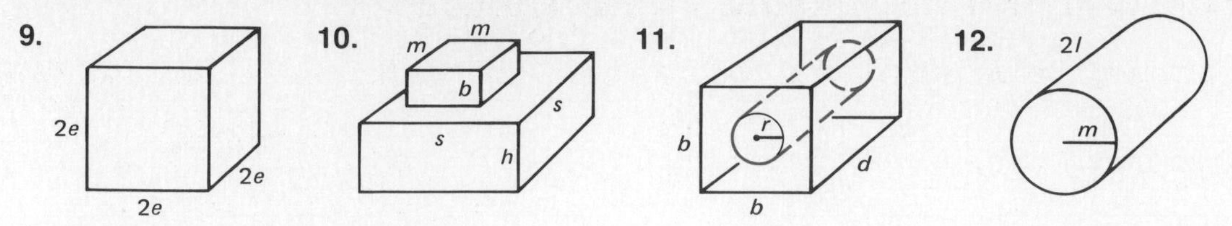

Write each rule as a formula.

13. The perimeter (P) of a rectangle equals the sum of twice the width (w) and twice the length (l).
14. The distance (d) traveled by any moving object equals the product of the uniform rate (r) and time (t).
15. The number of liters capacity of a container (c) is found by dividing the volume in cubic centimeters (V) by 1000.
16. The distance away (d), in kilometers, of lightning is found by dividing the number of seconds (N) between the flash and its accompanying thunder by 3.
17. The first 200 kilowatt hours cost 7 cents each. Additional kilowatt hours (n) cost 4 cents each. Write a formula for the total cost (C) in cents.
18. The temperature in degrees Celsius (t) can be found by counting the chirps made by a cricket in 15 seconds (N) and subtracting 15.

B 19. The first 3 minutes of a long-distance call cost 85 cents. Each additional minute costs 15 cents. Write a formula for the cost of the call in dollars.

Write a formula for the perimeter. Write a formula for the area.

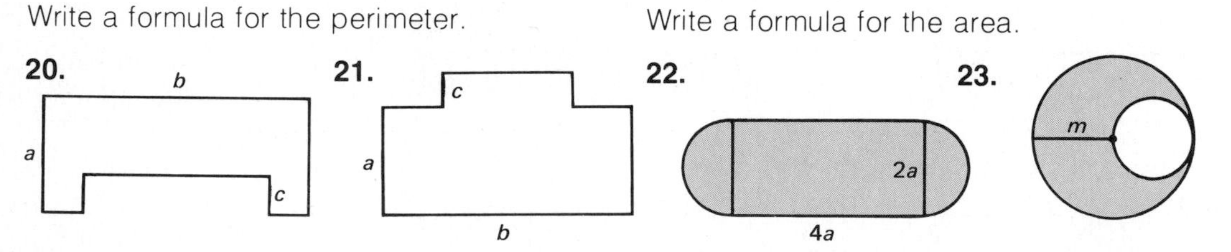

C 24. Find the cost of the canvas needed to make a tent having the measurements shown in the diagram. Allow one-tenth extra for seams and waste. Estimate the price of canvas at $5/m².

2.25 m
2 m
3 m
2 m

25. Find the cost to the nearest dollar of the paint for putting one coat on this garage. Allow 5 m² for painting under the eaves. Estimate the cost of paint at $15 for 3.8 liters. One liter of paint covers about 12.5 m².

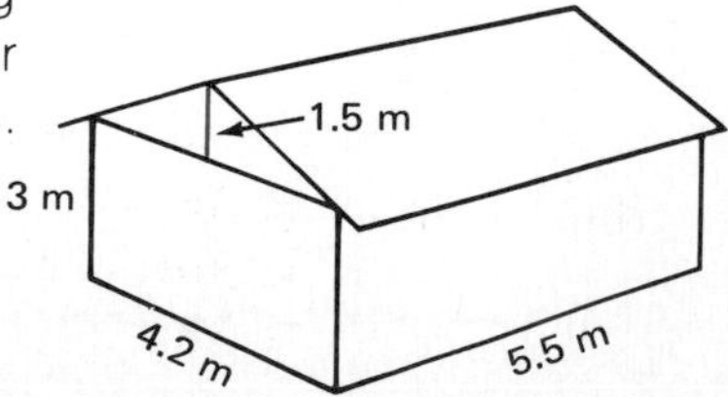

4-5 WRITING FORMULAS FROM TABLES

By studying the data in a table, you may find a formula for relating the corresponding numbers.

Note that *data* is the plural of *datum*.

EXAMPLE 1 During an antique automobile race, these data were recorded for the 1926 automobile. Write a formula that relates d and t.

Elapsed time in hours (t)	0	1	2	3	4
Distance in kilometers (d)	0	20	40	60	80

SOLUTION Distance in kilometers is 20 times the number of hours.

Ⓜ $$d = 20t$$

$\text{km} = \frac{\text{km}}{\text{h}} \cdot \text{h}$

EXAMPLE 2 The following table shows the number of sides, s, of a polygon and the number of triangles, N, formed by diagonals from one vertex of the polygon. Write a formula that relates N and s.

s	3	4	5	6
N	1	2	3	4

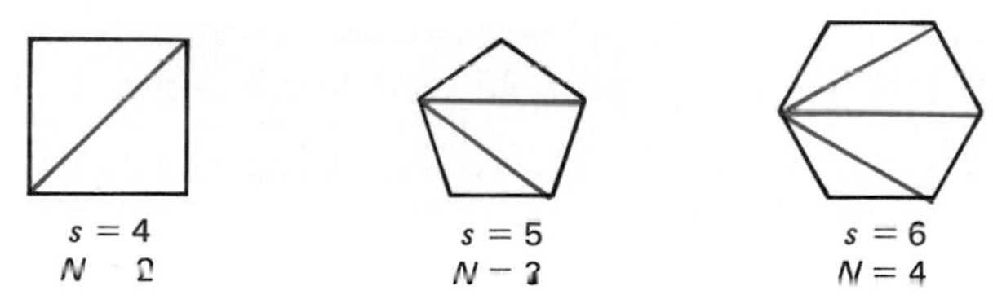

SOLUTION Each number for N is 2 less than the corresponding number for s.

Ⓜ $$N = s - 2$$

EXAMPLE 3 Write a formula that relates P and s as shown here. Then complete the table.

s	1	2	3	4	5	6
P	4	7	10	?	?	?

SOLUTION Each number for P is 1 more than 3 times s.

Ⓜ $$P = 3s + 1$$

Evaluate the formula for $s = 4$, $s = 5$, and $s = 6$.

Ⓜ

$$P = 3s + 1 = 3(4) + 1 = 13$$

$$P = 3s + 1 = 3(5) + 1 = 16$$

$$P = 3s + 1 = 3(6) + 1 = 19$$

CLASSROOM EXERCISES

For each exercise write a formula that expresses a relationship between the numbers. Then complete the table.

1.

Number of liters of gasoline (n)	1	2	3	4	5	6
Cost in dollars (C)	0.25	0.50	0.75	?	?	?

2.

Interest in dollars (i)	1	2	3	4	5	6
Total amount in dollars (A)	46	47	48	?	?	?

3.

x	1	2	3	4	5	6
y	3	5	7	?	?	?

4.

x	1	2	3	4	5	6
y	1	3	5	?	?	?

EXERCISES

A For each exercise write a formula that expresses a relationship between the numbers. Then complete the table.

1.

s	1	2	3	4	6	10
P	3	6	9	?	?	?

2.

s	1	2	3	4	8	12
P	4	8	12	?	?	?

3.

C	1	2	3	5	10	20
S	9.5	10.5	11.5	?	?	?

4.

M	1	2	3	4	12	17
S	11.5	12.5	13.5	?	?	?

5.

l	1	2	3	5	10	17
A	2.5	5	7.5	?	?	?

6.

w	1	2	4	7	10	23
A	1.5	3	6	?	?	?

B 7.

R	1	2	4	5	25	110
I	110	55	27.5	?	?	?

8.

n	0	1	2	3	4	5
N	−5	−2	1	?	?	?

9.

s	1	2	3	4	12	15
A	1	4	9	?	?	?

10.

e	1	2	3	4	9	10
V	1	?	27	?	?	1000

C Copy the word that correctly completes each sentence.

11. For two variables, x and y, such that $xy = k$, k a positive constant, as x increases, y (increases, decreases).

12. For two variables, x and y, such that $y = kx$, k a positive constant, as x increases, y (increases, decreases).

CHECKING YOUR UNDERSTANDING

WORDS

formula

CONCEPTS

- A formula expresses a mathematical relationship in a concise form. It may be used to help solve any problem involving that relationship. [4-1 to 4-5]

PROCESSES

- Find the value for a variable in a formula when given a value for each of the other variables. [4-1]

  1. $A = \frac{1}{2}bh$, $b = 1.5$, $h = 3$. Find A.

  2. $h = \frac{2A}{b + d}$, $A = 15$, $b = 2$, $d = 7$. Find h.

- Solve a problem using a formula. [4-2, 4-3]

  3. Find the distance traveled in 3 hours at the average rate of 70 kilometers per hour. Use the formula $d = rt$.

  4. Find the perimeter of an isosceles triangle whose base measures 12 cm and whose sides measure 10 cm each. Use $P = b + 2s$.

- Write a formula for a mathematical relationship or rule given as a word sentence or suggested by a diagram or table. [4-4, 4-5]

  5. The average of three numbers, p, q, and r, is $\frac{1}{3}$ their sum.

6.

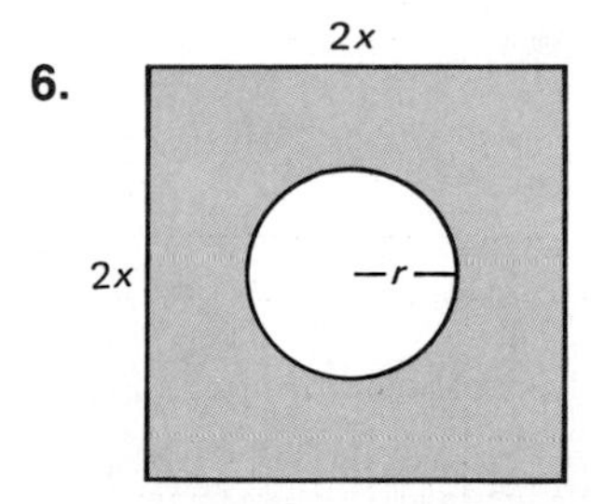

Area of region shown by shading = ?

7.

h	1	2	3	6	8
j	3	5	7	13	17

formula: ?

USING THE CONSTANT FEATURE OF YOUR CALCULATOR

Some calculators have a built-in "constant" feature that allows you to efficiently perform the same operation several times. Try the following.

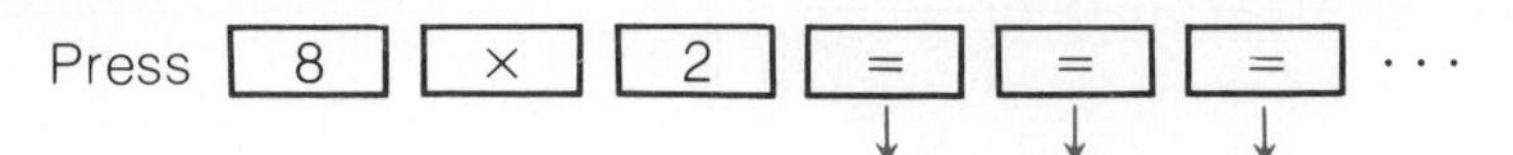

If the display shows 16 32 64 and so on, your calculator has a built-in constant. It is performing the sequence of instructions "multiply by two" every time you press the Equals key. This feature also will work with addition, subtraction and division.

If your calculator does not have a built-in constant, it may have a Constant key. This key sometimes looks like this [K]. You should check your calculator manual for directions on how to use this feature.

EXAMPLE 1 Use the calculator to simplify $91 - 8 - 8 - 8 - 8$.

SOLUTION This requires performing the same step (subtract 8) several times. The constant feature of the calculator may be used.

Press 91 [−] 8 [=] [=] [=] [=]

The display will show 59.

EXAMPLE 2 Use the calculator to simplify 3^5.

SOLUTION Recall that $3^5 = 3 \times 3 \times 3 \times 3 \times 3$.

Press 3 [×] 3 [=] [=] [=] [=].

The display will show 243.

EXAMPLE 3 Use the calculator to simplify $14 \cdot 5^4$.

SOLUTION The order of operations requires that 5^4 be simplified first.

Press 5 [×] 5 [=] [=] [=] [×] 14 [=]

The display will show 8750.

EXAMPLE 4 Find the circumference of the circles with diameters whose measures are 1, 2, 3, 4, and 5.
Use the formula $C = \pi d$, with $\pi = 3.14$.

SOLUTION Press 1 [×] 3.14 [=] 2 [=] 3 [=] 4 [=] 5 [=]

The display will show 3.14, 6.28, 9.42, 12.56, and 15.7.

EXERCISES

Use the constant feature of your calculator to simplify.

1. $47 - 3 - 3 - 3 - 3 - 3$
2. $32 + 7 + 7 + 7 + 7 + 7 + 7$
3. $96 \div 2 \div 2 \div 2 \div 2$
4. $972 \div 3 \div 3 \div 3 \div 3 \div 3$
5. 2^8
6. 4^5
7. $(-3)^4$
8. $(-7)^4$
9. $(-7)5^3$
10. $12(-4)^5$
11. $4(-1 \cdot 1)^4$
12. $3.7(1.2)^4$

Use the constant feature of your calculator to evaluate.

13. $4x^3$ for $x = 1.6$
14. $7t^3$ for $t = 0.5$
15. $0.3y^5$ for $y = -2$
16. $-6r^4$ for $r = -3$
17. $-1.7z^4$ for $z = -1.2$
18. $-8s^4$ for $s = 1.1$

Use your calculator and the constant feature to help you answer the following.

19. In $3 \cdot 3 \cdot 3 \cdot \cdots$, how many times must you use 3 as a factor to have 177 147 as the product?

20. In $15 \cdot 2 \cdot 2 \cdot 2 \cdot \cdots$, how many times must you use 2 as a factor to have 61440 as a product?

21. You have $655.36 in the bank. If you withdraw one-half of the amount left in the bank every day, after how many withdrawals will you have less than $1.00 left in the bank?

There is a tax of 7.5¢ on each dollar spent. Find the tax on each amount.

22. $2
23. $6
24. $45
25. $3.50
26. $12.98
27. $18.37

Use your calculator to investigate the following.

28. What happens when a fraction is used repeatedly as a factor?
(for example, $\frac{1}{2} \cdot \frac{1}{2} \cdot \frac{1}{2} \cdot \cdots$)

29. What happens for the following series of key strokes on a calculator with a built-in constant?

1 [+] 3 [+/−] [=] [+/−] [=] [+/−] [=] ...

OBJECTIVE: Rewrite formulas to express unknown quantities in terms of known quantities.

4-6 REWRITING FORMULAS

A relationship may be described by a formula in different ways. A formula is most useful when numbers that generally are known are represented in one member, and a number that is to be found is represented as the other member.

The most meaningful and most useful form for a formula depends upon the situation in which it is to be used.

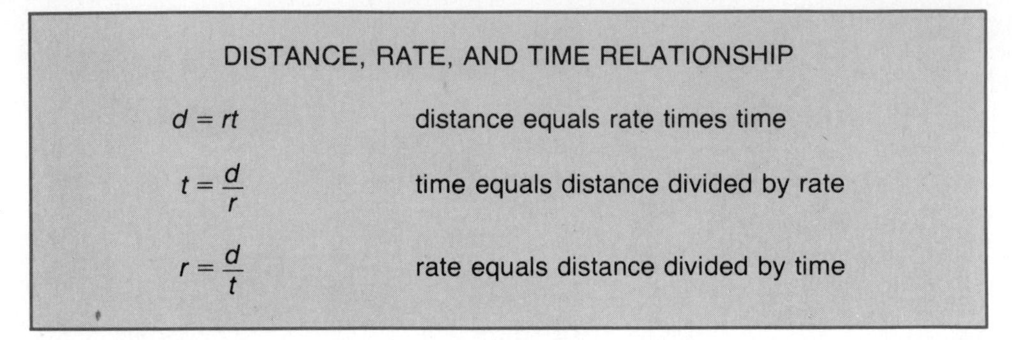

DISTANCE, RATE, AND TIME RELATIONSHIP

$d = rt$	distance equals rate times time
$t = \frac{d}{r}$	time equals distance divided by rate
$r = \frac{d}{t}$	rate equals distance divided by time

The formula $r = \frac{d}{t}$ is the most useful for finding the rate.

For the three forms shown in Example 1, the unit equations are:

$$\text{km} = \frac{\text{km}}{\text{h}} \cdot \text{h}$$

$$\text{h} = \frac{\text{km}}{\frac{\text{km}}{\text{h}}}$$

$$\frac{\text{km}}{\text{h}} = \frac{(\text{km})}{(\text{h})}$$

EXAMPLE 1 The Hernandez family drove 300 kilometers. They drove steadily for 5 hours. Find the rate they traveled.

SOLUTION

$d = rt$	$t = \frac{d}{r}$	$r = \frac{d}{t}$
$300 = r \cdot 5$	$5 = \frac{300}{r}$	$r = \frac{300}{5}$
$\frac{300}{5} = r$	$5r = 300$	$= 60$
$60 = r$	$r = \frac{300}{5}$	
	$= 60$	

CONCLUSION The Hernandez family traveled 60 kilometers per hour.

EXAMPLE 2 The formula $P = 4s$ gives the perimeter, P, of a square when the length, s, of a side is known. Write a new formula that gives the length of a side when the perimeter is known.

It is conventional but not necessary to represent the "unknown" as the left member.

SOLUTION $P = 4\boxed{s}$

$\frac{P}{4} = \boxed{s}$, or $\boxed{s} = \frac{P}{4}$

EXAMPLE 3 Use the formula $i = prt$. Write a new formula that gives the time when the principal, rate, and interest are known.

Ⓜ **SOLUTION**

$$i = pr\boxed{t}$$

$$\frac{i}{pr} = \boxed{t}, \text{ or } \boxed{t} = \frac{i}{pr}$$

When writing a new formula from a given formula, we want to express a number to be found in terms of the known numbers. In effect, we are solving an equation (the given formula) for the unknown number. We may check the result just as we do for equations.

EXAMPLE 4 Write a formula for the width of a rectangle in terms of a known perimeter and length. Check your result.

SOLUTION Begin with the formula for the perimeter, P, in terms of length, l, and width, w. Then, solve for w.

Ⓜ

$$P = 2l + 2\boxed{w}$$

$$P - 2l = 2\boxed{w}$$

$$\frac{P - 2l}{2} = \boxed{w}, \text{ or}$$

$$\boxed{w} = \frac{P - 2l}{2}$$

CHECK Replace w by $\frac{P - 2l}{2}$ in $P = 2l + 2w$.

$$P = 2l + 2w$$

$$P \stackrel{?}{=} 2l + 2\left(\frac{P - 2l}{2}\right)$$

$$P \stackrel{?}{=} 2l + P - 2l$$

$$P = P \quad \checkmark$$

WRITING A DIFFERENT FORMULA FOR A RELATIONSHIP

1. Write the formula in its given form.
2. Locate the variable for the unknown number in the formula.
3. Use the Properties of Equality to write a new formula so that the variable for the unknown is one of the two members.

CLASSROOM EXERCISES

Write a new formula by solving for the circled variable.

1. $P = 3\textcircled{s}$
2. $S = C + \textcircled{M}$
3. $P = 2\textcircled{l} + 2w$
4. $A = \dfrac{\textcircled{h}}{n}$
5. $A = \dfrac{h}{\textcircled{n}}$
6. $A = \dfrac{a + \textcircled{b} + c}{3}$

EXERCISES

A Write a new formula by solving for the circled variable.

1. $A = \textcircled{p} + i$
2. $A = p + \textcircled{i}$
3. $S = C + M + \textcircled{G}$
4. $P = a + \textcircled{b} + c$
5. $F = \textcircled{m}a$
6. $F = m\textcircled{a}$
7. $A = \dfrac{\textcircled{a} + b + c}{3}$
8. $A = \dfrac{a + b + \textcircled{c}}{3}$
9. $D = \dfrac{M}{\textcircled{V}}$
10. $A = \dfrac{h}{\textcircled{n}}$
11. $s = \dfrac{1}{2}\textcircled{a}t^2$
12. $E = \dfrac{1}{2}\textcircled{m}v^2$
13. $P = 2\textcircled{b} + 2s$
14. $P = 2l + 2\textcircled{w}$
15. $i = \textcircled{p}rt$
16. $i = pr\textcircled{t}$
17. $S = R - 2\textcircled{w}$
18. $S = R - \dfrac{1}{4}\textcircled{W}$

B

19. $F = \dfrac{Wv^2}{a\textcircled{r}}$
20. $F = \dfrac{\textcircled{m}v^2}{r}$
21. $F = \dfrac{\textcircled{W}v^2}{ar}$
22. $S = \pi\textcircled{d}h + 2\pi r^2$
23. $D = 180(\textcircled{n} - 2)$
24. $m = 0.98(\textcircled{h} - 102)$

C

25. $V = \dfrac{W}{\textcircled{T} - t}$
26. $S = \dfrac{W}{W - \textcircled{w}}$
27. $S = \dfrac{\textcircled{W}}{\textcircled{W} - 6}$

1.

$1/\dfrac{1}{x} = x$

The Reciprocal key [1/x] on your calculator replaces the number in the display by its reciprocal. Predict what should happen if you enter any non-zero number into the display and then press the Reciprocal key several times. Try it and test your prediction.

CHAPTER REVIEW

Copy and complete each table. Use the formula given. [4-1]

1. $E = 3h$

h	0	0.4	2	$3\frac{1}{2}$
E	?	?	?	?

2. $r = \frac{100}{t}$

t	$\frac{1}{2}$	4.5	5	12
r	?	?	?	?

3. $s = 4.9t^2$

t	0	1	2	2.5	10
s	?	?	?	?	?

Evaluate the left member for the numbers given.

4. $r = \frac{d}{t}$ for $d = 150$, $t = 2.5$

5. $c = 1.75 + 0.05t$ for $t = 7$

6. $C = 2\pi r$ for $r = 2.5$

7. $i = prt$ for $p = 1000$, $r = 0.08$, $t = 5$

Solve. [4-2]

8. Use $t = \frac{d}{r}$. Find the driving time from New York City to Miami, Florida, a distance of 2200 km, for the rate of 88 km/h.

9. A body falls toward earth for 20 seconds. Use $s = 4.9t^2$ to find the distance it falls in meters.

The formula gives meters when time is given in seconds. The 4.9 incorporates this fact.

10. \$1500 is invested at $8\frac{1}{2}\%$ simple interest per year. Use $V = p + prt$. Find the value of the investment after 5 years.

Solve. [4-3 to 4-5]

11. Find the perimeter of a rectangle having length $3\frac{1}{2}$ and width $6\frac{1}{4}$.

12. Find the circumference of a circle with diameter length 5.0.

13. Find the area of a triangle with base length 6 and height 3.1.

14. Find the area of a circle with diameter length 5.

15. Find the volume of a cylinder with radius length 5 and height 4.

16. Find the volume of a sphere with radius length 5.

17. Find the area of each face of this rectangular solid. →

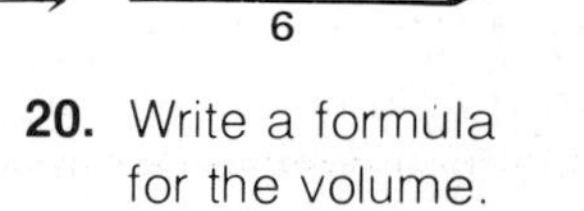

18. Write a formula for the perimeter.

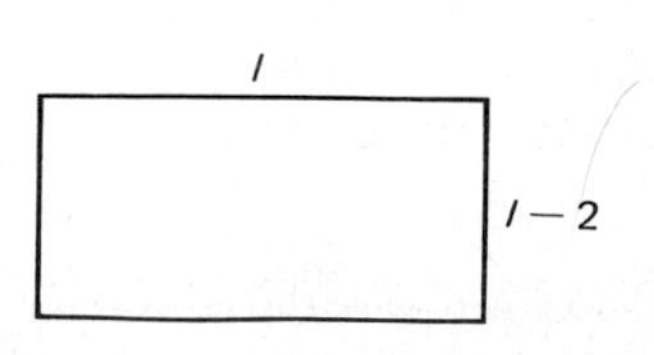

19. Write a formula for the area of the shaded part.

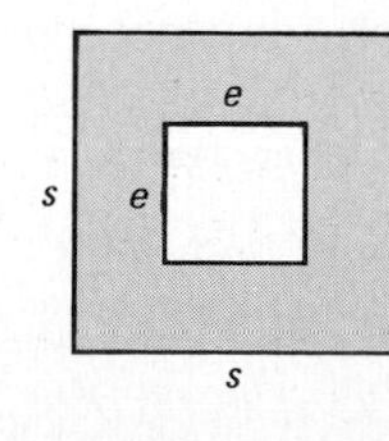

20. Write a formula for the volume.

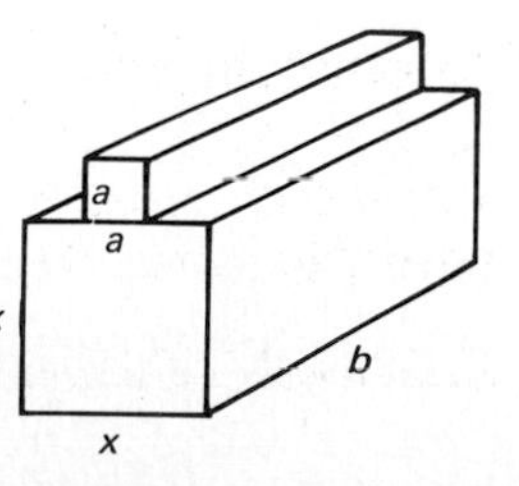

21. Write as a formula: The cost (C) is the product of the price per item (p) and the number of items (n).

22. Write a formula that relates c and n. Give the numbers that complete the table.

n	0	1	2	3	12
c	5	7	9	?	?

23. Write a formula that relates c and i. Give the numbers that complete the table.

i	1	2	5	10	15
c	2.54	5.08	12.7	?	?

Solve each formula for the variable shown in color. [4-6]

24. $C = 2\pi \boxed{r}$ **25.** $i = \boxed{p}rt$ **26.** $P = 2\boxed{a} + b$ **27.** $B.A. = \frac{\boxed{h}}{A.B.}$

CAPSULE REVIEW

Write the letter of the best response.

1. The area of a parallelogram with base length 5 cm and height 3.5 cm is

a. 8.75 cm **b.** 8.75 cm^2 **c.** 17.5 cm **d.** 17.5 cm^2 **e.** 35 cm^2

2. The perimeter of a parallelogram with height 3 and sides of lengths 4 and 5 is

a. 8 **b.** 9 **c.** 10 **d.** 12 **e.** 18

3. The volume of a cylinder with radius length 4 cm and height 10 cm is

a. 2010 cm^3 **b.** 502.4 cm^2 **c.** 2010 cm^2 **d.** 251.2 cm^3 **e.** 502.4 cm^3

4. The area of a triangle with base length 5 cm and height 3.5 cm is

a. 8.75 cm **b.** 8.75 cm^2 **c.** 17.5 cm **d.** 17.5 cm^2 **e.** 35 cm^2

5. For $C = 2\pi r$, as numbers for r increase, numbers for C

a. increase **b.** decrease **c.** are unchanged **d.** double **e.** are halved

6. For $r = \frac{d}{t}$, as numbers for d increase, numbers for r

a. increase **b.** decrease **c.** are unchanged **d.** double **e.** are halved

7. For $r = \frac{d}{t}$, as numbers for t decrease, numbers for r

a. increase **b.** decrease **c.** are unchanged **d.** double **e.** are halved

8. For $B.A. = \frac{h}{A.B.}$, as $A.B.$ increases and h remains constant, $B.A.$

a. increases **b.** decreases **c.** is unchanged **d.** doubles **e.** is halved

9. For $P = 2l + 2w$, as l decreases, P

a. increases **b.** decreases **c.** is unchanged **d.** not enough information

CHAPTER TEST

1. Use the formula $d = rt$. Find the distance an airplane travels in 2 hours flying at 600 km/h.
2. Julio earns $3 an hour at his job. Write a formula that relates his earnings (E) and the number of hours (h) he works.
3. A pitcher's earned-run average (ERA) is found by the formula $ERA = \frac{9\ ER}{IP}$, for which ER represents the number of earned runs and IP represents the number of innings pitched. Melissa pitched six innings and gave up 2 earned runs. What was her earned-run average?
4. An object dropped from the top of a building reaches the ground in 3 seconds. Use the formula $s = 4.9t^2$ to find the building's height in meters.
5. Write a formula showing the relationship between the perimeter (P) of a rectangle and its length (l) and width (w).
6. Use the formula $A = \pi r^2$. Find the area of a circle which has a radius length 10 cm.
7. Jean Washington is paid $250 a week plus $0.25 for each dollar in sales(s). Write a formula showing her weekly pay (P).
8. There are 100 centimeters in 1 meter. Write a formula showing the relationship between a number of meters (k) and a number of centimeters (n).
9. Write a formula that relates B and n.
10. Give the numbers that complete the table.

n	0	1	2	3	4	5
B	0	5	10	15	?	?

11. Write a formula that relates k and r.
12. Give the numbers that complete the table.

r	1	2	3	4	5
k	6	7	8	?	?

13. $P = 4s$. Write a formula that gives the length of a side of a square when the perimeter is known.
14. $A = lw$. Write a formula that gives the length of a rectangle when the area and width are known.

Write the letter of the best response.

15. Use $i = prt$. The interest earned by $500 invested at 6% per year for 2 years is
    a. $10 **b.** $12 **c.** $30 **d.** $60 **e.** $100
16. Use $d = rt$. Jason walks for 3 hours at 6 km/h. How far does he walk?
    a. 0.5 km **b.** 2 km **c.** 3 km **d.** 9 km **e.** 18 km
17. Which formula relates the circumference of a circle to its diameter length?
    a. $C = \pi d$ **b.** $C = 2\pi d$ **c.** $C = \frac{d}{\pi}$ **d.** $C = \frac{2d}{\pi}$ **e.** $C = \pi d^2$

18. The price of a bar of soap is $0.45. Which formula relates the cost (C) in dollars to the number of bars of soap (n)?

a. $C = 0.45 + n$ **b.** $C = n - 0.45$ **c.** $C = 0.45n$ **d.** $C = \frac{n}{0.45}$ **e.** $C = \frac{0.45}{n}$

19. Which formula relates G and t for the numbers shown in the table.

t	0	1	2	3
G	1	3	5	7

a. $G = t + 1$ **b.** $G = 2t + 1$ **c.** $G = t + 2$

d. $G = 2t$ **e.** $G = 4t - 1$

20. $d = rt$ gives distance in terms of rate and time. Which formula correctly gives rate in terms of distance and time?

a. $r = dt$ **b.** $r = d - t$ **c.** $r = t - d$ **d.** $r = \frac{t}{d}$ **e.** $r = \frac{d}{t}$

CUMULATIVE REVIEW

Give a word or symbol to complete each sentence.

1. $-x$ is the __?__ of x.

2. $\frac{y}{z}$ is the __?__ of $\frac{z}{y}$.

3. A number that can be shown in the form $\frac{a}{b}$ with a and b both integers and $b \neq 0$ is a __?__ number.

4. The sentence "$A = s^2$" is called the __?__ for the area of a square.

5. $\frac{11}{16}$ __?__ $\frac{11}{15}$ (Use >, <, or =.)

6. -12 is a __?__ of the equation $x + 8 = -4$.

Briefly answer each question. Refer to the concept suggested.

7. $3^6 \cdot 3^4 = 3^{10}$ Why?

8. $6^8 \div 6^3 = 6^5$ Why?

9. The real numbers are related to the points of a number line in a special way. How?

10. The truth of a compound sentence (formed by joining two simple sentences using the words "or" or "and") depends upon the truth of the simple sentences. Explain.

11. The multiplication property used in solving inequalities differs from the multiplication property used in solving equations. How?

Graph each set.

12. all real numbers less than or equal to 4

13. the negative integers greater than -8

Graph each solution set.

14. $-4x + 11 = -17$

15. $7y \geq -49$

16. $x \leq -4$ or $x \geq 2$

17. $x \geq -10$ and $x \leq 5$

18. $|x| < 6$

19. $|x| > 3$

Evaluate.

20. $-4x + \frac{2}{3}y$ for $x = 12$ and $y = -21$

21. $(-2)^3x^4$ for $x = -3$

22. $-4a^2b^3 - 7ab$ for $a = -5$ and $b = \frac{1}{2}$

Simplify.

23. $36 + 15 \div 3 - 2 \cdot (4 + 16) \div 5$

24. $-7a + 6b - 12 + 9a - 13b + 4$

25. $-29 + 16$

26. $4\frac{3}{5} + \left(-11\frac{1}{10}\right)$

27. $\frac{7y^2}{8} + \frac{5y^2}{6}$

28. $\frac{3x}{4} - \frac{5x}{3}$

29. $(-3) \cdot (-8) \cdot (-2) \cdot (-1)$

30. $(-5x^2) \cdot (6x^3)$

31. $(-3h)(-9k)$

32. $\left(\frac{-12x^4}{7y}\right) \cdot \left(\frac{14y^2}{3x}\right)$

33. $(48) \div (-3)$

34. $\left(-4\frac{1}{5}\right) \div \left(-4\frac{9}{10}\right)$

35. $\frac{24y^7}{3y^4}$

36. $\frac{-72x^5z^3}{6x^4z^5}$

37. $\left(\frac{8y^2}{9x^3}\right) \div \left(\frac{16y^5}{15x^7}\right)$

Solve.

38. $x + 24 = 6$

39. $y - 18 = -3$

40. $-7x = 28$

41. $\frac{y}{-3} = -12$

42. $5x + (-49) = -84$

43. $8y + 15 = -4y + 75$

44. $y - 6 > 10$

45. $x + 8 < -4$

46. $7x > 35$

47. $-9y \le 54$

48. $3x + 19 < -23$

49. $5y - 16 \ge -3y + 24$

50. The sum of two consecutive even integers is 34. Find the integers.

51. The difference of two numbers is 44. One number is 18 larger than two times the other. Find the numbers.

Write the letter of the best response.

52. $\frac{\pi^x}{\pi^{x-2}} =$ **a.** π^{2x-2} **b.** π^2 **c.** π^{2x} **d.** π^x

53. The inequality $-\frac{x}{3} \ge 4$ may be simplified to

a. $x \le -12$. **b.** $x \ge -12$. **c.** $-x \le 12$. **d.** $12 \le x$.

54. The graph at the right represents the solution set for

−3 −2 −1 0 1 2 3

a. $|x| > 3$. **b.** $|x| \ge 3$. **c.** $x < -3$ or $x \ge 3$. **d.** $x < -3$ and $x \ge 3$.

55. For $a = 2$ and $b = -3$, $-|a^2b^3| =$

a. 108. **b.** −108. **c.** 54. **d.** −54.

56. For $a = -1$ and $b = 4$, $|ab| - b \cdot |a| =$

a. 0. **b.** 8. **c.** −8. **d.** 4.

57. $4 \div 2 + 3 \cdot 5 =$

a. $4 \div [(2 + 3) \cdot 5]$ **b.** $4 \div [2 + (3 \cdot 5)]$ **c.** $[4 \div (2 + 3)] \cdot 5$ **d.** $(4 \div 2) + (3 \cdot 5)$

CHAPTER 5

Problem Solving: Using Equations

An important goal of an algebra course is learning the use of algebra as a problem-solving tool. Many of the word problems you solve in this course are provided simply to give you practice in working with this tool. Far more important than the word problems is the procedure you learn to use. Good procedure is an excellent problem-solving skill, applicable in a wide variety of situations.

OBJECTIVES: Use equations to solve problems involving percent, earning and spending, and distance, rate, and time.

5-1 ALGEBRAIC REPRESENTATION

When using algebra to solve a problem, one of the first steps is to write a symbol to represent a number to be found. That symbol, in turn, may be used to form other expressions that represent other numbers.

EXAMPLE 1 Each record plays for 23 minutes. Represent the number of hours that several records will play.

(M) **SOLUTION** Use
- n for the number of records.
- $23n$ for the number of minutes the records will play. $\quad \frac{\text{min}}{\text{record}} \cdot \text{records} = \text{min}$
- $\frac{23n}{60}$ for the number of hours the records will play. $\quad \frac{\text{min}}{\frac{\text{min}}{\text{h}}} = \text{h}$

EXAMPLE 2 Megan rode her bicycle at 20 kilometers per hour. Using one variable, represent the distance Megan rode. Then represent the time Megan spent riding.

SOLUTION From $d = rt$ (distance = rate · time), we find $\frac{d}{r} = t$.

 Use
- d for the number of kilometers Megan rode.
- $\frac{d}{20}$ for the number of hours Megan rode. $\quad \frac{\text{km}}{\frac{\text{km}}{\text{h}}} = \text{h}$

In the statement of a problem, a mathematical relationship may be given by a word sentence. After creating the symbols and writing the expressions for the numbers involved, we use the symbols and expressions to replace the word sentence by a number sentence.

EXAMPLE 3 The length of a rectangular region is 4 times its width. The area of the region is 400 square meters. Write an equation that relates the area to the width.

(M) **SOLUTION** $A = lw$ gives the area for a rectangle.

Use
- w for the width in meters.
- $4w$ for the length in meters. $\quad$ (dimensionless) · m = m

$400 = 4w(w)$ $\quad \text{m}^2 = \text{m} \cdot \text{m}$

$400 = 4w^2$

EXAMPLE 4 The length of the shortest side of a triangle is one-half that of a second side. The length of the third side is 5 less than the sum of the lengths of the other two sides. The perimeter of the triangle is 40. Write an equation that relates the perimeter to the length of one side.

Ⓜ **SOLUTION** $P = a + b + c$ gives the perimeter for a triangle.

Use
- m for the length of the second side.
- $\frac{m}{2}$ for the length of the shortest side.
- $m + \frac{m}{2} - 5$ for the length of the third side.

$$40 = m + \frac{m}{2} + m + \frac{m}{2} - 5$$

For some problems, it may be necessary to first write the word sentence for the central mathematical relationship. Also, it may be helpful to arrange the symbols and expressions in a chart.

EXAMPLE 5 Lee, Bea, and Jean work together raking leaves. Lee works twice as many hours as Bea, and Jean works twice as many hours as Lee. Each is paid $5 per hour. They are paid $70 for the job. Write an equation that relates the number of hours worked to the total pay.

Ⓜ **SOLUTION** The sum of the dollars earned by each is 70. Make a chart. Use h for the number of hours Bea worked.

The chart format is an alternative to the list format.

	Number of Hours Worked	Number of Dollars Earned
Bea	h	$5h$
Lee	$2h$	$5(2h)$
Jean	$2(2h)$	$5(2)(2h)$

Margin notes beside the rows:
- Bea: $\frac{\$}{h} \cdot h = \$$
- Lee: (dimensionless) $\cdot$ h = h; $\frac{\$}{h} \cdot h = \$$
- Jean: (dimensionless) $\cdot$ h = h; $\frac{\$}{h} \cdot h = \$$

$$B_\$ + L_\$ + J_\$ = 70$$

$\$ + \$ + \$ = \$$

$$5h + 5(2h) + 5(2)(2h) = 70$$

CLASSROOM EXERCISES

Use one variable to represent the numbers in each exercise.

1. a number of years and the number of months in those years
2. a number of years and the number of centuries in those years
3. three consecutive numbers
4. Jon is now 3 times as old as Jan. Represent their ages now and their ages 5 years ago. Use a chart.

For each exercise, write an equation. Use one variable.

5. The width of a rectangle is one-half the length. The area of the rectangle is 200 square meters.

6. The length of the base of a triangle is 5 centimeters. The area of the triangle is 45 square centimeters.

EXERCISES

A Use one variable to represent the numbers in each exercise.

1. Represent three consecutive even integers, the smallest of which is given by $2n$.

2. Represent three consecutive odd integers, the largest of which is given by $2n + 1$.

3. Joe's hourly pay rate is 3 times Flo's. Represent the hourly and the weekly pay for each for a 40-hour week. Use a chart.

4. Sam's weekly salary is $\frac{3}{4}$ Pam's salary. Represent the weekly and the annual salary for each. Use a chart.

5. A car travels 100 km/h for a certain number of hours. Represent the time and distance traveled.

6. A car travels 110 km at a constant rate. Represent the rate and the time.

For each exercise, write an equation. Use one variable.

7. In degrees, the measure of one angle of a triangle is twice that of the second angle. The measure of the third angle is 3 times that of the second. The sum of the measures is 180.

8. In degrees, the measure of one angle of a triangle is 30 more than that of another. The measure of the third is 10 greater than twice that of the smallest. The sum of the measures is 180.

9. The width of a rectangle is $\frac{1}{3}$ its length. Its area is 100.

10. The length of the base of a triangle is 8 centimeters. The area of the triangle is 72 square centimeters.

B 11. Heather has a regular $37\frac{1}{2}$-hour-per-week job and also a part-time job for 20 hours a week. The hourly rate for the part-time job is $1\frac{1}{4}$ times the rate for the regular job. Represent the total weekly wages in simplest form.

C 12. A number of liters of fuel is used to travel 400 kilometers. Represent the number of liters of fuel used and the rate of use in liters per 100 kilometers.

Error IS $\frac{1}{0}$ REALLY UNDEFINED?

$\frac{1}{x}$ is undefined for $x = 0$. What happens on your calculator when you enter 5 [÷] 0 [=]? What happens when you enter 0 [1/x]?

5-2 PERCENT

The word **percent** may be thought of as meaning "per hundred," or, more conveniently, "hundredths." The symbol for percent is %. Thus, 6% means "6 per hundred," "6 hundredths," or simply 0.06.

FORMS FOR HUNDREDTHS

Percent	Decimal	Fraction
6%	0.06	$\frac{6}{100}$
65%	0.65	$\frac{65}{100}$
6.5% or $6\frac{1}{2}$%	0.065	$\frac{6.5}{100}$ or $\frac{65}{1000}$
0.5% or $\frac{1}{2}$%	0.005	$\frac{0.5}{100}$ or $\frac{5}{1000}$
0.6%	0.006	$\frac{0.6}{100}$ or $\frac{6}{1000}$
650%	6.50	$\frac{650}{100}$

In a percent problem, there usually are three numbers involved. When we know any two of these numbers, we may use an algebraic equation to find the third number.

EXAMPLE 1 What number is 3% of 120?

Ⓜ SOLUTION Use n for the number.

$n = 3\%$ of 120
$n = 0.03(120)$
$n = 3.6$

The symbol "%" is never used in an equation beyond a "word equation" such as $n = 3\%$ of 120.

CONCLUSION 3.6 is 3% of 120.

EXAMPLE 2 169 is 65% of what number?

Ⓜ SOLUTION Use n for the number.

$169 = 65\%$ of n.
$169 = 0.65n$
$$n = \frac{169}{0.65}$$
$n = 260$

CONCLUSION 169 is 65% of 260.

EXAMPLE 3 26 is what percent of 65?

Ⓜ **SOLUTION** Use r for the percent in decimal form.

$$26 = r \cdot 65$$
$$r = \frac{26}{65}$$
$$r = 0.40$$

CONCLUSION 26 is 40% of 65.

EXAMPLE 4 On a test, Lyn had 48 answers correct. There were 60 test questions. Give Lyn's score as a percent.

Ⓜ **SOLUTION** 48 is some percent of 60.
Use r for the percent in decimal form.

$$48 = r \cdot 60$$
$$r = \frac{48}{60}$$
$$r = 0.80$$

CONCLUSION Lyn's score was 80%.

CLASSROOM EXERCISES

Solve. Use an algebraic equation.

1. What number is 60% of 40?
2. 8 is what percent of 160?
3. What percent of 50 is 75?
4. 60 is 40% of what number?
5. Find $7\frac{1}{2}$% of $4000.
6. Find 120% of 75.
7. A hockey team won 14 games and lost 6. What percent of the games played did it win?

EXERCISES

[A] Solve. Use an algebraic equation.

1. What number is 4% of 180?
2. What number is 250% of 6?
3. 18 is what percent of 72?
4. 72 is what percent of 18?
5. What percent of 250 is 50?
6. What percent of 1.2 is 1.5?
7. 84 is 400% of what number?
8. 27 is $37\frac{1}{2}$% of what number?

Solve. Use an algebraic equation.

9. A student scored 54 correct answers for a test having 72 items. Give the student's score as a percent.
10. A student scored 91 correct answers for a test having 125 items. Give the student's score as a percent.
11. A tennis player has won 9 of the last 15 matches. What percent of the matches did the player lose?
12. A family spends 25% of its monthly income for rent. The rent is $250 per month. Find the family's monthly income.

13. A chair was made to sell for \$55. A discount of \$10 is allowed for cash payment. The discount is what percent of the original price?

14. What number is $33\frac{1}{3}\%$ of 0.750?

15. What number is $\frac{1}{4}\%$ of 2?

16. 1.6 is 0.1% of what number?

17. 4.8 is 0.2% of what number?

B **18.** A baseball team won 15 games and lost 12. What percent of the games played did it win?

19. A radio originally priced at \$90 was sold for \$72. The sale price was what percent of the original price?

20. The state sales tax for an automobile was \$295. The price of the automobile was \$4538.46. Find the state sales-tax percent.

21. The amount of state sales tax for a refrigerator was \$37. The price of the refrigerator was \$822.22. Find the state sales-tax percent.

C **22.** Eighty percent of a company's annual income is from long-term contracts. Of this contract income, 22% is from international contracts. The gross income of the firm is \$1.3 billion per year. Find to the nearest \$100 000 the annual income from international contracts.

23. In a school, 60% of the students belong to the Outing Club. Eighty percent of the club members take part in less than 50% of the club activities. 240 members take part in less than 50% of the club activities. Find the number of students in the school.

MAGIC SQUARES

A magic square of order n is an n-by-n square arrangement of the natural numbers from 1 to n^2 so that the sum of the numbers in each row, column, and diagonal is the same. A 3-by-3 magic square is shown at the right.

The sum of all the numbers in any magic square is the sum of the first n^2 natural numbers. The sum may be found by the formula $S = \frac{n^2(n^2+1)}{2}$. The sum of the numbers in any row, column, or diagonal is $\frac{S}{n}$.

Therefore, $$\frac{S}{n} = \frac{n(n^2+1)}{2}.$$

8	1	6
3	5	7
4	9	2

		1	8	15
	5	7	14	
4	6	13		
10	12			3
11			2	9

		48	1			28
	47				27	29
46				26		
			25			
		24				4
21	23				3	
22			49	2		

What is the sum of the numbers in one row of a magic square of each order?

1. 3 **2.** 4 **3.** 5 **4.** 6 **5.** 7 **6.** 2

Copy and complete the

7. 5-by-5 magic square. **8.** 7-by-7 magic square.

5-3 PERCENT INCREASE AND DECREASE

A quantity is often increased or decreased by a certain part of itself. When such a change is expressed in terms of percent, it is called the *percent increase* or the *percent decrease*.

EXAMPLE 1 A jacket, regularly priced at \$32.50, is advertised for sale at "20% off". Find the sale price of the jacket.

Ⓜ SOLUTION The sale price equals \$32.50 less 20% of \$32.50.

Use s for the sale price of the jacket.

$$s = 32.50 - 0.20(32.50)$$

\$ = \$ − (dimensionless) · \$

$$s = 32.50 - 6.50$$

$$s = 26.00$$

20% OFF

CONCLUSION The sale price of the jacket is \$26.00

EXAMPLE 2 Last year 12 students signed up for the volunteer program. This year there is a 50% increase in that number. How many students signed up this year?

Ⓜ SOLUTION The number of students who signed up this year equals 12 increased by 50% of 12.

Use n for the number who signed up this year.

$$n = 12 + 0.50(12)$$

students = students + (dimensionless) · students

$$n = 12 + 6$$

$$n = 18$$

CONCLUSION 18 students signed up this year.

EXAMPLE 3 The Humane Society picked up 60 stray dogs this month. This is a decrease of 25% from the number picked up last month. How many stray dogs were picked up last month?

Ⓜ SOLUTION The number of stray dogs picked up last month decreased by 25% of that number equals 60.

Use n for the number picked up last month.
Use $0.25n$ for the amount of decrease.

(dimensionless) · dogs = dogs

$$n - 0.25n = 60$$

dogs − dogs = dogs

$$0.75n = 60$$

$$n = \frac{60}{0.75}$$

$$n = 80$$

CONCLUSION There were 80 stray dogs picked up last month.

EXAMPLE 4 The number of cars that are allowed to park in the lot will be increased from 24 to 32. What is the percent increase?

Ⓜ **SOLUTION** 24 increased by what percent of 24 gives 32?

Use r for the percent increase in decimal form.

cars + (dimensionless) · cars = cars

$$24 + r \cdot 24 = 32$$
$$r \cdot 24 = 8$$
$$r = \frac{8}{24}, \text{ or } \frac{1}{3}$$
$$r = 0.333\cdots$$

CONCLUSION The percent increase is $33\frac{1}{3}\%$.

Sometimes the percent decrease is called the *percent discount*.

EXAMPLE 5 The price of an automobile was reduced from \$7000 to \$6500. Find the percent discount.

Ⓜ **SOLUTION** \$7000 decreased by what percent of \$7000 gives \$6500?

Use r for the percent discount in decimal form.

\$ − (dimensionless) · \$ = \$

$$7000 - r \cdot 7000 = 6500$$
$$r \cdot 7000 = 500$$
$$r = \frac{500}{7000}$$
$$r \doteq 0.07$$

CONCLUSION The percent discount is about 7%.

CLASSROOM EXERCISES

Solve. Use an algebraic equation.

1. 14 is increased by 50%. Find the result.
2. A number decreased by 25% gives 45. Find the number.
3. By what percent must 18 be increased to give 27?
4. 36 decreased by what percent gives 27?
5. A set of garden tools is offered for sale at 20% off. The regular price is \$38. Find the sale price.
6. A stove was reduced in price from \$450 to \$400. Find the percent discount.
7. The monthly rent for an apartment was raised from \$300 a month to \$315 a month. Find the percent increase.
8. A store advertised tires at 20% off. Find the original price of a tire that has a sale price of \$52.

EXERCISES

A Solve. Use an algebraic equation.

1. 35 is decreased by 20%. Find the result.

2. 3.5 is decreased by 20%. Find the result.

3. 60 is increased by 125%. Find the result.

4. 4000 is increased by $5\frac{1}{2}$%. Find the result.

5. 12 decreased by what percent gives 6?

6. 16 increased by what percent gives 20?

7. By what percent must 2 be increased to give 5?

8. By what percent must 500 be increased to give 545?

9. What number increased by 25% gives 10?

10. What number increased by $9\frac{1}{2}$% gives 2190?

11. A state sales-tax is $5\frac{1}{2}$%. Find the amount of sales tax for an item priced at $1500.

12. A state sales-tax is $3\frac{1}{2}$%. Find the amount of sales tax for an item priced at $17.50.

13. The monthly rent for an apartment was increased from $260 per month to $273 per month. What percent increase is this?

14. The price of pocket-size calculators decreased from $500 to $5 over a 10-year period. What percent decrease is this?

15. The value of an automobile decreased from $7000 to $6650 in one year. Find the percent decrease. (Note: The annual percent decrease is called the *annual depreciation*.)

16. The market value of a house increased from $40 000 to $42 800 in one year. Find the percent increase. (Note: The annual percent increase is called the *annual appreciation*.)

A department store is offering a discount of "20% to 40% off" all items. Find the sale price for each item in Exercises 17-20.

	Item	Original Price	Percent Discount	Sale Price
17.	Washing Machine	$299	40%	?
18.	Stereo	$160	30%	?
19.	Curling Iron	$7.95	20%	?
20.	Camera	$25.40	25%	?

B **21.** The annual cost of basic insurance coverage for a teen-aged driver is $600. There is a 10% discount when a student is on the honor roll. Also, there is a 15% discount when a student has passed the driver education course. Find the annual cost of basic coverage for a student who meets both requirements.

C **22.** The value of a house increased from $75 000 to $120 000 in 8 years. Give the average annual appreciation rate as a percent.

23. The value of a boat decreased from $20 000 to $15 000 in 3 years. Give the average annual depreciation rate as a percent.

5-4 EARNING AND SPENDING

Related expressions having a single variable may be useful in situations that involve earning and spending.

EXAMPLE 1 A salesperson works for a salary plus commission. The weekly salary is \$150. The commission for each item sold is \$3. The total pay for one week was \$330. How many items were sold that week?

(M) SOLUTION Total pay equals salary plus commission.

Use n for the number of items sold.
$3n$ for the commission for the week in dollars.

$\frac{\$}{\text{item}} \cdot \text{items} = \$$

$\$ = \$ + \$$

$$330 = 150 + 3n$$
$$180 = 3n$$
$$60 = n$$

Many applications in mathematics involve rate in some form, and hence a rate equation. Such an equation has the form $\frac{A}{B} \cdot (\text{number of } B) = \text{number of } A$ such as $\frac{\text{km}}{\text{h}} \cdot \text{hours} = \text{kilometers}$, or $\frac{\$}{\text{item}} \cdot \text{items} = \text{dollars}$, or $\frac{\$}{\text{unit}} \cdot \text{units} = \text{dollars}$.

CONCLUSION There were 60 items sold.

CHECK Is \$330 equal to one week's salary plus the commission for 60 items?

$$330 \stackrel{?}{=} 150 + 3(60)$$
$$330 = 330 \checkmark$$

EXAMPLE 2 Karen, Lani, and Michael work together on an outdoor job. Karen works twice as many hours as Lani. Michael works twice as many hours as Karen. Their hourly pay rates are the same. How should the \$56 pay for the job be divided among Karen, Lani, and Michael?

(M) SOLUTION The sum of the number of dollars earned by each is 56.

Use L for the number of dollars earned by Lani.
$2L$ for the number of dollars earned by Karen.
$2(2L)$ for the number of dollars earned by Michael.

(dimensionless) · \$ = \$

(dimensionless) · \$ = \$

$\$ + \$ + \$ = \$$

$$L_\$ + K_\$ + M_\$ = 56$$
$$L + 2L + 4L = 56$$
$$7L = 56$$
$$L = 8$$

Also, $2L = 16$ and $2(2L) = 32$.

CONCLUSION Lani earns \$8, Karen \$16, and Michael \$32.

CHECK Is the sum of what Lani, Karen, and Michael receive equal to 56?

$$8 + 16 + 32 \stackrel{?}{=} 56$$
$$56 = 56 \checkmark$$

EXAMPLE 3 A city spent \$228 000 for new vans and pickup trucks. There were twice as many vans as trucks. The price for a truck was \$5000. The price for a van was \$7000. How many vans and pickup trucks did the city buy?

Ⓜ **SOLUTION** Cost of the trucks plus cost of the vans was \$228 000.

Use
- n for the number of new trucks. $\frac{\text{vans}}{\text{truck}} \cdot \text{trucks} = \text{vans}$
- $2n$ for the number of new vans.
- $5000n$ for the cost in dollars of the trucks. $\frac{\$}{\text{truck}} \cdot \text{trucks} = \$$
- $7000(2n)$ for the cost in dollars of the vans. $\frac{\$}{\text{van}} \cdot \text{vans} = \$$

$$\text{cost}_t + \text{cost}_v = 228\,000$$
$$5000n + 7000(2n) = 228\,000 \qquad \$ + \$ = \$$$
$$5000n + 14\,000n = 228\,000$$
$$19\,000n = 228\,000$$
$$n = \frac{228\,000}{19\,000}$$
$$n = 12 \qquad \text{Also, } 2n = 24.$$

CONCLUSION The city bought 12 pickup trucks and 24 vans.

CHECK The check is left for the student.

CLASSROOM EXERCISES

Solve.

1. A salesperson earns a salary of \$200 per week plus a commission of \$5 per item sold. One week, the salesperson earned \$350. How many items did the person sell that week?
2. A set of new stereo records is to include twice as many vocal records as instrumental records. The price of a vocal record is \$6. The price of an instrumental record is \$8. How many of each type can be bought for \$40?

EXERCISES

[A] Solve.

1. Three carpenters named Alpers, Betta, and Gamoff work together on a job. Alpers works twice as long as Betta, and Gamoff works half as long as Alpers. Each carpenter earns the same hourly rate. The total amount paid for the job is \$2000. How much does each carpenter receive?
2. On a job, Chris worked twice as many hours as Lee, and Lee worked twice as many hours as Kim. Each earned the same hourly rate. The total pay was \$2100. Find the amount each person earned.
3. A college student sells small household items on a salary-plus-commission plan. The basic salary is \$130 per week. The commission is 25 cents for each item sold. How many items must be sold in a week to give an income of \$200 for the week?
4. A night-school student sells small electrical appliances part time on a salary-plus-commission plan. The basic

salary is $60 per week. A commission of $5 is also earned for each item sold. How many items must be sold each week to give a weekly income of $100?

5. Two trucks carry different-sized payloads. One truck carries $3n$ metric tons valued at $3000 per ton. The other truck carries n metric tons valued at $8000 per ton. The total value of both payloads is $51 000. Find the number of metric tons each truck carries.

6. A homemaker is making new slipcovers for two chairs. One chair requires 1.5 times as much fabric as the other. The budget allows $200 for this project. Find the amount that can be spent for fabric for each chair.

B **7.** A family has budgeted $160 to replace the tires on the family car. Two regular tires and two mud/snow tires are needed. The price of the mud/snow tires is 1.1 times the price of regular tires. Find the maximum price that can be paid for a tire of each type.

8. The operator of a fast-food stand receives a weekly salary of $140. There is a commission of 5 cents for each fish sandwich sold and 8 cents for each hamburger sold. Twice as many fish sandwiches as hamburgers are sold at this stand. Find the number of each type of sandwich that must be sold each week to give the operator an income of $500 a week.

C **9.** The owner of a hairdressing salon needs to make a profit of $500 per week. There are profits of $1.50 for a hairwash-and-set, $3 for a haircut, and $5.50 for a permanent. For each 100 hairwash-and-sets, there are 25 haircuts and 15 permanents. Find the number of customers per week needed to give the desired profit.

10. A fuel retailer makes a profit of 25 cents per 100 liters on regular gasoline. The profit for no-lead gas is 30 cents per 100 liters and for premium is 40 cents per 100 liters. For every 100 liters of regular gas sold, 50 liters of no-lead and 40 liters of premium are sold. Find the number of one-hundred liters of each type of gas that must be sold to give a weekly profit of $500.

DOES 10% ALWAYS EQUAL 10%?

Sue worked at a store for $3.00 an hour. She agreed to accept a 10% increase in pay during December when sales were above average and a 10% decrease in pay during January when sales were not so good.

How much did Sue earn per hour

1. before December? **2.** during December? **3.** during January?

4. Explain.

Which of the following is correct?

5. 10 is 25% more than 8, so 8 is 75% of 10.

6. 8 is 80% of 10, so 10 is 20% more than 8.

5-5 DISTANCE, RATE, AND TIME

Two numbers may represent measurements of different quantities. A comparison of such numbers is a *rate*. In general, a rate may be spoken of in terms of the first measured amount *per* the second measured amount.

RATES

	Write	Read
Walk 7 kilometers in 5 hours	7 km/5 h	7 kilometers per 5 hours
Drive 80 kilometers in 1 hour	80 km/1 h or 80 km/h	80 kilometers per hour
Pump 100 liters in 60 seconds	100 L/60 s or 100 L/min	100 liters per 60 seconds or 100 liters per minute
Spread 600 grams on each square meter.	600 g/m²	600 grams per square meter

In the formula $d = rt$, or the formula $r = \frac{d}{t}$, r represents a rate. It compares the distance traveled with the time spent traveling that distance. The rate of an object also is called its *speed*.

Other rates: $\frac{\$}{\text{week}}, \frac{\$}{\text{year}}, \frac{\$}{\text{dozen}}$

fuel-consumption rate: $\frac{\text{liters}}{100 \text{ km}}$

production rates: $\frac{\text{units}}{\text{time}}$

unit price: $\frac{\$}{\text{kg}}$

EXAMPLE 1 A 747 and a DC-8 jet aircraft pass each other flying in opposite directions. The average speed for the 747 is 1030 km/h. For the DC-8, it is 960 km/h. Find the distance between the airplanes after 2.5 hours.

Ⓜ SOLUTION

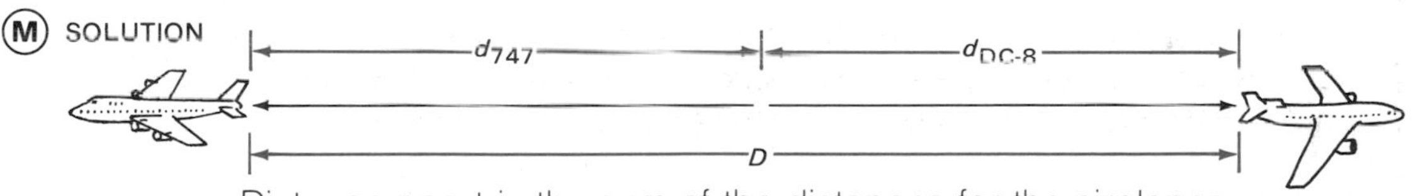

Distance apart is the sum of the distances for the airplanes.

Use D for the distance apart.

$$D = d_{747} + d_{DC-8}$$
$$D = r_{747}t_{747} + r_{DC-8}t_{DC-8}$$
$$D = (1030)(2.5) + (960)(2.5)$$
$$D = 2575 + 2400$$
$$D = 4975$$

$\text{km} = \frac{\text{km}}{\text{h}} \cdot \text{h} + \frac{\text{km}}{\text{h}} \cdot \text{h}$

CONCLUSION After 2.5 hours, the airplanes are 4975 kilometers apart.

EXAMPLE 2 Two joggers who are 9 kilometers apart begin to jog toward each other. The rate for jogger A is 10 km/h. The rate for jogger B is 12.5 km/h. In how many hours will they meet? How far will each have jogged?

Ⓜ SOLUTION

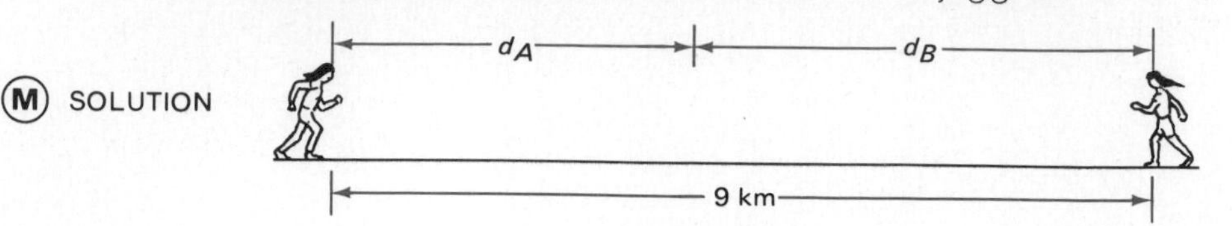

The sum of the distances is 9 km.

$\frac{\text{km}}{\text{h}} \cdot \text{h} = \text{km}$

Use
- t for the number of hours until the joggers meet.
- $10t$ for the number of kilometers jogged by A.
- $12.5t$ for the number of kilometers jogged by B.

$\text{km} + \text{km} = \text{km}$

$$d_A + d_B = 9$$
$$10t + 12.5t = 9$$
$$22.5t = 9$$
$$t = 0.4$$

Also, $10t = 4$ and $12.5t = 5$.

CONCLUSION The joggers will meet in 0.4 hours, or 24 minutes. One will have jogged 4 km, the other 5 km.

CHECK The sum of the distances jogged is 9 km. ✔

EXAMPLE 3 Two antique cars are driven from the same place to an automobile rally. The rate of one car is 1.5 times the rate of the other. In 4 hours the faster car is 80 km ahead of the slower car. Find the rate for each.

Ⓜ SOLUTION The difference of the distances is 80 km.

Use r for the rate of the slower car in kilometers per hour.

$\text{h} \cdot \frac{\text{km}}{\text{h}} = \text{km}$

(dimensionless) $\cdot \frac{\text{km}}{\text{h}} = \frac{\text{km}}{\text{h}}$, $\text{h} \cdot \frac{\text{km}}{\text{h}} = \text{km}$

	rate	· time =	distance
Slower car	r	4	$4r$
Faster car	$1.5r$	4	$4(1.5r)$

$\text{km} - \text{km} = \text{km}$

$$d_F - d_S = 80$$
$$4(1.5r) - 4r = 80$$
$$6r - 4r = 80$$
$$2r = 80$$
$$r = 40$$

Also, $1.5r = 60$.

CONCLUSION The cars are traveling 40 km/h and 60 km/h.

CHECK The check is left for the student.

An hourly wage is a *rate of payment* for work. The total wages (W) equals the product of the hourly rate (r) and the number of hours worked (t). We can show this with the formula $W = rt$.

EXAMPLE 4 A skilled and an unskilled worker work together on a job. The hourly rate of the skilled worker is 3 times the hourly rate of the unskilled worker. They work for 5 hours and are paid $65 for the job. Find the hourly wage rate for each worker.

Ⓜ SOLUTION The sum of the wages for the workers is $65.
Use r for the hourly rate of the unskilled worker.

Note the structural similarity to Example 3. See also, Exercise 4, p. 168.

	rate	· time	= wages
Unskilled	r	5	$5r$
Skilled	$3r$	5	$5(3r)$ or $15r$

$$\text{h} \cdot \frac{\$}{\text{h}} = \$$$

$$(\text{dimensionless}) \cdot \frac{\$}{\text{h}} = \frac{\$}{\text{h}}, \quad \text{h} \cdot \frac{\$}{\text{h}} = \$$$

$$W_{\text{unskilled}} + W_{\text{skilled}} = 65$$
$$5r + 15r = 65$$
$$20r = 65$$
$$r = 3.25$$
$$\text{Also, } 3r = 9.75.$$

$$\$ + \$ = \$$$

CONCLUSION The hourly wage rates are $3.25 per hour for the unskilled worker and $9.75 per hour for the skilled worker.

CHECK Is the sum of their wages equal to 65?

$$5(3.25) + 5(9.75) \stackrel{?}{=} 65$$
$$65 = 65 \quad ✓$$

CLASSROOM EXERCISES

Solve. Use an algebraic equation.

1. Two planes take off from the same airport at the same time and fly in opposite directions. Their rates are 800 km/h and 900 km/h. Find the elapsed flying time when they are 5100 km apart.

2. An experienced worker and an inexperienced worker together are paid $54 for 3 hours work. The rate for the experienced worker is 1.5 times the rate for the inexperienced worker. Find the hourly rate for each.

3. Yen Yen and Hau Yee are 2.5 km apart and walk toward each other at rates of 3.5 km/h and 4 km/h. After how long do they meet?

4. Two automobiles enter an expressway at the same time and travel in the same direction. Car A travels 88 km/h and car B travels 80 km/h. In how many hours will car A be 30 km ahead of car B?

EXERCISES

A Solve. Use an algebraic equation.

1. Two joggers start from different points and travel toward each other. The rate for one jogger is 5.6 km/h and the rate for the other is 6.0 km/h. The joggers meet in 1.5 hours. How far apart were their starting points?
2. A worker earns $5.60 per hour on one job and $6 per hour on another. Find the total amount earned by working 1.5 hours on each job.
3. Bernardo and Maki work together to paint a house. Bernardo is paid twice the rate Maki is paid. For 1.5 hours work, Bernardo earns $7.50 more than Maki. Find the hourly rate for each.
4. Two runners start from the same starting line and run in the same direction. The rate of one runner is twice the rate of the other. After 1.5 hours, the distance between the runners is 7.5 km. Find the rate for each runner.
5. Two cyclists start together and ride in the same direction. The rate of one cyclist is 24 km/h. The rate of the other cyclist is 20 km/h. In how many hours will they be 10 km apart?
6. Two trailer trucks depart from the same loading area at the same time and travel in opposite directions. The rate of one truck is twice the rate of the other. In 3 hours they are 360 km apart. Find the rate for each truck.
7. A private plane and a transport jet leave airports that are 2280 km apart. They fly toward each other (at different altitudes) at 190 km/h and 570 km/h. In how many hours will they pass each other?
8. Two runners start at the same time and proceed in opposite directions at the rates of 14 km/h and 16 km/h. In how many hours will they be 10 km apart?
9. Two freight trains start at the same time from two points 480 km apart and travel toward each other at the same rate. They meet in 6 hours. Find the rate of each.
10. The Santa-Cruz Skipper runs $4\frac{1}{2}$ hours at a certain rate and 3 hours at 40 km/h. The entire distance is 390 kilometers. Find the first rate.

B

11. The top speed of one racing car is 0.9 of the top speed of another. In a race, the faster car is in a position 10 km ahead of the other after one-half hour. Find the rate for each car.
12. A worker is paid time-and-a-half for overtime work. The wages paid for 40 regular hours and 12 overtime hours were $400.20. Find the rate for overtime pay.
13. At 11 A.M. Rosetta left Boston and traveled at a rate of 30 km/h. At 1 P.M. Brigette left to overtake her at a rate of 85 km/h. How long did it take Brigette to overtake Rosetta?

C

14. Runner 56 starts from the starting line and runs at a rate of 11 km/h. Runner 88 leaves the starting line 6 minutes later and runs at 16 km/h. In how many hours will Runner 88 overtake Runner 56?
15. The sediment in an ancient lake was laid down in two layers per year. The summer rate for depositing sediment was 1.1 times the winter rate. Over a period of 6.5 million years, a thickness of 200 meters of sedimentary rock was formed. Find the winter and summer rates for rock formation in millimeters per year.

OBJECTIVES: Solve equations containing parentheses. Use parentheses in algebraic representations.

5-6 PARENTHESES IN EQUATIONS

An expression containing parentheses may be simplified by first *clearing the expression of parentheses*. The Multiplication Properties of One and Negative One, and the Distributive Property are used to clear parentheses.

EXAMPLE 1 Simplify $4(a + b) - 3a$; $4(a - b) - 3a$; $-4(a + b) - 3a$, and $-4(a - b) - 3a$.

Ⓜ SOLUTION

$$\begin{aligned} &4(a + b) - 3a \\ &= 4a + 4b - 3a \\ &= a + 4b \end{aligned}$$

$$\begin{aligned} &4(a - b) - 3a \\ &= 4a - 4b - 3a \\ &= a - 4b \end{aligned}$$

$$\begin{aligned} &-4(a + b) - 3a \\ &= (-4)a + (-4)b - 3a \\ &= -4a - 4b - 3a \\ &= -7a - 4b \end{aligned}$$

$$\begin{aligned} &-4(a - b) - 3a \\ &= (-4)a - (-4)b - 3a \\ &= -4a + 4b - 3a \\ &= -7a + 4b \end{aligned}$$

EXAMPLE 2 Simplify $-(x + y)$ and $-(3x - 7y)$.

Ⓜ SOLUTION

$$\begin{aligned} -(x + y) &= -1(x + y) \\ &= (-1)x + (-1)y \\ &= -x + (-y) \\ &= -x - y \end{aligned}$$

$$\begin{aligned} -(3x - 7y) &= -1[3x + (-7y)] \\ &= (-1)3x + (-1)(-7y) \\ &= -3x + 7y \end{aligned}$$

EXAMPLE 3 Simplify $(y - 5) - (3y + 4)$.

Ⓜ SOLUTION

$$\begin{aligned} (y - 5) - (3y + 4) &= (y - 5) + [-(3y + 4)] \\ &= (y - 5) + (-3y - 4) \\ &= y - 5 - 3y - 4 \\ &= -2y - 9 \end{aligned}$$

EXAMPLE 4 Simplify $4a - 3(a - b)$.

Ⓜ SOLUTION

$$\begin{aligned} 4a - 3(a - b) &= 4a + [-3(a - b)] \\ &= 4a + (-3a + 3b) \\ &= 4a - 3a + 3b \\ &= a + 3b \end{aligned}$$

When solving an equation containing parentheses, it usually is a good idea to first clear parentheses.

EXAMPLE 5 Solve $(6x - 5) - (6 - x) = 3$.

Ⓜ SOLUTION

$$\begin{aligned} (6x - 5) - (6 - x) &= 3 \\ 6x - 5 - 6 + x &= 3 \\ 7x - 11 &= 3 \\ 7x &= 14 \\ x &= 2 \end{aligned}$$

CHECK

$$\begin{aligned} (6x - 5) - (6 - x) &= 3 \\ (6 \cdot 2 - 5) - (6 - 2) &\overset{?}{=} 3 \\ 3 &= 3 \checkmark \end{aligned}$$

EXAMPLE 6 Solve $3(x - 5) - 4(2x - 4) = -2(x - 11)$.

Ⓜ SOLUTION

$$\begin{aligned} 3(x - 5) - 4(2x - 4) &= -2(x - 11) \\ 3x - 15 - 8x + 16 &= -2x + 22 \\ -5x + 1 &= -2x + 22 \\ -5x + 2x &= 22 - 1 \\ -3x &= 21 \\ x &= -7 \end{aligned}$$

CHECK

$$\begin{aligned} 3(x - 5) - 4(2x - 4) &= -2(x - 11) \\ 3(-7 - 5) - 4[2(-7) - 4] &\overset{?}{=} -2(-7 - 11) \\ 3(-12) - 4(-18) &\overset{?}{=} -2(-18) \\ 36 &= 36 \checkmark \end{aligned}$$

Parentheses between parentheses are **nested parentheses**. To solve equations containing nested parentheses, clear the innermost parentheses first.

EXAMPLE 7 Solve $-(-3x - 3(-2 + x)) = 4(-3x + 3(2 - x))$.

Ⓜ SOLUTION

$$\begin{aligned} -(-3x - 3(-2 + x)) &= 4(-3x + 3(2 - x)) \\ -(-3x + 6 - 3x) &= 4(-3x + 6 - 3x) \\ -(-6x + 6) &= 4(-6x + 6) \\ 6x - 6 &= -24x + 24 \\ 6x + 24x &= 24 + 6 \\ 30x &= 30 \\ x &= 1 \end{aligned}$$

CHECK

$$\begin{aligned} -(-3x - 3(-2 + x)) &= 4(-3x + 3(2 - x)) \\ -(-3(1) - 3(-2 + 1)) &\overset{?}{=} 4(-3(1) + 3(2 - 1)) \\ -(-3 - 3(-1)) &\overset{?}{=} 4(-3 + 3(1)) \\ 0 &= 0 \checkmark \end{aligned}$$

CLASSROOM EXERCISES

Simplify.

1. $4(2p - 3) - 4$
2. $-3(2x - 1) - 4$
3. $-7(-x + 4) - 4$
4. $8 - 3(-3y + 1)$
5. $2(4x - 3) - 4(x - 5)$
6. $(a + 5) - (-6 + 3a)$

Solve.

7. $3x - (4 - 2x) + 5 = 6$
8. $(4m - 3) - 5(m + 1) = (5m + 2)(3) - 10$
9. $2(x - 1) - (3x + 4) = (x + 6) - (x - 4)$
10. $4 - (2 - (x - 1)) = 8$

EXERCISES

A Simplify.

1. $3(m - n) - 4(n - m)$
2. $c(c - 5) - 5(c^2 + 2c)$
3. $8\left(\frac{1}{2}a - \frac{1}{4}b\right) + 18\left(-\frac{1}{2}a + \frac{1}{3}b\right)$
4. $-0.4(25x + 10y) + 6(-0.2x - y)$

Solve.

5. $3(x + 6) = 21$
6. $2(x + 4) = 32$
7. $6x - (3x - 4) = 14$
8. $2x - (13 - 2x) = 61$
9. $5(x - 1) = 6(x - 3)$
10. $4(m - 5) = 5(m - 7)$
11. $4(x - 3) - 6(x + 1) = 0$
12. $5(x + 4) - 4(x + 3) = 0$
13. $6(x - 2) - 2(x - 5) - 2(x + 6) = 0$
14. $3(2x - 3(x + 1)) = 0$
15. $3(5 - n) - 4(2n - 7) = -11 - (10 + 3n)$
16. $20h - (5h + 9) - (7 - 9h) = (12h - 5)$

B Simplify.

17. $ab(a^2 - ab + b^2) - 3a(a^2b + ab^2)$
18. $m^2(m - 1) - m(m^2 + 2m - 4)$

Solve.

19. $3(4y + 8) - 2.4y = 2(0.8y + 4)$
20. $2x - 5(0.8x - 1.8) + 5(x + 4) = 41$
21. $3x + 0.2(x - 30) = x - 0.1(8x - 30)$
22. $3x + \frac{1}{5}(x - 30) = x - \frac{1}{10}(8x - 30)$

C Simplify.

23. $3x - (2x - 2(x - (x - 1)) + 2)$
24. $12x - (3x + (4x - (3x + 2x)))$

Solve.

25. $\frac{4}{5}(12 - x) = \frac{2}{5}x$
26. $0.4(x - 0.3(3 - x)) = 0.3(1.2 - 2(x + 0.4))$
27. $\frac{2}{5}(12 - x) = \frac{4}{5}x$
28. $x + 0.2(x - 8 - 2(8 - 0.3(5 - x) - x)) = 0$

5-7 ALGEBRAIC REPRESENTATION USING PARENTHESES

Unless an algebraic expression is a monomial, it must be enclosed by parentheses when used with another algebraic expression to show subtraction, multiplication, or division.

To subtract $x + 4$ from y	write $y - (x + 4)$	not $y - x + 4$
To multiply $x + 4$ by y	write $y(x + 4)$	not $yx + 4$
To divide y by $x + 4$	write $y \div (x + 4)$	not $y \div x + 4$

EXAMPLE 1 Billy is 1 year older than Yvonne. Represent their ages in months.

years + years = years

$\frac{\text{months}}{\text{year}} \cdot \text{years} = \text{months}$

Ⓜ SOLUTION Use
- y for Yvonne's age in years.
- $y + 1$ for Billy's age in years.
- $12y$ for Yvonne's age in months.
- $12(y + 1)$ for Billy's age in months.

EXAMPLE 2 From home, the school is 3 kilometers closer than the park. Represent each distance in meters.

km − km = km

$\frac{\text{m}}{\text{km}} \cdot \text{km} = \text{m}$

Ⓜ SOLUTION Use
- p for the distance to the park in kilometers.
- $p - 3$ for the distance to the school in kilometers.
- $1000p$ for the distance to the park in meters.
- $1000(p - 3)$ for the distance to the school in meters.

EXAMPLE 3 Today, I shall keep track of how many hours I am awake. Represent the number of minutes I am asleep today.

h − h = h

$\frac{\text{min}}{\text{h}} \cdot \text{h} = \text{min}$

Ⓜ SOLUTION Use
- x for the number of hours I am awake today.
- $24 - x$ for the number of hours I am asleep.
- $60(24 - x)$ for the number of minutes I am asleep.

EXAMPLE 4 Ty has 1 more than 3 times the number of nickels that Jo has. Represent the number of nickels and the value of the nickels that each has.

Ⓜ **SOLUTION** Use

n	for the number of nickels Jo has.
$3n + 1$	for the number of nickels Ty has.
$5n$	for the value, in cents, of Jo's nickels.
$5(3n + 1)$	for the value, in cents, of Ty's nickels.

$\frac{¢}{\text{nickel}} \cdot \text{nickels} = ¢$

EXAMPLE 5 On Monday the vending machine collected 3 fewer dimes than half the number it collected on Sunday. Represent the number of dimes it collected on Sunday. Represent the value in dollars of the dimes it collected on Monday.

Ⓜ **SOLUTION** Use

d	for the number of dimes collected Sunday.
$\frac{1}{2}d - 3$	for the number of dimes collected Monday.
$0.10\left(\frac{1}{2}d - 3\right)$	for the value in dollars of the dimes collected Monday.

$\frac{\$}{\text{dime}} \cdot \text{dimes} = \$$

EXAMPLE 6 This week a truck made 2 fewer deliveries than triple the number it made last week. On each delivery its load amounted to 5 metric tons. Represent the number of deliveries it made last week. Represent the number of metric tons it delivered this week.

Ⓜ **SOLUTION** Use

n	for the number of deliveries last week.
$3n - 2$	for the number of deliveries this week.
$5(3n - 2)$	for the number of metric tons delivered this week.

$\frac{t}{\text{delivery}} \cdot \text{deliveries} = t$

EXAMPLE 7 A long-distance telephone rate is 17 cents for the first minute plus 12 cents for each additional minute. Represent the cost of a long-distance call at this rate.

Ⓜ **SOLUTION** Use

n	for the number of minutes talked.
$n - 1$	for the number of minutes talked at the rate of 12¢/min.
$17 + 12(n - 1)$	for the cost of the telephone call in cents.

$\text{min} - \text{min} = \text{min}$

$¢ + \frac{¢}{\text{min}} \cdot \text{min} = ¢$

CLASSROOM EXERCISES

Represent each number by an algebraic expression.

1. the value in cents of $n - 1$ nickels
2. the value in dollars of $2n + 1$ dimes
3. the number of minutes in $4n - 2$ hours
4. the number of millimeters in $3n - 1$ centimeters
5. Represent the cost in dollars for a taxicab ride of $5n$ kilometers. The rate is \$1.75 for the first kilometer and 35 cents for each additional kilometer.
6. Represent the cost in dollars for $500n$ kW · h of electricity at a basic service charge of \$4.75, 6¢/kW · h for the first 200 kW · h, and 5¢/kW · h for each additional kilowatt hour.
7. Represent the cost in dollars for $10n$ cubic meters of household gas. The rate is 32¢/m³ for the first 1.5 cubic meters, and 28¢/m³ thereafter. There is a basic service charge of \$2.75.

EXERCISES

Represent each number by an algebraic expression.

A

1. the number of months in $n - 1$ years
2. the number of minutes in $24 - t$ hours
3. the total pay in dollars for $n - 3$ hours of work at the rate of \$3.50/h
4. the total pay in dollars for $2w + 1$ weeks at the rate of \$140/week
5. the distance traveled in kilometers at the rate 35 km/h for $t + 1$ hours
6. the distance traveled in kilometers at the rate $k + 1$ km/h for 3 hours
7. the rate for traveling a distance of $2.5k - 1$ km in 4 hours
8. the time for traveling a distance of $1.5k + 1$ km at the rate of 5 km/h
9. the number of metric tons hauled at the rate of 5 metric tons per trip for $10 - n$ trips
10. the number of metric tons hauled at the rate of $t - 1$ metric tons per trip for 28 trips
11. the cost in dollars for m kW · h of electricity at 6¢/kW · h for the first 200 kW · h and 5¢/kW · h thereafter
12. the cost in dollars for e kW · h of electricity at 9¢/kW · h for the first 100 kW · h and 7¢/kW · h thereafter
13. the cost in dollars for an operator-assisted telephone call that lasts $2n$ minutes at the rate of \$2.25 for the first 3 minutes and 38 cents per minute thereafter
14. the cost in dollars for an operator-assisted telephone call that lasts $3n$ minutes at the rate of \$2.15 for the first 3 minutes and 36 cents per minute thereafter
15. the cost in dollars for $2000n$ printed business cards at \$25 for the first 1000 cards and 1 cent per card thereafter

B

16. the area of a rectangle having length 5 and width $l - 3$
17. the perimeter of a square having side length $s - 5$
18. the perimeter of a rectangle having length $w + 4$ and width $w - 3$
19. the total value of 100 grams of gold at $26 + n$ dollars per gram and 80 grams of silver at $2 + m$ dollars per gram
20. the total value of 500 grams of gold at $26 - n$ dollars per gram and 750 grams of silver at $1.50 + m$ dollars per gram

21. the total value of 8% of d dollars and 7% of $1000 - d$ dollars

22. the total value of $9\frac{1}{2}$% of $d + 1$ dollars and $10\frac{1}{2}$% of $5000 - d$ dollars

C **23.** $2r$% of $800 - d$ dollars

24. $(r + 1)$% of $3d$ dollars

25. The pressure in water increases at the rate of 101 kPa per 10 meters of depth. Represent the water pressure at the depth $2n - 3$ meters.

26. Represent the sum $x + x + x + \cdots$ when there are $n + 1$ addends.

CHECKING YOUR UNDERSTANDING

WORDS

clearing parentheses	percent decrease	percent increase
percent	percent discount	rate

CONCEPTS

- Replacing a percent by another form, usually a decimal form, is necessary for computation. [5-2]
- An equation generally is easier to solve if first it is cleared of parentheses. [5-6]

PROCESSES

- Represent one or more numbers with algebraic symbols and expressions involving one variable. Use parentheses when necessary. [5-1, 5-7]

  1. Bobbi works 5 days a week and earns $5.75 an hour. Represent the number of hours Bobbi works in a day. Represent the amount she earns in a week.

  2. Andy had 3 fewer nickels than he had dimes. Represent the difference in the values of the two types of coins.

- Solve problems involving percent or rate. [5-2 to 5-5]

  3. 150 is 32% of what number?

  4. Abby earns $4 per hour. Cass earns $7 per hour. On one job Cass worked twice as long as Abby. Together they earned $27. How much did each earn?

  5. Two airplanes leave the same city and fly in opposite directions. One is traveling 700 kilometers per hour and the other 800 kilometers per hour. How long will it be before they are 600 kilometers apart?

- Solve an equation containing parentheses. [5-6]

  6. $3x - (x + 4) = 2$

  7. $5x + 2(4x - 5) = 42$

OBJECTIVE: Use equations to solve problems involving numbers, coins, age, and geometric relationships.

5-8 NUMBER PROBLEMS

A problem about numbers provides practice in writing algebraic expressions. Then, when a word sentence in the problem suggests an equation, the expressions are used to replace the word sentence by the equation. Solving the equation is the next step in solving the problem. Each solution of the equation suggests a conclusion for the problem, but each should be checked to see that it agrees with the problem situation.

EXAMPLE 1 The product of 5 and a number increased by 3 is 32. Find the number.

(M) SOLUTION Use $\left[\begin{array}{ll} n & \text{for the number.} \\ n+3 & \text{for the number increased by 3.} \end{array}\right.$

$$\begin{aligned} 5(n+3) &= 32 \\ 5n + 15 &= 32 \\ 5n &= 17 \\ n &= \tfrac{17}{5}, \text{ or } 3\tfrac{2}{5} \end{aligned}$$

CONCLUSION The number is $3\frac{2}{5}$.

CHECK Is 5 times the sum of $3\frac{2}{5}$ and 3 equal to 32?

$$\begin{aligned} 5\left(3\tfrac{2}{5} + 3\right) &\stackrel{?}{=} 32 \\ 32 &= 32 \ \checkmark \end{aligned}$$

EXAMPLE 2 One number is 8 less than another. When 3 times the smaller is subtracted from 4 times the larger, the difference is 47. Find each number.

(M) SOLUTION 1 Use $\left[\begin{array}{ll} n & \text{for the larger number.} \\ n-8 & \text{for the smaller number.} \end{array}\right.$

$$\begin{aligned} 4n - 3(n-8) &= 47 \\ 4n - 3n + 24 &= 47 \\ n + 24 &= 47 \\ n &= 23 \end{aligned}$$

Also, $n - 8 = 15$.

Ⓜ SOLUTION 2 Use $\left[\begin{array}{l} n \text{ for the smaller number.} \\ n+8 \text{ for the larger number.} \end{array}\right.$

$$4(n+8) - 3n = 47$$
$$4n + 32 - 3n = 47$$
$$n = 15$$
$$\text{Also, } n + 8 = 23.$$

CONCLUSION The smaller number is 15. The larger number is 23.

CHECK The check is left for the student.

CLASSROOM EXERCISES

Solve.

1. A number is decreased by 6. The result is multiplied by 5. This result is 2 more than the number. Find the number.
2. One number is 4 larger than another. When twice the larger is added to the smaller, the sum is 62. What are the numbers?
3. One number is six times another. The sum of the two numbers is 98. Find the numbers.
4. The difference of two numbers is 14. When twice the larger is subtracted from 4 times the smaller, the difference is 4. Find each number.
5. The difference of two numbers is 9. Their sum is 15. Find each number.
6. One number is 6 less than another. When 4 times the larger is subtracted from 12 times the smaller, the remainder is 16. Find each number.
7. The sum of two numbers is 47. Twice the larger increased by 3 times the smaller gives the sum 106. Find each number.

EXERCISES

A Solve.

1. When 19 is subtracted from three times a number, the remainder is 110. Find the number.
2. One number is twice another number. When the larger is diminished by 10, the result is 2 greater than the smaller. Find the numbers.
3. One number is 4 less than another. The sum of the numbers is 320. Find the numbers.
4. One number is 10 more than another. The sum of the numbers is 126. Find each number.

B

9. One number is 32 larger than another. Their sum is 800. Find each number.
10. The sum of two numbers is 62. The larger number increased by 18 equals the smaller number increased by 32. Find the numbers.
11. Three numbers have the sum 119. The second number is 8 greater than the first, and the third is 3 greater than the second number. Find the three numbers.

C

12. Find 3 consecutive even integers whose sum is 26 more than 4 times the smallest number.
13. Two numbers are in the ratio 2 to 3. The larger number is represented by $6x + 3$. Represent the smaller number.

5-9 COIN PROBLEMS

In solving problems that involve money, we must keep in mind two ideas. One idea is the *number* of coins of a given type, and the other is the *value* of those coins. Also, we may know certain facts about the *total number* of all coins or their *total value*.

EXAMPLE 1 A parking meter contains \$1.15 in nickels and dimes. There are 2 more nickels than dimes. Find the number of coins of each type.

Ⓜ SOLUTION The sum of the values of the coins is \$1.15, or 115¢. Use d for the number of dimes.

$\frac{¢}{\text{dime}} \cdot \text{dimes} = ¢$

coins + coins = coins, $\frac{¢}{\text{nickel}} \cdot \text{nickels} = ¢$

	Number	Value in Cents
Dimes	d	$10d$
Nickels	$d + 2$	$5(d + 2)$

$¢ + ¢ = ¢$

$$\begin{aligned} \text{value}_D + \text{value}_N &= 115 \\ 10d + 5(d + 2) &= 115 \\ 10d + 5d + 10 &= 115 \\ 15d &= 105 \\ d &= 7 \qquad \text{Also, } d + 2 = 9. \end{aligned}$$

CONCLUSION There are 7 dimes and 9 nickels in the parking meter.

CHECK Do 7 dimes and 9 nickels have a value of \$1.15?

$$\begin{aligned} 10(7) + 5(9) &\stackrel{?}{=} 115 \\ 115 &= 115 \ \checkmark \end{aligned}$$

EXAMPLE 2 A vending machine contains \$102 in nickels, dimes, and quarters. There are 50 more quarters than dimes and 10 more dimes than nickels. Find the number of coins of each type.

Ⓜ SOLUTION The sum of the values of the coins is \$102, or 10 200¢. Use n for the number of nickels.

Working in dollars also is acceptable.

$\frac{¢}{\text{nickel}} \cdot \text{nickels} = ¢$

coins + coins = coins, $\frac{¢}{\text{dime}} \cdot \text{dimes} = ¢$

coins + coins = coins, $\frac{¢}{\text{quarter}} \cdot \text{quarters} = ¢$

	Number	Value in Cents
Nickels	n	$5n$
Dimes	$n + 10$	$10(n + 10)$
Quarters	$(n + 10) + 50$	$25(n + 60)$

$$\begin{aligned} \text{value}_N + \text{value}_D + \text{value}_Q &= 10\,200 \\ 5n + 10(n + 10) + 25(n + 60) &= 10\,200 \\ 5n + 10n + 100 + 25n + 1500 &= 10\,200 \\ 40n + 1600 &= 10\,200 \\ 40n &= 8600 \\ n &= 215 \end{aligned}$$

¢ + ¢ + ¢ = ¢

Also, $n + 10 = 225$, and $n + 60 = 275$.

CONCLUSION There are 215 nickels, 225 dimes, and 275 quarters.

CHECK Are 215 nickels, 225 dimes, and 275 quarters worth $102?

$$5(215) + 10(225) + 25(275) \stackrel{?}{=} 10\,200$$
$$10\,200 = 10\,200 \checkmark$$

EXAMPLE 3 A coin-sorting machine contains 50 coins in nickels and dimes. The value of all the coins is $4.55. Find the number of coins of each type in the machine.

(M) SOLUTION The sum of the values of the coins is $4.55. Use d for the number of dimes.

Working in cents also is acceptable.

	Number	Value in Dollars
Dimes	d	$0.10d$
Nickels	$50 - d$	$0.05(50 - d)$

coins − coins = coins, $\frac{\$}{\text{dime}} \cdot \text{dimes} = \$$, $\frac{\$}{\text{nickel}} \cdot \text{nickels} = \$$

$$\begin{aligned} \text{value}_D + \text{value}_N &= 4.55 \\ 0.10d + 0.05(50 - d) &= 4.55 \\ 0.10d + 2.50 - 0.05d &= 4.55 \\ 0.05d &= 2.05 \\ d &= 41 \end{aligned}$$

$ + $ = $

Also, $50 - d = 9$.

CONCLUSION There are 41 dimes and 9 nickels in the machine.

CHECK The check is left for the student.

CLASSROOM EXERCISES

Solve.

1. The nickels and dimes in my bank are worth $1.80. I have six more nickels than dimes. How many of each coin do I have?

2. There are 15 nickels and dimes on a table. The value of the coins is 90 cents. Find the number of each type of coin.

3. A vending machine contains quarters, dimes, and nickels worth $56.80. There are 10 more quarters than dimes. The number of dimes is 2 less than 3 times the number of nickels. Find the number of each type of coin.

EXERCISES

A Solve.

1. A boy has 3 more dimes than quarters. The total value of the coins is \$1.70. Find the number of each type of coin.
2. A girl has 4 more quarters than dimes. The total value of the coins is \$2.05. Find the number of each type of coin.
3. A parking meter contains nickels and dimes. There is one more dime than twice the number of nickels. The total value of the coins is \$1.60. Find the number of coins of each type.
4. A coin-operated washing machine contains nickels and quarters. There is one less nickel than three times the number of quarters. The total value of the coins is \$19.95. Find the number of coins of each type.
5. A coin-sorting machine contains half dollars, dimes, and nickels worth \$3.60. There are 3 times as many nickels as half dollars and 2 more nickels than dimes. How many of each type of coin are in the machine?
6. A coin-sorting machine contains quarters, dimes, and nickels worth \$12.60. There are 3 more nickels than dimes. The number of quarters is 3 more than twice the number of dimes. Find the number of each type of coin in the machine.
7. 21 nickels and dimes are worth \$1.65. Find the number of each type of coin.
8. 160 nickels and dimes are worth \$14.30. Find the number of each type of coin.

B

9. A collection of money worth \$10.70 consists of nickels, dimes, and quarters. There are 10 more quarters than nickels. The number of dimes is 2 less than 3 times the number of nickels. Find the number of coins of each kind.
10. Jack has 4 more dimes than nickels. After spending 2 nickels and 3 dimes he has coins worth 90 cents left. How many of each type of coin does he have left?
11. Jill has 4 more nickels than dimes. After spending 3 nickels and 2 dimes she has coins worth 15 cents left. How many of each type of coin does she have left?

C

12. Among her 30 coins, Lucia has an equal number of quarters and nickels. She also has some dimes. By changing the quarters for dimes, and the dimes and nickels for quarters, she would have 31 coins. How many coins of each type does Lucia have?

0.6666667

IMPROVISING INVERSES

1. If the Reciprocal key [1/x] is broken on your calculator, how might you still enter the reciprocal of 1.5?
2. If the Change Sign key [+/−] is broken on your calculator, how might you still enter −1.5?

5-10 AGE PROBLEMS

Problems that involve age give you practice in thinking about time relationships in the past, present, and future.

EXAMPLE 1 A mother is 9 times as old as her son. In 3 years she will be only 5 times as old as her son will be. Find the present age of each.

(M) SOLUTION The age of the mother in 3 years will equal 5 times the age of the son in 3 years.
Use s for the present age in years of the son.

Note that one variable is chosen and all numbers are given it terms of it.

	Age Now	Age in 3 Years
Son	s	$s + 3$
Mother	$9s$	$9s + 3$

years + years = years

(dimensionless) · years + years = years

$$9s + 3 = 5(s + 3)$$
$$9s + 3 = 5s + 15$$
$$4s = 12$$
$$s = 3. \quad \text{Also, } 9s = 27.$$

CONCLUSION The son is 3 years old at present. The mother is 27.

CHECK In 3 years will the mother's age be 5 times her son's?

$$27 + 3 \stackrel{?}{=} 5(3 + 3)$$
$$30 = 30 \checkmark$$

EXAMPLE 2 Portia is 17 years old. Her father is 42. In how many years will her father be twice as old as Portia will be?

(M) SOLUTION Her father's age in a certain number of years will be twice Portia's age.
Use t for the number of years until the above occurs.

	Age Now	Age in t Years
Portia	17	$17 + t$
Father	42	$42 + t$

years + years = years

years + years = years

$$42 + t = 2(17 + t)$$
$$42 + t = 34 + 2t$$
$$8 - t$$

CONCLUSION In 8 years Portia's father will be twice as old as Portia.

CHECK The check is left for the student.

CLASSROOM EXERCISES

Solve.

1. Sono is 8 years older than Fumio. In 3 years, twice Sono's age will equal 3 times Fumio's age. Find the present age for each.
2. The sum of the ages of Ivette and Hector is 50 years. Ivette's age 8 years from now will equal 2 times Hector's age then. Find the present age for each.

EXERCISES

A Solve.

1. Roberta now is 3 times as old as Ricky. Five years from now she will be twice as old as Ricky is then. Find both ages.
2. Sofia is 5 times as old as her cousin. Four years from now she will be 3 times as old as her cousin. Find both ages.
3. Doris is three years older than Jennifer. The sum of their ages is 29. Find their ages.
4. Janet is twice as old as Joanne. The sum of their ages is 108. What are their ages?
5. Frank is 4 times as old as Carla. In 10 years he will be twice as old as Carla will be. How old is each?
6. Vicente is 3 times as old as Consuela. In 10 years he will be twice as old as Consuela will be. Find the present age for each.
7. Otto is 10 years older than Yusef. In 8 years, twice Otto's age will equal 3 times Yusef's age. How old is each at present?
8. Walter is 8 years older than Ray. In 6 years 5 times Walter's age will equal 9 times Ray's age. How old is each at present?
9. Stefan is 14 years old. His mother is 38. How many years ago was the mother exactly 5 times as old as Stefan?
10. Teri is 12 years old. Her mother is 40. How many years ago was the mother exactly 5 times as old as Teri?

B

11. A man was 30 years old when his son was born. The father's age is 6 years greater than 3 times the son's age. How old is each at present?
12. A woman was 25 years old when her daughter was born. The mother's present age is 10 years more than 4 times her daughter's present age. Find the present age of each.
13. Sol is 20 years older than Troy. Five years from now, Troy will be $\frac{3}{5}$ as old as Sol. How old is each now?
14. Estella is $\frac{1}{3}$ as old as her father and two years younger than her brother. The sum of the ages of the three is 67 years. Find the age of each.
15. Elsie said to the class, "The sum of Herman's age and my age is 38 years. Four times my age 10 years ago is 2 greater than Herman's age 5 years ago." How old is each?

C

16. Professor Riddel told the class "The sum of my age and the age of this book is 139 years. Four times my age 10 years ago was 51 years greater than the age of the book then." How old is Professor Riddel and how old is the book?

5-11 GEOMETRY PROBLEMS

Geometric relationships enable us to use a single variable when we represent the measures of different parts of some geometric figures.

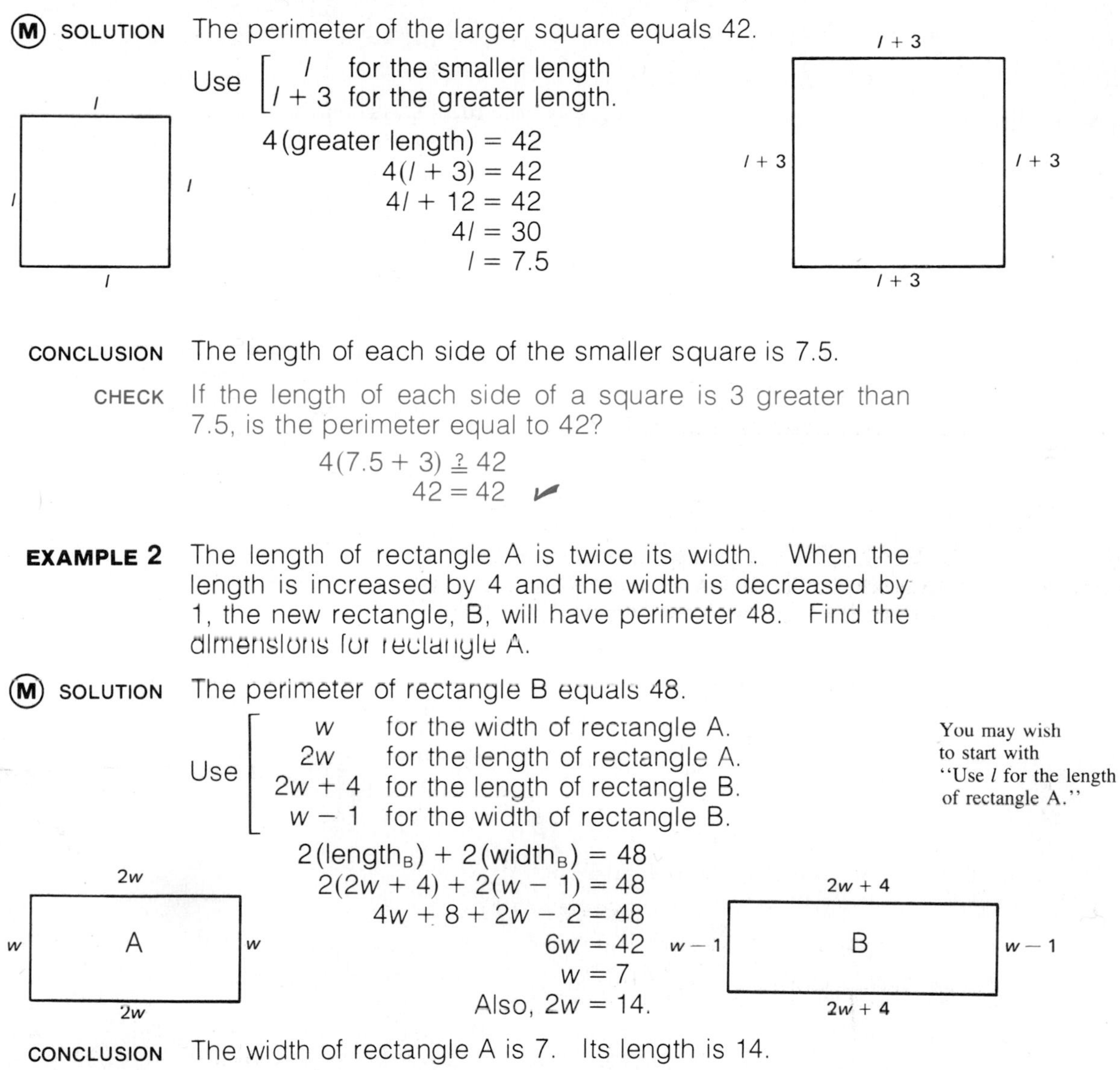

EXAMPLE 1 When the lengths of the sides of a square are increased by 3, the perimeter of the larger square will be 42. Find the length of each side of the smaller square.

Ⓜ **SOLUTION** The perimeter of the larger square equals 42.

Use $\left[\begin{array}{ll} l & \text{for the smaller length} \\ l+3 & \text{for the greater length.} \end{array}\right.$

$$\begin{aligned} 4(\text{greater length}) &= 42 \\ 4(l+3) &= 42 \\ 4l + 12 &= 42 \\ 4l &= 30 \\ l &= 7.5 \end{aligned}$$

CONCLUSION The length of each side of the smaller square is 7.5.

CHECK If the length of each side of a square is 3 greater than 7.5, is the perimeter equal to 42?

$$\begin{aligned} 4(7.5+3) &\stackrel{?}{=} 42 \\ 42 &= 42 \ \checkmark \end{aligned}$$

EXAMPLE 2 The length of rectangle A is twice its width. When the length is increased by 4 and the width is decreased by 1, the new rectangle, B, will have perimeter 48. Find the dimensions for rectangle A.

Ⓜ **SOLUTION** The perimeter of rectangle B equals 48.

Use $\left[\begin{array}{ll} w & \text{for the width of rectangle A.} \\ 2w & \text{for the length of rectangle A.} \\ 2w+4 & \text{for the length of rectangle B.} \\ w-1 & \text{for the width of rectangle B.} \end{array}\right.$

You may wish to start with "Use l for the length of rectangle A."

$$\begin{aligned} 2(\text{length}_B) + 2(\text{width}_B) &= 48 \\ 2(2w+4) + 2(w-1) &= 48 \\ 4w + 8 + 2w - 2 &= 48 \\ 6w &= 42 \\ w &= 7 \\ \text{Also, } 2w &= 14. \end{aligned}$$

CONCLUSION The width of rectangle A is 7. Its length is 14.

CHECK The check is left for the student.

EXAMPLE 3 The length of a rectangle is 3 larger than its width. The perimeter is 5 times the width. Find the length and width of the rectangle.

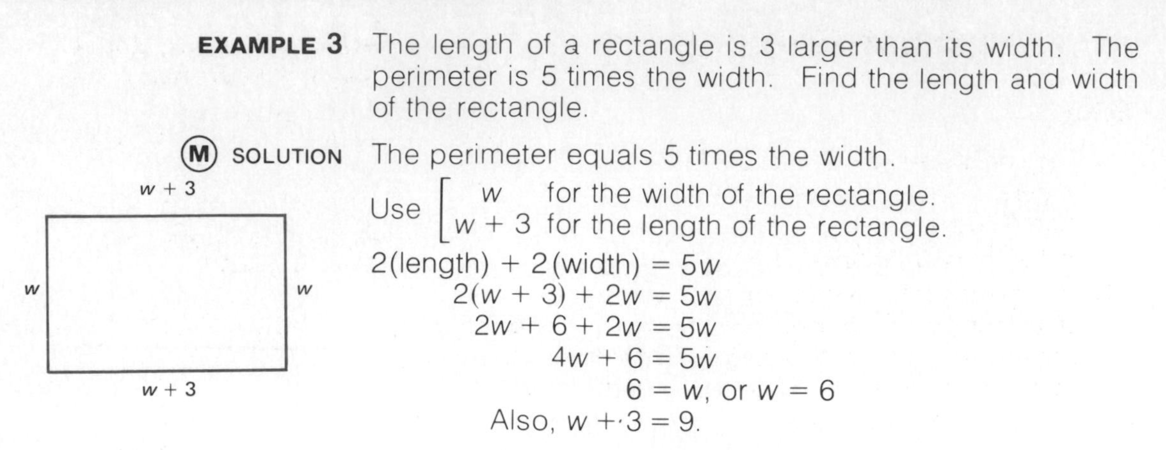

Ⓜ **SOLUTION** The perimeter equals 5 times the width.

Use $\left[\begin{array}{ll} w & \text{for the width of the rectangle.} \\ w+3 & \text{for the length of the rectangle.} \end{array}\right.$

$$\begin{aligned} 2(\text{length}) + 2(\text{width}) &= 5w \\ 2(w+3) + 2w &= 5w \\ 2w + 6 + 2w &= 5w \\ 4w + 6 &= 5w \\ 6 &= w, \text{ or } w = 6 \end{aligned}$$

Also, $w + 3 = 9$.

CONCLUSION The length of the rectangle is 9. The width is 6.

CHECK Is the perimeter 5 times the width?

$$2 \cdot 9 + 2 \cdot 6 \stackrel{?}{=} 5 \cdot 6$$
$$30 = 30 \ \checkmark$$

For the following example, we use the fact that the sum of the degree measures of the angles of a triangle is 180.

EXAMPLE 4 The degree measure of one angle of a triangle is 12 larger than that of another. The degree measure of the third angle is 48 larger than twice that of the smallest angle. Find the degree measure of each angle of the triangle.

Ⓜ **SOLUTION** The sum of the degree measures of the angles of a triangle is 180.

degrees + degrees = degrees {

Use $\left[\begin{array}{ll} m & \text{for the measure of the smallest angle.} \\ m+12 & \text{for the measure of another angle.} \\ 2m+48 & \text{for the measure of the third angle.} \end{array}\right.$

degrees + degrees + degrees = degrees

$$\begin{aligned} m + (m+12) + (2m+48) &= 180 \\ m + m + 12 + 2m + 48 &= 180 \\ 4m + 60 &= 180 \\ 4m &= 120 \\ m &= 30 \end{aligned}$$

Also, $m + 12 = 42$, and $2m + 48 = 108$.

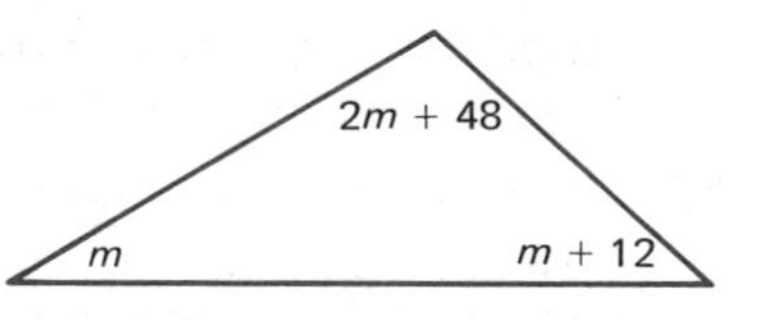

CONCLUSION The measures of the angles of the triangle are 30°, 42°, and 108°.

CHECK The sum of 30, 42, and 108 is 180. ✓

CLASSROOM EXERCISES

Solve.

1. The perimeter of a rectangle is 70 meters. The length is 7 meters less than twice the width. Find the dimensions of the rectangle.
2. The measure in degrees of one angle of a triangle is 20 less than another. The measure of the third angle is three times the sum of the other two. Find the measure of each angle.

EXERCISES

A Solve.

1. The perimeter of a triangle is 25 cm. The lengths of the sides of the triangle are x, $x + 2$, and $x + 2$. Find the length of each side.
2. The perimeter of a triangle is 37 cm. The lengths of the sides of the triangle are x, $2x + 1$, and $2x + 1$. Find the length of each side.
3. The perimeter of a rectangle is 102 cm. The width is w and the length is $w + 3$. Find the dimensions of the rectangle.
4. The perimeter of a rectangle is 252 cm. The length is l and the width is $l - 2$. Find the dimensions of the rectangle.
5. The perimeter of a rectangle is 147 meters. The length is 15 meters less than 5 times the width. Find the dimensions of the rectangle.
6. The perimeter of a rectangle is 367 meters. The length is 31 meters less than 5 times the width. Find the dimensions of the rectangle.
7. The perimeter of a pentagon, Figure 1, is 38.3 cm. The lengths of the sides are x, $x - 2$, $x - 2$, $x + 1$, and $x + 1$. Find the length of each side.

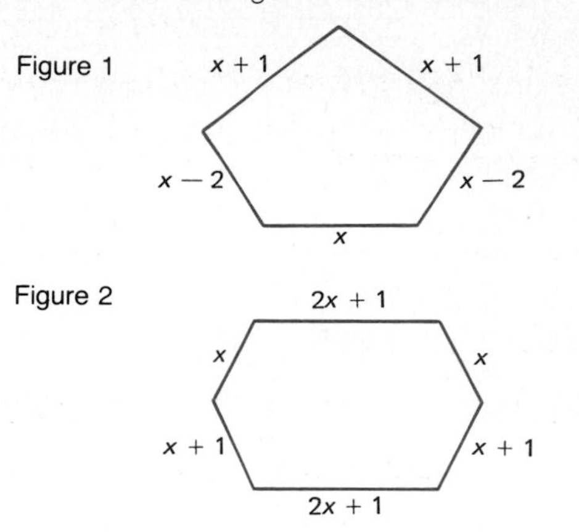

8. The perimeter of a hexagon, Figure 2, is 100 cm. The length of each of the two longest sides is $2x + 1$. Find the length of each of the two longest sides.
9. The length of a rectangle is twice its width. If the length is increased by 6 m and the width is decreased by 2 m, the perimeter is 44 m. Find the dimensions of the original rectangle.

B

10. The measure in degrees of one angle of a triangle is 115 greater than that of another. The measure of the third angle is 9 greater than twice that of the smallest. How large is each angle?
11. The perimeter of a triangle is 117 meters. The length of the second side is $\frac{1}{9}$ of the length of the first side. The length of the third side is $\frac{1}{3}$ of the length of the first side. Find the lengths of the sides of the triangle.

C

12. The measure in degrees of $\angle A$ is twice that of $\angle B$ and one less than that of $\angle C$. If the sum of the measures of the 3 angles is at least 61, what is the least possible measure of $\angle A$?

CHAPTER REVIEW

Represent the related variables by algebraic symbols. [5-1]

1. a number of items and the price per item in cents when the total cost of the items is $5

2. an hourly wage rate, the weekly wage at that rate, the annual wage at that rate (Assume a 40-hour work week and a 50-week work year.)

Replace by an equation.

3. The area of a rectangle having length three times the width is 25.

Solve. [5-2]

4. What number is 70% of 125?

5. 60 is 125% of what number?

6. 30 is what percent of 80?

7. What percent of 600 is 3?

8. 65 out of a possible 172 people voted in an election. What percent of the people voted?

Solve. [5-3 to 5-5]

9. A number decreased by 25% of the number gives 80. Find the number.

10. By what percent is 16 increased to give 24?

11. Find the percent discount for an item reduced in price from $25 to $18.

12. On a given day, an ice cream vendor had sales amounting to $344.40. The vendor sold 6 times as many 60-cent cones as 50-cent cones. How many of each type of cone were sold?

13. Two motorcyclists start from the same place at the same time and ride in the same direction. One cyclist travels at 1.5 times the rate of the other. After 2.5 hours the distance between the cyclists is 48 km. Find the rate for each.

Simplify. [5-6]

14. $-2(x - y) - 3x$

15. $(r + 3) - (-3 + r)$

16. $3(a^2 + 5a - 2) - 3(-2 + 5a + a^2)$

Solve.

17. $2(t - 7) + 5(6 - t) = 1$

18. $\frac{1}{5}(5x + 10) = \frac{1}{2}(4x - 6)$

19. $7(2y - 1) + 3y = -3(y + 2) + 7$

20. $2(3x + 3) - 2x = 8 - 4(2x - 6)$

Represent by algebraic symbols. [5-7]

21. the cost of a telegram containing $3n$ words when the first 10 words cost $1.50 and each additional word costs 8 cents

Solve. [5-8 to 5-11]

22. The sum of two numbers is 4. When 10 times the smaller is added to 4 times the larger, the sum is 4. Find each number.

23. Natalie has 28 coins consisting of dimes and quarters. They are worth \$3.25. Find the number of each kind of coin.

24. Pierre is 10 years older than Juliette. In 8 years, Pierre's age will be 2 years less than twice Juliette's age. Find the present age of each.

25. The measure of one angle of a triangle is 15° less than that of another. The measure of the third angle is 3 times the sum of the other two. Find the measure of each angle.

CAPSULE REVIEW

Write the letter of the best response.

1. When $2n$ represents a distance in meters, the distance in kilometers is

a. $1000(2n)$ **b.** $\frac{2n}{1000}$ **c.** $\frac{1000}{2n}$ **d.** $\frac{2(1000)}{n}$ **e.** $\frac{2}{1000n}$

2. a represents Lee's age in years. Lee's age in months 3 years from now is

a. $12a + 3$ **b.** $\frac{12}{a} + 3$ **c.** $\frac{a}{12} + 3$ **d.** $a + 36$ **e.** $12a + 36$

3. 60 is 30 percent of what number?

a. 2 **b.** 18 **c.** 180 **d.** 200 **e.** 1800

4. The price of an item was increased from \$5800 to \$6090. The percent increase in the price is

a. 2.9% **b.** 4.76% **c.** 5% **d.** 29% **e.** 50%

5. What number is 60% of 30?

a. 2 **b.** 18 **c.** 180 **d.** 200 **e.** 1800

6. 60 is what percent of 30?

a. 2 **b.** 18 **c.** 180 **d.** 200 **e.** 1800

7. $3 - (3 - 3x) - 3(-3 + x) =$

a. 3 **b.** 9 **c.** $6x + 9$ **d.** $-6x + 9$ **e.** $-6x - 3$

8. A salesperson's salary is \$175 per week plus a commission of 20% of the sales for the week. The amount of sales needed to give a weekly income of \$250 is

a. \$213 **b.** \$225 **c.** \$250 **d.** \$375 **e.** \$425

9. Two runners leave from points that are 42 kilometers apart and run toward each other. The rate of the faster runner is 15 km/h and that of the slower runner is 13 km/h. How long will it take them to meet?

a. 1.5 h **b.** $\frac{2}{3}h$ **c.** 1.6 h **d.** 21 min **e.** 1 h

CHAPTER TEST

1. The total cost for a number of like items is \$4. Represent the number of items and the price per item in cents.
2. Write an equation for this information. The area of a rectangle having width one-fourth the length is 20.
3. Find 30% of 60.
4. 30 is what percent of 75?
5. The population of Falls City was 50 000 in 1970. It increased 20% between 1970 and 1980. What was the population in 1980?
6. A \$30 sweater is marked "15% off." Find the new selling price.
7. Andrew, Luz, and Diego work on a job and are paid \$60.00. Luz works twice as long as Andrew. Diego works three times as long as Andrew. Their hourly pay rates are the same. How much should each receive?
8. Two airplanes leave an airport at the same time and fly in opposite directions. One flies at 350 km/h. The other flies at 450 km/h. How far apart are the airplanes after 2 hours?
9. The hourly output of one machine is 3 times the hourly output of another machine. In four hours the machines produce 192 items. Find the hourly output of each machine.
10. Simplify $5a - (3a + 2)$.
11. Simplify $3(a - b) + 2(a + b)$.
12. Use a to represent Angela's age in years. Express in months Angela's age 2 years from now.
13. Use b to represent Brian's height in centimeters. Express in meters Brian's height after he grows 3 centimeters.
14. One number is 3 larger than another number. The sum of 10 times the larger number and 3 times the smaller number is 4. Find the two numbers.
15. One number is 5 times another. The sum of 7 times the smaller number and 3 times the larger number is 11. Find the two numbers.
16. A parking meter contains 10 more nickels than dimes. The value of the nickels and dimes is \$3.20. Find the number of each type of coin.
17. A vending machine contains nickels, dimes, and quarters. It has 20 more dimes than quarters and 20 more nickels than dimes. The value of the coins is \$16.80. Find the number of each type of coin.
18. Jennifer is six years older than Christopher. Three years ago she was twice as old as Christopher. How old is Jennifer now?
19. Michael is 17 years old and Kathryn is 14. How many years ago was Michael twice as old as Kathryn?
20. The length of a rectangle is 5 centimeters more than the width. Its perimeter is 28 centimeters. Find the length and width.

21. The measure of one angle of a triangle is 25° larger than the measure of the smallest angle. The measure of the third angle is 32° larger than the measure of the smallest angle. Find the measures of all three angles.

Write the letter of the best response.

22. When m represents time in minutes, what represents time in seconds?

a. $\frac{m}{60}$ **b.** $\frac{m}{100}$ **c.** $60m$ **d.** $100m$ **e.** $3600m$

23. 70% of a number is 280. What is the number?

a. 196 **b.** 210 **c.** 250 **d.** 350 **e.** 400

24. Production was 20 000 units one week and 21 800 units the next week. What was the percent of increase?

a. 1.8% **b.** 9% **c.** 18% **d.** 109% **e.** 180%

25. A college student sells subscriptions to magazines for a salary plus commission. The salary is \$125 a week. The commission for each subscription sold is \$2.25. The total pay for one week was \$230.75. How many subscriptions were sold?

a. 47 **b.** 43 **c.** 157 **d.** 48 **e.** 52

26. Two bicyclists leave locations which are 105 kilometers apart and ride toward each other. One goes 15 km/h. The other goes 20 km/h. In how many hours will they meet?

a. 3 h **b.** 5.25 h **c.** 7 h **d.** 14 h **e.** 21 h

27. $6x + 5 - (2x - 3) =$

a. $4x - 2$ **b.** $4x + 2$ **c.** $4x + 8$ **d.** $8x + 2$ **e.** $8x + 8$

28. x represents Sara's age in days. Sara's age *in hours* 10 days from now may be given as

a. $\frac{x}{24} + 10$ **b.** $\frac{x + 10}{24}$ **c.** $24x + 10$ **d.** $24(x + 10)$ **e.** $x + 240$

29. One number is 4 times as large as another. When 4.5 is added to the smaller number it equals the larger number. Find the smaller number.

a. 0.9 **b.** 1.5 **c.** 4.5 **d.** 6 **e.** 7.5

30. Boris has 6 more nickels than dimes. The value of his nickels and dimes is \$1.50. How many dimes does Boris have?

a. 8 **b.** 10 **c.** 12 **d.** 14 **e.** 16

31. Melissa is 18 years old and Ryan is 4. In how many years will Melissa be twice Ryan's age?

a. 28 **b.** 21 **c.** 14 **d.** 10 **e.** 8

32. The measures of two angles of a triangle are each twice the measure of the smallest angle. What is the measure of the smallest angle?

a. 72° **b.** 45° **c.** 42° **d.** 39° **e.** 36°

CHAPTER 6
Operations With Polynomials

When you work with mathematics, you learn the meaning and use of symbols. Is this not basically what you have been doing for much of your life? The meanings of symbols in mathematics are quite definite, precise, and understood to represent the same ideas by millions of people. Is this not *basically* true of symbols in general?

OBJECTIVES: Add and subtract polynomials. Multiply and divide a polynomial by a monomial.

6-1 ADDING POLYNOMIALS

Polynomials may be added by writing them one after another and then combining like terms. They may also be added by writing them so that like terms are in columns, and then adding the terms in each column.

EXAMPLE 1 Add $2a + 3b + 4$, $4a - b - 2$, and $3a - 1$.

Ⓜ SOLUTION 1

$$\begin{aligned} & (2a + 3b + 4) + (4a - b - 2) + (3a - 1) \\ &= 2a + 3b + 4 + 4a - b - 2 + 3a - 1 \\ &= 2a + 4a + 3a + 3b - b + 4 - 2 - 1 \\ &= 9a + 2b + 1 \end{aligned}$$

Ⓜ SOLUTION 2

$$\begin{array}{l} 2a + 3b + 4 \\ 4a - b - 2 \\ \underline{3a - 1} \\ 9a + 2b + 1 \end{array}$$

One way to check your addition is by using a number for each variable. In this check, 2 is used for a and 3 for b, although almost any numbers could be used.

CHECK

$$\begin{array}{rcrcr} 2(2) + 3(3) + 4 &=& 4 + 9 + 4 &=& 17 \\ 4(2) - 3 - 2 &=& 8 - 3 - 2 &=& 3 \\ \underline{3(2) - 1} &=& \underline{6 - 1} &=& \underline{5} \\ 9(2) + 2(3) + 1 &=& 18 + 6 + 1 &=& 25 \end{array} \quad \left.\begin{matrix}17\\3\\5\end{matrix}\right\} 25$$

EXAMPLE 2 Find the sum of $2x^3 + 3x^2 - 7x + 1$, $x^3 - 4x^2 - 5x + 3$, and $3x^3 + 2x^2 - 4x - 2$. Check by using 2 for x.

Ⓜ SOLUTION

$$\begin{array}{r} 2x^3 + 3x^2 - 7x + 1 \\ x^3 - 4x^2 - 5x + 3 \\ \underline{3x^3 + 2x^2 - 4x - 2} \\ 6x^3 + x^2 - 16x + 2 \end{array}$$

CHECK

$$\begin{array}{rcrcr} 2(2)^3 + 3(2)^2 - 7(2) + 1 &=& 16 + 12 - 14 + 1 &=& 15 \\ (2)^3 - 4(2)^2 - 5(2) + 3 &=& 8 - 16 - 10 + 3 &=& -15 \\ \underline{3(2)^3 + 2(2)^2 - 4(2) - 2} &=& \underline{24 + 8 - 8 - 2} &=& \underline{22} \\ 6(2)^3 + (2)^2 - 16(2) + 2 &=& 48 + 4 - 32 + 2 &=& 22 \end{array} \quad \left.\begin{matrix}15\\-15\\22\end{matrix}\right\} 22$$

EXAMPLE 3 Find the sum of $3x^3 - 2y^3$, $x^2y + 2xy^2 + y^3$, and $-4x^3 - 7x^2y + 5xy^2 - 6y^3$.

Ⓜ SOLUTION

$$\begin{array}{rrrr} 3x^3 & & & -\ 2y^3 \\ & x^2y & +\ 2xy^2 & +\ \ y^3 \\ -4x^3 & -\ 7x^2y & +\ 5xy^2 & -\ 6y^3 \\ \hline -\ \ x^3 & -\ 6x^2y & +\ 7xy^2 & -\ 7y^3 \end{array}$$

CHECK The check is left for the student.

For an orderly solution, you should arrange the polynomials in decreasing or increasing powers of one of the variables. In Examples 2 and 3, the terms are arranged in decreasing powers of x.

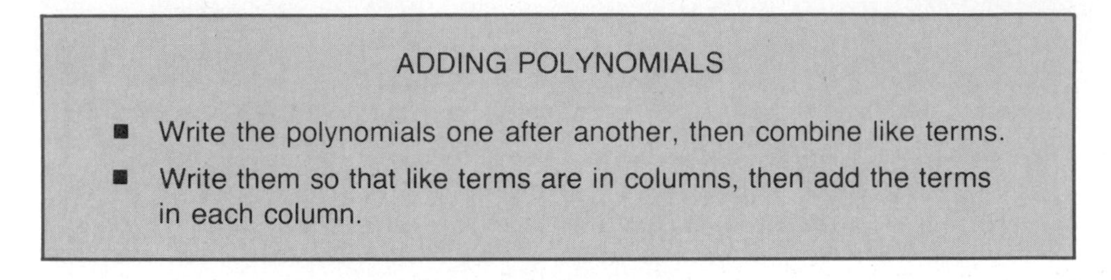

ADDING POLYNOMIALS

- Write the polynomials one after another, then combine like terms.
- Write them so that like terms are in columns, then add the terms in each column.

CLASSROOM EXERCISES

Add.

1. $$\begin{array}{r} 6x + 7 \\ \hline 3x + 5 \end{array}$$

2. $$\begin{array}{rrr} 4c & +\ 5b & -\ \ a \\ \hline -3c & -\ 5b & +\ 7a \end{array}$$

3. $$\begin{array}{rrr} x^2 & +\ \ xy & +\ \ y^2 \\ \hline 2x^2 & -\ 3xy & +\ 2y^2 \end{array}$$

4. $$\begin{array}{rrr} m^3 & +\ \ m^2 & +\ \ m \\ -5m^3 & -\ 7m^2 & -\ 7m \\ \hline -2m^3 & +\ 4m^2 & -\ 3m \end{array}$$

EXERCISES

A Add.

1. $$\begin{array}{rrr} -3k^2 & +\ 4k & -\ 6 \\ \hline 3k^2 & -\ 3k & -\ 5 \end{array}$$

2. $$\begin{array}{rrr} -2x^2 & +\ 5x & +\ 7 \\ \hline 6x^2 & +\ 2x & -\ 5 \end{array}$$

3. $$\begin{array}{rrr} -3k^2 & +\ \ 4k & -\ 9 \\ 2k^2 & -\ \ 5k & +\ 3 \\ \hline -k^2 & -\ 10k & +\ 1 \end{array}$$

4. $$\begin{array}{rrr} a^2 & -\ 4a & +\ 3 \\ -3a^2 & +\ 5a & -\ 2 \\ \hline a^2 & -\ 2a & -\ 5 \end{array}$$

5. $$\begin{array}{rrr} 3x^2 & -\ 5xy & -\ \ y^2 \\ 5x^2 & +\ 4xy & -\ 2y^2 \\ \hline -6x^2 & +\ 4xy & -\ 6y^2 \end{array}$$

6. $$\begin{array}{rrr} 3m^2 & -\ \ m & -\ 6 \\ m^2 & & -\ 4 \\ \hline & 4m & -\ 1 \end{array}$$

7. $$\begin{array}{rrr} 6x^2 & +\ 5x & -\ 3 \\ & -\ 6x & +\ 7 \\ \hline 5x^2 & & -\ 5 \end{array}$$

8. $$\begin{array}{rrr} x^4 & -\ \ ax^3 & \\ & -\ 2ax^3 & -\ \ bx^2 \\ \hline & ax^3 & +\ 4bx^2 \end{array}$$

9. $$\begin{array}{rrr} x^3 & -\ 3x^2 & -\ \ 2 \\ -4x^3 & -\ \ x^2 & +\ \ 1 \\ \hline x^3 & & -\ 10 \end{array}$$

Add.

10. $2x + 4y - 12$, $8x - 5y - 2$, and $-9x - 8y - 1$

11. $7a - 9b + c$, $-5a + c$, and $3a + 8b - 2c$

12. $-5x^2 - 3x + 2$, $-3x^2 + 6$, and $-4x^2 - 7x$

13. $7a^2 - 5a + 3$, $6a - 3$, and $5a^2 - 4$

14. $a^2 - b^2 + ab$, $b^2 - a^2 - ab$, and $4ab + b^2$

15. $5a + b + 4c$, $-3a - 6b$, and $4b - 6c + 5a$

16. $2x^2 - 3xy + y^2$, $-8xy - 9y^2 - x^2$, and $-3x^2 - 4y^2$

17. $13x + 4y - 12$, $18x - 5y - 2$, and $-9x - 8y - 4$

18. $6a^2 - 5b^2 + 8c - 5b + 3a$, $2c - 5b + 2a^2 + 6a - b^2$

19. $4x^2 + 8xy - 10y^2 + 6z^2$, $5y^2 - 2xy - 7x^2$

20. $a - b + c$, $2a + b - 3c$, and $a + b - c$

21. $4a + b + c$, $6c - 5b - 3a$, and $5b - 6c$

22. $\frac{1}{3}x + \frac{1}{4}y - \frac{1}{5}z$ and $\frac{1}{2}x - \frac{3}{4}y + \frac{4}{5}z$

23. $\frac{1}{2}a + \frac{1}{3}b - \frac{1}{4}c$ and $\frac{1}{3}a - \frac{1}{2}b - \frac{3}{4}c$

24. $\frac{2}{3}a^2 + \frac{1}{4}a - 3$, $\frac{1}{2}a^2 - a + \frac{2}{3}$, and $\frac{3}{4}a - \frac{1}{6}a^2$

25. $\frac{3}{4}x^2 - \frac{1}{5}x + 2$, $-\frac{1}{2}x^2 + \frac{1}{2}x$, and $2x^2 - 4x + 7$

26. $3.15x - 1.60y + 0.70z$ and $1.25x - 3.40y - 1.00z$

27. $2.40a - 5.60b - 0.15c$ and $-4.3a + 6.55 + 0.20c$

28. $4.2x^2 - 3.05x + 7$ and $5.3x - 2x^2 + 5$

29. $-6.2a^2 + 5.35a - 2$ and $-0.02a - 3.5a^2 + 0.05$

B **30.** $-4a^2b - 2ab^2 + 5b^3$, $6ab^2 - 3a^2b + 2b^3$, and $4a^2b + 8b^3$

31. $3(a - 2 - 4b) + 2(a - x - 4b) + 4(x + 5b - 2)$

32. $-2a(3b + 6a - 5c) + 4b(6a - 3b) + 2c(6a + 3b)$

33. The length of a rectangle is $3a + 1$. The width is $a - 6$. Find the perimeter.

34. The length of one side of a square is $x^2 - 6x + 4$. Find the perimeter.

35. Find the perimeter of a regular pentagon with sides of length $2x - 3y$.

36. Find the perimeter of a triangle with sides of lengths $2x^2 + 5x + 2$, $3x^2 - 2x + 7$, and $6x - 5$.

37. Find the sum of the lengths of the 12 edges of this rectangular solid.

38. Find the volume of this solid when $a = 3$, $b = 2$, and $c - 1$.

$b - c$

$a - c$

$a + b + c$

C Add.

39. $ax^2 + bx + c$ and $px^2 - qx + r$

40. $4bx^2 - 3bx + 7$ and $5cx^2 + 9x - 12$

41. $5x(x^2 - 3y + z) + 6(xy - 4z + 3)$

42. $-3a(-2a^2 + 5a + 2) + 3(a^3 - 5a^2 + 3a - 2)$

6-2 SUBTRACTING POLYNOMIALS

Instead of subtracting one polynomial from another, you may add the opposite of that polynomial to the other polynomial.

EXAMPLE 1 Subtract $x^2 - 4x + 3$ from $4x^2 + 2x + 1$. Check by using 2 for x.

Ⓜ SOLUTION Add the opposite. →

$$\begin{array}{r} 4x^2 + 2x + 1 \\ \underline{\overset{(-)}{}x^2 \overset{(+)}{-} 4x \overset{(-)}{+} 3} \\ 3x^2 + 6x - 2 \end{array}$$

CHECK Add the opposite. →

$$\begin{array}{rcrcr} 4(2)^2 + 2(2) + 1 & = & 16 + 4 + 1 & = & 21 \\ \underline{(2)^2 - 4(2) + 3} & = & \underline{4 - 8 + 3} & = & \underline{-1} \\ 3(2)^2 + 6(2) - 2 & = & 12 + 12 - 2 & = & 22 \end{array} \quad \left.\begin{array}{l}21\\-1\end{array}\right\} 22$$

EXAMPLE 2 Subtract $5x^3 + x^2 - 5x + 7$ from $x^3 + 4x$. Check by using 2 for x.

Ⓜ SOLUTION Add the opposite. →

$$\begin{array}{r} x^3 \qquad + 4x \\ \underline{\overset{(-)}{}5x^3 \overset{(-)}{+} x^2 \overset{(+)}{-} 5x \overset{(-)}{+} 7} \\ -4x^3 - x^2 + 9x - 7 \end{array}$$

CHECK Add the opposite. →

$$\begin{array}{rcr} 8 \quad + 8 \quad & = & 16 \\ \underline{40 + 4 - 10 + 7} & = & \underline{41} \\ -32 - 4 + 18 - 7 & = & -25 \end{array} \quad \left.\begin{array}{l}16\\41\end{array}\right\} -25$$

Another way to check your subtraction is by adding the result, or difference, to the polynomial being subtracted. The sum should equal the first polynomial used in the subtraction.

EXAMPLE 3 Subtract $3x^2 - x - 5$ from $5x^2 - 3 + 7$. Check by adding.

SOLUTION Add the opposite.

$$\begin{array}{r} 5x^2 - 3x + 7 \\ \underline{3x^2 - x - 5} \\ 2x^2 - 2x + 12 \end{array}$$

CHECK Add these polynomials.

$$\begin{array}{r} 3x^2 - x - 5 \\ \underline{2x^2 - 2x + 12} \\ 5x^2 - 3x + 7 \end{array} \checkmark$$

Polynomials may be subtracted by writing them one after another, indicating the difference, and then simplifying.

EXAMPLE 4 Subtract $2a^2 + 3b - 1$ from $4a^2 - 4b + 5$.

(M) SOLUTION

$$(4a^2 - 4b + 5) - (2a^2 + 3b - 1)$$
$$= 4a^2 - 4b + 5 - 2a^2 - 3b + 1$$
$$= 2a^2 - 7b + 6$$

CHECK $(2a^2 - 7b + 6) + (2a^2 + 3b - 1) \stackrel{?}{=} 4a^2 - 4b + 5$

$4a^2 - 4b + 5 = 4a^2 - 4b + 5$ ✓

> SUBTRACTING ONE POLYNOMIAL FROM ANOTHER
>
> Add the opposite of one polynomial to the other.

CLASSROOM EXERCISES

Subtract.

1. $\begin{array}{r} 7a^2 - b^2 \\ \underline{a^2 + b^2} \end{array}$

2. $\begin{array}{r} 5a^2 + 2b^2 \\ \underline{-3a^2 + 5b^2} \end{array}$

3. $\begin{array}{r} -3m + 5n \\ \underline{-7m - 2n} \end{array}$

4. $2x^2 - 3y$ from $4x^2 - 4y + 6$

5. $8a^2 + 4b^2 + 1$ from $4a^2 + 3b^2 - 5$

6. $12x^2 - 3y^2$ from $15x^2 + 2y^2$

7. $6x - 3y + z$ from $-2x + 5y + 7z$

EXERCISES

[A] Subtract.

1. $\begin{array}{r} 4x - 3y + z \\ \underline{2x - 7y - 3z} \end{array}$

2. $\begin{array}{r} 2a - 3b + 4c \\ \underline{a - b + 6c} \end{array}$

3. $\begin{array}{r} 2r - 4s + t \\ \underline{5r + s - t} \end{array}$

4. $\begin{array}{r} 2a - b \\ \underline{a + 7b - 6} \end{array}$

5. $\begin{array}{r} x^2 - 3x \\ \underline{4x^2 - x + 3} \end{array}$

6. $\begin{array}{r} 6x^2 + 5x - 3 \\ \underline{4x^2 - 7x + 4} \end{array}$

7. $\begin{array}{r} \frac{1}{2}a^2 - 2a + 3 \\ \underline{-4a^2 + \frac{3}{2}a - 5} \end{array}$

8. $\begin{array}{r} \frac{1}{5}m^2 + \frac{2}{3}m + \frac{1}{2} \\ \underline{\frac{3}{5}m^2 - \frac{1}{6}m - \frac{2}{3}} \end{array}$

9. $\begin{array}{r} -0.3x^2 - 0.5x + 0.07 \\ \underline{0.4x^2 + 0.3x + 0.35} \end{array}$

Subtract.

10. $2k + 3m - 6n$ from $4k + 6m$

11. $a - b + c$ from $2a - 5b - 3c$

12. $2a + 5b + 4c$ from $a - b + 6c$

13. $m^2 - 7m - 2$ from $m^2 + 10m + 13$

14. $\frac{3}{4}a - \frac{1}{4}b + \frac{1}{5}c$ from $\frac{1}{2}a - \frac{1}{3}b + \frac{2}{5}c$

15. $\frac{1}{10}a - \frac{1}{5}b - \frac{1}{2}c$ from $\frac{2}{5}a + \frac{1}{4}b - \frac{1}{2}c$

16. $0.2m + 0.35n + p$ from $0.3m - 0.45n - p$

17. $-0.5x + 0.3y + z$ from $6.2x + 0.5y - 2z$

18. $6x^2 - 0.5x$ from $-3x^2 + 0.7x - 0.2$

19. $-2a^2 - 0.5a - 0.03$ from $6a^2 - 5$

20. $a^2 + a^4 - 6$ from $3a^4 + a^2 - a + 4$

21. $4c^3 - 3c + 5c^2$ from $c + c^2 + 5c^3 - 1$

22. $a + 2b - 3c$ is how much greater than $-a - b - 5c$?

23. How much greater than $2a - b$ is $a + 3b + 2$?

B Simplify.

24. $(-a^3 + ab^2 - 2b^3) - (b^3 + a^3 - a^2b)$

25. $(16m^4n^2 - 3m^2n + 12) - (4m^4n^2 - 9)$

26. $(5n^2 - 4n + 5) - (3n^2 + 7n + 6)$

27. $(x^2 + 2x - 3) - (5x^2 - 4x - 7)$

28. $0 - (y - x)$

29. $(x^2 + y^2) - (x^2 - 2xy + y^2)$

C Subtract.

30. $x^2 - 3xy + 2a$ from the sum of $x^3 - 21$ and $2x^2 - 4xy$

31. $x^2 + 3x + 2$ from the sum of $4x^2 - 3x - 6$ and $-3x^2 + 5x + 8$

32. The perimeter of a triangle is $7x - 10$. The length of one side is $x - 6$ and the length of another is $2x + 1$. Find the length of the third side.

33. The perimeter of a rectangle is $10x - 20$. The length of one side is $2x - 7$. Find the sum of the lengths of the other sides.

34. The length of a rectangle is $x^2 - 4x + 9$ and the length exceeds the width by $7x - 2$. Write a formula for the perimeter of the rectangle.

Simplify.

35. $2(6x^2 - 2x - 5) - 3(x^2 + 7x + 2) + 3(4x^2 - 2x - 7)$

36. $-3(x^2 + 5x - 6) + 4(6x^2 - 2x - 7) - 5(-5x^2 - 4x + 2)$

THE BUSY BIRD

Two cyclists are 40 km apart. They ride towards each other. A bird flies from the first cyclist to the second, then back to the first, then back to the second, and so on. The first cyclist rides at 11 km/h. The second rides at 9 km/h. The bird flies at 15 km/h. How far will the bird fly before the two cyclists pass each other?

6-3 MULTIPLYING MONOMIALS

Soon you will need to multiply monomials with speed and accuracy. Recall that to find the product of two monomials, you must find a product for the coefficients and a product for the variables.

EXAMPLE 1 Multiply $3ab$ and $-2z$.

Ⓜ SOLUTION $(3ab)(-2z) = -6abz$

If the monomials include exponents, keep in mind what the exponents mean. For example, x^2 means $x \cdot x$; m^4 means $m \cdot m \cdot m \cdot m$; and $(2ab^2)^3$ means $(2ab^2)(2ab^2)(2ab^2)$.

Recall that an exponent indicates the number of times the base is used as a factor.

EXAMPLE 2 Multiply $4x$ and x.

Ⓜ SOLUTION $4x \cdot x = 4x^2$

EXAMPLE 3 Multiply x^4 and x^2.

SOLUTION $x^4 \cdot x^2 = (x \cdot x \cdot x \cdot x)(x \cdot x)$
$= x^6$

To find the product of two terms with the same base, you may add the exponents and show the base with this exponent sum.

EXAMPLE 4 Multiply z^3 and z^5.

Ⓜ SOLUTION $z^3 \cdot z^5 = z^{3+5}$
$= z^8$

EXAMPLE 5 Multiply $3y^3$, y, and $-y^2$

Ⓜ SOLUTION $(3y^3)(y)(-y^2) = -3(y^3yy^2)$
$= -3y^{3+1+2}$
$= -3y^6$

Recall the difference between $-y^2$ and $(-y)^2$.

To find the power of a power, you may multiply the exponents to find the exponent for the base.

EXAMPLE 6 Find the square of x^5.

Ⓜ SOLUTION 1
$(x^5)^2 = x^5 \cdot x^5$
$= x^{5+5}$
$= x^{10}$

Ⓜ SOLUTION 2
$(x^5)^2 = x^{5 \cdot 2}$
$= x^{10}$

EXAMPLE 7 Simplify $(x^2)^3$.

Ⓜ SOLUTION $(x^2)^3 = x^{2 \cdot 3}$
$= x^6$

EXAMPLE 8 Simplify $(-5x^4)^3$.

Ⓜ SOLUTION
$(-5x^4)^3$
$= (-5x^4)(-5x^4)(-5x^4)$
$= (-5)^3(x^4)^3$
$= -125x^{4 \cdot 3}$
$= -125x^{12}$

To find the power of a product, you may find the product of the powers.

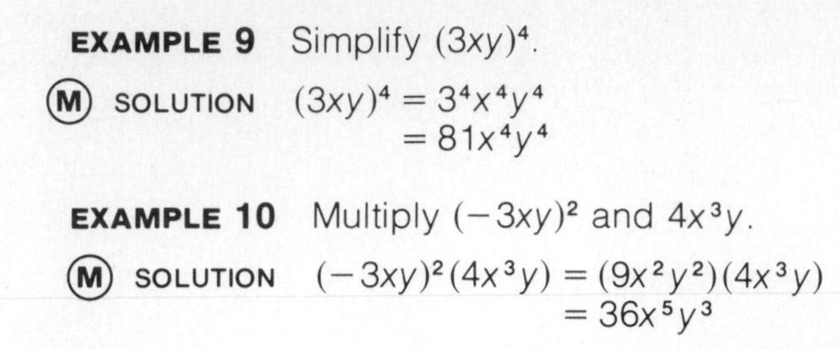

EXAMPLE 9 Simplify $(3xy)^4$.

Ⓜ SOLUTION $(3xy)^4 = 3^4x^4y^4$
$= 81x^4y^4$

EXAMPLE 10 Multiply $(-3xy)^2$ and $4x^3y$.

Ⓜ SOLUTION $(-3xy)^2(4x^3y) = (9x^2y^2)(4x^3y)$
$= 36x^5y^3$

MULTIPLYING MONOMIALS

- Find the product for the coefficients and the product for the variables.
- For two terms that have the same base, add the exponents.
  $x^a \cdot x^b = x^{a+b}$
- For the power of a power, multiply the exponents.
  $(x^a)^b = x^{a \cdot b}$
- For the power of a product, find the product of the powers.
  $(x \cdot y)^a = x^a \cdot y^a$

CLASSROOM EXERCISES

Multiply.

1. $(4xy)(2z)$
2. $(x)(x)$
3. $(2k)(4k^5)$
4. $(x^3)(x^5)$
5. $(b^3)(b^4)$
6. $(3a^2)(4a^3)$
7. $(5n^3)(-6n^2)$
8. $(x^3)^2$
9. $(-3x^2)^3$
10. $(a^2b^2)^3$
11. $(2x)^2(-3x)$
12. $(xy)^5$

EXERCISES

A Multiply.

1. $(2xy)(4w)$
2. $(-3ab)(8c)$
3. $(-7k)(-6mn)$
4. $(-mn)(2x)$
5. $(x^2)(x)$
6. $(r)(4r)$
7. $(9x)\left(\frac{1}{3}x^2\right)$
8. $\left(\frac{1}{2}y\right)\left(\frac{1}{5}y^2\right)$
9. $(-8h)(3h^3)$

10. $(-3a^2b)(4ab)$ **11.** $(0.1r)(-0.1r)$ **12.** $(-0.4w)(-5w)$
13. $(4xy)^3$ **14.** $(k^4)^3$ **15.** $(-4x^2)^3$
16. $(-6x^2)^2$ **17.** $(-2a^3b)^2$ **18.** $(-9a^3b^4)^2$
19. $(8y^2)^4$ **20.** $(xyz)^4$ **21.** $(4x^3y)^2$
22. $(2ab)^5$ **23.** $(ab)(bc)(ac)$ **24.** $(mn)(np)(ps)$

B **25.** $(2xy)^2(3x)$ **26.** $(-3b)^3(2bc^2)$ **27.** $(6a^2y)(-3ay^2)(a)$
28. $(-0.4w)(-6w^5)$ **29.** $\left(\frac{1}{2}x\right)^2$ **30.** $(a^4b^3)(-ab^2)^2$
31. $(-5a^2)^2(6ab)^2(-3ab^2)$ **32.** $(-10x^2y)^2(0.01x)^2(-0.1y)^2$ **33.** $\left(-\frac{1}{4}x^2\right)^2\left(\frac{4}{5}x\right)^3$

C Simplify.

34. $[(6x)^2]^3$ **35.** $[(2x^2)^2(4x)^2]^3$ **36.** $\left[(-3a^2)^3\left(\frac{1}{3}a^4\right)^3\right]^2$
37. $\left[(-2x^2)^3\left(-\frac{1}{4}x^4\right)^2(-2x^2)^3\right]^2$ **38.** $[(ab)^2(ac)^2]^4$ **39.** $[(a^b)^c]^d$
40. $x^{a+1} \cdot x^{a-1}$ **41.** $(x^{a+1})^2$ **42.** $(x^{2a})^3$
43. $(x^{n-1}y)(xy^{n+1})$ **44.** $(x^{n-1}y)^2(xy^{n+1})^2$ **45.** $(x^my^n)^2(-x^my^n)^3$

102868

HAPPY BIRTHDAY

With numeric dating a birthday of October 28, 1968 is written 10 28 68.

1. Try the following with your calculator. Be sure to press [=] after each step.

a. Enter the number of the month you were born.
b. Multiply by 5.
c. Add −4.
d. Multiply by 20.
e. Add 93.
f. Add the number of the day you were born.
g. Subtract 13.

What is special about the number that is now in the display?

2. Use your knowledge of algebra to explain what happened.

6-4 MULTIPLYING A POLYNOMIAL BY A MONOMIAL

To multiply a polynomial by a monomial, apply the Distributive Property. Multiply *each* term of the polynomial by the monomial.

$$a(b + c) = ab + ac$$
$$a(b + c + d) = ab + ac + ad$$

EXAMPLE 1 Multiply $2a - b + 6$ by 4.

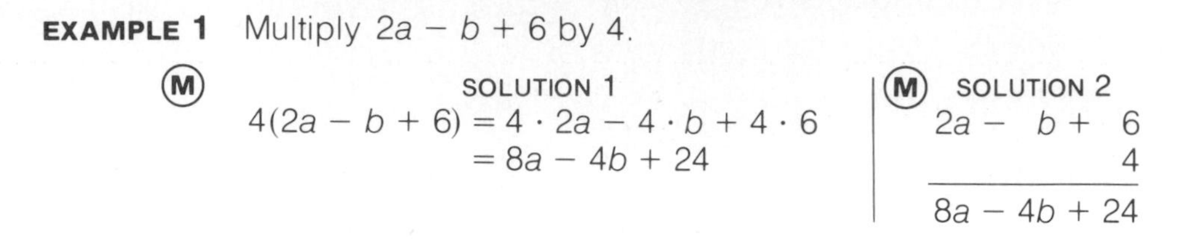

Ⓜ SOLUTION 1

$$4(2a - b + 6) = 4 \cdot 2a - 4 \cdot b + 4 \cdot 6$$
$$= 8a - 4b + 24$$

Ⓜ SOLUTION 2

$$\begin{array}{r} 2a - b + 6 \\ 4 \\ \hline 8a - 4b + 24 \end{array}$$

You can check multiplication by using a number for each variable in the same way you checked addition and subtraction.

EXAMPLE 2 Multiply $3x^2 - 4x + 1$ by $-2x$. Check by using 2 for x.

Ⓜ SOLUTION 1 $-2x(3x^2 - 4x + 1) = -6x^3 + 8x^2 - 2x$

CHECK

$$\begin{aligned} -2x(3x^2 - 4x + 1) &\stackrel{?}{=} -6x^3 + 8x^2 - 2x \\ -2 \cdot 2(3 \cdot 2^2 - 4 \cdot 2 + 1) &\stackrel{?}{=} -6 \cdot 2^3 + 8 \cdot 2^2 - 2 \cdot 2 \\ -4(12 - 8 + 1) &\stackrel{?}{=} -6 \cdot 8 + 8 \cdot 4 - 2 \cdot 2 \\ -4 \cdot 5 &\stackrel{?}{=} -48 + 32 - 4 \\ -20 &= -20 \ \checkmark \end{aligned}$$

Ⓜ SOLUTION 2

$$\begin{array}{r} 3x^2 - 4x + 1 \\ -2x \\ \hline -6x^3 + 8x^2 - 2x \end{array}$$

CHECK

$$\begin{array}{rcrcr} 3 \cdot 2^2 - 4 \cdot 2 + 1 = & & 12 - 8 + 1 = & & 5 \\ -2 \cdot 2 = & & -4 = & & -4 \\ \hline -6 \cdot 2^3 + 8 \cdot 2^2 - 2 \cdot 2 = & & -48 + 32 - 4 = & & -20 \end{array} \quad \left.\begin{array}{r}5\\-4\end{array}\right\} -20$$

MULTIPLYING A POLYNOMIAL BY A MONOMIAL

Multiply each term of the polynomial by the monomial.

CLASSROOM EXERCISES

Multiply.

1. $\begin{array}{r} 4x + 2y \\ 2x \\ \hline \end{array}$
2. $\begin{array}{r} 6a^2 - 5a + 6 \\ -3a \\ \hline \end{array}$
3. $\begin{array}{r} 4a + 2b + 1 \\ b \\ \hline \end{array}$
4. $\begin{array}{r} 6x^2 + 5x - 2 \\ -7 \\ \hline \end{array}$
5. $2a(a^2 + 3a - 4)$
6. $4x(x - y - 2)$
7. $5x(7x^2 + 2x - 3)$

EXERCISES

A Multiply.

1. $\begin{array}{r} 3x - 8y - 5 \\ 4 \\ \hline \end{array}$
2. $\begin{array}{r} 7a - 5b + 3 \\ 5 \\ \hline \end{array}$
3. $\begin{array}{r} -3b + c \\ -6 \\ \hline \end{array}$
4. $\begin{array}{r} -3x + 4y \\ -10 \\ \hline \end{array}$
5. $\begin{array}{r} 4x^2 - 5y \\ a \\ \hline \end{array}$
6. $\begin{array}{r} m + n - p \\ -c \\ \hline \end{array}$
7. $\begin{array}{r} 4a^2 + 7a - 10 \\ 2a \\ \hline \end{array}$
8. $\begin{array}{r} 7m^2 - m + 3 \\ 3m \\ \hline \end{array}$
9. $5(2a^2 + 7)$
10. $-4(5x^4 - 3x^2)$
11. $x(4ax^2 - 7a^2)$
12. $8m(m^3 - 2m)$
13. $a(3a^2 + 2)$
14. $-b(b^3 + 3b^2)$
15. $-y(-2a^2y + 10a)$
16. $-5(6a + b - 7)$
17. $-7(-c^2 + 2c + 3)$
18. $x(x^2 - 4x + 5)$
19. $2x(x^2 + x + 1)$
20. $-1(a + b - c)$
21. $-5(a^2 - 5a + 7)$
22. $d^2(12d^3 - 16d^2 + 12d)$
23. $3a^2(a^3 + 2a^2 - 6a)$
24. $16d(-2d^3 - 4d^2 + 15)$
25. $7m(3m^2 + 4m - 7)$
26. $a^2(-4a^4 + 3a^2 - 9)$
27. $-3a^4(a^2 - 2a + 5)$
28. $20x\left(\frac{1}{5}x^2 - \frac{3}{4}x\right)$
29. $12a\left(\frac{1}{6}a^3 - \frac{1}{2}a^2\right)$

B

30. $4ax^2(-9a^3x^2 + 8a^2x^3 + 6a^4x^4)$
31. $17b^3d^2(-4b^2d^2 - 11b^3d^3 - 5bd^4)$
32. $\frac{3}{4}(12a^2 - 16a + 8)$
33. $0.2(4m^2 + 5n + 8)$
34. $(-5x^2 + 7x - 3)2x^3$
35. $(-3y^4 - 4y^3 + 7y^2)(-2y)$
36. Find the area of a rectangle with base $4a - 6$ and width $2a$.
37. Find the cost of $7n - d$ articles at $2n$ cents each.
38. Find the area of a triangle with base $x + 8$ and altitude $2x$.
39. Explain why $A = p + prt$ may be used in place of $A = p(1 + rt)$.

C Multiply.

40. $-3xy^2z(-8x^2yz^3 - 10x^2y^2z^4 + 8x^4yz^2)$
41. $\frac{3}{4}x^2yz^2\left(-\frac{4}{5}xy^2z + \frac{8}{9}x^3yz^3 - \frac{12}{13}x^3y^4z^2\right)$

6-5 DIVIDING MONOMIALS

The fraction bar, —, may be used to indicate division. When this is done, it sometimes is easy to find common factors of the numerator and the denominator. This can help you simplify the quotient.

EXAMPLE 1 Divide x^6 by x^4.

SOLUTION 1

$$\frac{x^6}{x^4} = \frac{x^2x^4}{x^4}$$
$$= \frac{x^2}{1} \cdot \frac{x^4}{x^4}$$
$$= x^2 \cdot 1$$
$$= x^2$$

This is an application of the Multiplication Property of One.

SOLUTION 2

$$\frac{x^6}{x^4} = \frac{\overset{1\cdot 1\cdot 1\cdot 1}{\cancel{xxxx}xx}}{\underset{1\cdot 1\cdot 1\cdot 1}{\cancel{xxxx}}}$$
$$= x^2$$

EXAMPLE 2 Divide $18x^2y$ by $3xy$.

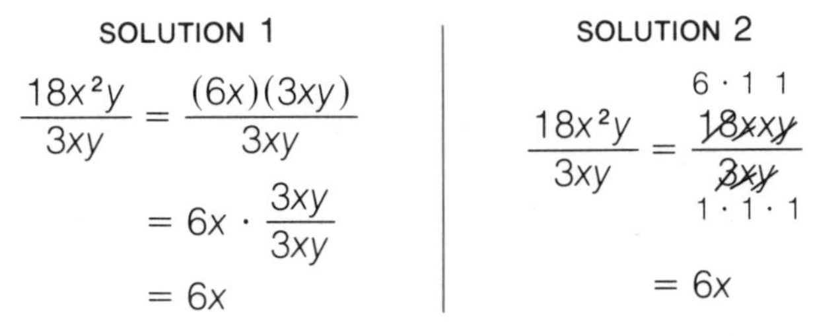

SOLUTION 1

$$\frac{18x^2y}{3xy} = \frac{(6x)(3xy)}{3xy}$$
$$= 6x \cdot \frac{3xy}{3xy}$$
$$= 6x$$

SOLUTION 2

$$\frac{18x^2y}{3xy} = \frac{\overset{6\cdot 1\ 1}{\cancel{18}\cancel{x}x\cancel{y}}}{\underset{1\cdot 1\cdot 1}{\cancel{3}\cancel{x}\cancel{y}}}$$
$$= 6x$$

When factors of the numerator and denominator are shown with exponents and the same base, you may subtract exponents.

EXAMPLE 3 Divide x^6 by x^4.

Ⓜ SOLUTION

$$\frac{x^6}{x^4} = x^{6-4}$$
$$= x^2$$

Compare with Example 1.

EXAMPLE 4 Divide. $\frac{16x^7y^5}{4x^4y^2}$

SOLUTION 1

$$\frac{16x^7y^5}{4x^4y^2} = \frac{\overset{1}{\cancel{4}} \cdot 4 \cdot \overset{1}{\cancel{x^4}} \cdot x^3 \cdot \overset{1}{\cancel{y^2}} \cdot y^3}{\underset{1\cdot 1\cdot 1}{\cancel{4}\cancel{x^4}\cancel{y^2}}}$$
$$= 4x^3y^3$$

Ⓜ SOLUTION 2

$$\frac{16x^7y^5}{4x^4y^2} = 4x^{7-4}y^{5-2}$$
$$= 4x^3y^3$$

Remember that the lesser exponent is subtracted from the greater exponent. The result is shown in the numerator or denominator according to whichever had the larger exponent. When the difference of the exponents is zero, the value of the factor is 1.

EXAMPLE 5 Divide $-27a^9b^4c^2$ by $9a^5b^7c^2$.

(M) SOLUTION

$$\frac{-27a^9b^4c^2}{9a^5b^7c^2} = \frac{-3a^{9-5}c^{2-2}}{b^{7-4}}$$
$$= \frac{-3a^4c^0}{b^3}$$
$$= \frac{-3a^4}{b^3},$$
$$= -\frac{3a^4}{b^3}$$

CHECK

$$\left(\frac{-3a^4}{b^3}\right)(9a^5b^7c^2) \stackrel{?}{=} -27a^9b^4c^2$$
$$-27a^9b^4c^2 = -27a^9b^4c^2 \checkmark$$

DIVIDING MONOMIALS

- Find the quotient for the coefficients and the quotient for the variables.
- For factors in the numerator and denominator that have the same base, subtract the smaller exponent from the larger exponent. Show the result in the numerator or denominator according to whichever had the larger exponent.

CLASSROOM EXERCISES

Simplify each quotient. Assume that no denominator equals 0.

1. $\frac{x^4}{x^3}$ **2.** $\frac{-m^7}{m^4}$ **3.** $\frac{10a^6}{2a^3}$ **4.** $\frac{a^4b^8}{ab^3}$

5. $\frac{-2x^{11}y^2}{x^2y}$ **6.** $\frac{42xy^3z}{7xyz}$ **7.** $\frac{-15x^5y^7z^{12}}{3z^4}$ **8.** $\frac{-100x^4y^2z^7}{-5x^4yz^6}$

EXERCISES

A Simplify each quotient. Assume that no denominator equals 0.

1. $\frac{24a^2}{2a}$
2. $\frac{52x^2}{13x}$
3. $\frac{a^2b^3c}{ab}$
4. $\frac{m^4}{m}$
5. $\frac{12xy^2}{4xy}$
6. $\frac{24a^2b}{6ab}$
7. $\frac{3b^4c^5d^2}{1.5bc^2d}$
8. $\frac{34x^7y^8}{2x^3y^4}$
9. $\frac{45x^4y^6}{3x^2y^2}$
10. $\frac{-a^7}{-a^5}$
11. $\frac{-4m^5}{2m}$
12. $\frac{-3m^5}{3}$
13. $\frac{-18a^3}{a}$
14. $\frac{-8m^4}{8m^4}$
15. $\frac{15x^2y}{-3xy}$
16. $\frac{21x^5y^4}{7xy}$
17. $\frac{36a^3b^3c}{9ab^3c}$
18. $\frac{48s^4t^7}{4s^3t^3}$
19. $\frac{-14a^2b^5c^4}{2ab^4c}$
20. $\frac{32r^2s}{4s}$
21. $\frac{4.4m^2n^5}{0.2mn^3}$
22. $\frac{-2.25r^7s^9}{1.5r^2s^5}$
23. $\frac{7.5p^5q}{-0.3p^2}$
24. $\frac{52x^3yz}{-4x^2z}$
25. $\frac{3a^3b^4}{9b^3c}$
26. $\frac{0.8x^3y^2z}{0.2xy^2z}$
27. $\frac{-0.25a^3b^2c^3}{-0.5a^2bc^3}$
28. $\frac{0.108a^6b^3c^5}{-0.12a^3b^2c^4}$

B

29. $\frac{(3x^2)(12xy)}{4y}$
30. $\frac{(6x)(3x^2y^2)}{9xy}$
31. $6x \div \frac{1}{2}x$
32. $6x^2 \div \frac{1}{3}x$
33. $\frac{1}{2}x^3 \div \frac{1}{3}x^2$
34. $5y \div 2\frac{1}{2}y$
35. $7m^4 \div 3\frac{1}{2}m^2$
36. $22a^3b^3c^3 \div 11a^3b^2c$
37. $24a^2bc^3 \div 8a^2bc^2$
38. $48xy^2z \div 2xy$
39. $\frac{(2x^3)(4x)^2}{2x}$
40. $\frac{(18x)(4x^2y^2)}{(6x)(3x^2y)}$
41. $\frac{(-5xy)^2(-2xy)^2}{-5x^2y^3}$
42. $\frac{(-21a^2b)(-2ab)^2}{-7a^3b}$
43. $\frac{6(rs)^4}{(14r^2s^2)(3rs^3)}$

C

44. $\frac{(0.5xyz^2)^3\left(\frac{1}{4}x^2y^2\right)}{(0.25x^3y^2)^2}$
45. $\frac{\left(\frac{2}{3}x^2y^2z\right)^2\left(\frac{4}{5}x^3y^2z^4\right)^2}{\left(\frac{2}{5}xyz\right)^4}$
46. $\frac{(2.5m^2n^2)^2(1.5mn^2)^2}{(0.55m^2n^2)^2}$
47. $\frac{\left(\frac{3}{8}a^3b^2c\right)^2 \cdot (abc)^4 \cdot \left(\frac{1}{2}a^2b\right)^2}{\left(\frac{3}{2}a^2bc^2\right)^3}$

SPEED TEST

It took 2 hours to complete the first half of a 160-km trip. What speed is needed for the second half to average 80 km/h for the entire trip?

6-6 DIVIDING A POLYNOMIAL BY A MONOMIAL

When a polynomial is multiplied by a monomial, each of its terms is multiplied by the monomial. Similarly, when a polynomial is divided by a monomial, each of its terms must be divided by the monomial.

EXAMPLE 1 Divide $60x^2 + 42x - 30$ by 2.

Ⓜ

SOLUTION 1

$$\frac{60x^2 + 42x - 30}{2}$$

$$= \frac{60x^2}{2} + \frac{42x}{2} - \frac{30}{2}$$

$$= 30x^2 + 21x - 15$$

SOLUTION 2

$$\begin{array}{r} 30x^2 + 21x - 15 \\ 2\overline{)60x^2 + 42x - 30} \\ \underline{60x^2 + 42x - 30} \\ 0 \end{array}$$

CHECK $2(30x^2 + 21x - 15) \stackrel{?}{=} 60x^2 + 42x - 30$

$60x^2 + 42x - 30 = 60x^2 + 42x - 30$ ✓

EXAMPLE 2 Divide $15x^3 - 40x^2 - 15x$ by $-5x$.

Ⓜ

SOLUTION 1

$$\frac{15x^3 - 40x^2 - 15x}{-5x}$$

$$= \frac{15x^3}{-5x} + \frac{-40x^2}{-5x} + \frac{-15x}{-5x}$$

$$= -3x^2 + 8x + 3$$

SOLUTION 2

$$\begin{array}{r} -3x^2 + 8x + 3 \\ -5x\overline{)15x^3 - 40x^2 - 15x} \\ \underline{15x^3 - 40x^2 - 15x} \\ 0 \end{array}$$

CHECK $-5x(-3x^2 + 8x + 3) \stackrel{?}{=} 15x^3 - 40x^2 - 15x$

$15x^3 - 40x^2 - 15x = 15x^3 - 40x^2 - 15x$ ✓

EXAMPLE 3 Divide $5x^3y^2 + 2x^2y^2 - 15xy$ by $5xy$

Ⓜ

SOLUTION 1

$$\frac{5x^3y^2 + 2x^2y^2 - 15xy}{5xy}$$

$$= \frac{5x^3y^2}{5xy} + \frac{2x^2y^2}{5xy} + \frac{-15xy}{5xy}$$

$$= x^2y + \tfrac{2}{5}xy - 3$$

SOLUTION 2

$$\begin{array}{r} x^2y + \tfrac{2}{5}xy - 3 \\ 5xy\overline{)5x^3y^2 + 2x^2y^2 - 15xy} \\ \underline{5x^3y^2 + 2x^2y^2 - 15xy} \\ 0 \end{array}$$

CHECK $5xy(x^2y + \tfrac{2}{5}xy - 3) \stackrel{?}{=} 5x^3y^2 + 2x^2y^2 - 15xy$

$5x^3y^2 + 2x^2y^2 - 15xy = 5x^3y^2 + 2x^2y^2 - 15xy$ ✓

DIVIDING A POLYNOMIAL BY A MONOMIAL

Divide each term of the polynomial by the monomial.

CLASSROOM EXERCISES

Simplify each quotient. Assume that no denominator equals zero.

1. $(27x - 12) \div 3$

2. $(10k^2 + 5k - 5) \div 5$

3. $(6x + 3y) \div -3$

4. $(12x + 8y) \div -4$

5. $(4x^3 - 2x^2 + 12x) \div (-2x)$

6. $15y^4 - 10y^3 + 5y \div (5y)$

7. $\dfrac{21x^3 + 6x^2 + 15x}{-3x}$

8. $\dfrac{-12a^4 + 20a^3 - 8a^2}{4a}$

EXERCISES

A Simplify each quotient. Assume that no denominator equals zero.

1. $(3x - 9) \div 3$

2. $(12x - 6) \div 3$

3. $(24a^3 + 6a^2) \div -3$

4. $(14m^2 - 21m) \div -7$

5. $(-5x^2 + 15x) \div 5$

6. $(-21a^3 - 18a^2) \div -3$

7. $(-15x^3 + 24x^2 - 12x) \div -3$

8. $(-24a^4 + 36a^2 + 12a) \div -6$

9. $(x^2 + x) \div x$

10. $(x^3 - x^2) \div x^2$

11. $\dfrac{-4a^3 + 16a^2 - 10a}{-2}$

12. $\dfrac{24m^3 - 16m^2 - 8m}{8}$

13. $\dfrac{8x^5 - 10x^4 + x^3}{x^3}$

14. $\dfrac{a^{10} - a^9 + a^7}{a^3}$

15. $\dfrac{8a^3 - 4a^2 + 4a}{-4a}$

16. $(35a^7 + 42a^5 + 21a^3) \div 7a^2$

17. $(-28b^6 + 32b^4 - 16b^2) \div 4b^2$

18. $(-36x^4 + 42x^3 - 24x^2) \div 6x$

19. $(45x - 33x^2 + 18x^3) \div 3x$

20. $(27a^2 - 45a^3 - 63a^4) \div 9a^2$

21. $(48x^3 - 72x^2 + 60x) \div 12x$

22. $(45x^5 - 60x^4 + 75x^3) \div 15x^2$

23. $(-77x^5 + 88x^3 - 22x) \div -11x$

24. $(25x^4 - 50x^3 + 100x^2) \div 25x$

25. $(-120x^6 + 150x^5 - 180x^4) \div -30x^3$

26. $(16x^2 + 32x^4) \div -8x$

B **27.** $(ab - ac) \div a$

28. $(\pi R - \pi r) \div \pi$

29. $(\pi r^2 - \pi rh) \div \pi r$

30. $(16a^7 + 44a^6 - 32a^5 - 28a^4) \div -4a^2$

31. $(8x^2y^3 + 4x^3y^4 - 2xy^3) \div (2xy^3)$

32. $(-15a^2b^3 - 21a^3b^2 - 6a^4b) \div (3a^2b)$

33. $(-45a^7b^2 + 30a^5b^3 - 60a^3b^4) \div (15ab)$

34. $(-56x^7y^2 + 72x^6y^3 - 64x^5y^4) \div (8x^4y^2)$

35. $(-400x^7y^3 + 320x^6y^4 - 160x^5y^3) \div (-20x^3y^2)$

36. $(-64x^6y^3z + 128x^5y^4z^2) \div (32x^4y^2z)$

37. $(-39a^4b^2 + 91a^3b^3 - 52a^2b^4) \div (-13ab)$

38. $(4.2ab^2 - 0.49a^2b) \div (0.07ab)$

39. $\left(\frac{3}{4}m^2n^2 + \frac{5}{4}mn^3\right) \div \left(\frac{1}{4}mn\right)$

C **40.** $(-3.6x^4y^5z^2 + 0.28x^5y^6z^3 + 40x^6y^7z^4) \div (0.04x^4y^2z)$

41. $(35x^5y^7 - 64x^6y^6 + 21x^7y^5) \div 5x^3y^4$

42. At $2y$ cents each, how many pencils can be bought for $(8y^2 + 6y)$ cents?

43. How long will it take to travel an^2 kilometers if you travel n kilometers a day?

44. If you save c cents a day, how many days are needed to save $(bc + c)$ cents?

45. Express the number of dekameters in a length of x kilometers and $50y$ meters.

CHECKING YOUR UNDERSTANDING

CONCEPTS

- The sum or difference of two polynomials may be simplified by combining like terms. [6-1, 6-2]
- To multiply or divide a polynomial by a monomial, multiplying or dividing each term of the polynomial by the monomial is necessary. [6-4, 6-6]

PROCESSES

- Add and subtract polynomials. [6-1, 6-2]

1. $(2x^2 - 5x + 7) + (-3x^2 + 7x - 4)$

2. $(-2x^2 - 4x + 5) - (5x^2 + 3x - 2)$

- Multiply and divide by a monomial. [6-3 to 6-6]

3. $(-3x^2)(2x)$

4. $(-2r^2)^4$

5. $\dfrac{20x^3y^2}{-4x^2y}$

6. $(3a^4b^2c^2) \div (-6ab^4c^2)$

7. $(-7c^2)(2c^2 - 9c + 15)$

8. $(-8x^3 + 4x^2 + 2x) \div (-2x)$

OBJECTIVES: Multiply and divide polynomials by polynomials. Solve problems using equations which contain products of polynomials.

6-7 MULTIPLYING POLYNOMIALS

To multiply polynomials, apply the Distributive Property. Multiply *each* term of one polynomial by each term of the other.

$$\begin{aligned}(r+s)(b+c) &= (r+s)b+(r+s)c\\ &= rb+sb+rc+sc\end{aligned}$$

$$\begin{aligned}(r+s)(b+c+d) &= (r+s)b+(r+s)c+(r+s)d\\ &= rb+sb+rc+sc+rd+sd\end{aligned}$$

EXAMPLE 1 Multiply $x + 2$ and $x + 5$.

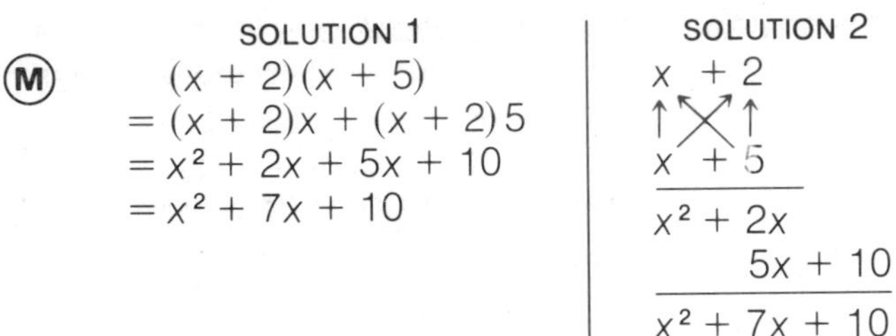

SOLUTION 1

$$\begin{aligned}&(x+2)(x+5)\\ &= (x+2)x+(x+2)5\\ &= x^2+2x+5x+10\\ &= x^2+7x+10\end{aligned}$$

SOLUTION 2

$$\begin{array}{r} x + 2\\ x + 5\\ \hline x^2 + 2x \qquad\\ 5x + 10\\ \hline x^2 + 7x + 10\end{array}$$

EXAMPLE 2 Multiply $a^2 - 3b^2 + 4ab$ and $2a - b$.
Check by using 4 for a and 3 for b.

SOLUTION First, arrange the terms of the polynomials according to decreasing or increasing powers of a variable. In the following, the greatest power of a is first, the next greatest power of a is second, and so on.

$$\begin{array}{rrrrcr} a^2 + & 4ab - & 3b^2 & & \text{—CHECK}\longrightarrow & 16+48-27 = 37\\ & 2a - & b & & \longrightarrow & 8-3 = 5\\ \hline 2a^3 + & 8a^2b - & 6ab^2 & & & 185\\ - & a^2b - & 4ab^2 + & 3b^3 & & \updownarrow\\ \hline 2a^3 + & 7a^2b - & 10ab^2 + & 3b^3 & \longrightarrow & 128+336-360+81 = 185\end{array}$$

> **MULTIPLYING POLYNOMIALS**
>
> 1. Multiply each term of one polynomial by each term of the other.
> 2. Combine like terms.

CLASSROOM EXERCISES

Multiply.

1. $\begin{array}{r} x + 1 \\ \underline{x + 1} \end{array}$
2. $\begin{array}{r} x + 2 \\ \underline{x + 3} \end{array}$
3. $\begin{array}{r} y + a \\ \underline{y - a} \end{array}$
4. $\begin{array}{r} b - 2 \\ \underline{b - 2} \end{array}$
5. $\begin{array}{r} c + 3 \\ \underline{c - 1} \end{array}$
6. $(x - 2y)(x - y)$
7. $(y + 3)(y + 4)$
8. $(2s - 3t)(3s + 4t)$

EXERCISES

A Multiply.

1. $(x + 2)(x + 2)$
2. $(x + 4)(x + 4)$
3. $(a + 3)(a + 2)$
4. $(c + 2)(c + 4)$
5. $(r - 1)(r - 2)$
6. $(x - 4)(x - 4)$
7. $(c + 5)(c - 8)$
8. $(x - 7)(x + 7)$
9. $(r - 6)(r + 6)$
10. $(r + s)(r - s)$
11. $(x - 3y)(2x + y)$
12. $(m - 3n)(2m - 5n)$
13. $(2x - 3y)(3x - 2y)$
14. $(5m + 3n)(m - 5n)$
15. $(m - n)(4m + n)$
16. $(x - 3y)(5x + 2y)$
17. $(a^2 - 6a + 9)(a - 1)$
18. $(2x - 1)(x^2 - x + 1)$
19. $(4x^2 + 4x - 3)(2 - x)$
20. $(6x^2 - 3x - 5)(3 - x)$
21. $(x + 1)(x^2 + 3x - 2)$
22. $(z + 2)(z^2 - 3z + 5)$
23. $(2x - 1)(x^2 + 3x + 5)$

B

24. $(a^2 - b^2)(a - 2b)$
25. $(4a + 1)^2$
26. $(2x - 3y)^2$
27. $(3x - 2y)^3$
28. $(2x + z)^3$
29. $(a - b)^3$
30. $(a + b)^3$
31. $4x^2 + (x + 2)^2$
32. $-3y(y - 2)^2$
33. $(3a - b)(2a + 3b) - (4a + b)(2a - b)$
34. $(2y + 5)(y - 6) - (3y + 1)(y - 8)$
35. $(x - 1)(2x - 1) - (3x + 1)(x - 2)$
36. $(3c - 1)^2 - (2c + 4)^2$
37. The base of a parallelogram is $x + 2y$. Its altitude is $x - 2y$. Find its area.
38. Find the area of a square with side of length $2x + 3$.

C Multiply.

39. $(x^2 + 2x - 1)(x^2 - x + 3)$
40. $(2a^2 + a - 2)(a^2 + 3a + 5)$
41. $(a^n + 3)^3$
42. $(x - y)^4$
43. $(2 - b^n)^3$

6-8 MULTIPLYING POLYNOMIALS IN EQUATIONS

When you solved equations containing a polynomial multiplied by a monomial, you first cleared the parentheses.

EXAMPLE 1 Solve $3 - 2(3x + 2) = 7$.

Ⓜ SOLUTION

$$\begin{aligned} 3 - 2(3x + 2) &= 7 \\ 3 - 6x - 4 &= 7 \qquad \text{(multiplying } (3x + 2) \text{ by } -2) \\ -6x - 1 &= 7 \\ -6x &= 7 + 1 \\ -6x &= 8 \\ x &= -\tfrac{4}{3} \end{aligned}$$

CHECK

$$\begin{aligned} 3 - 2(3x + 2) &= 7 \\ 3 - 2\left(3\left(-\tfrac{4}{3}\right) + 2\right) &\stackrel{?}{=} 7 \\ 3 - 2(-4 + 2) &\stackrel{?}{=} 7 \\ 3 - 2(-2) &\stackrel{?}{=} 7 \\ 7 &= 7 \ \checkmark \end{aligned}$$

Now you will solve equations containing a polynomial multiplied by a polynomial. To do these, always remember to find the product of the polynomials before clearing the parentheses.

EXAMPLE 2 Solve $8 - (x - 5)(x + 2) = 3 - x^2$.

Ⓜ SOLUTION

$$8 - (x - 5)(x + 2) = 3 - x^2 \longrightarrow$$

$$\begin{array}{r} x - 5 \\ x + 2 \\ \hline x^2 - 5x \qquad \\ + 2x - 10 \\ \hline x^2 - 3x - 10 \end{array}$$

$$\begin{aligned} 8 - (x^2 - 3x - 10) &= 3 - x^2 \longleftarrow \\ 8 - x^2 + 3x + 10 &= 3 - x^2 \\ -x^2 + 3x + 18 &= 3 - x^2 \\ -x^2 + x^2 + 3x &= 3 - 18 \\ 3x &= -15 \\ x &= -5 \end{aligned}$$

CHECK

$$\begin{aligned} 8 - (x - 5)(x + 2) &= 3 - x^2 \\ 8 - (-5 - 5)(-5 + 2) &\stackrel{?}{=} 3 - (-5)^2 \\ 8 - (-10)(-3) &\stackrel{?}{=} 3 - 25 \\ -22 &= -22 \ \checkmark \end{aligned}$$

CLASSROOM EXERCISES

Solve and check.

1. $3(x + 6) = 21$
2. $(5x - 1) = 6(x - 3)$
3. $6x - (3x - 4) = 14$
4. $2x - (13 - 2x) = 61$
5. $15 + 6x = 7(x - 2)$
6. $5(x + 4) - 4(x + 3) = 0$
7. $3x - 8 = 3(7 - x)$
8. $3 - (x + 29) = 12x$
9. $3c - 4(c + 2) = 5$
10. $(x + 2)(x + 1) = x^2 + 8$
11. $(x + 1)(x + 1) = x^2 + 9$
12. $4 + (x - 2)^2 = x^2 + 6$

EXERCISES

A Solve and check.

1. $9x - (3x - 18) = 36$
2. $8x - (2x + 5) = 0$
3. $9x - (5x - 2) = 8$
4. $2p - (4 - p) = 0$
5. $5(2p + 3) = 2(4p - 1)$
6. $5(2 - 3x) = 15 - (x + 7)$
7. $40 = 16 - 4(9 - 3k)$
8. $5x + 2(4x - 5) = 30$
9. $-(5x + 4) - 6x = 7$
10. $y + (2y - 1) = 2$
11. $3(2 - y) = 5(3 - y)$
12. $3c - (c + 2) = 2$
13. $14 = 5x + 3(2 - x)$
14. $2(3x + 1) - 2(15 - 4x) = 0$
15. $(x + 1)^2 - x^2 = 7$
16. $(x - 5)^2 = x^2 + 5$
17. $(x - 1)^2 - (x + 1)^2 = 4$
18. $(2x - 1)(2x + 3) = 4x^2 + 9$
19. $x - 3(x + 4) = 2$
20. $(x - 2)(x - 6) - (x - 8)(x - 3) = 0$

B

21. $(x - 3)^2 - (2x - 1)^2 = 3(2 - x^2)$
22. $(5x + 7)(6x - 2) - 15x(2x - 3) = 35$
23. $(3x + 5)(4x - 1) - 2(3x - 1)(2x + 3) = 0$
24. $3(4x - 3)^2 - (x + 6)(x - 5) = 47x^2 - 16$
25. $(4x + 1)(2x - 5) - 2(6x - 1)(6x + 1) + 37 = -64x^2$
26. $4(x \quad 6)^2 \quad (x \quad 1)^2 \quad 3x(x \quad 8) = \quad 11$
27. $(x - 2)(x + 2)(x - 3) = (x - 1)^3 - 1$
28. $(x - 1)(x + 1)(x - 2) = x^3 - 2x^2 - 3$
29. $(x - 3)(x + 4)(x + 3) = x^2(x + 4)$
30. $(x - 3)^3 - (x - 2)^3 = -3x(x - 4) - 19$

C Solve for x.

31. $(c + d)x = m(c + d)$
32. $(a - b)x = 2(a - b)$
33. $\frac{1}{3}(2acx) = b$

A MENTAL BLOCK

A block has a mass of 12 kg plus $\frac{1}{2}$ a block. Find the mass of the block.

0.89 INFLATION

The Constant feature of a calculator is useful for working with problems related to the inflation (or increase) of prices.

An *inflation rate* tells us how much prices increase over a period of time. For example, an annual inflation rate of 12% means that prices increase 12% per year. Each year, prices are 1.12 times as great as they were the previous year.

EXAMPLE Suppose an inflation rate of 12% is predicted for each of the next five years. Estimate what the price may be five years from now for a bicycle that presently sells for $85.

SOLUTION

Present price in dollars	85
Price after one year	$(1.12)(85)$
Price after two years	$(1.12)^2(85)$
Price after three years	$(1.12)^3(85)$
Price after four years	$(1.12)^4(85)$
Price after five years	$(1.12)^5(85)$

Press 85 [×] 1.12 [=] [=] [=] [=] [=]

The display will show 149.79904

CONCLUSION In five years the price should be about $150.

Copy and complete this chart. Assume the inflation rate will be $12\frac{1}{2}\%$ per year for 10 years.

	Item	Present Price	Price in 5 Years	Price in 10 Years
1.	Loaf of bread	$0.61	?	?
2.	Pair of jeans	$16	?	?
3.	Radial tire	$75	?	?
4.	Motorcycle	$1 500	?	?
5.	Automobile	$7 500	?	?
6.	House	$90 000	?	?

6-9 PROBLEM SOLVING: UNIFORM MOTION PROBLEMS

Problems that involve distance, time, and a uniform rate are called uniform motion problems. The formula $d = rt$ gives the distance traveled when the uniform rate and the time of travel are known.

EXAMPLE 1 Two airplanes start from the same place and fly in opposite directions. One airplane travels 100 kilometers per hour faster than the other. Two hours later they are 2260 kilometers apart. Find the rate of each.

Ⓜ SOLUTION

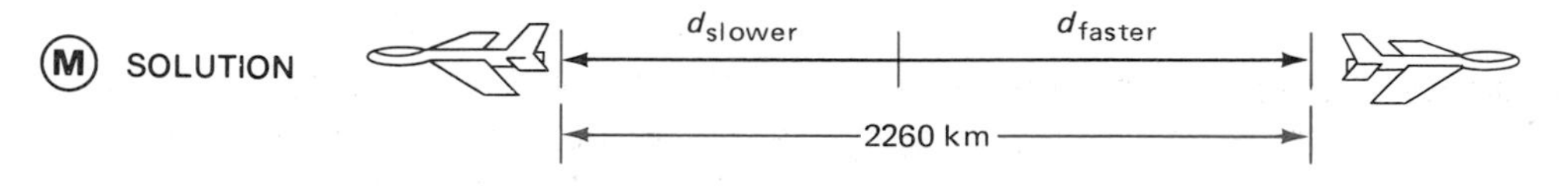

The sum of the distances is 2260 km.

Use r for the rate of the slower airplane in kilometers per hour.

	rate	· time	= distance	
Slower airplane	r	2	$2r$	$h \cdot \frac{km}{h} = km$
Faster airplane	$r + 100$	2	$2(r + 100)$	$h \cdot \frac{km}{h} = km$

$\frac{km}{h} + \frac{km}{h} = \frac{km}{h}$

$$\begin{aligned} d_{slower} + d_{faster} &= 2260 \\ 2r + 2(r + 100) &= 2260 \\ 2r + 2r + 200 &= 2260 \\ 4r &= 2060 \\ r &= 515 \\ \text{Also, } r + 100 &= 615. \end{aligned}$$

$km + km = km$

CONCLUSION The rate for the slower airplane was 515 km/h. The rate for the faster airplane was 615 km/h.

CHECK Will the two airplanes, one with a rate of 515 km/h and the other with a rate of 615 km/h, be 2260 km apart in 2 hours?

$$\begin{aligned} 2 \cdot 515 + 2 \cdot 615 &\stackrel{?}{=} 2260 \\ 1030 + 1230 &\stackrel{?}{=} 2260 \\ 2260 &= 2260 \ \checkmark \end{aligned}$$

EXAMPLE 2 A fully-loaded produce truck travels to a market at 60 km/h. It leaves at 6 A.M. The return trip begins at 3 P.M. It is made at 80 km/h and takes 1.5 hours less time. Find the total travel time for the trip to and from the market.

Ⓜ SOLUTION

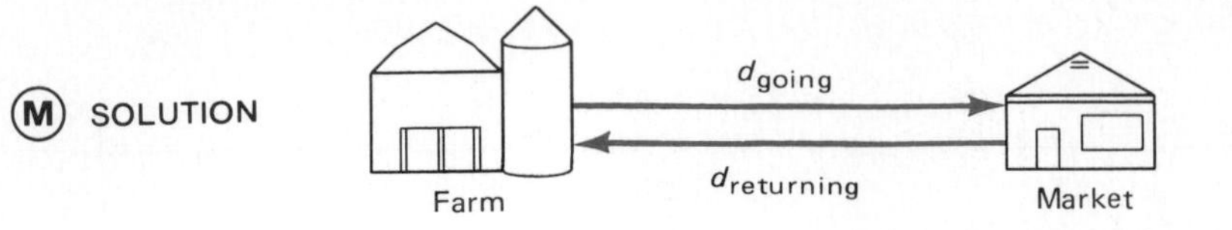

The distance to market equals the return distance.

Use t for the time in hours for the trip to market.

	rate ·	time =	distance
Going	60	t	$60t$
Returning	80	$t - 1.5$	$80(t - 1.5)$

$\frac{\text{km}}{\text{h}} \cdot \text{h} = \text{km}$

$\text{h} - \text{h} = \text{h}, \quad \frac{\text{km}}{\text{h}} \cdot \text{h} = \text{km}$

$\text{km} = \text{km}$

$$
\begin{aligned}
d_{going} &= d_{returning} \\
60t &= 80(t - 1.5) \\
60t &= 80t - 120 \\
120 &= 20t \\
t &= 6 \\
\text{Also, } t - 1.5 &= 4.5.
\end{aligned}
$$

CONCLUSION The total time for the trip was 10.5 hours.

CHECK Is the distance traveled in 6 hours at 60 km/h equal to the distance traveled in 4.5 hours at 80 km/h?

$$
\begin{aligned}
60(6) &\stackrel{?}{=} 80(4.5) \\
360 &= 360 \checkmark
\end{aligned}
$$

EXAMPLE 3 An hour after Bill left on a bicycle trip, his family found that he had forgotten a package. Debbie, an older sister, started after Bill in her car. If Bill was traveling at the rate of 12 km/h and Debbie drove at the rate of 60 km/h, how long did it take Debbie to catch up with Bill?

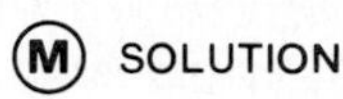

SOLUTION

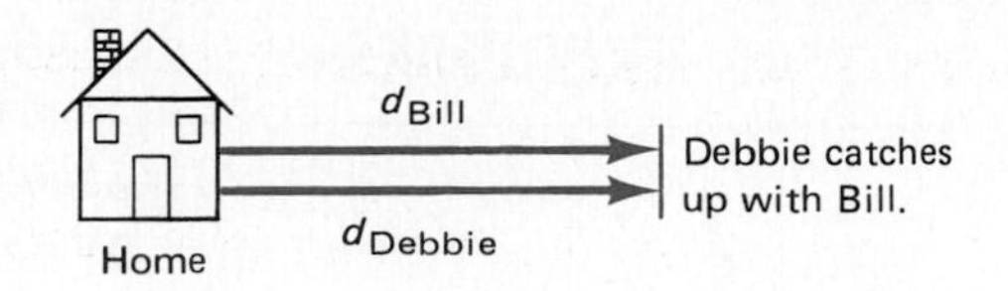

The distance Debbie travels equals the distance Bill travels.

Use t for the number of hours it took Debbie to catch up with Bill.

	rate	time	= distance
Debbie	60	t	$60t$
Bill	12	$t + 1$	$12(t + 1)$

$\frac{km}{h} \cdot h = km$

$h + h = h, \quad \frac{km}{h} \cdot h = km$

$$d_{Debbie} = d_{Bill}$$
$$60t = 12(t + 1)$$
$$60t = 12t + 12$$
$$48t = 12$$
$$t = \frac{1}{4}$$

$km = km$

CONCLUSION It took Debbie $\frac{1}{4}$ hour to catch up with Bill.

CHECK Did Debbie, who drove at a rate of 60 km/h for $\frac{1}{4}$ hour, travel the same distance as Bill, who bicycled at a rate of 12 km/h for $1\frac{1}{4}$ hours?

$$60\left(\frac{1}{4}\right) \stackrel{!}{=} 12\left(1\frac{1}{4}\right)$$
$$15 = 15 \checkmark$$

CLASSROOM EXERCISES

Solve.

1. Joe travels 18 km/h. Dave travels 30 km/h in the opposite direction. How many hours has Dave traveled when they are 90 km apart?

2. Jane rode her bike at a rate of 8 km/h. One hour later Lisa started after Jane on her bike. Lisa caught up with Jane in 2 hours. What was Lisa's rate?

3. Luis and Joel are 25 km apart and walk toward each other at the rates of 3.5 km/h and 4 km/h respectively. After how long do they meet?

4. Two automobiles, starting from Chicago, travel east and west respectively. The first travels 0.8 as fast as the second. In 4 hours they are 648 kilometers apart. Find the rate of each.

EXERCISES

A Solve.

1. Al travels 8 km/h. Ben leaves from the same place at the same time as Al and travels 20 km/h in the opposite direction. How many hours has Ben traveled when they are 180 km apart?

2. Two cars move toward each other from points that are 288 km apart. The speeds of the cars are 64 km/h and 56 km/h. In how many hours will they meet?

3. Portland, Oregon, and Seattle, Washington, are about 280 km apart by road. Driver A leaves Portland for Seattle at 8 o'clock and driver B leaves Seattle for Portland at 9 o'clock on the same road. Driver A travels at the rate of 70 km/h. Driver B travels at the rate of 80 km/h. At what time will the drivers pass each other?

4. Sue and Beth started from the same place and traveled in opposite directions at 70 km/h and 30 km/h respectively. Sue started 3 hours before Beth. How long had Beth traveled when they were 360 km apart?

5. A boat started from Norfolk towards Annapolis at 10 km/h. Two hours later another boat started from Norfolk to Annapolis at 14 km/h. How long did it take the second boat to overtake the first?

6. Dawn rides her bicycle at an average rate of 14 km/h. Four hours later Sharon starts after Dawn on a motorcycle and overtakes her in 2 hours. What is Sharon's rate?

7. Consuela walks from A to B at 3 km/h and returns by bicycle at 12 km/h. Her return journey takes $2\frac{1}{4}$ hours less time than her outward journey. Find her time for the entire journey.

8. A jet airplane traveled for 5 hours at its regular cruising speed. At the end of that time it had to turn back towards its base, moving at three-fourths the speed it had on its outward journey. After flying back for 6 hours, the airplane still had 400 km to go to reach its base. Find the regular speed of the airplane.

9. A train traveling 80 km/h left a station 30 minutes before a second train traveling 88 km/h. How soon did the second train overtake the first?

10. A taxi traveling 44 km/h is followed 10 minutes later by another taxi which travels 66 km/h. In how many minutes will the second taxi overtake the first?

11. Two cities A and B are 268 km apart. At 3 P.M. Mary starts from A towards B at 74 km/h and half an hour later Bob starts from B towards A at 80 km/h. At what time will they meet and how far will each have driven by that time?

12. Two airplanes start at the same time from cities 2448 km apart. They meet in $1\frac{1}{2}$ hours. The rate of one airplane is 288 km/h less than the rate of the other. What is the rate of each?

B 13. A rancher drove to town at a rate of 64 km/h and returned at 80 km/h. How much time was taken for each direction if the total driving time was 1 hour 21 minutes?

14. A light airplane flew the 342 km from Nashville to Atlanta in $1\frac{1}{2}$ hours. On the return flight, the rate of the airplane increased by 16 kilometers per hour

due to a tail wind. How long did the return flight take?

15. Teresa walks at a rate of 3 km/h. How far can she walk and then ride a bicycle back at the rate of 12 km/h if she must be back $2\frac{1}{2}$ hours after she starts?

16. In 2 hours 42 minutes, how far can an airplane go out and return if the rate going is 448 km/h and the rate returning is 560 km/h?

17. A jet airplane flying at an average speed of 864 km/h passes over Kennedy Airport in New York City at 3:00 P.M. An hour later, a supersonic jet following the same course passes Kennedy Airport. It overtakes the slower jet at 4:45 P.M. What was the average speed of the supersonic jet?

C **18.** An airplane requires 6 hours less time for a trip of 360 km than an automobile that travels at one fourth the rate of the airplane. How fast does each travel?

19. The Indianapolis Speedway is 4 km around. How long will it take a driver going 250 km/h to gain a lap on a driver going 240 km/h?

A MODEL FOR THE PRODUCT OF TWO BINOMIALS

The product of two binomials may be shown using rectangles and their areas.

EXAMPLE Use a rectangle to show the product of $x + 2$ and $2x + 3$.

SOLUTION

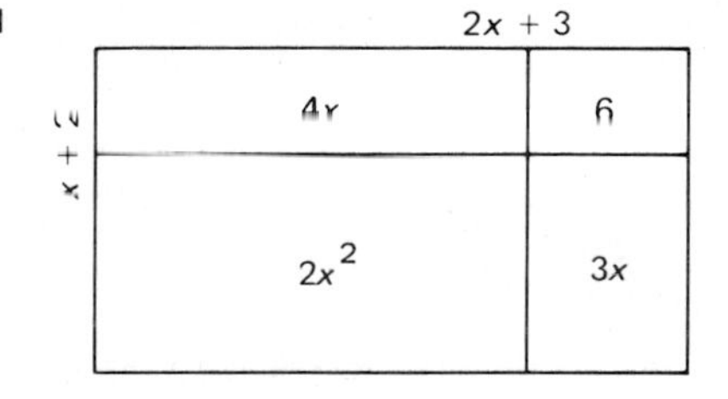

$$(x + 2)(2x + 3)$$
$$= 2x^2 + 4x + 3x + 6$$
$$= 2x^2 + 7x + 6$$

Draw a rectangle to show each product.

1. $(x + 3)(x + 2)$ **2.** $(2x + 1)(x + 4)$ **3.** $(3x + 5)(5x + 3)$

Draw a square to show each product.

4. $(x + 3)^2$ **5.** $(2x + 1)^2$ **6.** $(3x + 4)^2$

Try to show each of these with a picture.

7. $(x - 2)^2 = x^2 - 4x + 4$ **8.** $(x - 3)(x + 3) = x^2 - 9$

6-10 PROBLEM SOLVING: WORK PROBLEMS

Many work problems involve the relationship

amount of work done = rate of work · time spent working.

EXAMPLE 1 One printing press can print 4000 copies an hour, and another can print 6000 an hour. After the first press has been running 2 hours, the second press is started. How soon after the second press is started will 40 000 copies be printed?

Ⓜ **SOLUTION** The sum of the numbers of copies printed by both machines is 40 000.

Use t for the number of hours the second press runs.

$\frac{\text{copies}}{\text{h}} \cdot \text{h} = \text{copies}$

$\text{h} + \text{h} = \text{h}, \quad \frac{\text{copies}}{\text{h}} \cdot \text{h} = \text{copies}$

	rate	· time	= work
Second press	6000	t	$6000t$
First press	4000	$t + 2$	$4000(t + 2)$

copies + copies = copies

$$w_{\text{second}} + w_{\text{first}} = 40\,000$$
$$6000t + 4000(t + 2) = 40\,000$$
$$6000t + 4000t + 8000 = 40\,000$$
$$10\,000t = 40\,000 - 8000$$
$$10\,000t = 32\,000$$
$$t = 3\tfrac{1}{5}$$

Also, $t + 2 = 5\frac{1}{5}$.

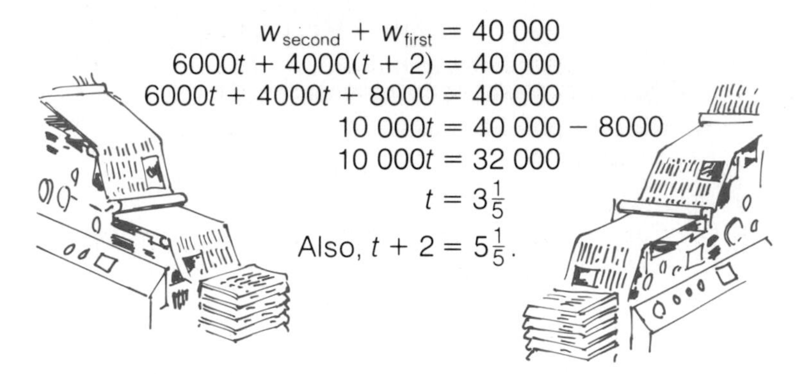

CONCLUSION In $3\frac{1}{5}$ hours after the second press is started, 40 000 copies will be printed.

CHECK If the second press runs for $3\frac{1}{5}$ hours and the first for $5\frac{1}{5}$ hours, will they print 40 000 copies?

$$6000 \cdot 3\tfrac{1}{5} + 4000 \cdot 5\tfrac{1}{5} \stackrel{?}{=} 40\,000$$
$$19\,200 + 20\,800 \stackrel{?}{=} 40\,000$$
$$40\,000 = 40\,000 \checkmark$$

To solve some work problems, it is necessary to find what part of the work can be done in one unit of time.

EXAMPLE 2 Jan can do a piece of work in 3 days and Francesca can do the same work in 2 days. How long will it take them to do the work if they work together?

SOLUTION The work done by Jan together with the work done by Francesca equals the whole piece of work.

Since Jan can do all the work in three days, her rate is $\frac{1}{3}$ of the work per day. Since Francesca can do all the work in 2 days, her rate is $\frac{1}{2}$ of the work per day.

Ⓜ Use t for the number of days needed to do the work when Jan and Francesca work together.

	rate	· time =	work
Jan	$\frac{1}{3}$	t	$\frac{1}{3}t$
Francesca	$\frac{1}{2}$	t	$\frac{1}{2}t$

$\frac{\text{work}}{\text{d}} \cdot \text{d} = \text{work}$

$\frac{\text{work}}{\text{d}} \cdot \text{d} = \text{work}$

$$work_J + work_F = work_{complete}$$
$$\frac{1}{3}t + \frac{1}{2}t = 1$$
$$\frac{5}{6}t = 1$$
$$5t = 6$$
$$t = \frac{6}{5}, \text{ or } 1\frac{1}{5}$$

$\frac{1}{3}$ is the fraction of the complete job that Jan can do in 1 day. $\frac{1}{3}t$ is the fraction of the complete job that Jan can do in t days. Similarly $\frac{1}{2}t$ is the fraction of the complete job that Francesca can do in t days. The sum of these two fractions is 1, the complete job.

CONCLUSION Jan and Francesca, working together, could do the work in $1\frac{1}{5}$ days.

CHECK If Jan can do $\frac{1}{3}$ of the work in 1 day and Francesca can do $\frac{1}{2}$ of the work in 1 day, can they, working together, complete the work in $\frac{6}{5}$ days?

Completing this check is left for the student.

CLASSROOM EXERCISES

Solve.

1. Mike can mow the lawn in 45 minutes. Phil can mow it in 30 minutes. How long would it take if they work together?
2. Susan can finish a job in $5\frac{1}{2}$ days. Her father can do it in $3\frac{1}{2}$ days. How long will it take them to finish the job working together?

EXERCISES

A Solve.

1. Jeff can mow the lawn in 2 hours. Jessie can mow it in 3 hours. How long will it take them if they work together?
2. Lola can complete a job in 8 days. Carol can do the same job in 10 days. How long will it take them to do the job together?
3. One printing press can print 4000 copies an hour. Another can print 3000 copies an hour. After the first press has been going 3 hours, the second press is started. How soon after the start of the second press will 50 500 copies be printed?
4. One photocopying machine can make 50 copies per minute. A second machine can make 24 copies per minute. After the first machine has been going 20 minutes, the second machine is started. How soon after the start of the second machine will 2850 copies be made?
5. Bonita can shovel the snow off the driveway in $1\frac{1}{2}$ hours. Abel can shovel it in $\frac{3}{4}$ of an hour. How long will it take them if they work together?
6. Frank can dig a trench in 15 hours. His father can dig it in 9 hours. How long will it take Frank and his father to dig the trench working together?
7. A tank can be filled in 7 hours by water passing through one valve. It can be filled in 3 hours by water passing through another valve. How long does it take for the tank to be filled when both valves are open?
8. One pipe can fill a tank in $2\frac{1}{2}$ hours. Another can empty the tank in $3\frac{1}{3}$ hours. When both pipes are left open, how long will it take to fill the tank?
9. Hugh can do a job in 15 hours. Joan can do it in 12 hours. Gina can do it in 10 hours. How long would it take them to do the job working together?

B

10. Mary can grade a set of papers in 45 minutes. Jane can grade the set in 50 minutes. Frances can grade the set in 40 minutes. How long will it take all three working together to do the grading?
11. Adele can make a quilt in 6 days, Gary in 10 days, and Sarah in 15 days. Adele and Gary work for 3 days. How long will it take Gary and Sarah to finish?
12. Peg and Joy can each gather a basket of berries in 18 minutes. Marla takes 27 minutes. They have to gather 10 baskets of berries and all work for 30 minutes. How long will it take Joy to finish after the others stop working?

C

13. When two machines operate for the same time, they can complete a certain job in 5 hours. The faster machine could do the whole job alone in $6\frac{2}{3}$ hours. What is the ratio of their speeds?
14. A tank can be filled in 9 hours by one pipe and in 5 hours by another pipe. It is emptied by a third pipe in 15 hours. How long will it take to fill the tank when the three pipes are open?
15. Mark can paint the fence around his house in 15 hours. His sister Jean can do it in 18 hours. Mark paints for 7 hours alone and then turns over the rest of the job to Jean. How long will it take Jean to finish painting the fence?

6-11 PROBLEM SOLVING: MIXTURE PROBLEMS

In mixture problems, we assume that the value of a mixture equals the combined values of the ingredients. In turn, the value of an ingredient is the product of the number of units of the ingredient and the value of each unit. When solving a mixture problem, it often is helpful to make a sketch.

EXAMPLE 1 Clover seed worth \$1.60 a kilogram is added to timothy seed worth \$1.00 a kilogram to make a mixture worth \$1.20 a kilogram. How many kilograms of clover seed and timothy seed are needed for 300 kg of the mixture?

This is another example of a rate situation. See the note on p. 162.

Ⓜ SOLUTION The sum of the values of the clover seed and the timothy seed equals the value of the mixture.

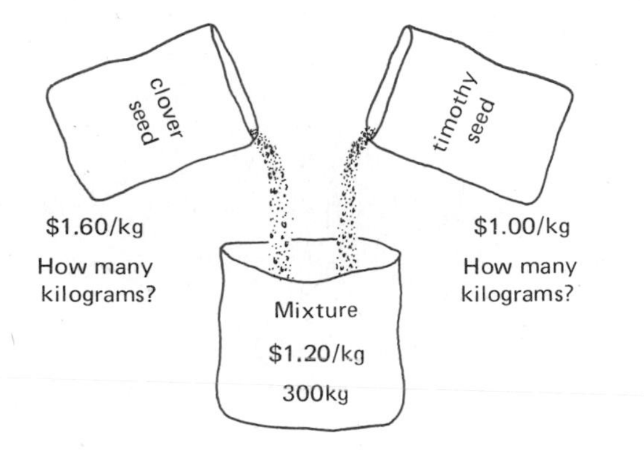

Use x for the number of kilograms of clover seed.

	unit value ·	number of units =	value
clover seed	1.60	x	$1.60x$
timothy seed	1.00	$300 - x$	$1.00(300 - x)$
mixture	1.20	300	$1.20(300)$

$\frac{\$}{kg} \cdot kg = \$$

kg − kg = kg, $\frac{\$}{kg} \cdot kg = \$$

$\frac{\$}{kg} \cdot kg = \$$

$$\begin{aligned} value_c + value_t &= value_m \\ 1.60x + 1.00(300 - x) &= 1.20(300) \\ 1.60x + 300 - x &= 360 \\ 0.60x &= 60 \\ x &= 100 \end{aligned}$$

Also, $300 - x = 200$.

\$ + \$ = \$

CONCLUSION 100 kg of clover seed and 200 kg of timothy seed are needed.

Does this conclusion agree with the problem situation? Try a check. Then turn the page and compare.

CHECK (Example 1) Is 100 kg of clover at \$1.60/kg and 200 kg of timothy seed at \$1.00/kg equal in value to 300 kg of a mixture worth \$1.20/kg?

$$100(1.60) + 200(1.00) \stackrel{?}{=} 300(1.20)$$
$$160 + 200 \stackrel{?}{=} 360$$
$$360 = 360 \checkmark$$

In mixture problems that involve percent, remember that you must compare a part to the total amount.

EXAMPLE 2 A 10% solution of iodine contains 10% iodine and 90% alcohol. How much pure alcohol must be added to one liter of a 10% solution of iodine to produce a 6% solution of iodine?

(M) SOLUTION

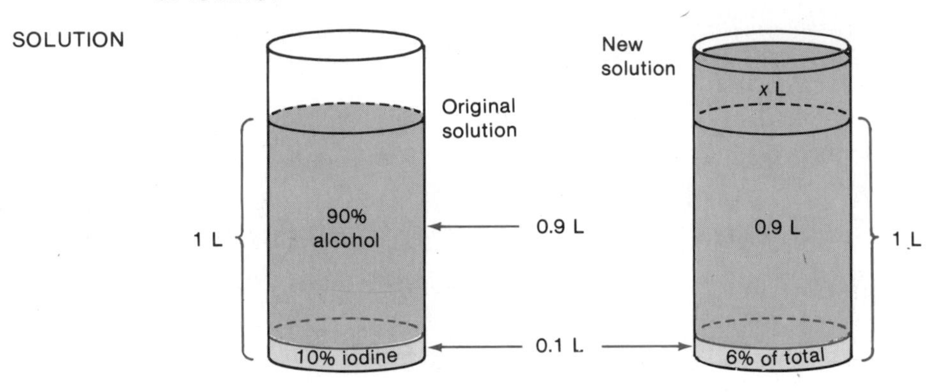

The amount of iodine remains constant.
10% of the original solution equals 6% of the new solution.

Use x for the number of liters of pure alcohol to be added to the solution.
$1 + x$ for the number of liters of the new solution.

L + L = L

(dimensionless) · L = (dimensionless) · L

$$0.10(1) = 0.06(1 + x)$$
$$0.10 = 0.06 + 0.06x$$
$$0.04 = 0.06x$$
$$M_{100} \quad 4 = 6x$$
$$x = \tfrac{2}{3}, \text{ or approximately } 0.67$$

CONCLUSION About 0.67 liter of alcohol should be added to the original solution.

CHECK Is 10% of 1 liter of solution equal to 6% of 1.67 liters of solution?

Completing this check is left for the student.

For comparison or to serve as a check, redo this example based on the alcohol content.

CLASSROOM EXERCISES

Solve.

1. How many kilograms of nuts worth $4.00 a kilogram should be mixed with 20 kg of nuts worth $3.20 a kilogram to produce a mixture worth $3.40 a kilogram?
2. How much water must be added to 4 liters of an 80% alcohol solution to make a solution that is 60% alcohol?

EXERCISES

A Solve.

1. How many kilograms of cashew nuts worth $6.60 a kilogram must be mixed with 10 kilograms of pecans worth $8.50 a kilogram to make a mixture worth $7.10 a kilogram?
2. How many kilograms of coffee worth $4.00 a kilogram must be mixed with 6 kilograms of coffee worth $4.75 a kilogram to make a mixture worth $4.45 a kilogram?
3. Peppermint tea costs $8.20 a kilogram. Licorice tea costs $6.40 a kilogram. How many kilograms of each kind must be used to make a 30-kilogram mixture worth $7.60 a kilogram?
4. Clover honey, selling for $5.20 a kilogram, is blended with alfalfa honey, selling for $3.20 a kilogram. The resulting mixture sells for $4.60 a kilogram. How much of each kind of honey is needed for 20 kilograms of the mixture?
5. Two kinds of coffee are blended to produce a mixture of 25 kilograms worth $5.20 a kilogram. The costs of the two kinds of coffee are $4.00 and $5.60 a kilogram. Find how many kilograms of each kind are blended.
6. Sue blends cream cheese worth $1.80 a kilogram, cheddar cheese worth $3.30 a kilogram, and blue cheese worth $3.60 a kilogram to make a cheese spread mixture worth $3.20 a kilogram. She uses 1 kg of cream cheese and 2 kg of cheddar. How much blue cheese does she use?
7. How many liters of water must be added to 10 L of a 95% solution of ammonia to make a solution that is 80% ammonia?
8. A 12-liter antifreeze solution of water and alcohol is 20% alcohol. How much pure alcohol must be added to make the solution 40% alcohol?
9. An alloy of copper and zinc consists of 75 kg of copper and 25 kg of zinc. How many kilograms of pure copper must be added to the alloy so that it will be 80% copper?
10. There are 8 L of alcohol in a mixture of 24 L of alcohol and water. How many liters of alcohol must be added to make a mixture that is 50% alcohol?
11. How many kilograms of water must be added to 40 kg of a 15% salt solution to produce a 10% salt solution?

B

12. Some Girl Scouts wish to make a mixture of two kinds of cookies which they can sell at 92 cents a kilogram. They use 12 kg of cookies that sell for x cents a kilogram and 18 kg of cookies that sell for $(x + 20)$ cents a kilogram. For how much per kilogram can each of these two kinds of cookies be sold?
13. An order of birdseed cost $14. It contained one kind of seed worth 60 cents a kilogram and another worth 50 cents a kilogram. There were 5 more kilograms of the 60-cent seed than of the 50-cent seed. How many kilograms of each kind were in the order?

14. How many liters of cream containing 40% fat must be mixed with 160 L of non-fat milk to make milk containing 8% fat?

15. A solution of 60 kg of salt and water is 5% salt. How much water must be evaporated so that the solution will be 10% salt?

C **16.** An automobile radiator contains 12 L of a mixture of water and antifreeze. The mixture is now 20% antifreeze. How much of the mixture must be drawn off and replaced by pure antifreeze to get a mixture containing 30% antifreeze?

17. At most, how many liters of antifreeze solution containing 40% glycerine should be drawn from a radiator containing 32 liters and replaced with water so that the new radiator solution is at least 20% glycerine?

18. Instead of being pure silver, a silver medal may be 0.9 pure, or "0.9 fine." How much pure silver must be melted with 5600 g of silver that is 0.6 fine to make it 0.9 fine?

19. There are two solutions of iodine, one of strength 8% and the other of strength 24%. How much of each solution should be mixed to obtain 16 mL of a 12% solution of iodine?

A PRIME INVESTIGATION

A whole number greater than 1 is a **prime number** if it has no whole number factors other than itself and 1. Study this chart:

Every number in column A has 2 as a factor.

Every number in column B has 3 as a factor.

Every number in column C has 2 as a factor.

Every number in column E has 6 as a factor.

A	B	C	D	E	F
2	3	4	5	6	7
8	9	10	11	12	13
14	15	16	17	18	19
20	21	22	23	24	25
26	27	28	29	30	31
32	⋯				

Thus, except for 2 and 3, there is no prime number in columns A, B, C, or E. All the prime numbers greater than 3 must be in columns D or F. This means that all prime numbers greater than 3 will be 1 less than or 1 greater than a multiple of 6.

1. Is every number in column F a prime number?
2. Is every number in column D a prime number?
3. How many numbers from 2 to 100 are prime numbers?
4. How many numbers from 101 to 200 are prime numbers? from 201 to 300?
5. Can you find a pattern?

6-12 DIVIDING POLYNOMIALS

The division of one polynomial by another is similar to the division of one number by another. Compare.

EXAMPLE 1 Divide 695 by 31. | Divide $x^2 - 8x + 17$ by $x - 3$.

SOLUTION

$$\begin{array}{r} 2 \\ 31\overline{)695} \end{array} \qquad \begin{array}{r} x \\ x - 3\overline{)x^2 - 8x + 17} \end{array}$$

$$\begin{array}{r} 2 \\ 31\overline{)695} \\ 62 \\ \hline 75 \end{array} \qquad \begin{array}{r} x \\ x - 3\overline{)x^2 - 8x + 17} \\ x^2 - 3x \\ \hline -5x + 17 \end{array}$$

$$\begin{array}{r} 22 \\ 31\overline{)695} \\ 62 \\ \hline 75 \end{array} \qquad \begin{array}{r} x - 5 \\ x - 3\overline{)x^2 - 8x + 17} \\ x^2 - 3x \\ \hline -5x + 17 \end{array}$$

$$\begin{array}{r} 22 \\ 31\overline{)695} \\ 62 \\ \hline 75 \\ 62 \\ \hline 13 \end{array} \qquad \begin{array}{r} x - 5 \\ x - 3\overline{)x^2 - 8x + 17} \\ x^2 - 3x \\ \hline -5x + 17 \\ -5x + 15 \\ \hline 2 \end{array}$$

$$695 \div 31 = 22 + \frac{13}{31} \qquad (x^2 - 8x + 17) \div (x - 3) = x - 5 + \frac{2}{x - 3}$$

CHECK Multiply 22 and 31. Then add the remainder. | Multiply $(x - 5)$ and $(x - 3)$. Then add the remainder.

$$\begin{array}{lr} & 22 \\ & 31 \\ \hline & 22 \\ & 66 \\ \hline & 682 \\ \text{Add} & 13 \\ \hline & 695 \end{array} \qquad \begin{array}{lr} & x - 5 \\ & x - 3 \\ \hline & x^2 - 5x \\ & -3x + 15 \\ \hline & x^2 - 8x + 15 \\ \text{Add} & 2 \\ \hline & x^2 - 8x + 17 \end{array} \checkmark$$

EXAMPLE 2 Divide $x^3 - 17xy^2 + 66y^3 - 5x^2y$ by $x - 6y$.

SOLUTION Arrange both polynomials in decreasing powers of x.

$$
\begin{array}{r l}
 & x^2 + xy - 11y^2 \\
x - 6y \,\big) & \overline{x^3 - 5x^2y - 17xy^2 + 66y^3} \\
 & x^3 - 6x^2y \\
\hline
 & \quad x^2y - 17xy^2 + 66y^3 \\
 & \quad x^2y - 6xy^2 \\
\hline
 & \qquad -11xy^2 + 66y^3 \\
 & \qquad -11xy^2 + 66y^3 \\
\hline
 & \qquad\qquad 0
\end{array}
$$

CHECK Multiplying
$x^2 + xy - 11y^2$ by $x - 6y$
is left for the student.

EXAMPLE 3 Divide $a^2 - 25$ by $a - 5$.

SOLUTION Since there is no term with a, $0a$ is inserted.

$$
\begin{array}{r l}
 & a + 5 \\
a - 5 \,\big) & \overline{a^2 + 0a - 25} \\
 & a^2 - 5a \\
\hline
 & \quad 5a - 25 \\
 & \quad 5a - 25 \\
\hline
 & \qquad 0
\end{array}
$$

CHECK The check is left for the student.

CLASSROOM EXERCISES

Divide. Check your results.

1. $x^2 - x - 6$ by $x - 3$
2. $y^2 + 4y + 4$ by $y + 2$
3. $12a^2 - 11ac + 2c^2$ by $4a - c$
4. $\dfrac{10x^2 + 29x + 21}{5x + 7}$
5. $\dfrac{y^3 - 7y + 6}{y - 2}$
6. $\dfrac{27y^2 - 24y + 8}{9y - 2}$

EXERCISES

A Divide. Check your results.

1. $m^2 + 8m + 12$ by $m + 2$
2. $c^2 + 11c + 24$ by $c + 3$
3. $x^2 - 9x + 20$ by $x - 4$
4. $x^2 - 12x + 35$ by $x - 5$
5. $y^2 - 9y + 15$ by $y - 2$
6. $x^2 - 7x + 14$ by $x - 3$
7. $2x^2 - 5x + 72$ by $x - 7$
8. $8x^2 + 3x + 4$ by $x - 3$
9. $x^2 - 4$ by $x + 2$
10. $x^2 - 16$ by $x + 4$
11. $x^2 - y^2$ by $x - y$
12. $a^2 - b^2$ by $a - b$
13. $h^2 - 64y^2$ by $h - 4y$
14. $a^2 - 28b^2$ by $a - 5b$
15. $4x^2 + x - 3$ by $x - 2$

16. $12x^2 - 11xy - 36y^2$ by $4x - 9y$

17. $8a^2 - 4ab - 12b^2$ by $2a - 3b$

18. $m^2 - 3mn - 88n^2$ by $m + 8n$

19. $r^2 - 8rs - 33s^2$ by $r + 3s$

B **20.** $2a^3b - 6a^2b + 18ab$ by $a^2 - 3a + 9$

21. $2x^3 + 11x - 3 - 9x^2$ by $2x - 3$

22. $4a^4 - 9a^2 + 6a - 1$ by $2a^2 - 1 + 3a$

23. $6x^3 - 18x + 12$ by $x - 1$

24. $a^3 - 1$ by $a - 1$

25. $a^3 + 1$ by $a + 1$

26. $a^3 + 8$ by $a + 2$

27. $x^3 - 27$ by $x - 3$

28. $x^3 + 64$ by $x + 4$

29. $27x^3 + 8$ by $3x + 2$

30. One factor of $x^5 + 1$ is $x + 1$. What is the other?

C Divide.

31. $a^4 + a^2b^2 + b^4$ by $a^2 - ab + b^2$

32. $a^3 - b^3 + c^3 - 3abc$ by $a + b + c$

33. $-7x^3 + 21 + 8x + 18x^2 + 6x^4$ by $3x^2 - 5x + 7$

34. $x^6 - y^6$ by $x^4 + x^2y^2 + y^4$

35. Find the number b for which $y + 3$ is a factor of $3y^2 + 2y + b$.

CHECKING YOUR UNDERSTANDING

CONCEPTS

- To multiply a polynomial by a polynomial, multiplying each term of one polynomial by each term of the other polynomial is necessary. [6-7]
- Dividing one polynomial by another is similar to dividing one number by another. [6-12]

PROCESSES

- Multiply and divide polynomials. [6-7, 6-12]

  1. $(2x + 2)(3x^2 - 4x + 5)$

  2. $(2x^2 - 13x + 15) \div (x - 5)$

- Solve equations that contain products involving polynomials. [6-8]

  3. $2(x - 5) - 3(10 - x) = 20$

  4. $(x - 2)(x + 3) = x(x + 4)$

- Solve a problem using an equation that contains products involving polynomials. [6-9 to 6-11]

  5. Two jet airplanes pass each other. One is flying north. The other is flying south at a rate 100 km/h faster than the first airplane. In two hours they are 3000 km apart. Find the rate of each.

  6. Machine A can package 3000 items an hour. Machine B can package 5000 items an hour. In one run of 26 000 items, machine A is used for 2 hours before machine B is turned on. How long must machine B run before the job is completed?

CHAPTER REVIEW

Find the sum for each set of polynomials. [6-1]

1. $3x + 2y + 7,\ 2x - y - 4,\ 4x - 1$
2. $5x^3 + 4x^2 - 6x + 7,\ x^3 - 3x^2 - 6x + 1,\ 2x^3 + 2x^2 - x$
3. $2x^3 - 3y^3,\ x^2y + 4xy^2 + y^3,\ -6x - 5x^2y + 5xy^2 - 4y^3$

Subtract. [6-2]

4. $2x^3 - x^2 + 3x + 1$ from $2x^3 + x^2 - 4x - 3$
5. $3m^3 + m^2 + 2m - 4$ from $7m^3 - 4m^2 - 4$
6. $t^3 - 3t^2r - 4r^2$ from $t^3 - 2t^2r - tr^2$

Multiply. [6-3]

7. $2ab$ and $-3c$
8. $5x^3$ and x^5
9. $-3x^2y$ and $-2xy^2z$

Simplify.

10. $(x^3)^4$
11. $(-2x^4)^3$
12. $(3x^2y)^4$

Simplify each product. [6-4]

13. $5(3m - n + 4)$
14. $-2x(-4x^2 - 3x + 2)$

Divide. [6-5]

15. $24a^2b$ by $8ab$
16. $-48x^6y^4b^2$ by $16x^2y^4b^6$
17. $18cd$ by $-72dc$

Simplify each quotient. [6-6]

18. $\dfrac{a^4 + a^3 - a^2}{-1}$
19. $\dfrac{x^6 - 5x^4 - x^3}{x^2}$
20. $\dfrac{3x^3 - 9x^2 + 3x}{-3x}$

Find the product. [6-7]

21. $(a + b)(a + b - c)$
22. $(3m - n)(m^2 + mn + 1)$
23. $(2x - 3y)(x^2 - 2y^2 + xy)$

Solve. [6-8]

24. $(a + 3)(a + 2) = (a - 3)(a - 1)$
25. $4x^2 - 4(x - 2)^2 = 4x$

Solve. [6-9]

26. One bicyclist rides 4 km/h faster than another. They ride in opposite directions for 3 hours and are then 72 km apart. Find the rate for each.

Solve. [6-10]

27. Haydee can mow the lawn in 2 hours. Jaime takes 3 hours for the job. How long would it take them if they mowed the lawn together.

28. Darrell can build a cabinet in 12 hours. Lionel can build one in 9 hours. After Darrell has worked on a cabinet for 5 hours, he is joined by Lionel. How long does it take them to finish the cabinet?

Solve. [6-11]

29. How many kilograms of coffee worth \$4 per kilogram must be mixed with 30 kg of coffee worth \$5 per kilogram to make a blend worth \$4.40 per kilogram?

30. How many liters of water must be added to 10 L of a 5% salt solution to produce a 4% salt solution?

Divide. [6-12]

31. $x^2 + 5x + 6$ by $x + 3$ **32.** $1 + 7x + 12x^2$ by $1 + 3x$ **33.** $4x^2 - 9$ by $2x - 3$

34. $6b^3 + 7ab^2 - 9a^2b + 2a^3$ by $3b - a$ **35.** $4x^2 - 16xy + 15y^2$ by $2x - 3y$

CAPSULE REVIEW

Write the letter of the best response.

1. $(6a^2b^3c)(-3a^2b^3c) =$

a. -2 **b.** $3a^2b^3c$ **c.** $-18a^2b^3c$ **d.** $-18a^4b^9c$ **e.** $-18a^4b^6c^2$

2. $xy^2 + x^2y =$

a. $2xy^2$ **b.** $2x^2y$ **c.** 0 **d.** $2x^2y^2$ **e.** none of these

3. When $3abc$ is subtracted from $-3a^2b^2c^2$, the difference is

a. 0 **b.** $6abc$ **c.** $-3a^2b^2c^2 - 3abc$ **d.** $3a^2b^2c^2 + 3abc$ **e.** $-6a^2b^2c^2$

4. The product of $(5x)^2$ and $5x$ is

a. $10x^2$ **b.** $125x^2$ **c.** $25x^2$ **d.** $125x^3$ **e.** $30x^2$

5. Which of these is (are) equivalent to $(-5x^8y^6)^2$?

A. $(25x^4y^4)(x^4y^4)$ B. $(5x^8y^6)(5x^8y^6)$ C. $25x^{16}y^{12}$

a. A only **b.** B only **c.** C only **d.** A and B only **e.** B and C only

6. The base, b, of a triangle is 2 units greater than its altitude, a. Both the base and the altitude are increased by 3 units. The area of the larger triangle is given by

a. $\frac{1}{2}(a + 3)(b + 3)$ **b.** $\frac{1}{2}(a + 3)(b + 5)$ **c.** $\frac{1}{2}(a + 5)(b + 5)$ **d.** $\frac{1}{2}(a + 5)(b + 3)$

7. The solution for $(x - 1)^2 + 1 = x^2$ is the same as the solution for

a. $(x + 1)^2 + 1 = x^2$ **b.** $(-1 + x)^2 + 1 = x^2$

c. $(-1 - x)^2 + 1 = x^2$ **d.** $(1 - x)^2 - 1 = x^2$

8. Jo can do a certain amount of work, w, in three 8-hour days. The amount of work Jo can do in one hour is

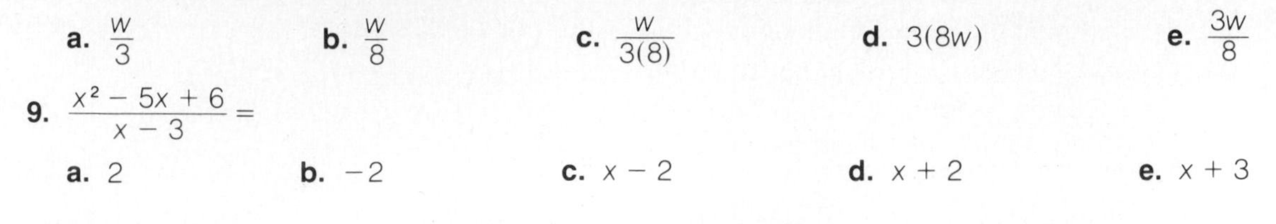

a. $\frac{w}{3}$ **b.** $\frac{w}{8}$ **c.** $\frac{w}{3(8)}$ **d.** $3(8w)$ **e.** $\frac{3w}{8}$

9. $\frac{x^2 - 5x + 6}{x - 3} =$

a. 2 **b.** -2 **c.** $x - 2$ **d.** $x + 2$ **e.** $x + 3$

CHAPTER TEST

1. Find the sum of $3a + 2b + c$, $4a + b$, and $a - 3c$.

2. Add.
$$\begin{array}{r} 3x^2 + 5x - 6 \\ x^2 + 3x + 7 \\ \underline{2x^2 \qquad\; - 2} \end{array}$$

3. Subtract.
$$\begin{array}{r} 4x^2 + 5x + 6 \\ \underline{x^2 - 2x + 3} \end{array}$$

4. Subtract $2a + b + c$ from $5a - b + 3c$.

5. Multiply $4x$ and $2x$.

6. Simplify $(3x)^2$.

7. Find the product. $4x(2x + 3)$

8. Multiply $5x^2 - 2x + 3$ by -2.

9. Simplify the quotient. $\frac{15x^2y}{3xy}$

10. Divide $-32x^8y^6$ by $8x^2y^2$.

11. Divide $9x^3 - 6x^2 + 15$ by 3.

12. Simplify the quotient. $\frac{2x^6 + 6x^4 + 4x^2}{2x^2}$

13. Multiply $x + 3$ and $x + 2$.

14. Multiply $x + 1$ and $x + 4$.

15. Solve. $3 + 2(x + 4) = 23$

16. Solve. $3(x - 1) - 2 = 7$

17. The distance between two towns is 76 kilometers. Two bicyclists ride from the towns toward each other. Pepe rides at 22 km/h. Julia starts one hour earlier than Pepe and rides at 20 km/h. Find the number of hours that Pepe rides until they meet.

18. Two motor boats leave the same place and travel in opposite directions. The rate of one motorboat is 5 km/h greater than that of the other. After 1.5 hours the distance between the boats is 49.5 km. Find the rate of each.

19. A large machine produces 200 parts per hour and a small machine produces 150 parts per hour. How many parts are produced when the large machine runs 6 hours and the small machine runs 4 hours?

20. Working alone, Jorge could paint the room in 3 hours. Working alone Michael could paint the room in 6 hours. How long would it take Jorge and Michael to paint the room if they work together?

21. Chemical A costs \$5 a liter and Chemical B costs \$30 a liter. A mixture of the two chemicals is produced that costs \$20 a liter. How many liters of each chemical are used in making a 10-liter mixture?

22. How many kilograms of $4 tea must be mixed with 10 kilograms of $7 tea to make a mixture worth $5 a kilogram?

23. Find the quotient. $x + 5\overline{)x^2 + 6x + 5}$

24. Divide $x^2 + 7x + 10$ by $x + 2$.

Write the letter of the best response.

25. The sum of $2a - 3b + 4c$, $3a - 2b$, and $4b + c$ is

a. $5a - 9b + 5c$ **b.** $9a - 5b + 5c$ **c.** $2a + 4b + 3c$
d. $5a + b + 3c$ **e.** $5a - b + 5c$

26. $x + 2$ subtracted from $x^2 + 6x + 6$ gives

a. $6x + 4$ **b.** $x^2 + 10$ **c.** $x^2 + 5x + 4$
d. $x^2 + 10x$ **e.** $x^2 + 7x + 8$

27. $3x^2$ multiplied by $2x$ gives

a. $12x$ **b.** $12x^2$ **c.** $5x^3$ **d.** $6x^3$ **e.** $6x^4$

28. $x + 6$ multiplied by 5 gives

a. $11x$ **b.** $x + 11$ **c.** $x + 30$ **d.** $5x + 11$ **e.** $5x + 30$

29. $12x^8y^6$ divided by $2x^2y$ gives

a. $6x^4y^6$ **b.** $6x^4y^5$ **c.** $6x^6y^5$ **d.** $10x^6y^5$ **e.** $10x^6y^6$

30. $8x^4 + 6x^2$ divided by $2x^2$ gives

a. $4x^2 + 3x$ **b.** $6x^2 + 4$ **c.** $4x^2 + 3$
d. $6x^2 + 4x$ **e.** $8x^4 + 4x^2$

31. $x + 1$ times $x + 2$ gives

a. $x^2 + 2$ **b.** $x^2 + 3x + 2$ **c.** $x + 2$
d. $x^2 + 3x + 3$ **e.** $x^2 + 2x$

32. The solution for $5x + 3(x - 2) = 2$ is

a. 0 **b.** $\frac{1}{6}$ **c.** $\frac{1}{2}$ **d.** 1 **e.** 2

33. Joan and Bill ran in a marathon race. Bill's time was 2.5 hours and Joan's time was 3 hours. Joan's rate was 3 km/h less than Bill's rate. Find the rate of each.

a. 45 km **b.** Joan 18 km/h, Bill 15 km/h **c.** Bill 6 km/h, Joan 3 km/h
d. Joan 3 h, Bill 2.5 h **e.** Bill 18 km/h, Joan 15 km/h

34. Brian can sort a stack of books in 30 minutes. Sarah can sort the books in 20 minutes. Working together, how many minutes would Brian and Sarah need to sort the books?

a. 10 **b.** 12 **c.** 14 **d.** 16 **e.** 18

35. How many kilograms of nuts costing $5 per kilogram must be mixed with 5 kg of nuts costing $8 per kilogram to make a mixture worth $6 per kilogram?

a. 6 **b.** 7 **c.** 10 **d.** 11 **e.** 12

36. $x^2 + 7x + 12$ divided by $x + 3$ gives

a. $x + 4$ **b.** $x - 4$ **c.** $x + 9$ **d.** $x^2 + 6x + 9$ **e.** $x^2 + 7x + 4$

CHAPTER 7
Special Products And Factoring

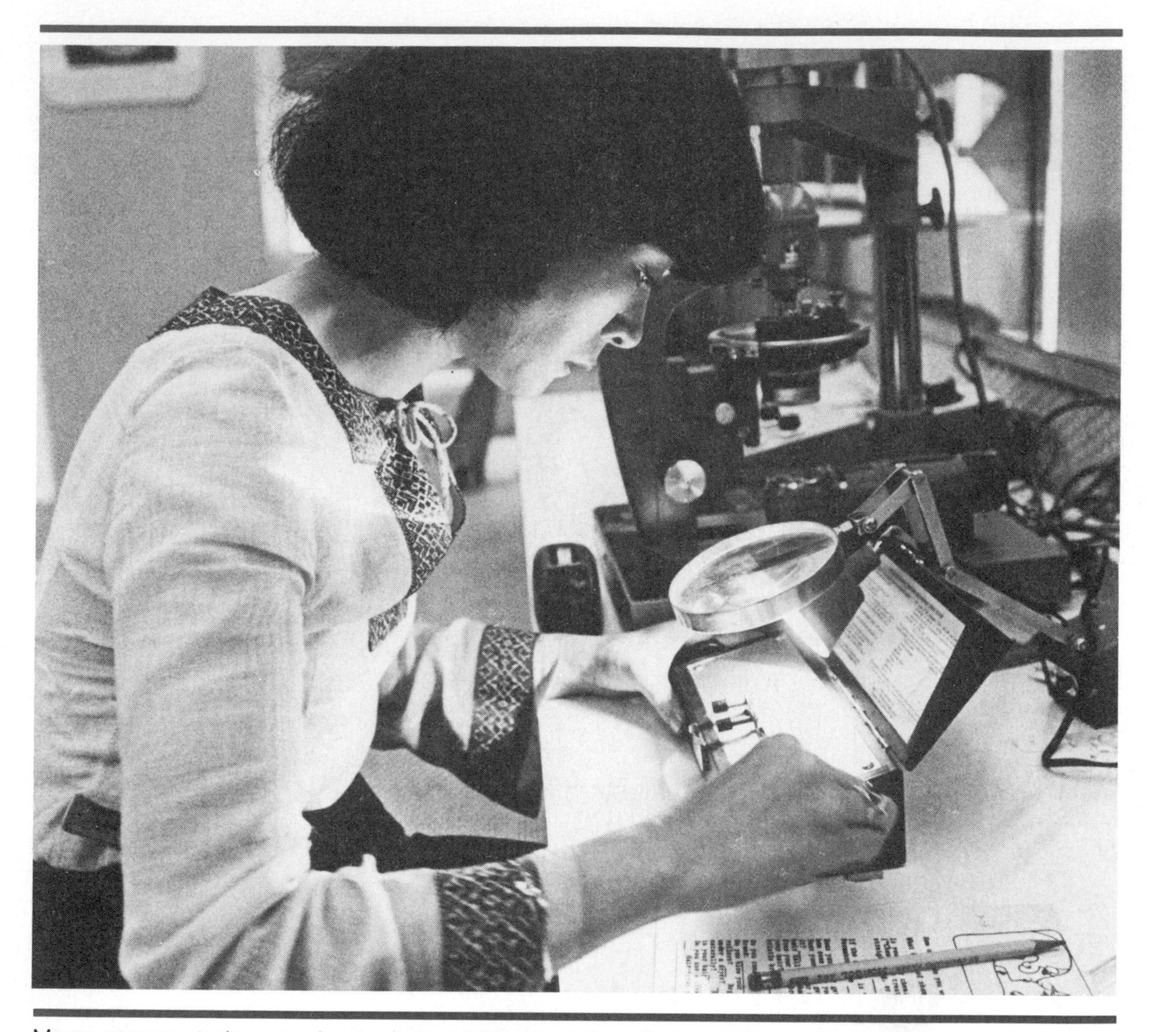

Many careers today require technical skills and knowledge different from what was necessary just a few years ago. Persons who provide personal services, such as hairstylists who now must know how to use sophisticated equipment for analyzing human hair, have to respond to the pressures from competition and the demands of an increasingly well-informed public.

OBJECTIVE: Factor a polynomial that has a monomial factor.

7-1 FACTORS, PRODUCTS, AND FACTORING

When two or more numbers are multiplied, each is said to be a **factor** of the product.

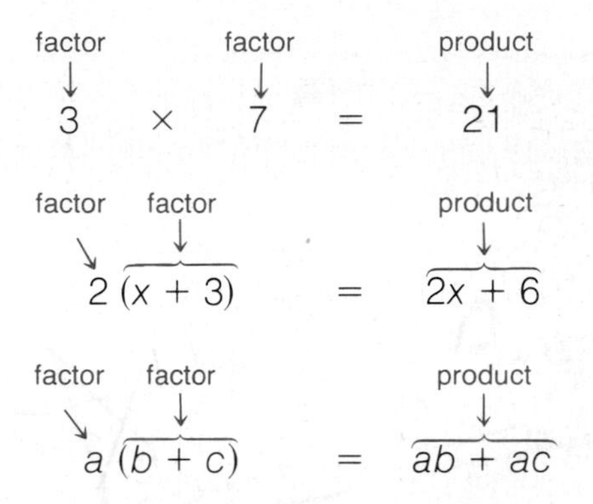

The fact that $a(b + c)$ and $ab + ac$ represent the same number is an application of the Distributive Property. Since $a(b + c)$ expresses the number as a product, we say that it is a **factored form** of $ab + ac$. One factor of $ab + ac$ is a, and the other is $(b + c)$. We call the process of finding the factors of a product **factoring**.

EXAMPLE 1 Express $3x + 3y$ in factored form.

(M) SOLUTION $3x + 3y = 3(x + y)$

EXAMPLE 2 Express $4xy + 3x$ in factored form.

(M) SOLUTION $4xy + 3x = x(4y + 3)$

EXAMPLE 3 Express $3(a + 2b)$ as a sum.

(M) SOLUTION $3(a + 2b) = 3a + 6b$

EXAMPLE 4 Find the missing factor in $3x + 6 = 3(?)$.

(M) SOLUTION $3x + 6 = 3(x + 2)$

The greatest counting number that is a factor of each of several counting numbers is the **greatest common factor** (G.C.F.) of those numbers. When factoring a polynomial, first look for the factors that its terms have in common. Use the greatest common factor of the terms as a factor of the polynomial.

EXAMPLE 5 Find the greatest common factor of 20, 30, and 45; of x^2, x^3, and x^4y^2; of a^2b^2 and ab^3.

SOLUTION

$20 = \boxed{5} \cdot 4$
$30 = \boxed{5} \cdot 6$
$45 = \boxed{5} \cdot 9$

4, 6, and 9 have no common factors greater than 1.

Therefore, the G.C.F. of 20, 30, and 45 is 5.

$x^2 = \boxed{x^2} \cdot 1$
$x^3 = \boxed{x^2} \cdot x$
$x^4y^2 = \boxed{x^2} \cdot x^2y^2$

1, x, and x^2y^2 have no common factors greater than 1.

Therefore, the G.C.F. of x^2, x^3, and x^4y^2 is x^2.

$a^2b^2 = \boxed{ab^2} \cdot a$
$ab^3 = \boxed{ab^2} \cdot b$

a and b have no common factors greater than 1.

Therefore, the G.C.F. of a^2b^2 and ab^3 is ab^2.

EXAMPLE 6 Factor $4x - 12$.

SOLUTION The G.C.F. of $4x$ and 12 is 4.

$$4x - 12 = 4(x - 3)$$

EXAMPLE 7 Factor $5x^4 - 15x^3 - 20x^2$.

SOLUTION The G.C.F. of 5, 15, and 20 is 5.
The G.C.F. of x^4, x^3, and x^2 is x^2.
The G.C.F. of the terms of the polynomial is $5x^2$.

$$5x^4 - 15x^3 - 20x^2 = 5x^2(x^2 - 3x - 4).$$

In factoring any polynomial, factoring should be continued until the polynomial factors are *prime*. Prime polynomials cannot be factored.

EXAMPLE 8 Factor $5x - 11y$.

SOLUTION The G.C.F. of $5x$ and $11y$ is 1. This polynomial cannot be factored. It is prime.

CLASSROOM EXERCISES

Find the greatest common factor for each set.

1. 35, 15, 10 **2.** 20, 28, 12 **3.** $4a$, $6b$ **4.** $4x$, $6x^2$

Express each sum in factored form.

5. $4x + 4y$ **6.** $2s^2 + s$

Express each factored form as a sum.

7. $3(y + x)$ **8.** $2(x^2 + 2)$

Find the missing factor.

9. $3x + 9 = ?(x + 3)$ **10.** $2a + 2 = 2(\ ?\ )$ **11.** $7t^2 + 28t = 7t(\ ?\ )$

Factor when possible.

12. $4a^2 + 2a$ **13.** $3x - 5$ **14.** $2x^3y - 6x^4 + 10x^2$

EXERCISES

A Find the greatest common factor for each set.

1. 72, 108, 63 **2.** 96, 104, 40 **3.** $8cd$, $6cy$
4. $15x^2$, $20xy^2$ **5.** $14c^3d^3$, $-21c^2d$ **6.** $24xy^2z^3$, $18xz^2$

Express each sum in factored form.

7. $3a + 3b$ **8.** $8x + 8y$ **9.** $5x^2 + 15$ **10.** $2a^2 + 4b$
11. $3x + 6y^2$ **12.** $0.3r^2s + rt$ **13.** $5x + 25yz^2$ **14.** $2ab + 10$
15. $5a^2 + 20b$ **16.** $7x + 28y$ **17.** $s^3r + s^2t^2$ **18.** $x^4y^2 + x^3$

Express each factored form as a sum.

19. $6(a + b)$ **20.** $2(a + b)$ **21.** $0.2(x + y)$ **22.** $r(s + t)$
23. $r^2(r^2 + s)$ **24.** $x^2(x + y)$ **25.** $9(b + 3)$ **26.** $5(x + 3y)$
27. $5(16s + r)$ **28.** $3(x + 3y)$ **29.** $x^2(x^4 + y^2)$ **30.** $a^2(x^3 + ab)$

Find the missing factor.

31. $6a + 6b = 6(?)$ **32.** $2a + 2b = ?(a + b)$ **33.** $x^2 - xy = x(?)$
34. $3x + 6 = 3(?)$ **35.** $4x - 2 = ?(2x - 1)$ **36.** $3x + 27 = ?(x + 9)$
37. $2x + 16 = 2(?)$ **38.** $3x + 12 = 3(?)$ **39.** $x^3 - x^2y = ?(x - y)$

Factor when possible.

40. $h^2 - 9h$ **41.** $5x^2 - 5x - 10$ **42.** $6x^2 + 48x + 72$
43. $5a - 7b + c$ **44.** $x^3y^3 + x^2y^2 + xy$ **45.** $x^3 - x^2 - 42x$
46. $a^4 + 7a^3 + 12a^2$ **47.** $5k^3 + 5k^2 - 60k$ **48.** $7p^5 + 70p^2 - 112p$
49. $180n - 360$ **50.** $\pi r^2 + \pi rl$ **51.** $2\pi r^2 + 2\pi rh$
52. $x^2y^3 - x^4y^5$ **53.** $x^4 - x^3 + x^2 - x$ **54.** $16a^2b - 2bc + 4b$

B

55. $42x^2y^3 - 35x^3y^4 - 14x^5y^6$

56. $3y^5 - 6y^4z - 9y^5z$

57. $27a^2b^3 - 18a^3b^2 + 9a^2b^3$

58. $56x^4y^3 + 28x^3y^2 - 63x^4y^3$

59. $12x^3 + 60x^2 - 64y$

60. $2.5a^2b^5 + 7.5b^3c + 9.5b^4$

61. $\frac{1}{2}x^4 - \frac{1}{8}x^3 + \frac{1}{4}x^2$

62. $\frac{1}{3}x^4y^3 + \frac{1}{4}x^4y + \frac{1}{12}x^3y$

Write an algebraic expression in factored form for the area A of each shaded region shown.

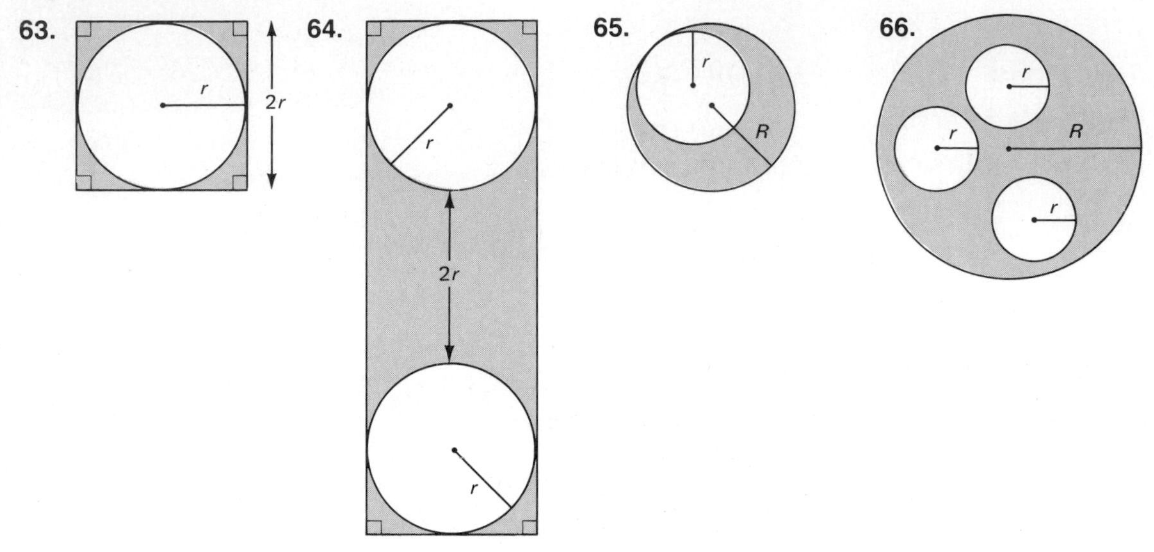

C

67. $S = \frac{1}{2}na + \frac{1}{2}nl$. Change this formula by factoring its right member.

68. Show that $T = 2(lw + lh + wh)$ is a formula for finding the total area of the rectangular solid in Figure 1.

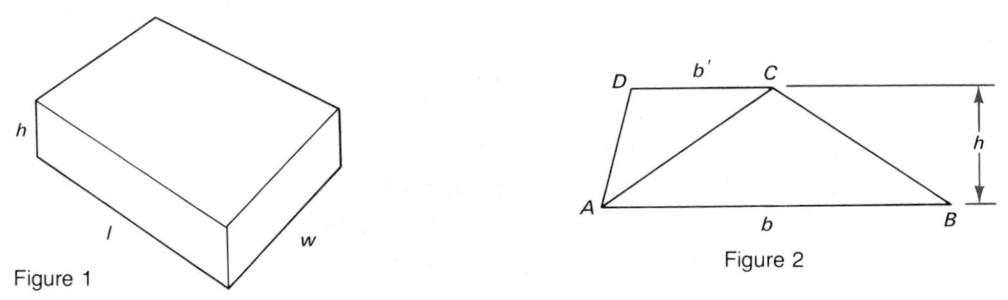

Figure 1

Figure 2

69. Trapezoid $ABCD$ in Figure 2 has height h and bases b and b'.

a. Write a formula for the area of $\triangle ABC$.

b. Write a formula for the area of $\triangle ADC$.

c. Write a formula for the area of $ABCD$.

d. Rewrite the formula for the area of $ABCD$ with the right member of the formula in factored form.

7-2 SQUARES AND SQUARE ROOTS OF MONOMIALS

To **square** a monomial means to use it twice as a factor. The result of squaring a monomial is the **square of the monomial**. Each of the two equal factors is a **square root**.

EXAMPLE 1 Square $4x^3y$

SOLUTION 1

$$(4x^3y)^2 = 4x^3y \cdot 4x^3y$$
$$= 16x^6y^2$$

SOLUTION 2

$$(4x^3y)^2 = 4^2(x^3)^2y^2$$
$$= 16x^6y^2$$

EXAMPLE 2 Find the square of the monomial $\frac{2}{3}r$.

SOLUTION 1

$$\left(\frac{2}{3}r\right)^2 = \left(\frac{2}{3}r\right)\left(\frac{2}{3}r\right)$$
$$= \frac{4}{9}r^2$$

SOLUTION 2

$$\left(\frac{2}{3}r\right)^2 = \left(\frac{2}{3}\right)^2 r^2$$
$$= \frac{4}{9}r^2$$

EXAMPLE 3 Simplify $(-6a^3b^4)^2$.

SOLUTION 1 $(-6a^3b^4)^2 = (-6a^3b^4)(-6a^3b^4)$
$= 36a^6b^8$

SOLUTION 2 $(-6a^3b^4)^2 = (-6)^2(a^3)^2(b^4)^2$
$= 36a^6b^8$

EXAMPLE 4 Find a square root of 16.

SOLUTION Since $4 \cdot 4 = 16$,
4 is a square root of 16.

Since $(-4)(-4) = 16$,
-4 is also a square root of 16.

EXAMPLE 5 Find the positive square root of 144.

SOLUTION Since $12 \cdot 12 = 144$ and $(-12)(-12) = 144$,
12 and -12 are the square roots of 144.
12 is the *positive* square root of 144.

Squaring a term with an exponent results in an exponent that is twice as large. Therefore, a square root of a term with an exponent may be found by taking one-half the exponent.

EXAMPLE 6 Find a square root of a^6b^4.

SOLUTION Since $a^6b^4 = (a^3b^2)(a^3b^2)$, a^3b^2 is a square root of a^6b^4.

EXAMPLE 7 Find a square root of $25p^8$.

SOLUTION Since $25p^8 = (5p^4)(5p^4)$, $5p^4$ is a square root of $25p^8$.

EXAMPLE 8 Find a square root of $\frac{25k^6}{36}$.

SOLUTION Since $\frac{25k^6}{36} = \left(\frac{5k^3}{6}\right)^2$, $\frac{5k^3}{6}$ is a square root of $\frac{25k^6}{36}$.

SQUARES AND SQUARE ROOTS OF MONOMIALS

- To square a monomial, multiply it by itself.
- To find a square root of a monomial, find a factor which, when squared, gives the monomial.

CLASSROOM EXERCISES

Square as indicated.

1. 3^2 **2.** $(-1)^2$ **3.** $(8m)^2$ **4.** $(3x^2)^2$ **5.** $(2x^3)^2$ **6.** $(3xy)^2$

Find a square root.

7. 4 **8.** 25 **9.** T^6 **10.** $16h^2$ **11.** $49x^4y^2$ **12.** $100x^4y^6$

EXERCISES

A Square as indicated.

1. 6^2 **2.** $(-3)^2$ **3.** $(-3r)^2$ **4.** $(-2y)^2$
5. $(-8m)^2$ **6.** $(7a)^2$ **7.** $(4x^3)^2$ **8.** $(6a^2)^2$
9. $(-2r^2s)^2$ **10.** $(5c^2t^4)^2$ **11.** $\left(\frac{1}{2}gt\right)^2$ **12.** $(-ab^2c^3)^2$
13. $(0.4x^2)^2$ **14.** $\left(\frac{1}{3}abc\right)^2$ **15.** $(10x^5)^2$ **16.** $(0.01a^9)^2$

Find a square root.

17. 49 **18.** 64 **19.** $\frac{1}{25}$ **20.** $\frac{1}{100}$ **21.** 81
22. 9 **23.** 144 **24.** r^6 **25.** a^2b^2 **26.** $25x^2$

27. $121p^4$ **28.** $225a^8$ **29.** $9m^2x^4$ **30.** $0.04c^2$ **31.** $100x^{10}$

32. $(x - y)^2$ **33.** $(a + b)^2$ **34.** a^2c^4 **35.** $25a^2b^4c^6$ **36.** $\frac{49a^2}{64}$

B Square each monomial.

37. $12.5x^3y^4$ **38.** $\frac{1}{16}r^2s^3$ **39.** $\frac{1}{13}x^4y^5$ **40.** $7.4a^7b^9$

41. $101x^{14}$ **42.** $9.7x^6$ **43.** $0.9a$ **44.** $1.1x^{13}$

Find a square root.

45. $\frac{4x^2}{9y^2}$ **46.** $\frac{16r^2}{25s^6}$ **47.** $\frac{49a^2}{64b^4}$ **48.** $\frac{36b^4}{144c^6}$

49. $0.49x^8y^{12}$ **50.** $1.21a^2b^6$ **51.** $\frac{(x + y)^2}{z^4}$ **52.** $\frac{(a + b)^6}{c^2d^4}$

C Simplify.

53. $(3y^2)^2 \cdot (2y)^2 \cdot (y^2)^2$ **54.** $\left(\frac{1}{10}x^2y^2\right)^2 \cdot (5xy^3)^2$

CHECKING YOUR UNDERSTANDING

WORDS

factoring
factored form
prime polynomial
square of a monomial
square root

CONCEPTS

- A polynomial may be factored when its terms have a common factor other than 1 or −1. [7-1]
- A term that can be written as the product of two equal factors has a square root. [7-2]

PROCESSES

- Factor a polynomial, when possible. [7-1]

1. $9x + 9y$ **2.** $x^3y + x^2y^2$ **3.** $4x^4 + 2x^3 + 6x^2 + 10x$

- Find the square or a square root of a monomial. [7-2]

4. $(3x^3)^2 =$ __?__ **5.** $(?)^2 = 81$ **6.** $(?)^2 = 36p^6r^8$

OBJECTIVES: Multiply two binomials. Factor a trinomial that has a binomial factor.

7-3 MULTIPLYING TWO BINOMIALS

To find the product of two polynomials, multiply each term of one polynomial by each term of the other. Then combine the like terms.

EXAMPLE 1 Multiply $3x - 4$ and $2x + 5$.

SOLUTION

The Long Method	The Short Method
$$\begin{array}{r} 3x - 4 \\ 2x + 5 \\ \hline 6x^2 - 8x \\ + 15x - 20 \\ \hline 6x^2 + 7x - 20 \end{array}$$	$(3x - 4)(2x + 5) = 6x^2 + 7x - 20$ (first terms: $6x^2$; last terms: -20; inner: $-8x$; outer: $+15x$)

EXAMPLE 2 Find the product of $2x - 3$ and $4x + 7$.

SOLUTION

1. The first term of the product is $(2x)(4x)$, or $8x^2$.
2. $(2x)(7) = 14x$ and $(-3)(4x) = -12x$.
   The middle term of the product is $14x + (-12x)$, or $2x$.
3. The last term of the product is $(-3)(+7)$, or -21.

Thus, $(2x - 3)(4x + 7) = 8x^2 + 2x - 21$.

When multiplying two binomials, try to do each step mentally, writing only your results.

EXAMPLE 3 Multiply $3a + 1$ and $a - 2$.

(M) SOLUTION $(3a + 1)(a - 2) = 3a^2 - 5a - 2$

EXAMPLE 4 Find the missing term in $(x + 4)(x + 2) = x^2 + 6x + \boxed{?}$

SOLUTION $(x + \boxed{4})(x + \boxed{2}) = x^2 + 6x + \boxed{8}$
8 is the missing term.

MULTIPLYING TWO BINOMIALS

1. Multiply their first terms.
2. Multiply the second term of each binomial by the first term of the other binomial. Combine like terms, if any.
3. Multiply the second terms of the two binomials.

CLASSROOM EXERCISES

Find the missing terms.

1. $(x + 1)(x + 2) = x^2 + 3x + (?)$

2. $(a - 3)(2a + 1) = (?) - 5a - 3$

3. $(m + 3)(4m + 1) = 4m^2 + (?) + 3$

4. $(2x + 4)(x - 1) = 2x^2 + (?) - 4$

5. $(3k - 1)(2k + 3) = (?) + 7k - (?)$

6. $(7c - 1)(c + 1) = 7c^2 + (?) - 1$

7. $(x + 2)(x - 5) = x^2 - (?) - 10$

8. $(2x - 3)(x + 1) = (?) - x - (?)$

9. $(m + 4)(2m + 1) = (?) + 9m + (?)$

10. $(4x + 2)(x + 3) = 4x^2 + (?) + 6$

Multiply.

11. $(a + 1)(a + 2)$

12. $(c + 1)(c + 1)$

13. $(c + 3)(c + 4)$

14. $(a - 2)(a - 2)$

15. $(c + 2)(c - 4)$

16. $(c + 3)(c - 4)$

EXERCISES

A Multiply.

1. $(x + 1)(x + 4)$

2. $(x + 2)(x + 5)$

3. $(a - 1)(a + 3)$

4. $(x - 2)(x + 3)$

5. $(a - 2)(a + 2)$

6. $(x - 6)(x - 6)$

7. $(c - 3)(c - 3)$

8. $(x + 5)(x + 3)$

9. $(1 + x)(1 + 2x)$

10. $(k + 3)(k + 7)$

11. $(2 - x)(7 + x)$

12. $(m - 7)(m - 7)$

13. $(x + 2)(-x - 5)$

14. $(y - 6)(-y + 3)$

15. $(a - 20)(a - 1)$

16. $(x + 4)(x - 15)$

17. $(y + 10)(y - 8)$

18. $(7c - 1)(2c + 3)$

19. $(7c - 1)(7c + 5)$

20. $(3p - 1)(2p + 3)$

21. $(4c + 1)(5c - 4)$

22. $(a + 2)(a + 4)$

23. $(8 + z)(8 - z)$

24. $(b - 2)(b - 7)$

25. $(z - 3)(3z - 1)$

26. $(3 - y)(2 + y)$

27. $(a - 1)(a + 2)$

28. $(6a - 1)(2a + 5)$
29. $(8x + 2)(3x - 2)$
30. $(t - 4)(t + 4)$
31. $(x + 4)(x - 10)$
32. $(2x + 3)(-2x + 4)$
33. $(x - 2)(2x + 1)$
34. $(2 - 5a)(2 - a)$
35. $(3 + 4b)(4 - 3b)$
36. $(3 + 6a)(2a - 4)$
37. $(12c - 5)(5c + 9)$
38. $(2n + 1)(n + 8)$
39. $(4x - 5)(2x + 4)$

B

40. $(x^2 - 3)(x^2 - 4)$
41. $(a + b)^2$
42. $(x - y)^2$
43. $(x^2 - 3y)(x^2 + 4y)$
44. $(10a - 1)(9a - 2)$
45. $(a^2 - 1)(a^2 - 4)$
46. $(x^2 - 1)(x^2 - 9)$
47. $(xy + 3)^2$
48. $(m + 8n)(m - 8n)$
49. $(2y - 5)(2y + 5)$
50. $(xy - 12)(xy + 1)$
51. $(3a - 4b)(3a + 4b)$
52. $(x^2 + y^2)(x^2 + 2y^2)$
53. $(x + 0.3)(x + 0.4)$
54. $\left(a - \frac{1}{2}\right)\left(a - \frac{1}{3}\right)$
55. $\left(b - \frac{1}{4}\right)\left(b + \frac{1}{3}\right)$
56. $(4n - 7p)(6n + 8p)$
57. $\left(9a - \frac{1}{2}b\right)\left(9a + \frac{1}{2}b\right)$
58. $(x + 0.1)(x + 0.1)$
59. $(2c + 0.3)(2c - 0.3)$
60. $\left(x + \frac{1}{2}\right)\left(x + \frac{1}{4}\right)$
61. $\left(a^3 - \frac{1}{5}\right)\left(a^3 + \frac{1}{5}\right)$
62. $\left(x + \frac{2}{3}y\right)\left(x - \frac{1}{3}y\right)$
63. $(m - 0.4n)(m - 0.1n)$

C

64. $\left[\left(3x + \frac{1}{2}\right)\left(3x - \frac{1}{2}\right)\right] + \left[\left(5x + \frac{2}{3}\right)\left(5x - \frac{2}{3}\right)\right]$
65. $\left[\left(x - \frac{1}{2}y\right)\left(x - \frac{1}{2}y\right)\right] + \left[(x - 4y)\left(\frac{1}{4}x - y\right)\right]$

66. The sides of a square have length $(x + 2)$. Write an expression that contains no parentheses for the area of the square.

67. A square has area $x^2 - 6x + 9$. Each side of a second square is 1 unit shorter than that of the first square. Write an expression that contains no parentheses for the area of the second square.

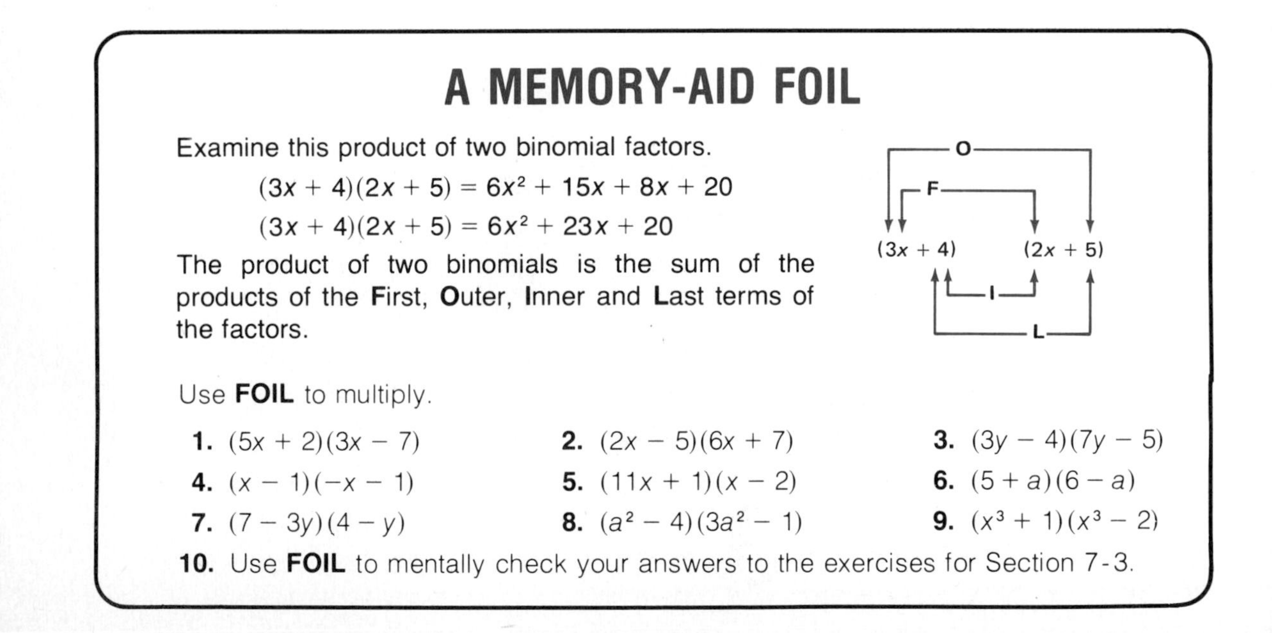

A MEMORY-AID FOIL

Examine this product of two binomial factors.

$$(3x + 4)(2x + 5) = 6x^2 + 15x + 8x + 20$$

$$(3x + 4)(2x + 5) = 6x^2 + 23x + 20$$

The product of two binomials is the sum of the products of the **F**irst, **O**uter, **I**nner and **L**ast terms of the factors.

Use **FOIL** to multiply.

1. $(5x + 2)(3x - 7)$
2. $(2x - 5)(6x + 7)$
3. $(3y - 4)(7y - 5)$
4. $(x - 1)(-x - 1)$
5. $(11x + 1)(x - 2)$
6. $(5 + a)(6 - a)$
7. $(7 - 3y)(4 - y)$
8. $(a^2 - 4)(3a^2 - 1)$
9. $(x^3 + 1)(x^3 - 2)$

10. Use **FOIL** to mentally check your answers to the exercises for Section 7-3.

7-4 FACTORING A POLYNOMIAL OF THE FORM $ax^2 + bx + c$

When two binomials are multiplied, the product is either a binomial, a trinomial, or a four-term polynomial.

$(x + 2)(x - 2) = x^2 - 4$, a binomial
$(x + 2)(x - 3) = x^2 - x - 6$, a trinomial
$(x + a)(y + b) = xy + ay + bx + ab$, a polynomial with four terms.

When the product of two binomials is a trinomial, it can be written in the form $ax^2 + bx + c$. When such a trinomial is the product of two binomials, those binomials may be found by reversing the method used in finding the product. There is no general rule for factoring trinomials of this kind, so study the examples very carefully.

EXAMPLE 1 Factor $x^2 + 6x + 8$.

SOLUTION The first terms of the two binomial factors are x and x.

$$x^2 + 6x + 8 = (x \ ? \ )(x \ ? \ )$$

Since there are no minus signs in the trinomial, there are no minus signs in the factors.

$$x^2 + 6x + 8 = (x + ?)(x + ?)$$

The product of the last terms of the binomials must be 8. Their sum must be 6. The terms are 4 and 2.

Ⓜ $$x^2 + 6x + 8 = (x + 4)(x + 2)$$

EXAMPLE 2 Factor $x^2 - 2x - 15$.

SOLUTION The first terms of the two binomial factors are x and x.

$$x^2 - 2x - 15 = (x \ ? \ )(x \ ? \ )$$

The -15 tells us that one of the operation signs in the factors is plus and one is minus.

$$x^2 - 2x - 15 = (x + ?)(x - ?)$$

The product of the last terms of the binomials must be 15. Their difference must be 2. The terms are 5 and 3.

$$x^2 - 2x - 15 \stackrel{?}{=} (x + 5)(x - 3)$$
or $$x^2 - 2x - 15 \stackrel{?}{=} (x + 3)(x - 5).$$

Checking both possibilities shows that

Ⓜ $$x^2 - 2x - 15 = (x + 3)(x - 5).$$

EXAMPLE 3 Factor $x^2 - 9x + 18$.

SOLUTION The first terms of the two factors are x and x.

$$x^2 - 9x + 18 = (x \ ? \ )(x \ ? \ )$$

The + 18 tells us that the operation signs in the factors are alike. Since the sign before $9x$ is minus, the signs in both factors must be minus.

$$x^2 - 9x + 18 = (x - ?)(x - ?)$$

The product of the last terms of the binomials must be 18. Their sum must be 9. The terms are 3 and 6.

Ⓜ $$x^2 - 9x + 18 = (x - 3)(x - 6)$$

EXAMPLE 4 Factor $x^2 - xy - 12y^2$

SOLUTION The first terms of the two factors are x and x. The last terms of the factors each include y.

$$x^2 - xy - 12y^2 = (x \ ? \ y)(x \ ? \ y)$$

The − 12 tells us that the operation signs in the factors are different.

$$x^2 - xy - 12y^2 = (x + ?y)(x - ?y)$$

The product of the last terms of the binomials must be $12y^2$. Their difference must be $1y$. The terms are $4y$ and $3y$.

$$x^2 - xy - 12y^2 \stackrel{?}{=} (x + 4y)(x - 3y)$$

or $x^2 - xy - 12y^2 \stackrel{?}{=} (x + 3y)(x - 4y)$.

Checking both possibilities shows that

Ⓜ $$x^2 - xy - 12y^2 = (x + 3y)(x - 4y).$$

EXAMPLE 5 Factor $8x^2 - 22x + 15$.

SOLUTION The first terms of the factors are either x and $8x$, or $2x$ and $4x$. The + 15 tells us that the operation signs of the factors are alike. The $- 22x$ tells us that they must be minus. The last terms of the factors are 1 and 15, or 3 and 5.

The eight possible pairs of binomials are:

1. $(x - 1)(8x - 15)$ 2. $(x - 15)(8x - 1)$
3. $(x - 3)(8x - 5)$ 4. $(x - 5)(8x - 3)$
5. $(2x - 1)(4x - 15)$ 6. $(2x - 15)(4x - 1)$
7. $(2x - 3)(4x - 5)$ 8. $(2x - 5)(4x - 3)$

Only one of the combinations gives $- 22x$ as the middle term of the product. By trial we find that

Ⓜ $$8x^2 - 22x + 15 = (2x - 3)(4x - 5).$$

EXAMPLE 6 Factor $x^2 + x + 1$.

SOLUTION The first terms of two binomial factors would have to be x and x.

$$x^2 + x + 1 = (x \ ?\ )(x \ ?\ )$$

The operation signs in the trinomial are all plus. The signs in each binomial would have to be plus.

$$x^2 + x + 1 = (x + ?)(x + ?)$$

The last terms of the factors would each have to be 1. Does $x^2 + x + 1 = (x + 1)(x + 1)$? No. This trinomial cannot be factored. It is prime.

CLASSROOM EXERCISES

Factor when possible.

1. $a^2 + 4a + 4$
2. $x^2 + x - 6$
3. $x^2 - 4x + 3$
4. $x^2 + x - 10$
5. $x^2 - xy - 6y^2$
6. $2x^2 + 5x + 2$

EXERCISES

A Factor when possible.

1. $c^2 + 5c + 4$
2. $y^2 + 4y + 3$
3. $z^2 + 7z + 10$
4. $x^2 + 6x + 9$
5. $y^2 + 12y + 36$
6. $k^2 + 8k + 15$
7. $m^2 + 8m + 12$
8. $1 + 2a + a^2$
9. $2 + 3x + x^2$
10. $z^2 + z + \frac{1}{4}$
11. $y^2 + y + \frac{2}{9}$
12. $y^2 + 5y + 8$
13. $m^2 + m - 30$
14. $m^2 - m - 30$
15. $c^2 - c - 20$
16. $m^2 - 2m - 63$
17. $x^2 + 7x - 18$
18. $x^2 + 5x - 14$
19. $y^2 - 6y - 40$
20. $2 - c - c^2$
21. $4 - 3p - p^2$
22. $y^2 + 1.4y - 0.72$
23. $z^2 - 4.6z - 0.96$
24. $c^2 - 5c - 9$
25. $x^2 - 5x + 4$
26. $x^2 - 8x + 15$
27. $y^2 - 11y + 18$
28. $x^2 - 4x + 4$
29. $y^2 - 10y + 25$
30. $y^2 - 19y + 84$
31. $x^2 - 13x + 40$
32. $3 - 4b + b^2$
33. $12 - 7c + c^2$
34. $x^2 - 1.5x + 0.54$
35. $y^2 - 3.5y + 9.6$
36. $y^2 - 16y + 24$
37. $x^2 + 3xy + 2y^2$
38. $y^2 + 10yz + 21z^2$
39. $m^2 + 8mn + 12n^2$
40. $x^2 + xy - 12y^2$
41. $m^2 + 2mn - 8n^2$
42. $c^2 - 6cd + 5d^2$
43. $h^2 - 9hk + 18k^2$
44. $x^2 - 12xy + 36y^2$
45. $a^2 - 9ab + 8b^2$
46. $c^2 + 6cd - 8d^2$
47. $x^2 - xy + y^2$
48. $7x^2 + 9x + 2$

49. $5y^2 + 17y + 14$

50. $15z^2 + 22z + 8$

51. $3c^2 + 8c + 5$

52. $9x^2 + 3x - 2$

53. $6p^2 - 25p - 25$

54. $3 - 10k - 8k^2$

55. $5x^2 - 17x + 14$

56. $2p^2 - 9p + 4$

57. $2 - 11c + 12c^2$

58. $12 - 32b + 5b^2$

59. $3x^2 - 13x - 20$

60. $4y^2 - 9y + 15$

B **61.** $3a^2 - 2ab - 5b^2$

62. $21c^2 - 58cd + 21d^2$

63. $15m^2 - 22mn - 5n^2$

64. $8x^2 + 2xy - 3y^2$

65. $42c^2 - 79cd + 35d^2$

66. $-mn + m^2 - 42n^2$

67. $5xy - 3y^2 + 2x^2$

68. $z^6 - z^3 - 20$

69. $k^6 - 5k^3 - 14$

70. $a^2b^2 + ab - 6$

71. $x^2y^2 - 2xy - 24$

72. $5x^4y^6 + 7x^2y^3 - 12$

73. $8a^2b^4 + 14ab^2 - 15$

74. $x^3 + 7x^2 + 10x$

75. $2ax^2 - 2ax - 12a$

76. $12x^2 + 10x - 8$

77. $4q^2 + 14q - 8$

78. $18z^2 - 21z - 9$

79. The area of a rectangle is represented by the expression $2x^2 + x - 190$. What expressions may represent its length and width?

80. A dividend is $b^2 - 10b + 24$. Name a binomial divisor. Name the quotient.

C Simplify. Factor your result.

81. $3y^2(6x^2 - 7y^2) + 8x^2(-2y^2 + x^2)$

82. $3yz(2yz + 3) - 8(yz + 5)$

111111. PATTERNS IN SIX-DIGIT NUMBERS

In a six-digit number you could have three digits repeating, two digits repeating, or one digit repeating.

893 893 57 57 57 4 4 4 4 4 4

1. On your calculator, enter a six-digit number using the same three digits twice. Divide by 7, by 11, and then by 13. What is special about your result?
2. On your calculator, enter a six-digit number using the same two digits three times. Divide by 3, by 7, by 13, and then by 37. What is special about your result?
3. On your calculator, enter a six-digit number using the same digit six times. Divide by 3, by 7, by 11, by 13, and then by 37. What is special about your result?
4. Explain your results.

7-5 SQUARING BINOMIALS

We know that the square of a binomial is the product of the binomial and itself.

$(x+y)^2 = (x+y)(x+y)$	$(x-y)^2 = (x-y)(x-y)$
$(x+y)^2 = x^2 + 2xy + y^2$	$(x-y)^2 = x^2 - 2xy + y^2$

In the expression that results from squaring either binomial, $x + y$ or $x - y$, we note the following.

1. The first term, x^2, is the square of the first term, x, of the binomial.
2. The middle term, $2xy$, represents twice the product of the two terms x and y.
3. The last term, y^2, is the square of the second term, y, of the binomial.
4. The operation sign preceding the middle term matches the operation sign in the binomial. The operation sign preceding the third term is "plus" for both $(x + y)^2$ and $(x - y)^2$.

The trinomial resulting from this process is a **perfect-square trinomial**.

EXAMPLE 1 Square $x + 3$.

SOLUTION The first term of the product is the square of x, or x^2.
The middle term is twice the product of x and 3, or $6x$.
The last term is the square of 3, or 9.

Ⓜ $$(x + 3)^2 = x^2 + 6x + 9$$

EXAMPLE 2 Write $(2x + 3)^2$ as a trinomial.

SOLUTION The square of $2x$ is $4x^2$.
Twice the product of $2x$ and 3 is $12x$.
The square of 3 is 9.

Ⓜ $$(2x + 3)^2 = 4x^2 + 12x + 9$$

EXAMPLE 3 Write $(3x - 5y)^2$ as a trinomial.

SOLUTION $(3x)^2 = 9x^2$
Twice the product $(3x)(-5y) = -30xy$
$(-5y)^2 = 25y^2$

Ⓜ $$(3x - 5y)^2 = 9x^2 - 30xy + 25y^2$$

SQUARING A BINOMIAL

1. Square the first term.
2. Add twice the product of the two terms. The operation sign that will precede this result in the trinomial should agree with the operation sign in the binomial.
3. Add the square of the last term.

CLASSROOM EXERCISES

Square as indicated.

1. $(x + 1)^2$ **2.** $(y - 4)^2$ **3.** $(2m - 2)^2$
4. $(3x - 1)^2$ **5.** $(x - 2y)^2$ **6.** $(3 - x)^2$

EXERCISES

A Square as indicated.

1. $(x + 2)^2$ **2.** $(a + 3)^2$ **3.** $(c - d)^2$ **4.** $(4 - c)^2$
5. $(6 - x)^2$ **6.** $(10 - y)^2$ **7.** $(2a + 4)^2$ **8.** $(3a + 3)^2$
9. $(4a - 1)^2$ **10.** $(5a + 2)^2$ **11.** $(2x - 3)^2$ **12.** $(4x - 1)^2$
13. $(4x - 7)^2$ **14.** $(4x + 5)^2$ **15.** $(3x - 6)^2$ **16.** $(8x - 1)^2$
17. $(x - 9y)^2$ **18.** $(2x - y)^2$ **19.** $(3a + 2b)^2$ **20.** $(2y + 8w)^2$
21. $(-3x - 7)^2$ **22.** $(-2 - 7c)^2$ **23.** $\left(x - \frac{1}{2}\right)^2$ **24.** $\left(x + \frac{1}{5}\right)^2$
25. $(x - 0.5)^2$ **26.** $\left(a - \frac{1}{5}\right)^2$ **27.** $(x + 0.3)^2$ **28.** $(y - 1.2)^2$

B **29.** $(3x - 13)^2$ **30.** $(21 - 6a)^2$ **31.** $(2y + 31)^2$ **32.** $(7 - 53x)^2$
33. $[2(3a + 2b)]^2$ **34.** $-(x - 2y)^2$ **35.** $-2(a - 6b)^2$ **36.** $\left[\frac{1}{2}(2x - 6y)\right]^2$

C Simplify.

37. $\left(\frac{1}{2} - m\right)^2 + \left(\frac{3}{4} + m\right)^2$ **38.** $\left(x - \frac{2}{3}\right)^2 + \left(x + \frac{5}{2}\right)^2$ **39.** $(n - 0.3)^2 + (n + 2.4)^2$

BUSINESS AND OFFICE

There are approximately 5.5 million people employed in *sales* or related occupations. All of these jobs require the ability to work easily with numbers. Skill with the four basic operations on the set of rational numbers is sufficient for many of these jobs. In more advanced sales positions, however, an understanding of and a working knowledge of algebra is essential.

Here are some activities that occur regularly in more advanced sales positions that require knowledge of mathematics beyond arithmetic.

- The parent company asks you, the manager of one of its retail stores, to supply it with a list of items that you would like to feature in your store next month, and for each item to list the profit margin you feel the store could make.
- As credit manager, customers ask you to explain the finance charge on their average minimum charge-account balances for the previous month.
- Your clients ask you, as a securities salesperson for an investment firm, to supply them with the yield factor (return divided by cost) for each of the securities that you are recommending they buy.

MATHEMATICAL SAMPLER

1. You are a real-estate agent. A customer to whom you are showing a $50 000 house asks what the annual taxes are. You look at the listing sheet for the house and you find only the following information: the assessment factor for the town is 82.5%, and the tax rate is 52 mills per dollar of assessment. Find the taxes for this particular house.

2. You have two job offers. One has a starting salary of $12 500, guaranteed raises of 7.5% after each of the first two years, and additional benefits worth $1400 each year. The other has a starting salary of $13 500 with guaranteed raises of 9.75% each year. Which job offers you the better financial reward for the next three years?

7-6 PERFECT-SQUARE TRINOMIALS

A perfect-square trinomial is the product of two equal binomial factors. The binomial is a square root of the trinomial.

EXAMPLE 1 Find a square root of $x^2 + 8x + 16$.

SOLUTION The first term is the square of x. The third term is the square of 4. The middle term is the product of x and 4, or $4x$, taken twice. Therefore, $x^2 + 8x + 16 = (x + 4)^2$ and $x + 4$ is a square root of $x^2 + 8x + 16$.

EXAMPLE 2 Find a square root of $x^2 - 10x + 25$.

SOLUTION The first term is the square of x. The third term is the square of 5. It is also the square of -5. The middle term is the product of x and -5, or $-5x$, taken twice. Thus, $x^2 - 10x + 25 = (x - 5)^2$ and $x - 5$ is a square root of $x^2 - 10x + 25$.

EXAMPLE 3 Find a square root of $x^2 - 10x - 25$.

SOLUTION For $x - b$ to be a square root of $x^2 - 10x - 25$, b^2 must equal -25. There is no such real number b. Therefore, there is no binomial $x - b$, with b a real number, that is a square root of $x^2 - 10 - 25$.

EXAMPLE 4 Find a square root of $9x^2 + 24x + 16$.

SOLUTION $9x^2 = (3x)^2$, $16 = 4^2$, and $24x =$ the product of $3x$ and 4, taken twice. Thus, $9x^2 + 24x + 16 = (3x + 4)^2$ and $3x + 4$ is a square root of $9x^2 + 24x + 16$.

CHECKING FOR A PERFECT-SQUARE TRINOMIAL

1. Arrange the trinomial so that the powers of one variable are shown in decreasing order.
2. Check that the first term is a perfect square.
3. Check that the third term is a perfect square.
4. Check that the second term is twice the product of the square roots of the first and third terms.

CLASSROOM EXERCISES

Tell which of the following are perfect squares. Find a square root of each perfect-square trinomial.

1. $x^2 + 2x + 1$ **2.** $x^2 + 4x + 4$ **3.** $a^2 - 4a + 4$

4. $x^2 - 2x + 4$ **5.** $x^2 + 3x + 9$ **6.** $4x^2 + 4x + 1$

EXERCISES

A Tell which of the following are perfect squares. Find a square root of each perfect-square trinomial.

1. $x^2 + 6x + 9$ **2.** $x^2 + 10x + 25$ **3.** $x^2 - 14x + 49$

4. $m^2 - 20m + 100$ **5.** $4 - 4x + x^2$ **6.** $36 - 12y + y^2$

7. $y^2 - 14y - 36$ **8.** $4x^2 + 4x - 1$ **9.** $36x^2 - 12x + 1$

10. $16x^2 - 8x + 1$ **11.** $a^2 + 16a + 64$ **12.** $x^4 + x^2 + 1$

13. $64y^2 - 16yz + z^2$ **14.** $9k^2 + 12kt + 4t^2$ **15.** $9u^2 + 6uv + v^2$

16. $c^2 + \frac{2}{3}c + \frac{1}{9}$ **17.** $a^2 - a + \frac{1}{4}$ **18.** $4n^2 + 4nt + t^2$

B **19.** $25k^8 - 30k^4 + 9$ **20.** $100y^8 - 160y^4 + 64$ **21.** $4x^8 + 20x^4 + 25$

22. $9y^6 - 42y^3 + 49$ **23.** $x^2 - \frac{4}{3}x + \frac{4}{9}$ **24.** $-36x^2 + 1.8x + 2.25$

C Find b so that each trinomial is a perfect square.

25. $x^2 + 10x + b$ **26.** $x^2 + bx + 64$ **27.** $bx^2 - 12x + 9$

28. $x^2 - 2bx + 49$ **29.** $9x^2 + 6x + b$ **30.** $25x^2 + bx + 144$

31. $y = \frac{4k^2 + 4k + 1}{9}$ and $k = 3x - 1$. Find y in terms of x.

AN ALGEBRAIC FALLACY

Susie said, "I can prove that $1 = 3$."

She continued,
"Obviously, if $a = b$, then $ab^2 = b^3$ and $ab^2 - b^3 = a^3 - b^3$.
Divide both sides by $a - b$ to get $b^2 = a^2 + ab + b^2$.
Now, use 1 for a and b.
The results are $1 = 3$."

Find the error in this reasoning.

7-7 MULTIPLYING THE SUM OF TWO NUMBERS BY THEIR DIFFERENCE

A special product is obtained when the sum of two numbers is multiplied by their difference.

EXAMPLE 1 Multiply $x + 4$ and $x - 4$.

SOLUTION For $(x + 4)(x - 4)$,
the first term of the product is $x \cdot x$, or x^2.
The middle term of the product is $4x + (-4x)$, or 0.
The last term of the product is $(4)(-4)$, or -16.
Thus, $(x + 4)(x - 4) = x^2 - 16$.

EXAMPLE 2 Multiply $ab - 3$ and $ab + 3$.

SOLUTION For $(ab - 3)(ab + 3)$,
the middle term of the product is $(-3ab) + 3ab$, or 0.
Thus, $(ab - 3)(ab + 3) = a^2b^2 - 9$.

EXAMPLE 3 Multiply $a + b$ and $a - b$.

SOLUTION For $(a + b)(a - b)$,
the middle term of the product is $ab - ab$, or 0.
Thus, $(a + b)(a - b) = a^2 - b^2$.

EXAMPLE 4 Multiply $2x - 3$ and $2x + 3$.

(M) SOLUTION

$$\begin{aligned}(2x - 3)(2x + 3) &= 4x^2 + 6x - 6x - 9 \\ &= 4x^2 - 9\end{aligned}$$

EXAMPLE 5 Multiply $3x + 2y$ and $3x - 2y$.

(M) SOLUTION

$$\begin{aligned}(3x + 2y)(3x - 2y) &= 9x^2 + 6xy - 6xy - 4y^2 \\ &= 9x^2 - 4y^2\end{aligned}$$

MULTIPLYING THE SUM OF TWO NUMBERS BY THEIR DIFFERENCE

1. Square the first number.
2. Subtract the square of the second number.

CLASSROOM EXERCISES

Multiply.

1. $(x + 1)(x - 1)$
2. $(x - 3)(x + 3)$
3. $(a - c)(a + c)$
4. $(ab - 1)(ab + 1)$
5. $(xy - 2)(xy + 2)$
6. $(2x + 3)(2x - 3)$

EXERCISES

A Multiply.

1. $(c + 3)(c - 3)$
2. $(a + 5)(a - 5)$
3. $(x + 7)(x - 7)$
4. $(y + 9)(y - 9)$
5. $(2 + k)(2 - k)$
6. $(1 - x)(1 + x)$
7. $(ab - 1)(ab + 1)$
8. $(xy + 8)(xy - 8)$
9. $(m + n)(m - n)$
10. $(c - d)(c + d)$
11. $(-p + q)(-p - q)$
12. $(-r - s)(-r + s)$
13. $(3c - 1)(3c + 1)$
14. $(5x + 3)(5x - 3)$
15. $(10x + 9)(10x - 9)$
16. $(8r - 5)(8r + 5)$
17. $(2x + n)(2x - n)$
18. $(4s + 3t)(4s - 3t)$
19. $(3k - 5h)(3k + 5h)$
20. $(7m + 9n)(7m - 9n)$
21. $(r + 0.5)(r - 0.5)$
22. $(s + 0.8)(s - 0.8)$
23. $\left(\frac{3}{4}x - \frac{1}{2}y\right)\left(\frac{3}{4}x + \frac{1}{2}y\right)$
24. $\left(\frac{1}{7}x + \frac{1}{5}y\right)\left(\frac{1}{7}x - \frac{1}{5}y\right)$
25. $(0.3a + 0.5b)(0.3a - 0.5b)$
26. $(1.1r - 1.2s)(1.1r + 1.2s)$
27. $\left(abc - \frac{1}{3}\right)\left(abc + \frac{1}{3}\right)$

B

28. $(x^2 - 1)(x^2 + 1)$
29. $(x^2 + 8)(x^2 - 8)$
30. $(a + 5)(a - 5)(a^2 + 25)$
31. $(x - 3)(x + 3)(x^2 + 9)$
32. $(3x^2 - y^2)(3x^2 + y^2)$
33. $(r^3 + 2s^4)(r^3 - 2s^4)$
34. $(a^2 + b^2)(a + b)(a - b)$
35. $(m^2 + n^2)(m - n)(m + n)$
36. $(y^2 + z^2)(y^2 - z^2)(y^4 + z^4)$
37. $(h^2 + k^2)(h^2 - k^2)(h^4 + k^4)$
38. $(5c^2d^3 + 7e^5)(5c^2d^3 - 7e^5)$
39. $(3x^2y^4 - 8z^3)(3x^2y^4 + 8z^3)$

40. For the rectangle below, the length is 10 greater than the width.
a. If $x + 5$ represents the length, what expression represents the width?
b. What expression represents the area of the rectangle?

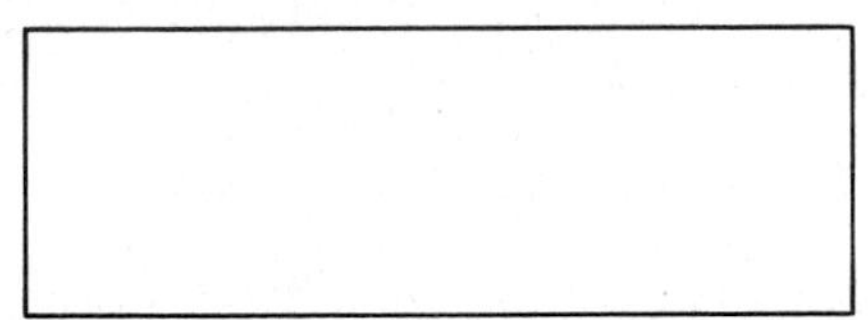

41. For the parallelogram below, the base is 18 greater than the altitude.
a. If $y - 9$ represents the altitude, what expression represents the base?
b. What expression represents the area of the parallelogram?

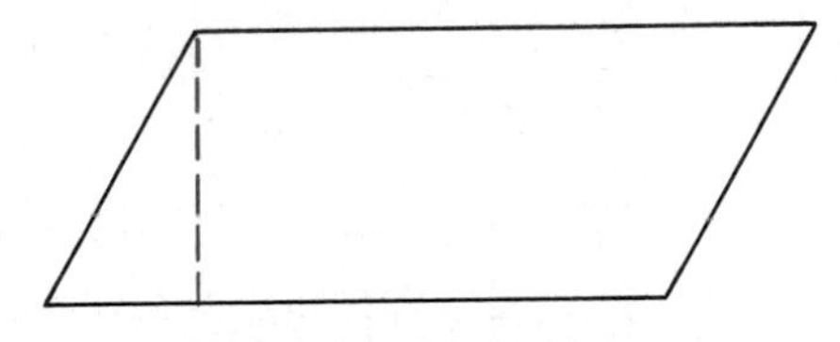

42. If the three factors of a product are $z + 6$, $z^2 + 36$, and $z - 6$, what expression represents the product?

C Multiply.

43. $[(a+b)-c][(a+b)+c]$

44. $[6x-(2b-3c)][6x+(2b-3c)]$

Rewrite each factor so that one is in the form $a+b$ and the other is in the form $a-b$. Then find the product.

45. $[4y^2-9-6xy+9x^2][-6xy+9x^2+9+4y^2]$

46. $[16z^2+40z+17][16z^2+40z+33]$

Write an expression that represents the volume of each.

47. **48.**

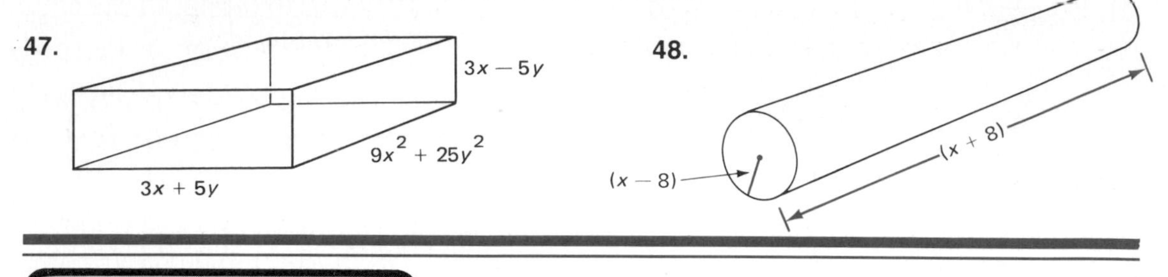

0.1666667

DISCOUNTS

Storekeepers find the Constant feature of a calculator useful for working with discounts.

EXAMPLE The chart shows present prices of tennis rackets in the store where you work. The store manager asks you to mark down the prices by 15%.

Eliminator	\$74.95
Competitor II	\$49.95
All-Pro	\$34.95
Super Lightweight	\$18.95
True Volley	\$12.95

SOLUTION Since each price is marked down by 15%, the new prices will be 85% of the present prices.

Press	74.95 [×] 0.85 [=]	49.95 [=]	34.95 [=]	18.95 [=]	12.95 [=]
Display	63.7075	42.4575	29.7075	16.1075	11.0075

CONCLUSION The marked down prices will be \$63.71, \$42.46, \$29.71, \$16.11, and \$11.01.

A record store is going to reduce album prices by $\frac{1}{6}$, or 16.7%. Copy and complete this chart.

Album category Present price	AA \$12.99	BB \$10.99	CC \$8.99	DD \$6.79	EE \$4.49	FF \$2.95
Reduced price	**1.** ?	**2.** ?	**3.** ?	**4.** ?	**5.** ?	**6.** ?

7-8 FACTORING THE DIFFERENCE OF TWO SQUARES

We know that the product of the sum and difference of two numbers is equal to the difference of the squares of the numbers. Now we reverse this process and find the two factors of the difference of two squares.

EXAMPLE 1 Factor $x^2 - y^2$.

SOLUTION A square root of x^2 is x and a square root of y^2 is y. The sum of the square roots is $x + y$. The difference of the square roots is $x - y$.

Thus, $x^2 - y^2 = (x + y)(x - y)$.

EXAMPLE 2 Factor $4c^4 - 25$.

SOLUTION A square root of $4c^4$ is $2c^2$. A square root of 25 is 5. One factor is $2c^2 + 5$ and the other is $2c^2 - 5$.

Thus, $4c^4 - 25 = (2c^2 + 5)(2c^2 - 5)$.

EXAMPLE 3 Factor $1 - 81n^2$.

SOLUTION A square root of 1 is 1. A square root of $81n^2$ is $9n$.

Thus, $1 - 81n^2 = (1 + 9n)(1 - 9n)$.

EXAMPLE 4 Factor $a^2b^4 - 0.01$

(M) SOLUTION $a^2b^4 - 0.01 = (ab^2 + 0.1)(ab^2 - 0.1)$

FACTORING THE DIFFERENCE OF TWO SQUARES

1. Find a square root of each of the squares.
2. Write the sum of these square roots as one factor. Write the difference of the square roots as the other factor.

CLASSROOM EXERCISES

Factor.

1. $a^2 - b^2$
2. $x^2 - 4$
3. $x^2 - 9$
4. $25 - c^2$
5. $a^2 - 4b^2$
6. $x^2 - 9y^2$
7. $9x^2 - 4$
8. $49x^2 - 1$
9. $1 - r^2$

EXERCISES

A Factor when possible.

1. $x^2 - m^2$ **2.** $c^2 - b^2$ **3.** $x^2 - 1$

4. $c^2 - 4$ **5.** $4 - c^2$ **6.** $c^2 - d^2$

7. $x^2 - 9$ **8.** $y^2 - 16$ **9.** $a^2 - 25$

10. $m^2 - 36$ **11.** $a^2 - 49$ **12.** $64 - x^2$

13. $1 + c^2$ **14.** $R^2 + r^2$ **15.** $4x^2 - 1$

16. $9x^2 - 1$ **17.** $36h^2 - 25$ **18.** $9x^2 - 100$

19. $25r^2 - 1$ **20.** $x^2 - \frac{1}{4}$ **21.** $m^2 - \frac{1}{9}$

22. $4s^4 - 49$ **23.** $1 - 9a^2$ **24.** $x^6 - y^6$

25. $49 - m^4$ **26.** $x^6 - 1$ **27.** $64x^2 - 49y^2$

28. $4r^2 - 64s^2$ **29.** $9p^2 - 81q^4$ **30.** $4x^2 - 36y^2$

31. $c^2d^2 - a^2b^2$ **32.** $1 - a^2b^2c^2$ **33.** $a^6b^8 - 121$

B **34.** $x^6y^4 - 1600$ **35.** $1.69x^8 - 0.81y^4$ **36.** $y^2z^2 - 6.25$

37. $9r^2 - \frac{1}{4}$ **38.** $\frac{25}{49}x^2 - \frac{9}{64}y^2$ **39.** $0.09x^2 - 0.16y^2$

C **40.** $x^{2a} - 9$ **41.** $(x + 4)^2 - x^2$ **42.** $z^2 - (z - 2)^2$

ANOTHER WAY TO FACTOR TRINOMIALS

An alternate way to factor quadratic trinomials requires squaring the coefficient of the first term.

EXAMPLE Factor $8x^2 - 22x + 15$.

SOLUTION First, multiply by 8 to get $64x^2 - 176x + 120$.
$64x^2 - 176x + 120 = (8x - a)(8x - b)$ for which
$-8a - 8b = -176$, or $a + b = 22$, and $ab = 120$.
The obvious integer solutions for a and b are 12 and 10.

$$64x^2 - 176x + 120 = (8x - 12)(8x - 10)$$
$$8(8x^2 - 22x + 15) = 4(2x - 3) \cdot 2(4x - 5)$$
$$8x^2 - 22x + 15 = (2x - 3)(4x - 5)$$

Factor using the above method.

1. $8x + 10x + 3$ **2.** $6x^2 - x - 12$ **3.** $12x^2 + 7x - 12$

4. $4b^2 + 4b - 3$ **5.** $3y^2 - 11y - 20$ **6.** $12x^2 + 32x + 5$

7. $6x^2 - 17x + 12$ **8.** $10a^2 + 19a + 6$ **9.** $12x^2 + 7rs - 12s^2$

7-9 TYPES OF FACTORING

When factoring an expression, first determine if it contains a monomial factor. If it does, be sure to find the greatest monomial factor common to all the terms.

EXAMPLE 1 Factor $ax - ay$.

(M) SOLUTION $ax - ay = a(x - y)$

EXAMPLE 2 Factor $6x - 12y$.

(M) SOLUTION $6x - 12y = 6(x - 2y)$

EXAMPLE 3 Factor $6a^2 - 9a^2y^2$.

(M) SOLUTION $6a^2 - 9a^2y^2 = 3a^2(2 - 3y^2)$

If there is no monomial factor, see if the expression is the difference of two squares or a perfect-square trinomial.

EXAMPLE 4 Factor $9a^2 - 25$.

(M) SOLUTION $9a^2 - 25 = (3a + 5)(3a - 5)$

EXAMPLE 5 Factor $a^2b^4 - 16c^2$.

(M) SOLUTION $a^2b^4 - 16c^2 = (ab^2 + 4c)(ab^2 - 4c)$

EXAMPLE 6 Factor $9x^2 + 12xy + 4y^2$.

(M) SOLUTION $9x^2 + 12xy + 4y^2 = (3x + 2y)(3x + 2y)$, or $(3x + 2y)^2$

If there is no monomial factor and the expression is a trinomial but not a perfect square, look for two different binomial factors. This may require that you try various combinations.

EXAMPLE 7 Factor $6a^2 + a - 12$.

(M) SOLUTION $6a^2 + a - 12 = (3a - 4)(2a + 3)$

EXAMPLE 8 Factor $3x^2 - x + 3$.

SOLUTION Trying various combinations using $(3x - \quad)(x - \quad)$ will show that $3x^2 - x + 3$ cannot be factored. $3x^2 - x + 3$ is prime.

CLASSROOM EXERCISES

Factor.

1. $2x + 6$
2. $3x^2 + 4x$
3. $6a^2 - 15ab^2$
4. $a^2b^6 - 36$
5. $4x^2 - 16y^2$
6. $x^2 + 4x + 4$
7. $x^2 + 5x - 24$
8. $a^2 + 6a - 40$
9. $c^2 - 16c + 63$
10. $y^2 + y - 10$
11. $x^2 - 3x - 18$
12. $x^2 - 7x - 30$

EXERCISES

A Factor the polynomials that are not prime.

1. $5x + 10$
2. $3x^2 - 18$
3. $x^2 + 4$
4. $a^2 + 9$
5. $2x^2 - 6x$
6. $\pi R + \pi r$
7. $abx + a$
8. $12x^8 - 10x^6$
9. $a^2 + 64$
10. $c^2 - 29$
11. $m^2 - 25$
12. $1 - z^2$
13. $c^2 + 2c + 1$
14. $m^2 - 10m + 25$
15. $a^2 - a - 42$
16. $6a^2 - 13a - 5$
17. $h^2 - 6h + 8$
18. $a^2 - 11ac + 18c^2$
19. $r^2 - 7r - 60$
20. $c^2 - 9c$
21. $6x^4 - 9x^2$
22. $p^2 - 6p + 9$
23. $y^2 - 4y + 4$
24. $x^2 - 3x - 10$
25. $p^2 - p - 56$
26. $9 - 4x^2$
27. $-2a^3 + 4ab^2 - 6ac^2$
28. $-3r^3 + 6rs^2 - 9rt^2$
29. $a^2 - 64b^2$
30. $m^2 - 14m + 49$
31. $-12 - x + x^2$
32. $2c^2 - 17c + 35$
33. $x^2 + 8x + 12$
34. $a^2 - 6ab^2 + 9b^4$
35. $16x^2 + 8xy + y^2$
36. $p^2 + p - 72$
37. $1 + x^2$
38. $x^2 + 16xy - 16x^2$
39. $25x^2 - 1$
40. $x^2 + 5xy - 36y^2$
41. $c^2d^2 - 7cd - 35$
42. $2x^2 + 3x + 1$
43. $x^2y^4 - w^2$
44. $a^2b^2 - d^2$
45. $4x^2 - 20x + 25$

B

46. $x^2 - 5xy - 36y^2$
47. $6y^2 - 8y - 14$
48. $2c^2 + 5c + 2$
49. $k^{10} + 2k^5 + 1$
50. $2b^2 + 5b - 3$
51. $a^2b^2 - 6abc + 9c^2$
52. $w^4x^4 - 81$
53. $x^4 + 8.5x^2 + 4.0$
54. $x^2 - x - 380$

C Factor.

55. $(a + b)^2 - 4(a + b) + 3$
56. $(x + y)^2 - 3(x + y) + 2$
57. $(x + 2)^2 - 4(x + 2) - 21$
58. $(y - 3)^2 - 2(y - 3) - 63$
59. $(x + y + z)^2 - (x - y + z)^2$
60. $12(s + t)^2 + 2(s^2 - t^2) - 24(s - t)^2$
61. $x^3 - x^2 - 9x + 9$ (Hint: x^2 is a factor of the first two terms. -9 is a factor of the last two terms.)

7-10 COMPLETE FACTORING

It is possible that some factors of an algebraic expression can themselves be factored. In factoring any expression, factoring should be continued until all factors are prime.

EXAMPLE 1 Factor $5x^2 - 5x - 60$ completely.

SOLUTION First find the greatest monomial factor common to the three terms.

$$5x^2 - 5x - 60 = 5(x^2 - x - 12)$$

The factor $x^2 - x - 12$ is a trinomial. It is not a perfect square, but by trying combinations, we find

$$x^2 - x - 12 = (x - 4)(x + 3).$$

Therefore, we write

(M)
$$\begin{aligned} 5x^2 - 5x - 60 &= 5(x^2 - x - 12) \\ &= 5(x - 4)(x + 3) \end{aligned}$$

EXAMPLE 2 Factor $a^4 - 1$.

SOLUTION Is there a monomial factor? No.
Is $a^4 - 1$ the difference of two squares? Yes.
Therefore,

$$a^4 - 1 = (a^2 + 1)(a^2 - 1).$$

$a^2 + 1$ cannot be factored, but $a^2 - 1$ is the difference of two squares.

$$a^2 - 1 = (a + 1)(a - 1)$$

Therefore, we write

(M)
$$\begin{aligned} a^4 - 1 &= (a^2 + 1)(a^2 - 1) \\ &= (a^2 + 1)(a + 1)(a - 1) \end{aligned}$$

FACTORING COMPLETELY

1. Find the greatest monomial factor common to all the terms.
2. Factor, if possible, any binomial or trinomial factors into prime factors.

CLASSROOM EXERCISES

Factor when possible.

1. $5a + 5$
2. $x^3 - x$
3. $k^2 - 1$
4. $2x^2 + 6x + 4$
5. $5y^2 + 10y + 5$
6. $b^4 - 81$
7. $k^2 + 2$
8. $x^3 - 25x$
9. $2a^4 - 2b^4$

EXERCISES

A Factor when possible.

1. $6a + 6$
2. $x^2 - 4x$
3. $4c^2 - 4$
4. $x^4 - a^4$
5. $x^4 + 7x^3 + 12x^2$
6. $4a^2 - 12a + 9$
7. $16a^2 - 4ab^2$
8. $5x^3 - 20xy^2$
9. $4c^2 - 9c$
10. $m^2 + 8m + 16$
11. $bx^2 - 9b$
12. $x^2 - 16x$
13. $3cx^2 + 7cx + 2c$
14. $a^2 - 25$
15. $a^2 - 25a$
16. $9x^3 - xy^2$
17. $\pi R^2 - \pi r^2$
18. $w^4 - 1$
19. $2\pi r^2 + 2\pi rh$
20. $a^4 - 16$
21. $a^4 - 16a$
22. $3x^2 - 6$
23. $x^3 - x$
24. $x^3 - x^2$
25. $x^5 - x^3$
26. $a^5 - a^4$
27. $a^4 + 1$
28. $a^4 - 16b^4$
29. $ax^2 - 4ay^2$
30. $5h^2 + 40h + 60$
31. $a^4 - 4a^2 + 3$
32. $10x^2 + 35x + 15$
33. $3a^3 + 8a^2 + 5a$
34. $12x^2 - 22x + 6$
35. $8a^2 + 16a + 8$
36. $8x^2 - 80x + 168$
37. $m^2 - 12m + 35$
38. $1 - x^2$
39. $4x^2 + 4x - 48$
40. $2\pi R - 2\pi r$
41. $p + pqt$
42. $abx^2 - ab$

B

43. $6a^2y^2 + 5ay^2 - 6y^2$
44. $x^4 - 2x^2y^2 + y^4$
45. $6c^2 - 54cd + 84d^2$
46. $\frac{1}{3}\pi R^2h + \frac{1}{3}\pi r^2h$
47. $9x^3 - 81xy^2$
48. $z^3 - 16z$
49. $A^2B^2 - 5AB^3 + 6B^4$
50. $a^2b^2 + a^2b - 12a^2$
51. $x^2 - 22x + 121$
52. $x^2 + 28xy + 196y^2$
53. $9a^2b^2 - 16c^2$
54. $12b^2 - 5b - 28$

C

55. $(49s^2 - 14rs + r^2) - 25$
56. $(x + y)^2 - (x - y)^2$
57. $(3a - b)^2 - (a + b)^2$
58. $[4x^2 - 12x + 9] - x^4$
59. $\left(x - \frac{1}{2}y + z\right)^2 - \left(x + \frac{1}{2}y - z\right)^2$
60. $\left(\frac{1}{2}a + \frac{1}{3}b\right)^2 + \left(\frac{1}{2}a^2 - \frac{2}{9}b^2\right) + \left(\frac{1}{2}a - \frac{1}{3}b\right)^2$
61. $(x^2 + 6x + 9)^2 - 5(x^4 - 18x^2 + 81) + 4(x^2 - 6x + 9)^2$
62. $[(x^2 - 2)^2 + 2x(x^2 - 2) + x^2] - [(x^2 - 6)^2 - 2x(x^2 - 6) + x^2]$

CHECKING YOUR UNDERSTANDING

WORDS

difference of two squares   perfect-square trinomial   square of a binomial

CONCEPTS

- To multiply two polynomials, multiplying each term of one by each term of the other is necessary. [7-3]

PROCESSES

- Multiply two binomials. [7-3, 7-5, 7-7]

1. $(4y + 2)(2y - 3)$ **2.** $(2x - 1)(2x - 1)$ **3.** $(3a - 2)(3a + 2)$

- Factor a trinomial or the difference of two squares. Factor completely. [7-4, 7-8 to 7-10]

4. $x^2 - 5x + 4$ **5.** $4x^2 - 4x + 1$ **6.** $3x^2 - 24x + 45$

7. $x^2 - 100$ **8.** $4x^2 - y^2$ **9.** $25x^2 - 36y^2$

10. $2x^2 - 8$ **11.** $5x^3 - 10x^2 - 15x$ **12.** $2x^2 - 4xy + 2y^2$

- Find the square of a binomial. Find a square root of a perfect-square trinomial. [7-5, 7-6]

13. $(3x - 1)^2$ **14.** $25x^2 - 10x + 1 = (?)^2$

RINGS AND THINGS

Consider a flat ring with inside radius r and outside radius R. The surface area of the ring may be found by subtracting the area of the small circle from the area of the large circle.

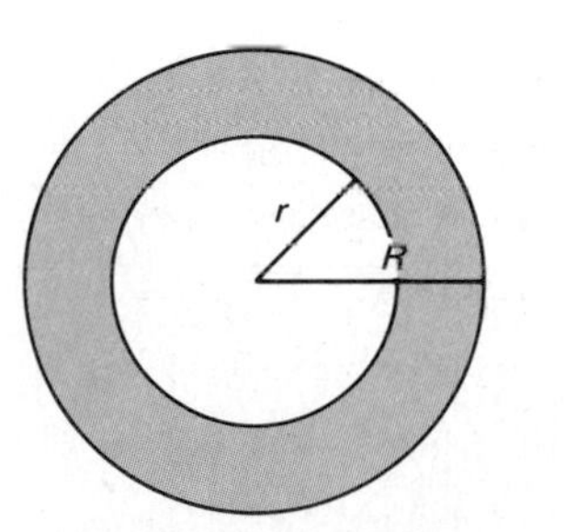

$$\text{Area of Ring} = \pi R^2 - \pi r^2$$
$$= \pi(R^2 - r^2), \text{ or } \pi(R + r)(R - r)$$

A large bullseye target is drawn with concentric circles 1 m, 2 m, 3 m, 4 m, and 5 m in radius. The center circle, middle ring and outer ring are painted black.

1. Find the area of the target that is black.

2. Find the area of the target that is white.

OBJECTIVES: Use factoring to solve equations. Use factoring to solve problems.

7-11 SOLVING EQUATIONS BY FACTORING

An equation with one member that is zero can sometimes be solved by factoring the other member. This method depends upon the fact that if a product is zero, then at least one of its factors is zero.

EXAMPLE 1 Solve $x^2 - 3x - 18 = 0$.

SOLUTION
$$x^2 - 3x - 18 = 0$$
$$(x - 6)(x + 3) = 0$$
Thus, $x - 6 = 0$ or $x + 3 = 0$

$x = 6$ | $x = -3$

CHECK

$$x^2 - 3x - 18 = 0$$
$$6^2 - 3(6) - 18 \stackrel{?}{=} 0$$
$$36 - 18 - 18 \stackrel{?}{=} 0$$
$$0 = 0 \checkmark$$

$$x^2 - 3x - 18 = 0$$
$$(-3)^2 - 3(-3) - 18 \stackrel{?}{=} 0$$
$$9 + 9 - 18 \stackrel{?}{=} 0$$
$$0 = 0 \checkmark$$

EXAMPLE 2 Solve $4x^2 = 25$.

Ⓜ SOLUTION
$$4x^2 = 25$$
$$4x^2 - 25 = 0$$
$$(2x + 5)(2x - 5) = 0$$
Thus, $2x + 5 = 0$ or $2x - 5 = 0$

$2x = -5$ | $2x = 5$

$x = -\frac{5}{2}$ | $x = \frac{5}{2}$

CHECK
$$4x^2 = 25$$
$$4\left(-\frac{5}{2}\right)^2 \stackrel{?}{=} 25$$
$$4\left(\frac{25}{4}\right) \stackrel{?}{=} 25$$
$$25 = 25 \checkmark$$
The check for $x = \frac{5}{2}$ is left for the student.

EXAMPLE 3 Solve $5x^2 = 2x$.

Ⓜ SOLUTION
$$5x^2 = 2x$$
$$5x^2 - 2x = 0$$
$$x(5x - 2) = 0$$
$x = 0$ or $5x - 2 = 0$

| $5x = 2$

| $x = \frac{2}{5}$

CHECK
$$5x^2 = 2x$$
$$5(0)^2 \stackrel{?}{=} 2(0)$$
$$0 = 0 \checkmark$$

The check for $x = \frac{2}{5}$ is left for the student.

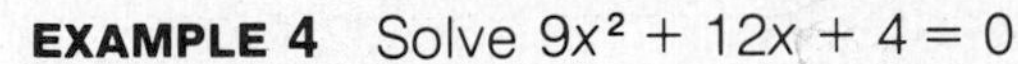

EXAMPLE 4 Solve $9x^2 + 12x + 4 = 0$

Ⓜ SOLUTION

$$9x^2 + 12x + 4 = 0$$
$$(3x + 2)(3x + 2) = 0$$
$$\text{Thus, } 3x + 2 = 0$$
$$3x = -2$$
$$x = -\frac{2}{3}$$

CHECK The check is left for the student.

SOLVING AN EQUATION BY FACTORING

1. If necessary, change the equation so that one member is zero.
2. Factor the other member.
3. Set each factor containing the variable equal to zero.
4. Solve the resulting equations.
5. Check each solution.

CLASSROOM EXERCISES

Solve by factoring.

1. $x^2 - 4 = 0$ **2.** $x^2 - 9 = 0$ **3.** $x^2 - 5x + 6 = 0$

4. $4x^2 = 9$ **5.** $3x^2 = 2x$ **6.** $6x^2 + x = 0$

EXERCISES

A Solve by factoring.

1. $x^2 + 2x = 15$ **2.** $x^2 + 3x + 2 = 0$ **3.** $m^2 - 4 = 0$

4. $x^2 - 1 = 0$ **5.** $x^2 - 3x = 0$ **6.** $x^2 + 5x = 0$

7. $x^2 + 6x = -9$ **8.** $x^2 - 35 = 2x$ **9.** $x^2 - 4x + 4 = 0$

10. $x^2 = 9$ **11.** $x^2 - 6x = 0$ **12.** $x^2 - 2x = 24$

13. $x^2 - 12x = -32$ **14.** $5y^2 - 17y = 0$ **15.** $4n^2 - 4$

16. $y^2 - 4y = 21$ **17.** $c^2 + 2 = 3c$ **18.** $4x^2 + 16x - 20 = 0$

19. $4x^2 = 36$ **20.** $y^2 - 8y = 0$ **21.** $2y^2 = 9y - 9$

22. $\pi r^2 - 2\pi r = 0$ **23.** $y(y + 2) = 15$ **24.** $d^2 + 8d = 0$

25. $x^2 = 16x$ **26.** $9x^2 = 27x$ **27.** $7x^2 = 28x$

28. $x^2 + x - 6 = 0$ **29.** $w^2 - 2w = 15$ **30.** $x^2 + 15 = -8x$

31. $2x^2 = x + 6$ **32.** $4x^2 + 4x = -1$ **33.** $3x^2 = 198 + 15x$

B Solve for x.

34. $\frac{x^2}{6} + \frac{x}{3} = \frac{1}{2}$ **35.** $x^2 = \frac{5}{2} - \frac{3x}{2}$ **36.** $6x^2 + \frac{13x}{2} = 7$

37. $x^2 + 25 = 1 \quad 10x$ **38.** $\frac{x^2}{2} = 6x$ **39.** $\frac{x^2}{12} + x + \frac{9}{4} = 0$

40. $\frac{x^2}{15} = \frac{x}{5} + \frac{2}{3}$ **41.** $(x - 3)(x - 5) = x - 5$ **42.** $(x - 4)(x - 5) = x - 5$

43. $x^2 - a^2 = 0$ **44.** $6x^2 + 7cx - 5c^2 = 0$ **45.** $12x^2 + 18xy - 12y^2 = 0$

46. $6x^2 + xy - 12y^2 = 0$ **47.** $\frac{x^2}{8} + yx = \frac{5y^2}{2}$ **48.** $\frac{y^2}{x} + 9x = 6y$

C **49.** $(2x - 1)(3x + 4) - 3(x - 1)(x + 2) = 18$ **50.** $(3x - 1)(3x + 1) - (2x - 1)(2x + 1) = 45$

USING SPECIAL PRODUCTS TO COMPUTE MENTALLY

The patterns for the special products can help us do some multiplications mentally.

$(x + y)^2 = x + 2xy + y^2$ | $(x - y)^2 = x^2 - 2xy + y^2$ | $(x + y)(x - y) = x^2 - y^2$

EXAMPLE 1 Multiply 42 and 42.

SOLUTION
$$\begin{aligned} &(42)^2 \\ &= (40 + 2)^2 \\ &= 1600 + 160 + 4 \\ &= 1764 \end{aligned}$$

EXAMPLE 2 Square 95.

SOLUTION
$$\begin{aligned} 95^2 - 5^2 &= (95 + 5)(95 - 5) \\ &= 100 \cdot 90 \\ &= 9000 \\ 95^2 &= 9000 + 5^2, \text{ or } 9025. \end{aligned}$$

Try these without using paper and pencil.

1. 39×41 **2.** 74×74 **3.** 23×17 **4.** 38×38

5. 63^2 **6.** 48^2 **7.** 55×45 **8.** 85×85

9. 19×19 **10.** 32×28 **11.** 51^2 **12.** 27^2

13. 67×53 **14.** 56^2 **15.** 92×92 **16.** 86×94

7-12 PROBLEM SOLVING: USING FACTORING

Some verbal problems give equations that can be solved by factoring.

EXAMPLE 1 One number is 6 times another number. Their product is 96. Find the numbers.

Ⓜ **SOLUTION** The product of a number and 6 times the number is 96.

Use x for one number.
$6x$ for the other number.

$$x(6x) = 96$$
$$6x^2 = 96$$
$$x^2 = 16$$
$$x^2 - 16 = 0$$
$$(x + 4)(x - 4) = 0$$

Therefore, $x + 4 = 0$ or $x - 4 = 0$.

$x = -4$ | $x = 4$

Also, $6x = -24$. | Also, $6x = 24$.

CONCLUSION The two numbers are -4 and -24, or 4 and 24.

CHECK The product of -4 and -24 is 96.
The product of 4 and 24 is 96. ✓

EXAMPLE 2 The difference of two numbers is 3. The sum of their squares is 29. What are the numbers?

Ⓜ **SOLUTION** The sum of the square of one number and the square of another number is 29.

Use n for one number.
$n + 3$ for the other number.

$$n^2 + (n + 3)^2 = 29$$
$$n^2 + n^2 + 6n + 9 = 29$$
$$2n^2 + 6n + 9 = 29$$
$$2n^2 + 6n - 20 = 0$$
$$2(n^2 + 3n - 10) = 0$$
$$2(n + 5)(n - 2) = 0$$

Therefore, $n + 5 = 0$ or $n - 2 = 0$.

$n = -5$ | $n = 2$

Also, $n + 3 = -2$. | Also, $n + 3 = 5$.

CONCLUSION The two numbers are -5 and -2, or 2 and 5.

CHECK Is the sum of the squares of -5 and -2 equal to 29?
Is the sum of the squares of 5 and 2 equal to 29?
Completing the check is left for the student.

EXAMPLE 3 A rectangular garden is 9 m long and 6 m wide. When the length and the width are changed by the same amount, the area becomes 44 m^2. Find the amount by which the length and width are changed.

Ⓜ **SOLUTION** The area of the new rectangular garden is 44 m^2.

$m + m = m$
$m - m = m$

Use
- x for the amount of change in meters.
- $9 + x$ for the new length in meters.
- $6 - x$ for the new width in meters.

$m \cdot m = m^2$

$$\text{length}_{\text{new}} \cdot \text{width}_{\text{new}} = 44$$
$$(9 + x)(6 - x) = 44$$
$$54 - 3x - x^2 = 44$$
$$10 - 3x - x^2 = 0$$
$$(2 - x)(5 + x) = 0$$

Therefore, $2 - x = 0$ or $5 + x = 0$.

$x = 2$	$x = -5$
Also, $9 + x = 11$ and $6 - x = 4$.	Also, $9 + x = 4$ and $6 - x = 11$.

CONCLUSION The length may be increased by 2 m and the width decreased by 2 m. Also, the length may be decreased by 5 m and the width increased by 5 m. Either way, the dimensions of the new rectangular garden will be 4 m by 11 m.

CHECK The area of a rectangular garden with dimensions 4 m by 11 m is 44 m^2. ✓

CLASSROOM EXERCISES

Solve.

1. The product of two consecutive integers is 90. Find the integers.
2. The product of two consecutive odd integers is 143. Find the integers.
3. The length of a rectangle is 3 greater than its width. The area of the rectangle is 54. Find the length and width.
4. The width of a rectangle is 9 m less than its length. The area of the rectangle is 70 m^2. Find the length and the width.
5. Find a number such that its square exceeds three times the number by 4.

EXERCISES

[A] Solve.

1. Find two numbers that differ by 6 and whose product is 135.
2. Find two consecutive even integers whose product is 120.

3. The difference of the squares of two consecutive integers is 21. Find the integers.

4. The difference of two numbers is 4. The difference of their squares is 40. Find the numbers.

5. The area of a rectangle is 176 cm^2. Find the dimensions of the rectangle when the length exceeds the width by 5 cm.

6. The square of a number is 56 more than the number itself. Find the number.

7. The sum of the degree measures of two angles is 90. The degree measure of one is the square of the degree measure of the other. Find the degree measure of each.

8. Mary said to Priscilla, "If six times my age in ten years is subtracted from the square of my present age, the result is 52." How old is Mary?

9. The square of a number is 5 less than 6 times the number. Find the number.

10. The sum of two numbers is 27. The sum of their squares is 389. Find the numbers.

11. If a number is increased by 6 and the sum is divided by 2, the resulting quotient will equal the square of the number. Find the number.

12. The lengths of the base and altitude of a triangle are equal. The area of the triangle is 128 m^2. Find the lengths of the base and altitude.

B **13.** A school band director planned to arrange the 55 band members in a marching formation so that there would be 6 more rows than the number of musicians in each row. Find the number of rows.

14. A farmer planted 360 cherry trees so there were 9 more trees in a row than the number of rows. How many rows were there?

15. A city lot is 12 m wide and 42 m long. How wide a strip must be cut off one end and one side to make the area of the lot 400 m^2?

16. A rectangular garden is 10 m wide and 25 m long. When the length is increased and the width is decreased by the same amount, the area becomes 216 m^2. Find the amount of change in the length and width.

17. A farmer wishes to build a granary for wheat that will hold 384 m^3. The bin is to be 3 m high and twice as long as it is wide. Find its length and width.

18. The number of cubic centimeters in a cube is three times the sum of the number of centimeters in all its edges. Find the length of each edge.

19. The length and width of a photographic print are 6 cm and 5 cm respectively. A white border of uniform width is placed around the print. The area of the border is 42 cm^2. Find the width of the border.

C **20.** A rectangular plot of ground is 20 m long and 15 m wide. The plot is surrounded by a walk of uniform width whose area is two thirds the area of the plot. Find the width of the walk.

21. One number exceeds another by d. The sum of the numbers is s. Find the numbers.

22. The perimeter of a rectangle is p. The length exceeds the width by d. Find the dimensions of the rectangle.

CHAPTER REVIEW

Multiply. [7-1]

1. $6(2a + 5)$ **2.** $r(3 - rs)$ **3.** $\pi(R^2 - r^2)$

Factor.

4. $8 - 4xy$ **5.** $5x - 10xy$ **6.** $a^3 + 3a^2b$

Simplify. [7-2]

7. $(6z)^2$ **8.** $(-8b)^2$ **9.** $(-3r^2s)^2$

Square each.

10. $4ab$ **11.** $-5abx$ **12.** $-7wx^3y^3$

Find a square root.

13. $36y^2$ **14.** $100m^8n^6$ **15.** $256x^4y^{16}$

Multiply. [7-3]

16. $(x + 3)(2x + 1)$ **17.** $(4w - 3)(w - 5)$ **18.** $(2x + y)(3x - 2y)$

Factor. [7-4]

19. $r^2 + r - 6$ **20.** $2x^2 - 15x + 7$ **21.** $3t^2 + 5t + 2$

Multiply. [7-5]

22. $(5s - 2)(5s - 2)$ **23.** $(m - 3n)(m - 3n)$ **24.** $(2b - 4c)(2b - 4c)$

Simplify.

25. $(2y - 6)^2$ **26.** $(5 - t)^2$ **27.** $(4x + 3y)^2$

Square.

28. $2x - 7$ **29.** $b - 3d$ **30.** $2a - 5b$

Factor. [7-6]

31. $x^2 + 4x + 4$ **32.** $4y^2 + 12y + 9$ **33.** $9n^2 - 12nm + 4m^2$

34. $1 + 2x + x^2$ **35.** $1 + 4h + 4h^2$ **36.** $64 - 96r + 36r^2$

Find a square root.

37. $t^2 + 14t + 49$ **38.** $4h^2 - 4h + 1$ **39.** $9p^2 + 12ps + 4s^2$

Multiply. [7-7]

40. $(3y + 4)(3y - 4)$ **41.** $(t - 4s)(t + 4s)$ **42.** $(7a + 2b)(7a - 2b)$

Factor. [7-8]

43. $49x^2 - 16$ **44.** $49x^2 - 16y^2$ **45.** $25a^2 - 9b^2$

Factor each polynomial that is not prime. [7-9]

46. $r^2 + r + 1$ **47.** $4y^2 + 12y + 9$ **48.** $25a^2 + 9b^2$

49. $x^2y^2 - 9$ **50.** $2x^2 + x - 10$ **51.** $x^2 - 7x + 10$

Factor completely. [7-10]

52. $3rs^2 - 12r$ **53.** $16s^2 - 196sq$ **54.** $2x^2 - 4x + 2$

55. $4sw^2 - 20sw + 25s$ **56.** $3x^3 - 3x^2 - 6x$ **57.** $4xy^3 + 14xy^2 + 6xy$

Solve. [7-11]

58. $x^2 + 3x = 0$ **59.** $6r^2 - 21r = 0$ **60.** $k^2 - 4k + 4 = 0$

61. $n^2 + 10n + 25 = 0$ **62.** $9x^2 - 4 = 0$ **63.** $w^2 + 3w - 10 = 0$

64. $2r^2 + 11r - 21 = 0$ **65.** $6x^2 - 27x + 12 = 0$ **66.** $12a^2 + 10a - 8 = 0$

Solve. [7-12]

67. Find a number so that twice the square of the number exceeds 8 times the number by 42.

68. The length of a rectangle is 3 greater than the width. When the length and width are each increased by 2, the area is increased by 58. Find the original length and width.

69. The area of a triangle is 90. The length of the altitude is 3 greater than the length of the base. Find the lengths of the base and altitude.

CAPSULE REVIEW

Write the letter of the best response.

1. Which number completes this sentence?
$(3x - 2)(2x + 3) = 6x^2 + \boxed{?}\,x - 6$

a. 4 **b.** 5 **c.** 6 **d.** 9 **e.** 13

2. Which is the square of $2t - 5$?

a. $4t^2 - 10t - 25$ **b.** $4t^2 - 20t - 25$ **c.** $4t^2 - 10t + 25$ **d.** $4t^2 - 20t + 25$

3. Which is a square root of $36t + 81 + 4t^2$?

a. $9 + 2t$ **b.** $6 + 2t$ **c.** $9 - 2t$ **d.** $6 - 2t$

4. Which is a perfect-square trinomial?

a. $4r^2 + 4r + 4$ **b.** $9x^2 + 7x + 16$ **c.** $4z^2 + 24z - 9$ **d.** $t^2 - 4t + 4$

5. Which do you get when you factor $4y^2 - 9b^2$?

a. $(2y + 3b)^2$ **b.** $(2y + 3b)(3b - 2y)$ **c.** $(2y - 3b)(2y + 3b)$ **d.** $(2y - 3b)^2$

6. Which do you get when you factor $4r^2 + 10r - 6$ completely?

a. $(2r + 6)(2r - 1)$ **b.** $(r + 3)(4r - 2)$ **c.** $2(r + 3)(2r - 1)$ **d.** $2(r - 3)(2r + 1)$

7. Which do you get when you factor $4x^2 - 16x$ completely?

a. $4(x - 4)(x + 4)$ **b.** $4x(x - 4)$ **c.** $(2x - 4)(2x + 4)$ **d.** $4(x - 2)(x + 2)$

8. Which way of rewriting the equation $3x^2 + 4x - 4 = 0$ is most helpful in solving it?

a. $x(3x + 4) - 4 = 0$ **b.** $(3x - 2)(x + 2) = 0$
c. $3x^2 + 4x = 4$ **d.** $3x + 4(x - 1) = 0$

9. The sum of two numbers is 18. One number plus the square of the other equals 174. Which equation will give the two numbers?

a. $x + (18 - x)^2 = 174$ **b.** $x + (18 + x)^2 = 174$
c. $(x - 18) + x^2 = 174$ **d.** $(x + 18) + x^2 = 174$

CHAPTER TEST

---

1. Write $5a + 5b$ in factored form.

2. Write the missing factor. $xy + 5x = x(?)$

3. Factor $7x + 14$.

4. Factor $ab + ac$.

5. Simplify $(5n)^2$.

6. Find a square root of $a^{16}b^2$.

7. Find the product. $(x + 2)(x + 3)$

8. Find the product. $(x - 10)(x + 14)$

9. Factor $x^2 + 7x + 12$.

10. Factor $x^2 - 2x - 8$.

11. Simplify $(x - 3)^2$.

12. Square $2x + 5$.

13. Find a square root of $a^2 - 12a + 36$.

14. Find a square root of $4n^2 + 12n + 9$.

15. Find the product. $(c + 7)(c - 7)$.

16. Find the product. $(3x - 4)(3x + 4)$

17. Factor $r^2 - 25$.

18. Factor $9x^2 - 4$.

19. Factor $x^2 - x - 20$.

20. Factor $x^2 + 2x + 1$.

21. Factor completely. $7x^2 - 7$

22. Factor completely. $5x^2 + 20x + 20$

23. Solve by factoring. $x^2 - 3x = 0$

24. Solve by factoring. $x^2 - 5x + 6 = 0$

25. The length of a rectangle is 5 greater than its width. The area is 14. Find the length and width of the rectangle.

26. The sum of a number and the square of the number is 12. Find the number.

Write the letter of the best response.

27. The factored form for $x^2 + 2x$ is

a. $x^2(1 + 2x)$ **b.** $x(x + 2)$ **c.** $2(x + x)$ **d.** $2(x + 2x)$ **e.** $x(x^2 + 2)$

28. Which of these is *prime*?

a. $2x + 2y$ **b.** $y^2 + 2y$ **c.** $3x + 6x^2$ **d.** $2a - 4b$ **e.** $2a + 3b$

29. Which is a square root of $9a^{100}$?

a. $3a^{10}$ **b.** $3a^{50}$ **c.** $3a^{100}$ **d.** $4.5a^{10}$ **e.** $4.5a^{50}$

30. The product of $a + 5$ and $a - 3$ is

a. $a^2 - 15$ **b.** $a^2 + 15$ **c.** $a^2 + 2$ **d.** $a^2 + 2a - 15$ **e.** $a^2 - 2a - 15$

31. Factors of $x^2 + 7x + 6$ are

a. $x - 1$ and $x + 7$
b. $x + 1$ and $x + 6$
c. $x + 1$ and $x + 7$
d. $x + 2$ and $x + 3$

32. $(x - 4)^2 =$

a. $x - 2$ **b.** $x + 2$ **c.** $x^2 + 16$ **d.** $x^2 - 8x - 16$ **e.** $x^2 - 8x + 16$

33. A square root of $a^2 + 16a + 64$ is

a. $a - 32$ **b.** $a - 8$ **c.** $a + 4$ **d.** $a + 8$ **e.** $a + 32$

34. $(n + 3)(n - 3) =$

a. $n^2 - 9$ **b.** $n^2 + 9$ **c.** $n^2 + 6n + 9$ **d.** $n^2 - 6n - 9$ **e.** $n^2 + 6$

35. Factors of $x^2 - 16$ are

a. $x - 4$ and $x - 4$
b. $x - 4$ and $x + 4$
c. $x + 4$ and $x + 4$
d. $x - 8$ and $x + 8$

36. Factors of $x^2 + 2x - 8$ are

a. $x - 4$ and $x + 2$
b. $x - 2$ and $x + 4$
c. $x + 1$ and $x - 8$
d. $x + 2$ and $x + 4$

37. $3x^2 - 3$ when factored completely gives

a. $3(x^2 - 1)$ **b.** $-3(x^2 - 1)$ **c.** $-3(x + 1)(x - 1)$ **d.** $3(x - 1)(x - 1)$ **e.** $3(x - 1)(x + 1)$

38. The solutions for $x^2 + x - 6 = 0$ are

a. -3 and 3 **b.** -3 and -2 **c.** -3 and 2 **d.** -2 and -2 **e.** -2 and 3

39. The width of a rectangle is 3 less than its length. The area is 40. The width of the rectangle is

a. 5 **b.** 8 **c.** 10 **d.** $18\frac{1}{2}$ **e.** 20

CHAPTER 8
More Problem Solving

A person may plan to be an artist, a butcher, a circus clown, or a dentist. There is always a chance, however, that to someone, someday, the person will be a teacher—an expert in history, mathematics, literature, crafts, sciences, or even how to live. It is a good idea to be prepared.

OBJECTIVE: Solve equations containing coefficients in fraction or decimal form.

8-1 CLEARING EQUATIONS OF FRACTIONS

Recall that the Multiplication Property allows us to multiply both members of an equation by the same number. If an equation contains fractions, the Multiplication Property lets us write a new equation that does not contain fractions. The process is called *clearing the equation of fractions*.

EXAMPLE 1 Solve $\frac{x}{3} - \frac{x}{5} = 6$.

SOLUTION

$$\frac{x}{3} - \frac{x}{5} = 6$$

Since 15 can be divided by both denominators 3 and 5, multiply both members of the equation by 15.

$$M_{15} \quad 15\left(\frac{x}{3} - \frac{x}{5}\right) = 15(6)$$

$$\frac{15x}{3} - \frac{15x}{5} = 15(6)$$

$$5x - 3x = 90$$

$$2x = 90$$

$$x = 45$$

CHECK

$$\frac{x}{3} - \frac{x}{5} = 6$$

$$\frac{45}{3} - \frac{45}{5} \stackrel{?}{=} 6$$

$$6 = 6 \checkmark$$

The smallest counting number that can be divided exactly by each of several counting numbers is the **least common multiple** (L.C.M.) of those numbers.

EXAMPLE 2 Solve $\frac{1}{3} + \frac{5x}{6} = \frac{7}{12}$.

SOLUTION

$$\frac{1}{3} + \frac{5x}{6} = \frac{7}{12}$$

The L.C.M. of the denominators 3, 6, and 12 is 12. Multiply both members by 12.

The least common multiple of the denominators is the same as the least common denominator (L.C.D.)

$$M_{12} \quad 12\left(\frac{1}{3} + \frac{5x}{6}\right) = 12\left(\frac{7}{12}\right)$$

$$\frac{12}{3} + \frac{12(5x)}{6} = 12\left(\frac{7}{12}\right)$$

$$4 + 10x = 7$$

$$10x = 3$$

$$x = \frac{3}{10}$$

CHECK The check is left for the student.

EXAMPLE 3 Solve $\frac{x}{3} + 12 = \frac{x + 12}{2}$.

Ⓜ SOLUTION

$$\frac{x}{3} + 12 = \frac{x + 12}{2}$$

The L.C.M. of 3 and 2 is 6.

$$M_6 \quad 6\left(\frac{x}{3} + 12\right) = 6\left(\frac{x + 12}{2}\right)$$

$$6\left(\frac{x}{3}\right) + 6(12) = 3(x + 12)$$

$$2x + 72 = 3x + 36$$

$$2x - 3x = 36 - 72$$

$$-x = -36$$

$$M_{-1} \quad x = 36$$

CHECK

$$\frac{x}{3} + 12 = \frac{x + 12}{2}$$

$$\frac{36}{3} + 12 \stackrel{?}{=} \frac{36 + 12}{2}$$

$$24 = 24 \checkmark$$

EXAMPLE 4 Solve $\frac{2x}{3} + \frac{3}{4}(28 - x) = 20$

Ⓜ SOLUTION

$$\frac{2x}{3} + \frac{3}{4}(28 - x) = 20$$

The L.C.M. of 3 and 4 is 12.

$$M_{12} \quad 12\left(\frac{2x}{3} + \frac{3}{4}(28 - x)\right) = 12 \cdot 20$$

$$12\left(\frac{2x}{3}\right) + 12\left(\frac{3}{4}\right)(28 - x) = 12 \cdot 20$$

$$8x + 9(28 - x) = 240$$

$$8x + 252 - 9x = 240$$

$$8x - 9x = 240 - 252$$

$$-x = -12$$

$$x = 12$$

CHECK The check is left for the student.

SOLVING A SIMPLE EQUATION CONTAINING FRACTIONS

1. Find the L.C.M. of all the denominators in the equation.
2. Multiply both members by the L.C.M. of the denominators.
3. Remove parentheses. (Sometimes it is better to remove parentheses *before* clearing the equation of fractions.)
4. Proceed to solve the resulting equation by combining terms and using the Properties of Equality.
5. Check your result.

CLASSROOM EXERCISES

Solve and check.

1. $\frac{x}{3} - \frac{x}{4} = 5$
2. $\frac{1}{2} + \frac{3x}{4} = \frac{5}{8}$
3. $\frac{1}{3} + \frac{4x}{9} = \frac{11}{18}$
4. $\frac{x}{4} + 10 = \frac{x + 3}{5}$
5. $\frac{x}{3} + 6 = \frac{x + 1}{4}$
6. $\frac{3x}{4} + \frac{2}{3}(20 - x) = 16$

EXERCISES

A Solve and check.

1. $\frac{x}{3} - \frac{x}{4} = 8$
2. $\frac{x}{2} - \frac{x}{5} = 6$
3. $\frac{x}{9} - \frac{x}{12} = -10$
4. $\frac{x}{8} - \frac{x}{10} = -9$
5. $\frac{x}{3} + \frac{x}{2} = 5$
6. $\frac{x}{6} + \frac{x}{9} = 15$
7. $\frac{x}{4} + \frac{x}{5} = -7$
8. $\frac{x}{8} + \frac{x}{12} = -16$
9. $\frac{1}{4} + \frac{5x}{6} = \frac{7}{12}$
10. $\frac{1}{6} + \frac{2x}{9} = \frac{17}{18}$
11. $\frac{2}{3} + \frac{7x}{12} = -\frac{3}{4}$
12. $\frac{3}{4} + \frac{5x}{12} = -\frac{2}{3}$
13. $\frac{1}{8} - \frac{3x}{4} = \frac{5}{12}$
14. $\frac{1}{12} - \frac{5x}{6} = \frac{7}{9}$
15. $\frac{3}{5} - \frac{9x}{10} = -\frac{1}{2}$
16. $\frac{7}{10} - \frac{11x}{15} = -\frac{4}{5}$
17. $\frac{x}{6} + 12 = \frac{x + 2}{4}$
18. $\frac{x}{8} + 4 = \frac{x + 1}{6}$
19. $\frac{x}{9} - 10 = \frac{x + 3}{8}$
20. $\frac{x}{5} - 15 = \frac{x + 5}{3}$
21. $\frac{x}{4} + 8 = -\left(\frac{x + 0}{3}\right)$
22. $\frac{x}{10} + 6 = -\left(\frac{x + 2}{5}\right)$
23. $\frac{x}{9} - 15 = -\left(\frac{x + 4}{6}\right)$
24. $\frac{x}{12} - 5 = -\left(\frac{x + 6}{8}\right)$
25. $\frac{2}{3}x + \frac{3}{4}(8 - x) = 12$
26. $\frac{4}{5}x + \frac{9}{10}(5 - x) = 15$
27. $\frac{5}{6}x - \frac{2}{3}(12 - x) = -20$

B

28. $\frac{3x + 1}{4} = 2 - \frac{3 - 2x}{6}$
29. $\frac{3(x - 4)}{5} - \frac{2(x - 3)}{10} = 0$
30. $\frac{x + 1}{2} = 1 - \frac{1 - 2x}{5}$
31. $\frac{x - 4}{9} + \frac{x + 2}{6} = \frac{1}{3}x$
32. $\frac{x - 12}{10} - \frac{2(2x + 1)}{3} + \frac{3(x - 2)}{2} = 0$

C

33. $\frac{x - 10}{5} + \frac{x - 8}{6} - \frac{x - 5}{10} = \frac{x - 11}{3} - \frac{5}{2}$
34. $\frac{2x - 1}{3} - \frac{x + 10}{6} = \frac{10 - 3x}{5} - \frac{x + 40}{2}$
35. $\frac{1}{4}x + 20 = \frac{x}{8} - \frac{5}{6}x + \frac{1}{2}x + 7$
36. $\frac{4}{5}x - 14 + \frac{7x}{10} = 23 + \frac{2}{3}x - \frac{x}{6}$

8-2 EQUATIONS CONTAINING DECIMALS; LEVER PROBLEMS

An equation containing decimal coefficients often may be solved efficiently by first *clearing the equation of decimals*. The process is similar to the process for clearing an equation of fractions.

Decimal	Decimal Places	Fraction	Denominator
0.3	1	$\frac{3}{10}$	10^1 or 10
1.23	2	$1\frac{23}{100}$	10^2 or 100
4.162	3	$4\frac{162}{1000}$	10^3 or 1000

When all of several denominators are powers of 10, the least common multiple of the denominators will be the largest denominator itself. The largest denominator is related to the most decimal places. Hence, to clear an equation of decimals, multiply both members by a power of 10 that is determined by the decimal having the most decimal places.

EXAMPLE 1 Solve $0.2x = 50$.

SOLUTION The only decimal in the equation has one decimal place. Multiply both members by 10.

Ⓜ

$$\begin{aligned} 0.2x &= 50 \\ M_{10} \quad 10(0.2x) &= 10 \cdot 50 \\ 2x &= 500 \\ x &= 250 \end{aligned}$$

CHECK

$$\begin{aligned} 0.2x &= 50 \\ 0.2(250) &\overset{?}{=} 50 \\ 50 &= 50 \checkmark \end{aligned}$$

EXAMPLE 2 Solve $0.3(2x - 4) - 0.025(x - 3) = 3.475$.

SOLUTION The most decimal places in any term is 3. Multiply both members by 10^3, or 1000.

Ⓜ

$$\begin{aligned} 0.3(2x - 4) - 0.025(x - 3) &= 3.475 \\ M_{1000} \quad 1000[0.3(2x - 4) - 0.025(x - 3)] &= 1000(3.475) \\ 300(2x - 4) - 25(x - 3) &= 3475 \\ 600x - 1200 - 25x + 75 &= 3475 \\ 575x &= 4600 \\ x &= 8 \end{aligned}$$

CHECK The check is left for the student.

A *lever* is a stiff board or bar which is supported by a *fulcrum*.

A lever will balance when the mass on one side times its distance from the fulcrum equals the mass on the other side times its distance from the fulcrum.

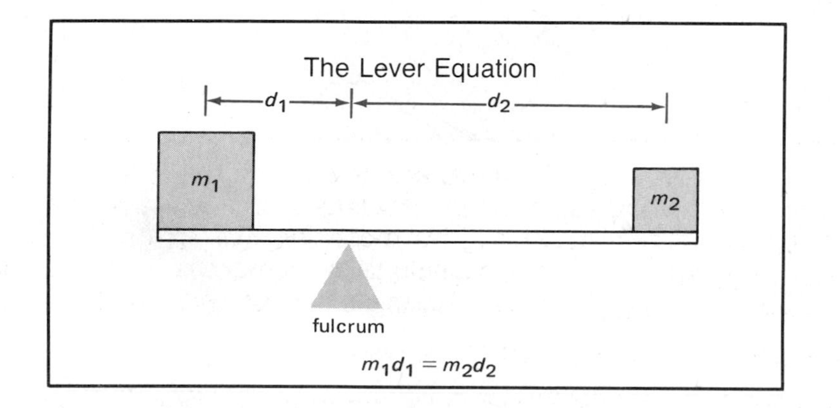

The distance is measured along the lever from the fulcrum to the foot of the perpendicular (to the lever) that contains the center of gravity of the object on the lever.

EXAMPLE 3 John, with a mass of 30 kilograms, sits 2 meters from the fulcrum of a seesaw. How far from the fulcrum should Melina, with a mass of 50 kilograms, sit to balance John?

(M) SOLUTION The Lever Equation gives the relationship.
Use d_M for the distance from the fulcrum to Melina.

kg · m = kg · m

$$mass_M \cdot d_M = mass_J \cdot d_J$$
$$50d_M = 30(2)$$
$$50d_M = 60$$
$$d_M = 1.2$$

d_m 2 m

Melina 50 kg

John 30 kg

CONCLUSION Melina should sit 1.2 meters from the fulcrum.

CHECK $50(1.2) \stackrel{?}{=} 30(2)$
$60 = 60$ ✓

EXAMPLE 4 A 6.0-kilogram iron ball balances a 3.6-kilogram iron ball on a lever. One ball is 1 meter farther from the fulcrum than the other. Find the distance from the fulcrum to each ball.

(M) **SOLUTION** The Lever Equation gives the relationship.

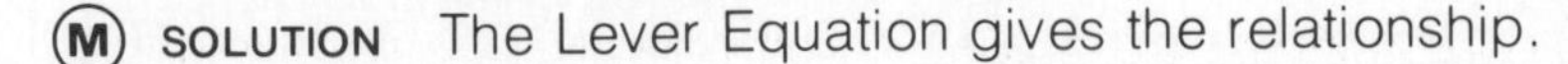

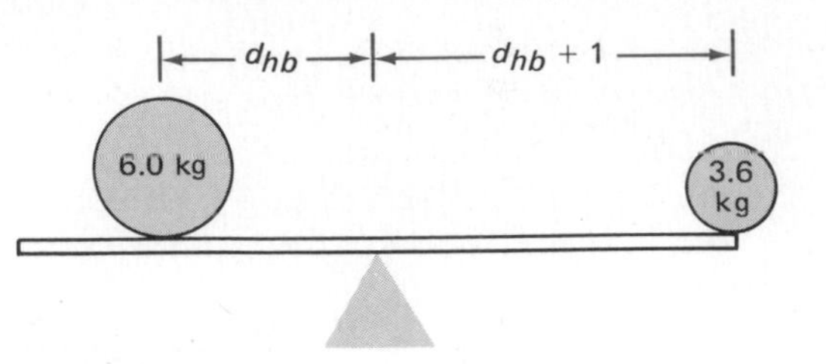

Use $\left[\begin{array}{l} d_{hb} \\ d_{hb} + 1 \end{array}\right.$ for the distance in meters to the heavier ball. / for the distance in meters to the lighter ball.

m + m = m

kg · m = kg · m

$$mass_{hb} \cdot d_{hb} = mass_{lb} \cdot d_{lb}$$
$$6.0d_{hb} = 3.6(d_{hb} + 1)$$
$$M_{10} \quad 60d_{hb} = 36(d_{hb} + 1)$$
$$60d_{hb} = 36d_{hb} + 36$$
$$24d_{hb} = 36$$
$$d_{hb} = 1.5 \quad \text{Also, } d_{hb} + 1 = 2.5.$$

CONCLUSION The heavier ball is 1.5 meters from the fulcrum. The lighter ball is 2.5 meters from the fulcrum.

CHECK The check is left for the student.

EXAMPLE 5 A bar on a mobile is 9 cm long. A mass of 26.4 grams will be hung at one end. A mass of 17.6 grams will be hung at the other. How far from the heavier end should the bar be attached to the mobile so that it balances?

(M) **SOLUTION** The Lever Equation gives the relationship.

Use $\left[\begin{array}{l} d_1 \\ 9 - d_1 \end{array}\right.$ for the distance to the 26.4-gram mass. / for the distance to the 17.6-gram mass.

cm − cm = cm

g · cm = g · cm

$$26.4d_1 = 17.6(9 - d_1)$$
$$M_{10} \quad 264d_1 = 176(9 - d_1)$$
$$264d_1 = 1584 - 176d_1$$
$$440d_1 = 1584$$
$$d_1 = 3.6$$

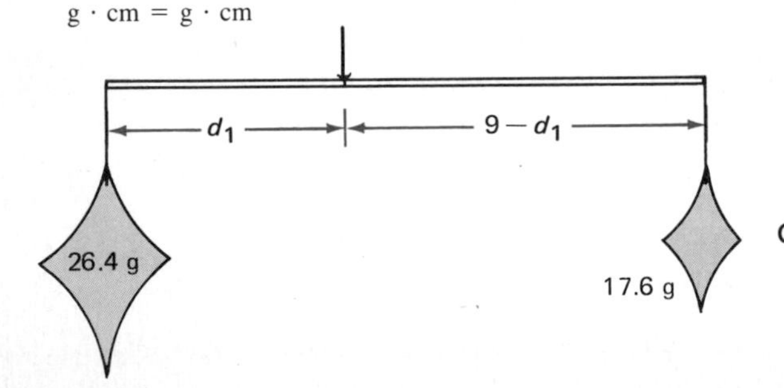

CONCLUSION To balance, the bar should be attached at a point 3.6 cm from the heavier end.

CHECK The check is left for the student.

CLASSROOM EXERCISES

Solve and check.

1. $0.2x = 5$
2. $0.12x - 1.4 = 0.04x + 0.2$
3. $0.5x - 4.0 = 0.3x + 1.8$
4. $0.45x = 1.8$
5. $0.07x - 0.42 = 5.6$
6. $0.02(x + 2) - 0.125(x - 4) = 0.645$
7. A 25-kilogram bag of sand is placed on a lever 1.6 m from the fulcrum. How far from the fulcrum should a 16-kilogram bag of sand be placed to balance the lever?

EXERCISES

A Solve and check.

1. $0.3x = 12$
2. $0.04x = 32$
3. $0.8x = 1.6$
4. $0.7x - 1.7 = 0.2x - 4.2$
5. $0.4x - 2.3 = 0.3x - 0.5$
6. $1.3x + 6.04 = 2.7x + 1.42$
7. $5.4x - 6.3 = 2.7x - 0.9$
8. $0.2x + 0.02 = 0.2$
9. $1.2x - 0.4 = 0.5$
10. $0.25(x + 2) - 0.75(x - 2) = 1.25$
11. $0.04(x + 5) - 0.375(x - 2) = 3.295$
12. $0.08(3x + 1) - 0.075(x - 1) = 2.465$
13. $0.03(x + 7) + 0.875(x - 4) = 4.855$
14. Alicia sits 2 meters from the fulcrum of a seesaw and balances Sonja who sits 2.4 meters from the fulcrum. Alicia has a mass of 48 kilograms. What is Sonja's mass?
15. Lorraine, with a mass of 52 kilograms, sits 1.2 meters from the fulcrum of a seesaw. How far from the fulcrum should Jessica, with a mass of 32 kilograms, sit to balance Lorraine?

B

16. $x = 4.25 - 0.25(2x - 1)$
17. $1.25x - 0.25(2x + 1) = 1.25$
18. $0.075x + 0.07(1000 - x) = 72$
19. $-0.006 + 0.296 = 0.15x - 0.07x$
20. $0.5(x + 0.2) + 0.07 - (0.3 - x) = 0.02$
21. $3(0.4x + 0.5) + 4(0.5x - 0.15) = 26$
22. A lever is 3.5 meters long. A 24.8-kilogram iron ball balances a 6.2-kilogram iron ball. Find the distance from the 6.2-kilogram iron ball to the fulcrum.
23. Two packages, one with a mass of 13.6 kilograms and one with a mass of 15.9 kilograms, are hung from the ends of a 1.8-meter rod. How far from the 15.9-kilogram mass must the fulcrum be for the two packages to balance?

C Solve for x.

24. $0.1ax + 0.01bx + 0.001cx = d$
25. $0.1h(x - k) + 0.01m(x + n) = p$

OBJECTIVE: Solve problems using equations that contain coefficients in fraction or decimal form.

8-3 "A FRACTION OF . . ."

When we talk about a certain fraction *of* a number, the word "*of*" means "times."

In Words	In Symbols
$\frac{1}{3}$ of x	$\frac{1}{3}x$
$\frac{2}{5}$ of the sum of x and 3	$\frac{2}{5}(x + 3)$
25% of 84	0.25(84)
$\frac{1}{2}$ of the people	$\frac{1}{2}b$, using b for the number of people
$\frac{3}{4}$ of the length	$\frac{3}{4}l$, using l for the length

EXAMPLE 1 10 is 4 larger than $\frac{2}{3}$ of a number. Find the number.

Ⓜ SOLUTION Use n for the number.

$$10 = \tfrac{2}{3}n + 4$$

M_3 $$30 = 2n + 12$$

$$18 = 2n$$

$$9 = n$$

CHECK $10 \stackrel{?}{=} \frac{2}{3}(9) + 4$

$10 = 10$ ✓

CONCLUSION The number is 9.

EXAMPLE 2 The difference of two numbers is 9. Two-thirds of the larger number plus $\frac{1}{6}$ of the smaller number equals 21. Find the numbers.

Ⓜ SOLUTION Use $\left[\begin{array}{l} x \text{ for the larger number.} \\ x - 9 \text{ for the smaller number.}\end{array}\right.$

$$\tfrac{2}{3}x + \tfrac{1}{6}(x - 9) = 21$$

M_6 $$4x + x - 9 = 126$$

$$5x = 135$$

$$x = 27$$ Also, $x - 9 = 18$.

CONCLUSION The two numbers are 27 and 18.

CHECK The check is left for the student.

EXAMPLE 3 The width of a rectangular building is $\frac{3}{4}$ of its length. The perimeter is 168 m. Find the length and width.

(M) **SOLUTION** 2(length) + 2(width) = perimeter

Use l for the length in meters.
$\frac{3}{4}l$ for the width in meters.

(dimensionless) · m = m

$$2l + 2\left(\frac{3}{4}l\right) = 168$$

(dimensionless) · m + (dimensionless) · m = m

$$2l + \frac{3}{2}l = 168$$

M_2

$$4l + 3l = 336$$
$$7l = 336$$
$$l = 48$$

Also, $\frac{3}{4}l = 36$

CONCLUSION The length of the building is 48 meters. The width is 36 meters.

CHECK Is the perimeter equal to 168?

$$2(48) + 2(36) \stackrel{?}{=} 168$$
$$168 = 168 \checkmark$$

CLASSROOM EXERCISES

Solve and check.

1. The sum of $\frac{1}{3}$ of a number and $\frac{1}{4}$ of the number is 14. Find the number.
2. The perimeter of a rectangular room is 22 m. The width is $\frac{5}{6}$ of the length. Find the dimensions of the room.
3. The perimeter of a rectangular TV screen is 52 cm. Its height is $\frac{6}{7}$ of its base. Find its dimensions.
4. The perimeter of a rectangular picture frame is 48 cm. Its width is $\frac{3}{5}$ of its length. Find its dimensions.

EXERCISES

A Solve and check.

1. 20 is 6 greater than $\frac{7}{8}$ of a number. Find the number.
2. 42 is 20 greater than $\frac{2}{5}$ of a number. Find the number.
3. The perimeter of a rectangular TV screen is 52 cm. Its height is $\frac{6}{7}$ of its base. Find its dimensions.
4. The perimeter of a rectangular picture frame is 48 cm. Its width is $\frac{3}{5}$ of its length. Find its dimensions.
5. The sum of $\frac{1}{7}$ of a number and $\frac{1}{4}$ of the number is 22. Find the number.
6. The sum of $\frac{1}{9}$ of a number and $\frac{1}{5}$ of the number is 28. Find the number.
7. If $\frac{1}{7}$ of a number is subtracted from $\frac{1}{3}$ of the number, the difference is 4. Find the number.
8. If $\frac{1}{12}$ of a number is subtracted from $\frac{1}{8}$ of the number, the difference is 9. Find the number.

B

9. Sharon's age now is $\frac{2}{5}$ of what it will be in 15 years. Find her present age.

10. Margarita's age now is $\frac{1}{6}$ of her mother's age. In 6 years she will be $\frac{2}{7}$ as old as her mother. Find Margarita's present age.

11. The perimeter of a triangular pillow is 85 cm. The lengths of two sides are each $\frac{5}{7}$ of the length of the base. Find the length of each side.

12. One number is $\frac{2}{7}$ of another number. Their sum is 57 more than 4 times the smaller. Find each number.

13. The difference of two numbers is 12. When one-half of their sum is subtracted from four-fifths of the larger, the difference is zero. Find the numbers.

14. Hazel's age is $\frac{2}{3}$ of Elizabeth's age. In 9 years she will be $\frac{3}{4}$ as old as Elizabeth. Find the present age of each.

C **15.** The difference of two numbers exceeds the smaller number by 4. The larger number exceeds one-half of their sum by 4. Find each number.

16. A father is 12 times as old as his son. In 6 years the son's age will be 2 years less than one-third of the father's age. Find the father's present age.

17. Gerry has quarters, nickels, and dimes worth \$4.50. There are half as many dimes as quarters, and three times as many nickels as dimes. How many coins of each kind does Gerry have?

18. There are 81 beads that are a single color, either red, white, or blue. There are $\frac{1}{2}$ as many red beads as there are white or blue beads. There are $\frac{4}{5}$ as many white beads as there are red or blue beads. There are $\frac{2}{7}$ as many blue beads as there are red or white beads. How many beads are there of each color?

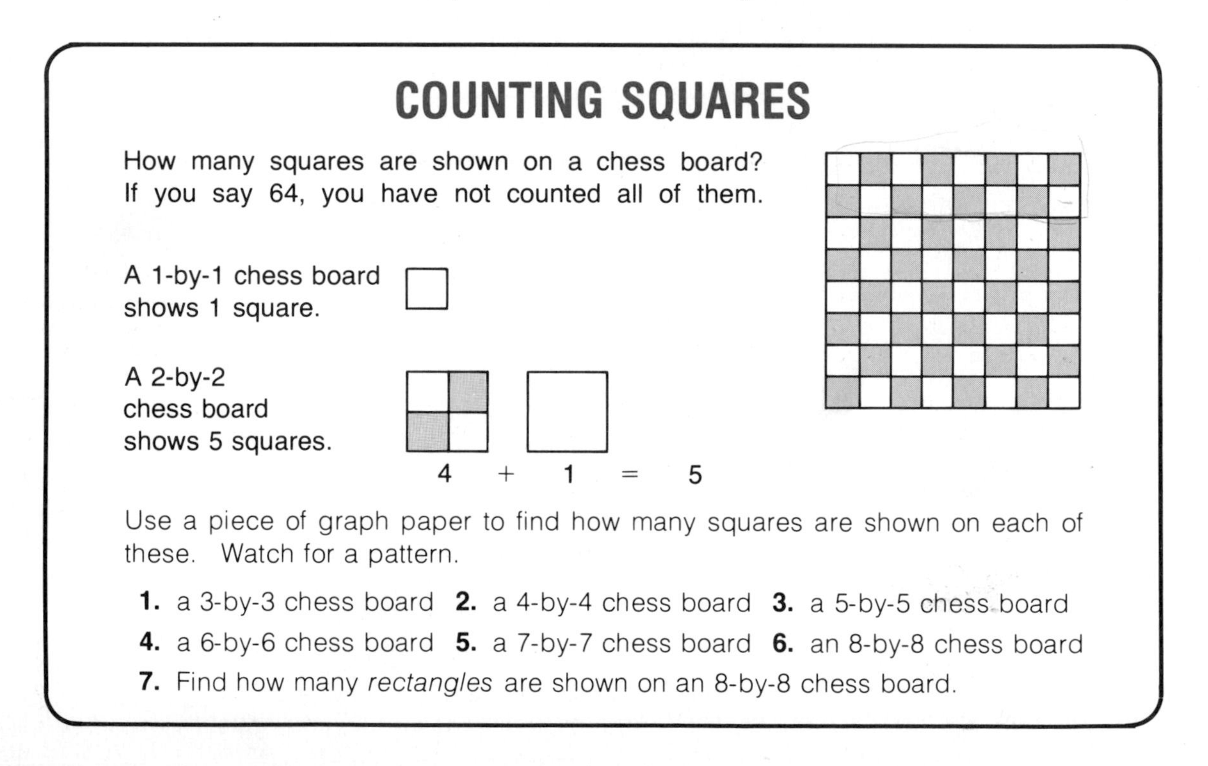

COUNTING SQUARES

How many squares are shown on a chess board? If you say 64, you have not counted all of them.

A 1-by-1 chess board shows 1 square.

A 2-by-2 chess board shows 5 squares.

4 + 1 = 5

Use a piece of graph paper to find how many squares are shown on each of these. Watch for a pattern.

1. a 3-by-3 chess board **2.** a 4-by-4 chess board **3.** a 5-by-5 chess board

4. a 6-by-6 chess board **5.** a 7-by-7 chess board **6.** an 8-by-8 chess board

7. Find how many *rectangles* are shown on an 8-by-8 chess board.

8-4 BUSINESS

Many problems in a business may be solved more easily with algebra than with arithmetic. Relationships among *cost*, *overhead*, *margin*, and *profit* may be given by formulas. Whenever a formula is used, the exact meaning of each symbol in the formula must be known.

Terms Used in Business	Symbol
Cost—the amount paid by a business to purchase an item	C
Overhead—the expense of doing business	O
Profit—the amount gained after expenses have been paid	P
Margin—the overhead plus the profit	M
Selling Price—the amount for which an item is sold	S

Relationships Used in Business	Formula
Selling Price = Cost + Overhead + Profit	$S = C + O + P$
Margin = Overhead + Profit	$M = O + P$
Selling Price = Cost + Margin	$S = C + M$

EXAMPLE 1 An item is purchased by a dealer for $150. At what price must the item be sold so that the margin will be 20% of the selling price?

We replace M by $0.20S$ to get an equation having just one unknown.

SOLUTION (M) Use $S = C + M$. Replace C by 150 and M by $0.20S$.

$$S = C + M$$
$$S = 150 + 0.20S$$
$$M_{100} \quad 100S = 15\,000 + 20S$$
$$100S - 20S = 15\,000$$
$$80S = 15\,000$$
$$S = 187.50$$

$\$ = \$ + (\text{dimensionless}) \cdot \$$

CONCLUSION The selling price should be $187.50.

CHECK The margin is $187.50 – $150, or $37.50.
Is $37.50 equal to 20% of $187.50?

$$37.50 \stackrel{?}{=} 0.20(187.50)$$
$$37.50 = 37.50 \checkmark$$

EXAMPLE 2 A merchant buys an item wholesale for \$31.20. The profit must be 15% of the selling price. 20% of the selling price is required to meet overhead expenses. Find the selling price for the item.

SOLUTION Use $S = C + O + P$.
Replace C by 31.20, P by $0.15S$, and O by $0.20S$.

(M)

$ = $ + (dimensionless) · $ + (dimensionless) · $

$$S = C + O + P$$
$$S = 31.20 + 0.20S + 0.15S$$
$$M_{100} \quad 100S = 3120 + 20S + 15S$$
$$100S - 20S - 15S = 3120$$
$$65S = 3120$$
$$S = 48$$

CONCLUSION The selling price for the item is \$48.

CHECK The profit is 15% of \$48, or \$7.20, and the overhead is 20% of \$48, or \$9.60. Is the sum of the cost, the profit, and the overhead equal to \$48?

$$31.20 + 7.20 + 9.60 \stackrel{?}{=} 48$$
$$48 = 48 \checkmark$$

CLASSROOM EXERCISES

Solve.

1. A dealer purchases an item for \$150. At what price must the item be sold so that the margin will be 25% of the selling price?
2. A merchant paid \$210 for a chair. The profit must be 10% of the selling price. The overhead is 15% of the selling price. What must be the selling price for this chair?

EXERCISES

A Solve.

1. The cost of an antique chair to a dealer is \$210. At what price must the chair be sold so that the margin will be 30% of the selling price?
2. The cost of a television set is \$450. At what price must the set be sold so that the margin is 25% of the selling price?
3. At what price should a merchant sell an item that cost \$96 so that the margin will be 20% of the selling price?
4. An importer bought a watch for \$24. At what price should the watch be sold so that the margin will be 75% of the selling price?
5. A sporting goods retailer paid \$132.60 for a set of golf clubs. The overhead is 12% of the selling price. The profit must be 20% of the selling price. At what price must the golf clubs be sold?
6. A dealer paid \$56 for a vacuum cleaner. The overhead is 14% of the selling price. The profit must be 16% of the selling price. At what price must the vacuum cleaner be sold?

7. A clothier bought a suit for $128. The overhead is 15% of the selling price. The profit is 21% of the selling price. At what price must the suit be sold?

8. At a 20%-off sale, a dress sold for $48.96. Find the original selling price.

9. At an end-of-the-year clearance sale a suit sold for $120.00. The suit had been discounted 25%. Find the original selling price.

10. At a 15% discount sale, a corn popper sold for $8.67. Find the original selling price.

11. After a reduction of 5%, a used car was sold for $2326.55. Find the original selling price.

B **12.** A dealer's margin for an item is to be 25% of the selling price. At what cost must the item be purchased so that it may be sold for $12?

13. A family bought a house for $45 000 and sold it for $49 500. The expenses for selling the house were $350. The profit was what percent of the cost?

14. For the information in Exercise 13, the profit was what percent of the selling price?

C **15.** The manager of an economy food store wishes to sell all goods at 15% more than cost. At what price must a lot of canned goods be purchased so that it may be sold for $3680?

16. The manager of a discount store wishes to sell all goods at 14% more than cost. At what price must a lot of paper goods be purchased so that it may be sold for $1254?

67108864

DOUBLING

The thickness of a sheet of paper folded in half is twice the thickness of the unfolded sheet. When the paper is folded in half again, the thickness is four times the original thickness.

1. When the paper is folded in half a third time, how does the thickness compare to the thickness of the unfolded sheet?

2. Suppose the paper could be folded in half 15 times. *Estimate* how the thickness would compare with the thickness of the unfolded sheet. Then use your calculator to compare thicknesses.

3. Suppose that a stack of 125 sheets of paper is 1 cm thick. Use your calculator to find what the thickness of one sheet would be if it could be folded 30 times.

4. Suppose a sheet of paper could be folded in half 27 times and the area of the folded part on top is 1 cm². *Estimate* the area of the unfolded sheet of paper. Then use your calculator to find what the area of the unfolded sheet would be.

8-5 SIMPLE INTEREST

Problems related to saving, lending, or borrowing money may be solved using formulas.

Borrowing and lending are relative terms. For example, money banked or invested is, in a sense, a loan.

The common time period is one year.

Terms Used in Saving, Lending, or Borrowing	Symbol
Principal—the amount of money invested or loaned	p
Interest—the amount of money paid for the use of the principal	i
Interest Rate—the amount of money paid for the use of one unit of the principal for one unit of time	r
Time—the time during which the money is invested or loaned	t
Amount—the sum of the principal and the interest	A

Relationships Used in Saving, Lending, or Borrowing	Formula
interest = principal · rate · time	$i = prt$
amount = principal + interest	$A = p + i$ or $A = p + prt$ or $A = p(1 + rt)$

Interest rates are usually given as a percent. An interest rate of 6% per year means that the interest for *each* dollar invested or loaned will be $0.06 for each year of the investment or loan. Also, we may say that the *annual rate* is 6%.

Annual means "yearly"

Example 1 is equivalent to finding the interest earned on an investment of $400 for $2\frac{1}{2}$ years with an interest rate of 6% for each year.

EXAMPLE 1 Find the interest on a loan of $400 for $2\frac{1}{2}$ years. The annual rate is 6%.

SOLUTION Use $i = prt$.

Replace p by 400, r by 0.06, and t by 2.5.

Ⓜ

$$i = prt$$
$$i = 400(0.06)(2.5)$$
$$i = 60$$

$$\$ = \$ \cdot \frac{\text{(dimensionless)}}{\text{year}} \cdot \text{years}$$

CONCLUSION The interest is $60.

EXAMPLE 2 At what annual rate will \$1260 produce \$382.20 simple interest in 4 years 4 months?

SOLUTION Use $i = prt$.

Replace i by 382.20, p by 1260, and t by $4\frac{1}{3}$ or $\frac{13}{3}$.

Ⓜ

$$\begin{aligned} i &= prt \\ 382.20 &= 1260 \cdot r \cdot \tfrac{13}{3} \\ 382.20 &= 5460r \\ \tfrac{382.20}{5460} &= r \\ 0.07 &= r \end{aligned}$$

$\$ = \$ \cdot \frac{\text{(dimensionle}}{\text{year}}$

CONCLUSION The rate is 7% per year.

CHECK Will \$1260 invested at 7% give \$382.20 simple interest in 4 years 4 months?

$$\begin{aligned} 382.20 &\stackrel{?}{=} 1260(0.07)\left(\tfrac{13}{3}\right) \\ 382.20 &= 382.20 \quad \checkmark \end{aligned}$$

EXAMPLE 3 \$2000 is invested. Find the value of the investment after 5 years if the interest rate is 8% for each year of the investment.

This problem is equivalent to finding the total repayment of a loan of \$2000 at 8% for 5 years.

SOLUTION Use $A = p + prt$.

Replace p by 2000, r by 0.08, and t by 5.

Ⓜ

$$\begin{aligned} A &= p + prt \\ A &= 2000 + 2000(0.08)(5) \\ A &= 2000 + 800 \\ A &= 2800 \end{aligned}$$

$\$ = \$ + \$ \cdot \frac{\text{(dimensionless)}}{\text{year}} \cdot \text{years}$

CONCLUSION The value after 5 years is \$2800.

EXAMPLE 4 After 4 years, the value of an investment is \$3720. The investment earned interest at the rate of 6% for each of the 4 years. Find the value of the original investment.

The equivalent loan problem is to find the amount that can be borrowed at 6% for 4 years when \$3720 is to be the loan payback.

SOLUTION Use $A = p + prt$.

Replace A by 3720, r by 0.06, and t by 4.

Ⓜ

$$\begin{aligned} A &= p + prt \\ 3720 &= p + p(0.06)(4) \\ 3720 &= p + 0.24p \\ M_{100} \qquad 372\,000 &= 100p + 24p \\ 372\,000 &= 124p \\ 3000 &= p \end{aligned}$$

$\$ = \$ + \$ \cdot \frac{\text{(dimensionless)}}{\text{year}} \cdot \text{years}$

CONCLUSION The original investment was \$3000.

CHECK The check is left for the student.

CLASSROOM EXERCISES

For the given information, find the interest, principal, rate, or time for an investment.

1. $p = \$4000$, $r = 5\%$, $t = 3$ years, $i = ?$
2. $p = \$4000$, $t = 6$ years, $r = 6\frac{1}{2}\%$, $i = ?$
3. $i = \$700$, $r = 14\%$, $t = 2$ years, $p = ?$
4. $p = \$2000$, $i = \$560$, $t = 2.5$ years, $r = ?$

Solve.

5. Find the interest earned on a principal of \$350 invested at 6% per year for $3\frac{1}{2}$ years.
6. The interest charged for a loan of \$480 for 5 years is \$240. Find the annual interest rate for the loan.

EXERCISES

A For the given information, find the interest, principal, rate, time, or value (A) for an investment.

1. $p = \$350$, $r = 7\%$, $t = 3$ years, $i = ?$
2. $p = \$560$, $r = 9\%$, $t = \frac{1}{2}$ year, $i = ?$
3. $p = \$6000$, $t = 5$ years, $r = 8\%$, $A = ?$
4. $A = \$1050$, $i = \$82.50$, $p = ?$

Solve.

5. Find the value after 5 years of an investment of \$9500 at 12% per year.
6. Find the value after 8 years of an investment of \$825 at 9% per year.
7. Sonya borrowed \$1200 at 9% annual interest for 2 years. How much interest did she pay?
8. Jim invested \$1200 at 9% annual interest for 3 years. How much interest did he earn?

B

9. The total amount to be paid back on a loan is \$8000 after 4 years. The annual rate is $7\frac{1}{2}\%$. Find the principal that was borrowed.
10. Find the annual rate (to the nearest 0.1%) for a loan of \$1200 when the total amount paid back after 5 years is \$1850.
11. How long (to the nearest 0.1 year) will it take an investment of \$4500 to increase to \$6000 at an annual simple-interest rate of $8\frac{1}{2}\%$?

C

12. How long will it take any investment at simple interest to triple in value at $10\frac{1}{2}\%$ per year?
13. Give a formula for the time required to double the value of an investment at r% annual simple interest.

DIAGONALS OF POLYGONS

A **diagonal** of a polygon is a segment joining two nonadjacent vertices. A triangle has no diagonals. A square has 2. A pentagon has 5. A hexagon has 9.

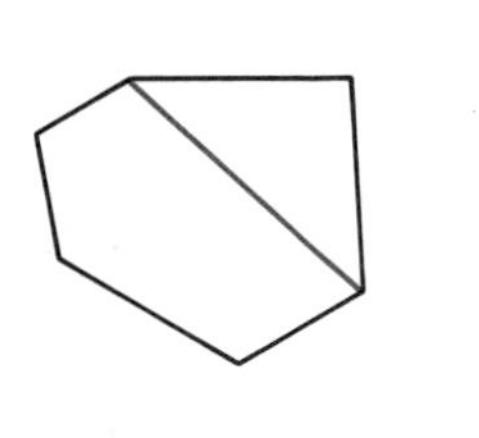

1. Develop a formula that gives the number of diagonals of a polygon when you know the number of sides.
2. Check your formula with the information given above or with sketches of other polygons.

8-6 SPORTS

A touchdown in football is worth 6 points. Points also may be won in other ways.

EXAMPLE 1 In one game, two football teams scored 46 points, including 4 points other than from touchdowns. How many touchdowns did they score?

Ⓜ **SOLUTION** Points from touchdowns plus 4 points equal 46 points.

Use t for the number of touchdowns.
$6t$ for the number of points from touchdowns.

$\frac{\text{points}}{\text{TD}} \cdot (\text{TDs}) = \text{points}$

points + points = points

$$6t + 4 = 46$$
$$6t = 46 - 4$$
$$6t = 42$$
$$t = 7$$

CONCLUSION The two teams scored 7 touchdowns.

CHECK Are 7 touchdowns and 4 more points worth 46 points?

$$7(6) + 4 \stackrel{?}{=} 46$$
$$46 = 46 \checkmark$$

Batting average in baseball or softball equals the number of hits divided by the number of times at bat.

$$\text{batting average } (BA) = \frac{\text{number of hits } (h)}{\text{number of times at bat } (AB)}$$

EXAMPLE 2 One season Janie had 37 hits and a batting average of .407. How many times was she at bat?

SOLUTION Use $BA = \frac{h}{AB}$. Find AB.

Ⓜ
$$BA = \frac{h}{AB}$$
$$0.407 = \frac{37}{AB}$$

M_{AB} $\quad 0.407AB = 37$

M_{1000} $\quad 407AB = 37\,000$

D_{407} $\quad AB = 90.9$

CONCLUSION Janie was at bat 91 times.

CHECK Checking that 37 hits in 91 times at bat gives a batting average of .407 is left for the student.

EXAMPLE 3 In a freestyle swimming race, Margot swam 0.35 meter per second faster than Louise. Margot won the race in 2 minutes 5 seconds. Louise finished 35 seconds later. What was the rate for each swimmer? What was the distance for the race?

Ⓜ **SOLUTION** The distance Louise swam equals the distance Margot swam. Use r for Louise's rate in meters per second.

$\frac{m}{s} \cdot s = m$

$\frac{m}{s} + \frac{m}{s} = \frac{m}{s}, \quad \frac{m}{s} \cdot s = m$

	rate	· time =	distance
Louise	r	160	$r \cdot 160$
Margot	$r + 0.35$	125	$(r + 0.35)125$

$$\begin{aligned} d_L &= d_M \\ r \cdot 160 &= (r + 0.35)125 \\ 160r &= 125r + 43.75 \\ 160r - 125r &= 43.75 \\ 35r &= 43.75 \\ r &= 1.25 \end{aligned}$$

Also, $r + 0.35 = 1.60$,
$r \cdot 160 = 200$,
and $(r + 0.35)125 = 200$.

CONCLUSION Louise swam 200 meters at 1.25 m/s. Margot swam 200 meters at 1.60 m/s.

CHECK Louise swam 1.25 m/s for 160 seconds and Margot swam 1.60 m/s for 125 seconds.

$1.25(160) \stackrel{?}{=} 1.60(1.25)$
$200 = 200$ ✓

CLASSROOM EXERCISES

Solve.

1. Last season Senta had 24 hits and a batting average of .400. How many times was Senta at bat?
2. A long-distance runner ran 1500 m in 5 minutes. Find the rate per minute.
3. Pamela runs 2 kilometers per hour faster than Brenda. They start a race at the same time. Pamela finishes in three-fourths of an hour and Brenda finishes one-eighth of an hour later. Find the rate for each.

EXERCISES

A Find the missing numbers for the chart.

		Times at Bat	Hits	Batting Average
1.	Johnson	564	138	?
2.	Leach	639	202	?
3.	Parker	677	?	.315
4.	Brown	486	?	.298

Solve.

5. One year the Westwood High School girls' basketball team won 12 games and lost 2. What percent of the total number of games did it win?

6. The Douglass Ducks made 3801 field goals out of 7883 attempts one season. What percent of its attempts did the team make?

7. The Dunbar Poets scored on 1836 out of 2316 free throws one year. On what percent of their free throws did they score?

8. An olympic runner ran a 10 000-meter race in 32 minutes. Find the rate in meters per minute.

9. A skater raced 500 meters in 45 seconds. Find the rate in meters per second.

10. Janet takes 3 hours to ride her bicycle the same distance that Lisa rides in 4 hours. Janet's average rate is 3 kilometers per hour more than Lisa's rate. Find the rate for each.

11. Barry takes 10 minutes to swim the same distance that Mark swims in 8 minutes. Mark's rate is $\frac{1}{4}$ meter per second more than Barry's rate. Find the rate for each.

B **12.** Earned run average (*ERA*) is computed my multiplying earned runs (*ER*) allowed by 9, then dividing by the number of innings pitched (*IP*). Write a formula for earned run average.

13. Use the formula from Exercise 12 to find a pitcher's *ERA* if 56 earned runs are given up in 206 innings.

14. Louis has an *ERA* of 5.00. If he pitches 6 more innings and gives up no more earned runs, he will lower his *ERA* to 4.5 Find how many innings he has pitched already.

15. Anita's batting average is .267. If she has 3 hits in her next 3 times at bat, her batting average will be .313. Find the number of hits she has already. Find the number of times she has been at bat.

16. The winning average of the West High School boys' softball team is .417. If it wins the next two games its average will be .500. Find the number of games already won. Find the number of games already played.

17. Ray's batting average is .350. By getting 2 hits in his next two times at bat, his batting average will be .409. Find the number of hits he has already. Find his number of times at bat.

C **18.** With 7 hits in 50 times at bat, Connie's batting average is .140. She wants to raise it to at least .333. She is at bat 3 times a game. For how many games would she have to have a perfect batting record to do this?

8-7 INVESTMENTS

A savings account in a bank is one type of investment. Buying shares of stock in a company is another. Buying bonds issued by an organization or by a government is a third type of investment.

Stocks and bonds are valuable to their owners in two ways. Their selling price may go up. Also, they may provide their owners with regular cash payments. Such cash payments (dividends) for a share of stock represent a share of the company profits. For bonds, the payments are the interest paid on the face value of the bond.

In any sale of stock, the cost (C) of the stock is the product of the price per share (p) and the number of shares (n).

$\$ = \frac{\$}{\text{share}} \cdot \text{shares}$

$$C_{\text{buying}} = p_{\text{buying}} \cdot n_{\text{bought}}$$
$$C_{\text{selling}} = p_{\text{selling}} \cdot n_{\text{sold}}$$

The gain (G) made by an investor who buys and sells a certain stock equals the difference between the selling price (C_s) and the original cost (C_b) to the investor.

$$G = C_s - C_b$$

EXAMPLE 1 A market price of $12\frac{3}{4}$ means that one share of stock sells for $12.75. Jaime Sánchez bought 40 shares of stock at $12\frac{3}{4}$. At what price per share should Jaime sell the stock to gain $55?

(M) SOLUTION

$$G = C_s - C_b$$
$$G = p_s n_s - p_b n_b$$

Use p for the selling price in dollars per share.

$\$ = \frac{\$}{\text{share}} \cdot \text{shares} - \frac{\$}{\text{share}} \cdot \text{shares}$

$$55 = p \cdot 40 - (12.75)40$$
$$55 = 40p - 510$$
$$565 = 40p$$
$$14.125 = p \text{, or } p = 14\tfrac{1}{8}.$$

CONCLUSION Jaime should sell the stock at $14\frac{1}{8}$.

CHECK Are 40 shares at $14\frac{1}{8}$ worth $55 more than 40 shares at $12\frac{3}{4}$?

$$40(14.125) \stackrel{?}{=} 40(12.75) + 55$$
$$565 = 565 \checkmark$$

The annual yield (Y) for a stock is the percent found by dividing the annual dividends (d) for one share of the stock by the price (p) paid for the share.

$$Y = \frac{d}{p} \text{ (expressed as a percent)}$$

A ratio or percent is dimensionless.

EXAMPLE 2 Last year, Joel Stein received \$6.30 in dividends for each share of a stock. He paid \$70 per share for the stock. Find the annual yield for Joel's stock.

SOLUTION Use $Y = \frac{d}{p}$.

Replace d by 6.30 and p by 70.

Ⓜ

$$Y = \frac{d}{p}$$

$$Y = \frac{6.30}{70}$$

$$Y = 0.09$$

$$(\text{dimensionless}) = \frac{\frac{\$}{\text{share}}}{\frac{\$}{\text{share}}}$$

CONCLUSION The annual yield for Joel's stock is 9%.

CHECK The check is left for the student.

Bonds often are issued at a face value, or par value, of \$1000 each, but the selling price may vary. The rate of interest (i) on a bond, although based upon the face value, does not always represent the actual yield. The yield is the percent found by dividing the interest earned by the price paid.

$$Y = \frac{i}{p} \text{ (expressed as a percent).}$$

EXAMPLE 3 A 6% \$1000 bond pays interest of \$60 per year. The bond is purchased at 120 (meaning \$120 for each \$100 of face value). What is the yield?

SOLUTION Use $Y = \frac{i}{p}$.

Replace i by 0.06(1000) and p by 120(10).

Ⓜ

$$Y = \frac{i}{p}$$

$$Y = \frac{0.06(1000)}{120(10)}$$

$$Y = 0.05$$

$$(\text{dimensionless}) = \frac{(\text{dimensionless}) \cdot \$}{\frac{\$}{\$100} \cdot \$100}$$

CONCLUSION The yield is 5%.

CHECK The check is left for the student.

When part of a sum of money is invested at one rate and part at another, it is called a *mixed investment*. Similarly, part of a sum of money may be borrowed at one rate and part at a different rate.

EXAMPLE 4 A family invested $8000, part at 6% and the remainder at 8% per year. The yearly income from the investments is $600. How much was invested at each rate?

Ⓜ **SOLUTION** The sum of the income from both investments is $600. Use n for the number of dollars invested at 6%.

	principal	· rate	· time =	interest
Amount at 6%	n	0.06	1	$0.06n$
Amount at 8%	$8000 - n$	0.08	1	$0.08(8000 - n)$

$\frac{\text{dimensionless}}{\text{year}} \cdot \text{years} \cdot \$ = \$$

$\$ - \$ = \$,\ \frac{\text{dimensionless}}{\text{year}} \cdot \text{years} \cdot \$ = \$$

$\$ + \$ = \$$

$$0.06n + 0.08(8000 - n) = 600$$

$$M_{100} \quad 6n + 8(8000 - n) = 60\,000$$

$$6n + 64\,000 - 8n = 60\,000$$

$$-2n = -4000$$

$$n = 2000$$

Also, $8000 - n = 6000$.

CONCLUSION The family invested $2000 at 6% and $6000 at 8%.

CHECK The check is left for the student.

CLASSROOM EXERCISES

Solve.

1. Yin Ho bought 5 shares of stock at $28\frac{1}{2}$ and sold them at $33\frac{1}{4}$. Find his gain on the investment.
2. A 7% $1000 bond pays $70 interest per year. The bond is purchased at 105. What is the yield?

EXERCISES

A Solve.

1. Susan bought 8 shares of stock at $46\frac{1}{2}$ and sold them at $53\frac{1}{4}$. Find her gain on the investment.
2. Steve bought 25 shares of stock at $8\frac{1}{4}$ and sold them at $10\frac{3}{4}$. Find his gain on the investment.
3. Lilia bought 12 shares of stock at $52\frac{1}{2}$. At what price per share must they be sold to gain $129?
4. Ralph bought 18 shares of stock at $11\frac{3}{4}$. At what price per share must they be sold to gain $81?
5. Andreas paid $90 per share for a stock. Last year each share paid $10.80 in dividends. Find the annual yield for the stock.
6. A 6% $1000 bond pays $60 in interest per year. The bond is purchased at 108. What is the yield?

7. The Nilssons borrowed $2850, part at 6% and the rest at 7%. The annual interest paid for the loan is $188. Find the amount borrowed at each rate.

8. The Schwartzes invested $3650, part at 8% and the rest at 7%. The annual interest earned is $262. Find the amount invested at each rate.

B 9. How may $8000 be invested, part at 7% and the rest at 6%, so that both investments produce equal income?

10. Two equal loans are made at 14% and $12\frac{1}{2}$%. Income from the $12\frac{1}{2}$% loan is $7500 less than income from the 14% loan. How much was loaned at each rate?

11. $5000 is invested at 6%. How much more invested at $9\frac{1}{2}$% will give total annual interest equivalent to 7%?

12. The owners of a small business have a $12 000 loan at 7%. How much money should they invest at $10\frac{1}{2}$% to meet their annual interest payments?

C 13. $6000 is to be loaned, part at 4% and part at 7%. Find the amount loaned at each rate so that the average rate is 6%.

14. Irena invested $12 000 at 8%. What amount should be invested at $7\frac{1}{2}$% so that the combined interest is equal to that of a single investment at 7.83%?

CHECKING YOUR UNDERSTANDING

WORDS AND SYMBOLS

clearing decimals   clearing fractions   least common multiple (L.C.M.)

CONCEPTS

- An equation generally is easier to solve if it first is cleared of fractions and decimals. [8-1, 8-2]
- A "fraction *of* a number" may be represented as the fraction *times* the number. [8-3]

PROCESSES

- Solve an equation containing fractions or decimals. [8-1, 8-2]

  1. $\frac{2}{3} + \frac{5}{6}x = \frac{7}{12}$ **2.** $\frac{1}{2}(x - 1) - \frac{1}{3}(x + 1) = \frac{7}{3}$ **3.** $1.3x - 17 = 7 + 0.7x$

- Solve a problem using an equation that includes fractions or decimals. [8-3 to 8-7]

  4. A block with a mass of 6.75 kilograms balances a block with a mass of 11.25 kilograms on a lever. One block is 1 meter farther from the fulcrum than the other. Find the distance from the fulcrum to the lighter block.

  5. The difference between one-half of a number and one-third of the number is 8. Find the number.

OBJECTIVES: Determine if two ratios are members of a proportion. Find the missing term in a proportion. Solve ratio and proportion problems.

8-8 RATIOS AND PROPORTIONS

We use ratios to compare numbers. Usually, we show the ratio of number a to number b ($b \neq 0$) in one of three forms.

A ratio is necessarily dimensionless.

a to b $\qquad$ $a{:}b$ $\qquad$ $\frac{a}{b}$

The third form suggests a fraction or the division indicated by the fraction. In fact, a ratio often is defined as the quotient $\frac{a}{b}$. Such a definition permits us to use, when working with ratios, the ideas we use when working with numbers. For example, to represent the ratio $a{:}b$ in simplest form, we may simplify the fraction $\frac{a}{b}$.

EXAMPLE 1 Write a ratio to compare the number of cents in the value of a quarter to the number of cents in the value of a dollar.

$\frac{¢}{¢}$ = (dimensionless)

Ⓜ **SOLUTION** $\dfrac{\text{value in cents for a quarter}}{\text{value in cents for a dollar}} = \dfrac{25}{100}$

The ratio also could be shown as 25 to 100 or 25 : 100.

EXAMPLE 2 Simplify the ratio 25 to 100.

SOLUTION Write the ratio in the form $\frac{25}{100}$.

The fraction $\frac{25}{100}$ simplifies to $\frac{1}{4}$.

CONCLUSION The ratio 1 to 4 is the simplest form for the ratio 25 to 100.

When numbers that are to be used in a ratio represent measurements, they should refer to the same unit of measure. When they represent numbers of objects, they should refer to the same type of object.

EXAMPLE 3 On the slide screen, Jill is shown as 1.2 meters tall. On the film Jill is shown as 3 millimeters tall. Write a ratio to compare Jill's height on the screen to her height on the film.

SOLUTION The unit of measure for both heights must be the same. Use millimeters.

Ⓜ
$$\frac{\text{height on screen in millimeters}}{\text{height on film in millimeters}} = \frac{1200}{3} = \frac{400}{1}$$

$\frac{\text{mm}}{\text{mm}}$ = (dimensionless).

CONCLUSION Jill's screen height is 400 times her film height.

CHECK Is 400 times Jill's height on the film (3 mm) equal to her height on the screen (1.2 m)?

$$400(0.003) \stackrel{?}{=} 1.2$$
$$1.2 = 1.2 \checkmark$$

An equation for which both members are ratios is a **proportion**. If the proportion $\frac{a}{b} = \frac{c}{d}$ is written $a:b = c:d$, we see two "outside" terms, a and d, called the *extremes*, and two middle terms, b and c, called the *means*. In a proportion, the product of the extremes equals the product of the means.

For the proportion $\frac{a}{b} = \frac{c}{d}$, $(a, b, c, d \neq 0)$, we can conclude that $ad = bc$. Also, when $ad = bc$ we may write the proportion $\frac{a}{b} = \frac{c}{d}$. When the ratio of two numbers equals the ratio of two other numbers, the numbers are said to be *in proportion*, or *proportional*.

EXAMPLE 4 Which of $\frac{6}{8}$, $\frac{8}{10}$, and $\frac{9}{12}$ are members of the same proportion?

SOLUTION In a proportion the product of the extremes equals the product of the means.

$\frac{6}{8} \stackrel{?}{=} \frac{8}{10}$	$\frac{6}{8} \stackrel{?}{=} \frac{9}{12}$	$\frac{8}{10} \stackrel{?}{=} \frac{9}{12}$
$60 \neq 64$	$72 = 72$	$96 \neq 90$

CONCLUSION $\frac{6}{8}$ and $\frac{9}{12}$ are members of the same proportion.

$$\frac{6}{8} = \frac{9}{12}$$

EXAMPLE 5 For what value of x are $\frac{x}{6}$ and $\frac{10}{15}$ equal?

SOLUTION $\frac{x}{6} = \frac{10}{15}$ when the product of the extremes equals the product of the means.

$$15x = 60$$
$$x = 4$$

CONCLUSION $\frac{x}{6}$ and $\frac{10}{15}$ are equal for $x = 4$.

CHECK The check is left for the student.

CLASSROOM EXERCISES

Write a ratio to compare the two measurements.

1. 2 m, 10 cm **2.** 20 seconds, 5 minutes **3.** 3 weeks, 1 year

Which are proportions?

4. $\frac{2}{3} \stackrel{?}{=} \frac{10}{15}$ **5.** $\frac{10}{11} \stackrel{?}{=} \frac{11}{12}$

Solve for x.

6. $\frac{x}{3} = \frac{1}{4}$ **7.** $\frac{3}{7} = \frac{x}{14}$

EXERCISES

A State each ratio in simplest form.

1. 40¢ to $1 **2.** 75 to 100 **3.** $3x$ to $8x$ **4.** a^2 to $3a^2$

5. an age of 15 years to an expected lifetime of 75 years

6. a 50-minute class period to a 6-hour school day

Two rectangular solids are shown at the right. State the ratio for each of the following in simplest form.

7. lengths, smaller to larger

8. lengths, larger to smaller

9. widths, larger to smaller

10. heights, smaller to larger

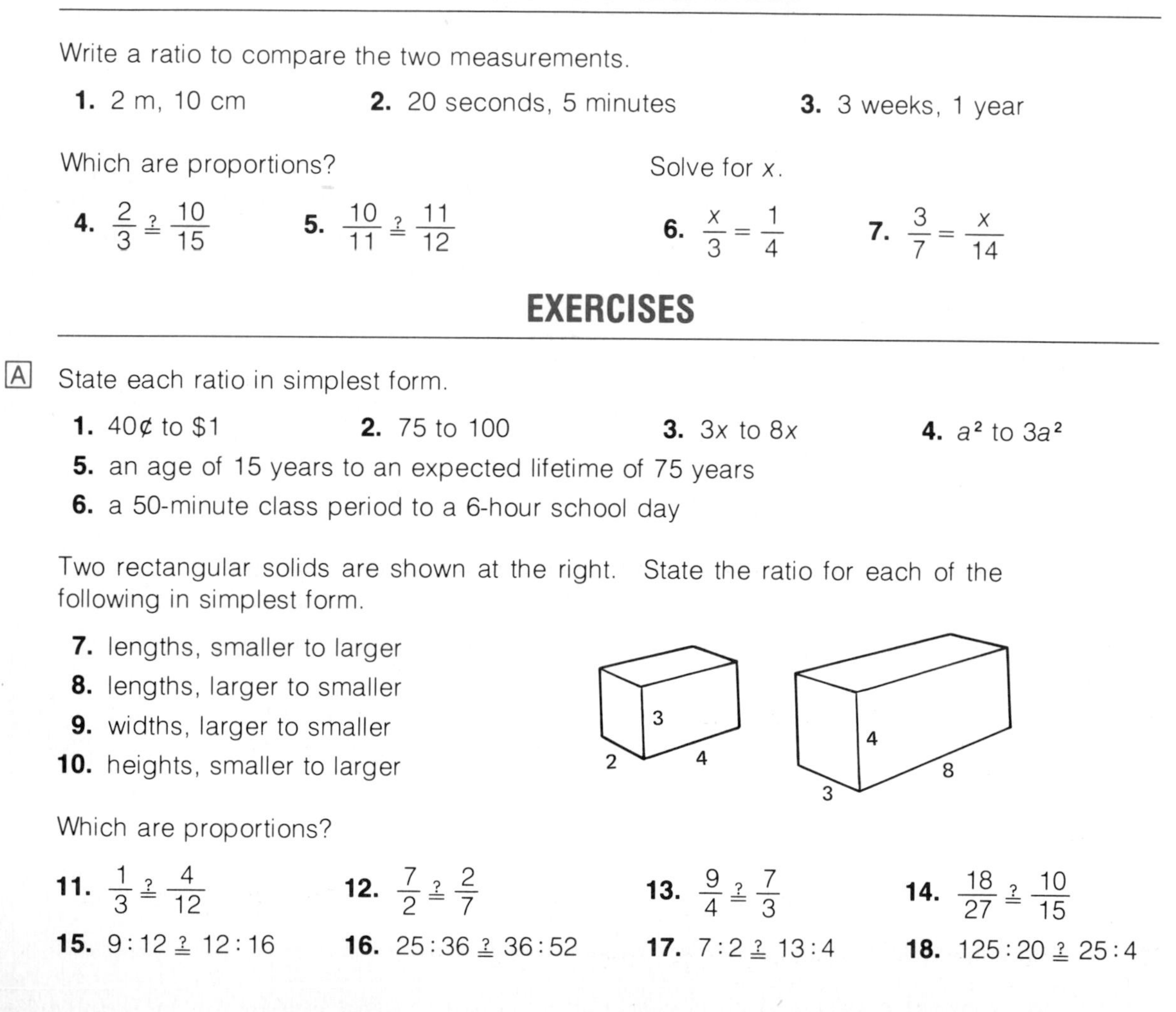

Which are proportions?

11. $\frac{1}{3} \stackrel{?}{=} \frac{4}{12}$ **12.** $\frac{7}{2} \stackrel{?}{=} \frac{2}{7}$ **13.** $\frac{9}{4} \stackrel{?}{=} \frac{7}{3}$ **14.** $\frac{18}{27} \stackrel{?}{=} \frac{10}{15}$

15. $9:12 \stackrel{?}{=} 12:16$ **16.** $25:36 \stackrel{?}{=} 36:52$ **17.** $7:2 \stackrel{?}{=} 13:4$ **18.** $125:20 \stackrel{?}{=} 25:4$

Solve for x.

19. $\frac{x}{3} = \frac{5}{6}$ **20.** $\frac{4}{8} = \frac{x}{16}$ **21.** $\frac{3}{x} = \frac{6}{1}$ **22.** $\frac{8}{12} = \frac{x}{27}$

B Give each ratio in simplest form.

23. the area of a 3-cm by 5-cm rectangle to the area of a 5-cm by 7-cm rectangle

24. the area of a square with a 3-cm side to the area of a square with a 9-cm side

25. the volume of a 3-cm by 5-cm by 2-cm rectangular solid to the volume of one that measures 6 cm by 15 cm by 4 cm

26. the circumference of a circle with a 4-centimeter radius to one with a 12-centimeter radius

Solve for x.

27. $\frac{x-2}{3} = \frac{4}{x+2}$ **28.** $\frac{x-3}{x+3} = \frac{x+5}{x-7}$

29. The ratio of live births in a population to deaths in that same population in one year is called the birth-to-death (B/D) ratio. Find the B/D ratio for each of these populations.

Population	Live Births/Year	Deaths/Year	B/D Ratio
A	20	15	?
B	21	3	?
C	150	120	?
D	10 427	750	?
E	654 321	123 456	?

30. A gear ratio is 7 : 4. If the larger gear has 140 teeth, how many teeth does the smaller gear have?

31. The ratio of the number of girls to the number of boys in a school is 5 : 6. If the numbers of girls and boys in a class have the same ratio and there are 15 girls, how many boys are there in the class?

C Solve for x.

32. $\frac{a}{c} = \frac{c}{x}$ **33.** $\frac{m}{x} = \frac{1}{3}$ **34.** For $7a - 4b = 0$, find $a : b$.

35. Find the teacher-pupil ratio in your classroom; in your school.

8-9 USING PROPORTIONS

Many problems may be solved using a proportion. In such cases, subscripts can be useful for setting up the proportion.

EXAMPLE 1 On a map, 3 centimeters represent 80 kilometers. How many kilometers do 9.6 cm represent?

Ⓜ **SOLUTION** The ratio of map distances equals the ratio of the actual distances.

$$\frac{d_{1,\text{ map}}}{d_{2,\text{ map}}} = \frac{d_{1,\text{ actual}}}{d_{2,\text{ actual}}}$$

Use d for the actual number of kilometers represented by 9.6 cm.

$$\frac{\text{cm}}{\text{cm}} = (\text{dimensionless}) = \frac{\text{km}}{\text{km}}$$

$$\frac{3}{9.6} = \frac{80}{d}$$

$$3d = 9.6(80)$$

$$d = 256$$

CONCLUSION 9.6 centimeters represent 256 kilometers.

CHECK The check is left for the student.

EXAMPLE 2 On an examination, Martha scored 135 on a 150-point scale. What would be her score on a 100-point scale?

SOLUTION The ratio of the scores possible must equal the ratio of the scores earned.

$$\frac{\text{score possible}_{150\text{ scale}}}{\text{score possible}_{100\text{ scale}}} = \frac{\text{score earned}_{150\text{ scale}}}{\text{score earned}_{100\text{ scale}}}$$

Use s for Martha's score on a 100-point scale.

$$\frac{\text{points}}{\text{points}} = (\text{dimensionless}) = \frac{\text{points}}{\text{points}}$$

$$\frac{150}{100} = \frac{135}{s}$$

$$150s = 100(135)$$

$$150s = 13\,500$$

$$s = 90$$

CONCLUSION Martha's score on a 100-point scale would be 90.

CHECK The check is left for the student.

Two numbers may represent measurements of different quantities. As we saw in Section 5-5, a comparison of such numbers is a *rate*. An equation in which both members are rates may be treated as a proportion.

EXAMPLE 3 The Smith family finds that it uses 5 loaves of bread in 2 weeks. At that rate, how many loaves will it use in a year (52 weeks)?

Ⓜ **SOLUTION** The rates of bread use are equal.
Use l for the number of loaves used in 52 weeks.

$$rate_{\text{shorter time}} = rate_{\text{longer time}}$$

$$\frac{loaves_{st}}{time_{st}} = \frac{loaves_{lt}}{time_{lt}}$$

$$\frac{5}{2} = \frac{l}{52}$$

$$5(52) = 2l$$

$$260 = 2l$$

$$130 = l$$

The ratio approach also may be used.
$\frac{5}{l} = \frac{2}{52}$, or
$\frac{l}{5} = \frac{52}{2}$.
$\frac{\text{loaves}}{\text{weeks}} = \frac{\text{loaves}}{\text{weeks}}$

CONCLUSION The Smith family will use 130 loaves of bread in a year.

CHECK The check is left for the student.

CLASSROOM EXERCISES

Solve using proportions.

1. In 2 hours, a student earns $6.30. How much will be earned in 5 hours?
2. Two slices of mushroom pizza cost 90¢. How much would 8 slices cost?
3. When 5 centimeters on a map represent 42 kilometers, how many kilometers do 12.5 centimeters represent?
4. When you score 19 on a 25-point biology quiz, what would be your score on a 100-point scale?

EXERCISES

A Solve each using a proportion.

1. Sue spends 36 minutes typing 3 pages of a report. How long will it take her to type 10 pages at the same rate?
2. Two concrete blocks have a mass of 4 kilograms. Find the mass of 500 blocks.

3. Regina earns \$220 for 5 days. How much will she earn for 30 days?
4. Dan traveled 1120 kilometers in two days. At this rate, how far would he travel in 13 days?
5. Roberto paid \$6.50 to rent a bicycle for two days. At this rate, how much would it cost him to rent a bicycle for 13 days?
6. If 20 spools of thread cost \$5.20, how much will 38 spools cost?
7. The ratio for two gears is 3 to 2. The large gear has 132 teeth. How many teeth does the small gear have?
8. The interest earned on \$500 is \$25. Find the interest earned on \$900 for the same rate and time.
9. 12 cm on a map represent 90 km. How many kilometers do 40 cm represent?
10. 24 cm on a map represent 192 km. How many centimeters represent 1000 km?

B

11. A person's hair grows approximately 50 millimeters every 2 months. How many millimeters will the hair grow in $1\frac{1}{2}$ years?
12. Marty and Leslie ride their bicycles 4.8 kilometers in $\frac{1}{2}$ hour. At this rate, how far would they travel in $3\frac{1}{4}$ hours?
13. Electric current and electromotive force are proportional. A current is 20 amperes when the electromotive force is 110 volts. Find the current when the electromotive force is 165 volts.
14. Brian owned 9 record albums and Harry owned 15. After both bought some new albums, the ratio of the number of Brian's albums to Harry's albums was 2:3. With the new albums, Harry owned 18 in all. How many albums did Brian buy?
15. Tony is preparing a tropical fruit salad. He wants a 3:1 ratio of papaya slices to kiwi slices. How many more kiwi slices must he add to a bowl containing 78 papaya slices and 13 kiwi slices?

C

16. A board is 3.54 m long. The board is cut into 2 pieces having lengths in the ratio 1 to 2. Find the length of each piece.
17. Two numbers are in a 2:3 ratio. The sum of the numbers is 80. Find the numbers.

DEEP THINKING REQUIRED

A zoo built a circular island for an otter exhibit. The swimming area surrounding the island contains 1125 m³ of water. The island is 20 m in diameter. The swimming area is 5 m wide. How deep is the water?

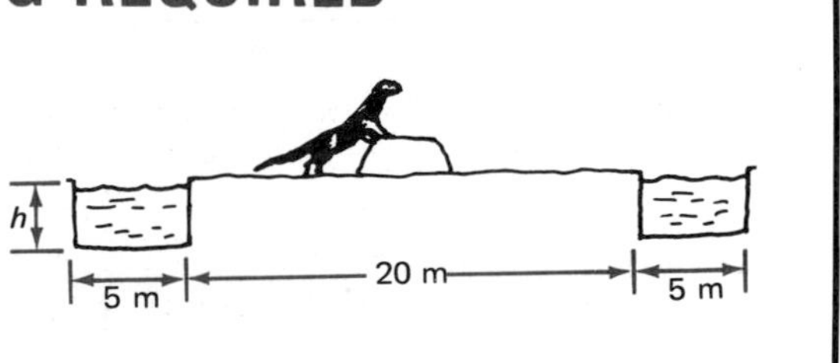

8-10 SIMILAR POLYGONS

Polygons that have the same shape are *similar* polygons. In such polygons, the measures of corresponding angles are equal and the lengths of corresponding sides are proportional.

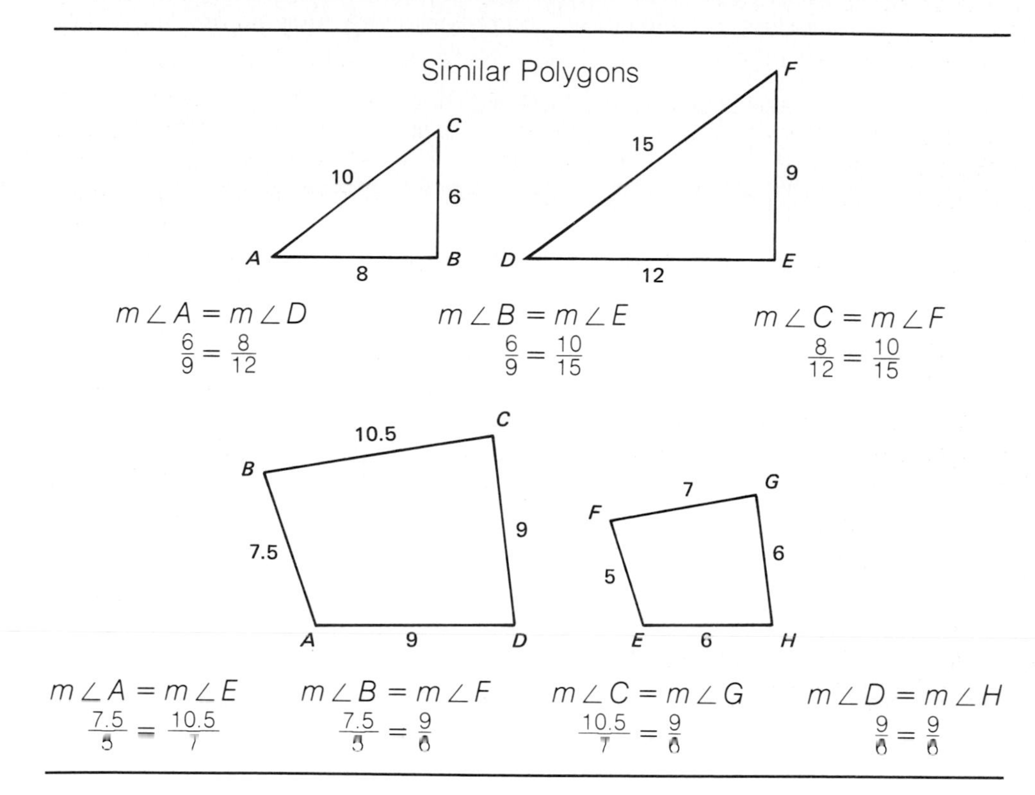

EXAMPLE 1 Are these rectangles similar?

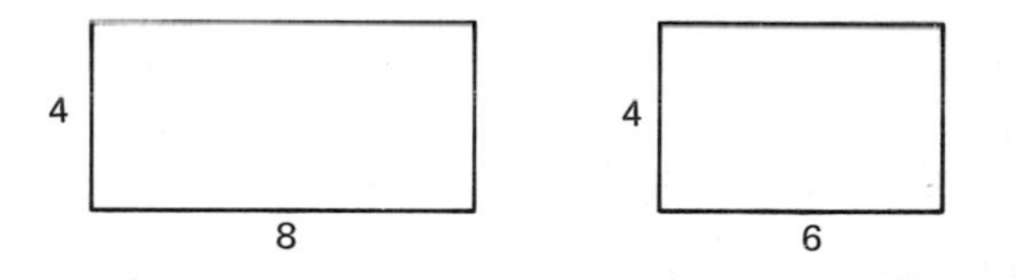

SOLUTION In any rectangle, all angles are *right angles*. The measure of each is 90°. Therefore, for two rectangles, any two corresponding angles have equal measure. For the rectangles shown, however, the lengths of corresponding sides are not proportional.

$$\frac{4}{4} \neq \frac{8}{6}$$

CONCLUSION These two rectangles are not similar.

EXAMPLE 2 Are these polygons similar?

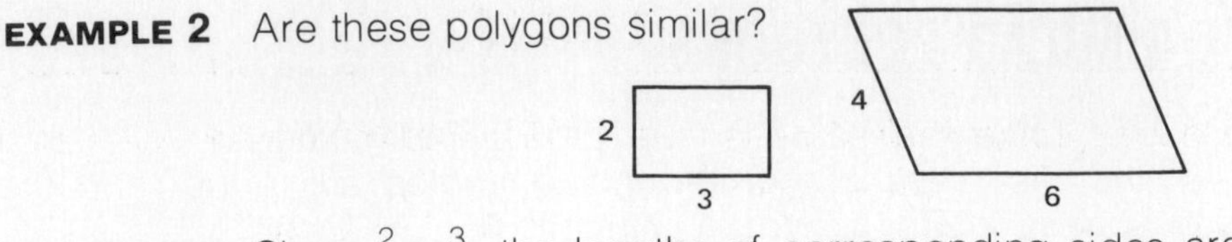

SOLUTION Since $\frac{2}{4} = \frac{3}{6}$, the lengths of corresponding sides are proportional. However, corresponding angles do not have equal measures.

CONCLUSION These two polygons are not similar.

EXAMPLE 3 The lengths of the sides of one triangle are 8 centimeters, 12 centimeters, and 15 centimeters. The length of the shortest side of a similar triangle is 6 centimeters. Find the lengths of the other two sides.

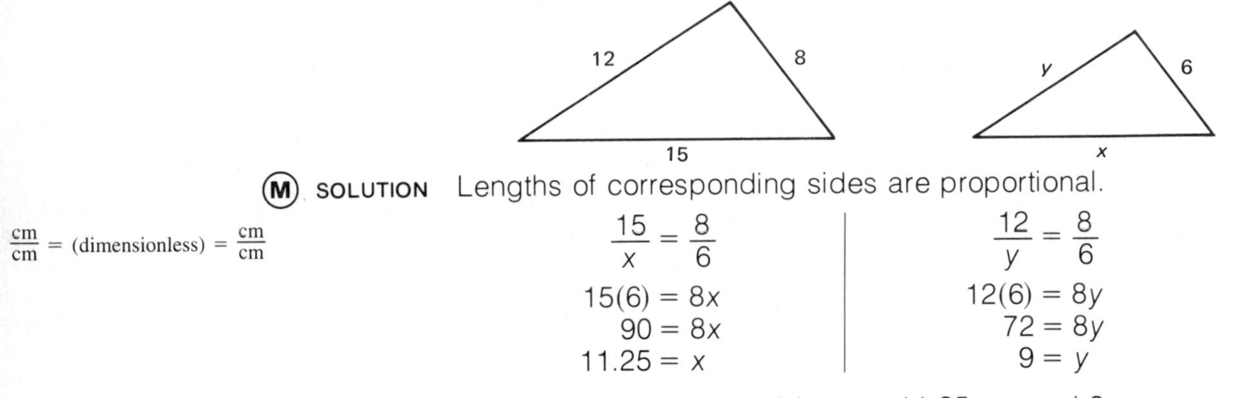

Ⓜ SOLUTION Lengths of corresponding sides are proportional.

$\frac{cm}{cm}$ = (dimensionless) = $\frac{cm}{cm}$

$$\frac{15}{x} = \frac{8}{6} \qquad\qquad \frac{12}{y} = \frac{8}{6}$$

$$15(6) = 8x \qquad\qquad 12(6) = 8y$$

$$90 = 8x \qquad\qquad 72 = 8y$$

$$11.25 = x \qquad\qquad 9 = y$$

CONCLUSION The lengths of the two sides are 11.25 cm and 9 cm.

CLASSROOM EXERCISES

Tell whether the polygons in each pair are similar. Explain your answer.

1.

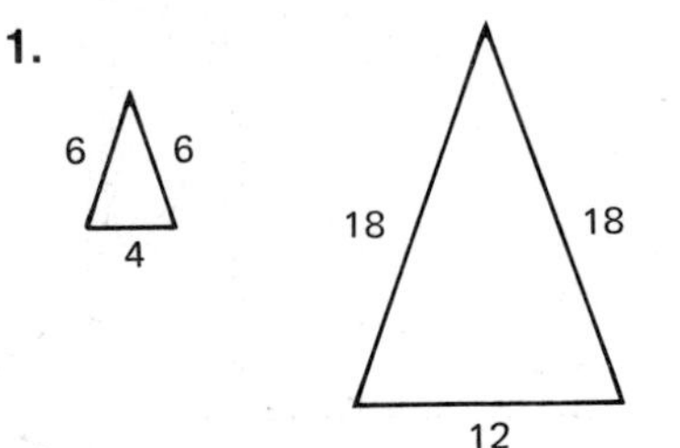

2.

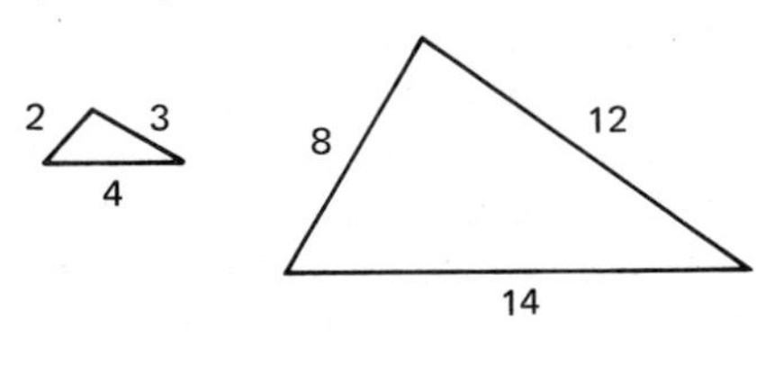

Solve.

3. The sides of one triangle have lengths 4 cm, 6 cm, and 8 cm. The longest side of a similar triangle is 12 cm. Find the lengths of the other two sides.

EXERCISES

A Tell whether the polygons in each pair are similar. Explain your answer.

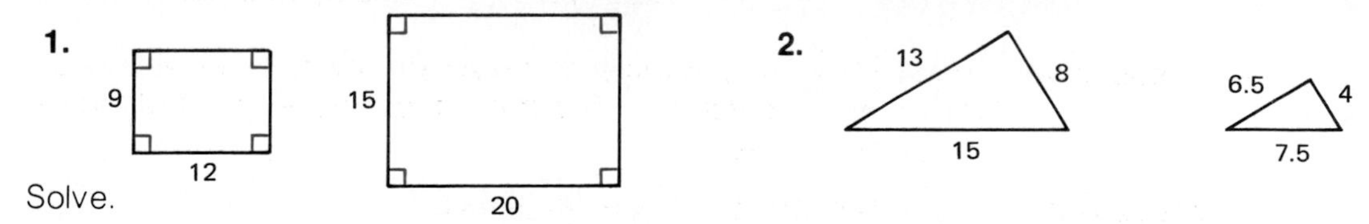

Solve.

3. The lengths of the sides of one triangle are 16 cm, 24 cm, and 30 cm. The length of the shortest side of a similar triangle is 12 cm. Find the lengths of the other two sides.

4. The lengths of the sides of one triangle are 5, 12, and 13 centimeters. Find the length of the shortest side of a similar triangle when its longest side is 91 centimeters.

5. The width and length of a rectangular room are 5 m and 6 m, respectively. The width of a similar rectangular room is 8 m. Find its length.

6. A rectangular lot is 60 meters wide and 75 meters long. A similar lot is 80 meters wide. Find its length.

B

7. The width and length of a rectangle are 5 m and 8 m, respectively. The length of a similar rectangle is 16 m. Find its width.

8. A flagpole 24 m high casts a shadow 16 m long. Find the length of the shadow cast by a telephone pole 7.5 m high.

9. The airline distances among three cities form a triangular flight route. The lengths of the sides of this triangle are 1300, 1500, and 2000 kilometers. Find the total length of a similar flight route when the length of the shortest side is 1050 kilometers.

10. A rectangular playground is 250 meters wide and 280 meters long. A similar playground is 200 meters wide. Find its perimeter.

C

11. To find the height of flagpole EF, pins are placed at A and B in a piece of cardboard so that A, B, and F are in a line. From the pin at B a plumb bob is suspended. Next, a pin is placed in the cardboard at C (where the plumb line crosses the line drawn from A to E). By measuring, it is found that $AE = 27$ m, $AC = 40.5$ cm, and $BC - 24$ cm. Find the height of the pole.

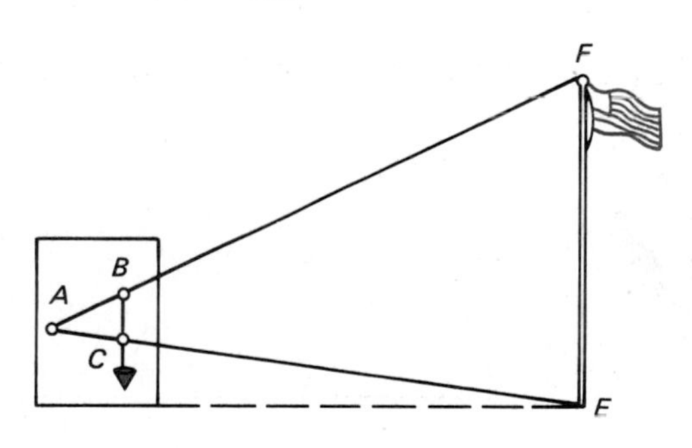

12. The base and height of a triangle are 24 cm and 20 cm, respectively. A similar triangle has an area of 750 cm². Find its dimensions.

CHAPTER REVIEW

Solve. [8-1, 8-2]

1. $\frac{t}{3} - 4 = \frac{2t}{4}$
2. $\frac{x}{3} + \frac{3}{4}(4 - x) = 3$
3. $\frac{3a + 2}{3} - 4 = \frac{3a + 1}{4}$
4. $0.99x = 198$
5. $3.92x - 0.6 = 3.72x$
6. $0.2(x - 4) - 0.025(3x - 2) = 0.25$
7. A 42-kilogram mass is placed at one end of a 4-meter beam. A 32-kilogram mass is placed at the other end. The beam is balanced on a fulcrum. How far is the fulcrum from the lighter mass?
8. The sum of $\frac{3}{4}$ of a number and $\frac{3}{2}$ of two less than the number is $10\frac{1}{2}$. Find the number. [8-3]
9. There were 6 more girls than boys at the meeting. Of the number attending, $\frac{5}{8}$ were girls. How many boys were at the meeting?
10. A dealer bought a television set for \$150 and sold it for \$180. Find the margin as a percent of the cost. [8-4]
11. For the information in Exercise 10, find the margin as a percent of the selling price.
12. Find the simple interest on a loan of \$1500 at 8% per year for 2 years. [8-5]
13. Find the annual rate at which \$2000 will produce \$300 simple interest in 2 years.
14. In a low-hurdles race, the winner ran 0.76 m/s faster than the second-place hurdler. The winner's time was 50 seconds. The second-place time was 55.25 seconds. Find the rate for each hurdler and the distance of the race. [8-6]
15. A family invested \$4000, part at 8% per year and the remainder at 7% per year. The annual income from the two investments totals \$296. Find the number of dollars invested at each rate. [8-7]
16. A motion picture film is 16 mm wide. On a theater screen, the width of the image from the film is 8 meters. Write the ratio of image width to film width. [8-8]
17. For what value of x are $\frac{x}{16}$ and $\frac{21}{28}$ equal?
18. A score of 56 points on a 70-point scale is equal to what score on a 100-point scale? [8-9]
19. Find lengths x and y for these similar triangles. [8-10]

20. Are these triangles similar?

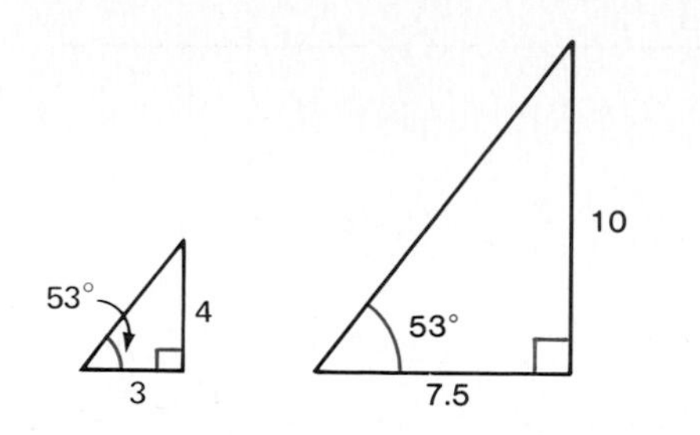

21. Are these polygons similar?

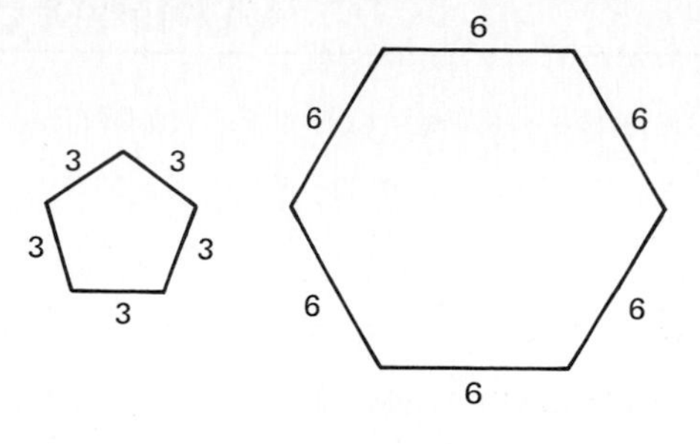

CAPSULE REVIEW

Write the letter of the best response.

1. $\frac{1}{2}$ of $\frac{1}{2}$ of $\frac{1}{2}$ equals

a. $\frac{1}{4}$ **b.** $\frac{1}{6}$ **c.** $\frac{1}{8}$ **d.** $\frac{3}{8}$ **e.** $\frac{3}{2}$

2. One-half of one and one-half equals

a. $\frac{1}{4}$ **b.** $\frac{1}{6}$ **c.** 1 **d.** $\frac{3}{2}$ **e.** $\frac{3}{4}$

3. A baseball player who had 75 hits for a batting average of .320 was at bat how many times?

a. 234 **b.** 240 **c.** 320 **d.** 426 **e.** 427

4. One-half of $10 000 is invested at 7%. At what annual rate must the other one-half be invested to give an annual interest income of $1000?

a. 9% **b.** 10% **c.** 11% **d.** 12% **e.** 13%

5. The ratio of 15 seconds to 2 minutes equals

a. $\frac{15}{2}$ **b.** $\frac{2}{15}$ **c.** $\frac{900}{2}$ **d.** $\frac{15}{120}$ **e.** $\frac{120}{15}$

6. The ratio of 3 kilograms to 30 grams equals

a. 1:10 **b.** 10:1 **c.** 1:100 **d.** 100:1 **e.** 1000:1

7. Two cities which are 500 kilometers apart are shown 5 centimeters apart on a map. Which ratio gives the scale for the map?

a. 100:1 **b.** 1000:1 **c.** 100 000:1 **d.** 10 000 000:1 **e.** 100 000 000:1

8. Which three numbers are *not* the lengths of the sides of a triangle similar to one with sides whose lengths are 10, 12, and 15?

a. 5, 6, 7.5 **b.** 15, 18, 22.5 **c.** 3.3, 4, 5 **d.** 1.0, 1.2, 1.5

9. Which ratio is not equal to the others?

a. $\frac{25}{10}$ **b.** $\frac{0.5}{0.2}$ **c.** $\frac{0.04}{0.16}$ **d.** $\frac{6}{2.4}$ **e.** $\frac{800}{320}$

CHAPTER TEST

1. What is the smallest counting number by which to multiply each member of $\frac{7x}{10} + 6 = \frac{3}{15}$ to clear the equation of fractions?

Solve.

2. $\frac{3x}{8} + \frac{1}{6} = \frac{5x}{12}$

3. $0.2x + 2.1 = 0.9x$

4. $1.68x - 0.39 = 2.46x$

5. Find $\frac{2}{3}$ of 0.624.

6. A number increased by $\frac{1}{4}$ of the number equals $\frac{5}{8}$. Find the number.

7. A merchant finds the cost of an item is $500, the selling price is $850, and the overhead is $200. Find the profit.

8. A product is purchased for $300. At what price must the product be sold so that the margin is 30% of the cost?

9. Find the simple interest on a loan of $600 at 18% for $\frac{1}{2}$ year.

10. $1000 is invested at an annual simple interest rate of 7%. Find the value of the investment after 3 years.

11. A field goal in basketball is worth 2 points. A free throw is worth 1 point. In one game the Eagles scored 86 points including 28 free throws. How many field goals did the Eagles score?

12. Dziki had 50 hits in 125 times at bat. Find Dziki's batting average.

13. Deanna bought 8 shares of stock at $25\frac{1}{4}$ and sold them at $30\frac{1}{2}$. For how much more than she paid for the stock did she sell it?

14. Amy bought an 8% $1000 bond for $1060. What is the annual yield for the bond?

15. A 10-kilogram box is 2 meters from the fulcrum of a lever. Find the mass of an object that is placed 4 meters from the fulcrum to balance the box.

16. A 400-gram object is 30 centimeters from the fulcrum of a lever. What distance from the fulcrum should a 500-gram object be placed to balance the lever?

17. For what value of x are the ratios $\frac{5}{8}$ and $\frac{x}{4}$ equal?

18. Kelly is 1.58 meters tall. In a picture, Kelly is 7.9 centimeters tall. Write a simplified ratio which compares Kelly's actual height to Kelly's height in the picture.

19. Joshua drinks 3 liters of milk every 2 days. At that rate, how many liters of milk will he drink in 30 days?

20. For a certain road map, 1 centimeter represents 20 kilometers. Two cities on the map are 12 centimeters apart. Find the actual distance between the cities.

21. The angles of one octagon are equal in measure to corresponding angles of another octagon. What must be true about the sides of the octagons if the octagons are similar?

22. The lengths of the sides of a triangle are 10 cm, 12 cm, and 16 cm. The shortest side of a similar triangle is 25 cm. Find the length of its longest side.

Write the letter of the best response.

23. The solution for $\frac{1}{8} + \frac{3x}{4} = \frac{5x}{12}$ is

a. $-\frac{3}{8}$ **b.** $-\frac{8}{3}$ **c.** $\frac{3}{28}$ **d.** $\frac{28}{3}$ **e.** $-\frac{3}{14}$

24. The solution for $0.3x + 5.76 = 0.12x$ is

a. −64 **b.** −32 **c.** 0.64 **d.** 0.32 **e.** 6.4

25. What is $\frac{5}{6}$ of 30?

a. 20 **b.** 25 **c.** 32 **d.** 36 **e.** 40

26. A product is purchased for $400. The price at which the product must be sold so that the margin is 20% of the selling price is

a. $480 **b.** $500 **c.** $580 **d.** $600 **e.** $640

27. The amount of simple interest earned on $500 invested at 6% for 3 years is

a. $18 **b.** $30 **c.** $90 **d.** $530 **e.** $590

28. A pitcher's earned run average is found by dividing 9 times the number of earned runs scored by the number of innings pitched. Angela pitched 4 innings and gave up 2 earned runs. What was her earned run average?

a. 0.222 **b.** 0.889 **c.** 1.125 **d.** 4.5 **e.** 18

29. Reyes bought 4 shares of stock at $87\frac{1}{2}$ and sold the stock at $75\frac{1}{4}$. How much did he lose on the stock?

a. $12.25 **b.** $12.75 **c.** $32.75 **d.** $49 **e.** $51

30. Heather, whose mass is 48 kilograms, sits 2.5 meters from the fulcrum of a lever. Nicole's mass is 40 kilograms. At what distance from the fulcrum must Nicole sit to balance Heather?

a. 2.1 m **b.** 2.3 m **c.** 2.8 m **d.** 3.0 m **e.** 3.2 m

31. Two cities which are 200 kilometers apart are pictured 4 centimeters apart on a map. Which ratio gives the scale of the map?

a. 5 000 000 : 1 **b.** 50 000 : 1 **c.** 50 : 1 **d.** 80 000 : 1 **e.** 800 : 1

32. David is paid $80 every 2 weeks. At that rate, his pay for 52 weeks is

a. $10 400 **b.** $8320 **c.** $6240 **d.** $4160 **e.** $2080

33. The lengths of the sides of a triangle are 3 cm, 4 cm, and 5 cm. The longest side of a similar triangle is 60 cm. How long is its shortest side?

a. 100 cm **b.** 80 cm **c.** 75 cm **d.** 45 cm **e.** 36 cm

CUMULATIVE REVIEW

Give the word(s) to complete each sentence.

1. In the equation $d = r \cdot t$, r represents the __?__.
2. The expression $2x + 5$ is called a __?__.
3. In the expression $(x + 4)(x + 2)$, $x + 4$ and $x + 2$ are called __?__.
4. The expression $6:9 = 2:3$ is called a __?__.
5. In the equation $i = prt$, p represents the __?__.

Briefly answer each question. Refer to the concept suggested.

6. $2x(3x - 6) = 6x^2 - 12x$. Why?
7. $\frac{2}{3}x - \frac{3}{5}y = 1$ can be rewritten as $10x - 9y = 15$. Why?
8. For 3 quarters and 4 dimes, the ratio of their values is not $3:4$. Why?
9. $-8x^2y - 12xy^2$ is not a prime polynomial. Why?
10. What properties of real numbers allow the sum $(-3x^2 + 5x - 9) + (4x^2 - 11x + 3)$ to be simplified to $x^2 - 6x - 6$?

Simplify each expression.

11. $4 + [(5 + 3) - 2]$
12. $9 + 8 \div 4 \cdot (11 - 9 \div 3)$
13. $2x^3 - 6x^2 + 4x + 5 + (7x^3 - 2x - 8) + (-9x^2 - 6x + 2)$
14. $-6y^3 + 4y^2 - 7y - 8 - (5y^3 - 8y^2 - 7y - 12)$
15. $(-6x^2y)(-7xy^2)$
16. $(-3x^2)^3$
17. $-5y(-6y^2 + 2y - 3)$
18. $(2x - y)(3x^2 - 2xy + 3y^2)$
19. $-54a^3b^4 \div 9a^2b$
20. $2x^3 + x^2 - 7x + 4 \div (x - 1)$
21. $(2m - 9)(3m + 7)$
22. $(3t - 4w)^2$
23. Evaluate $(-3a^2b)^2$ for $a = 2$ and $b = -3$.

Find a square root for each.

24. $81x^4y^8$
25. $4h^2 + 4h + 1$

Factor.

26. $12x - 8y$
27. $x^2 - x - 20$
28. $2y^2 + 5y - 12$
29. $6c^2 + cd - 12d^2$
30. $64y^2 - 81$
31. $2x^3y - 10x^2y - 48xy$

Graph the solution set.

32. $|x| < 5$
33. $x \geq 2$ *and* $x < 6$

Solve.

34. $(x - 6)(x + 3) = (x - 2)(x + 4)$

35. $3x - 2(3x - 5) = 19$

36. $\frac{2}{3}x + \frac{3}{4}x = 51$

37. $2.4x - 18 = -12 + 1.6x$

38. $15:25 = 36:x$

39. $3x^2 + 10x - 8 = 0$

40. Write an algebraic expression in one variable to represent the sum of one-fourth of a number and three.

41. What is the value in dollars of 3 half-dollars? 5 half-dollars? x half-dollars? $4x$ half-dollars? $2x + 3$ half-dollars?

42. An airplane leaves Portland, Oregon, headed for Miami, Florida. It flies at the rate of 450 kilometers per hour. An hour later, a second airplane leaves Portland for Miami. It flies at the rate of 600 kilometers per hour. How long will it take the second airplane to overtake the first?

43. One number is seven more than another. Three times the smaller is five less than twice the larger. Find the numbers.

44. Two cars leave from the same point and travel in opposite directions. One car travels 4 km/h faster than the other. After 4 hours they are 368 kilometers apart, find the rate of each car.

45. How many kilograms of tea selling at \$2.50/kg must be mixed with 8 kilograms of tea selling at \$4.00/kg to make a blend worth \$3.00/kg?

Write the letter of the best response.

46. Which is the square of $2x - 5$?

a. $4x^2 - 10x - 25$ **b.** $4x^2 - 10x + 25$ **c.** $4x^2 - 20x - 25$ **d.** $4x^2 - 20x + 25$

47. Which is equal to $a + b + c$?

a. $\frac{4(a + b) + c}{4}$ **b.** $\frac{4a + 4b + 4c}{4}$ **c.** $\frac{a + 5(b + c)}{5}$ **d.** $\frac{5a + b + c}{5}$

48. Which is equal to the ratio of 8.5 cm to 2 m?

a. 2 to 85 **b.** 17 to 400 **c.** 20 to 85 **d.** 17 to 40

49. Which is the factored form of $6b^2 + 11b + 3$?

a. $(6b - 1)(b - 3)$ **b.** $(6b + 3)(b + 1)$ **c.** $(3b + 1)(2b + 3)$ **d.** $(3b + 3)(2b + 1)$

50. 90 is what percent of 80?

a. 110% **b.** $112\frac{1}{2}\%$ **c.** $12\frac{1}{2}\%$ **d.** $88\frac{8}{9}\%$

51. Which algebraic expression represents the square of three less than the sum of x and y?

a. $(x + y - 3)^2$ **b.** $x^2 + y^2 - 3$ **c.** $x + y - 3^2$ **d.** $(x + y)^2 - 3$

52. A square root of $4h^2 + 8h + 4$ is

a. $(2h + 4)$ **b.** $4(h + 1)$ **c.** $(2h - 2)$ **d.** $(2h + 2)$

CHAPTER 9

Graphs, Linear Equations And Functions

On rare occasions, persons in the fine arts achieve unusual success early in their careers. For others it is more difficult and takes more time. During that time they must budget funds, pay attention to prices and costs, keep track of schedules, package and ship through the mails, fix equipment, submit funding proposals, and perform other tasks that require skills quite different from their artistic talents.

OBJECTIVE: Match ordered pairs of numbers and points in a plane.

9-1 NUMBER PAIRS AND POINTS IN A PLANE

We have seen with the number line how each point of a line may be associated with one real number. Now, we shall use two number lines to associate each point of a plane with two real numbers.

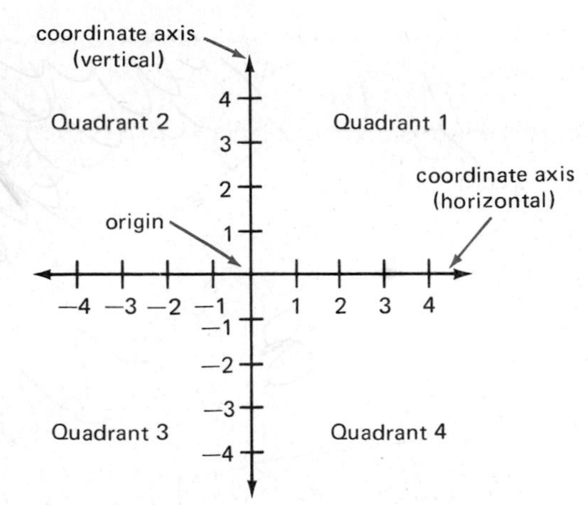

For any plane we may choose two perpendicular number lines that intersect at the zero point for each. This point is the **origin** and each number line is a **coordinate axis** for the plane, which now is called the **coordinate plane**. Pictures usually show one axis to be horizontal and the other axis to be vertical. The four parts of the plane that are separated from each other by the **axes** (plural for axis) are called **quadrants**. The quadrants customarily are numbered as shown.

Any point P in the coordinate plane may be associated with a pair of real numbers, one for each number line. These are called the **coordinates** of P. One way to find this number pair is to first move from the origin along the horizontal axis to the point directly below or above P. The number-line coordinate for this point is the first number associated with P. Then move up or down to P. The number-line coordinate from the vertical axis indicates how far up or down it is to P. This is the second number associated with P. The first number is called the **abscissa** of P. The second number is called the **ordinate** of P.

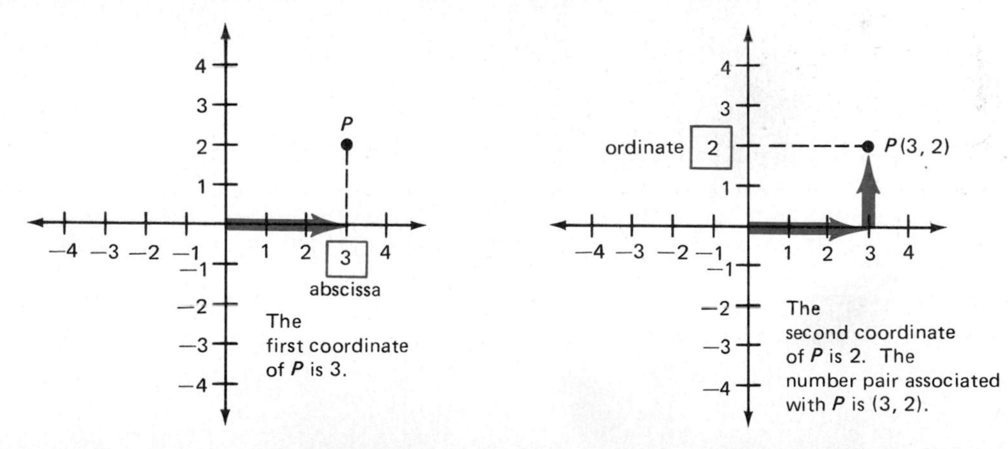

In associating a number pair with a point in the coordinate plane, mathematicians and scientists agree to give the number from the horizontal axis first and the number from the vertical axis second. Therefore, the point is said to correspond to an *ordered* number pair. Point P on the preceding page corresponds to the ordered number pair (3, 2). Sometimes we refer to a point in the coordinate plane by using *only* the ordered number pair, such as "point (3, 2)."

EXAMPLE 1 Find the coordinates of each point. Give the coordinates as an ordered number pair.

SOLUTION The coordinates
for A: (4, 3)
for B: $(-2, -3)$
for C: $(-3, 2)$
for D: (2, 0)

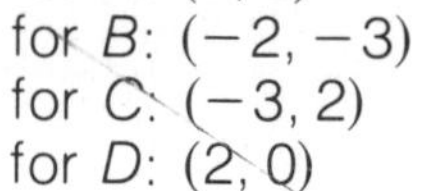

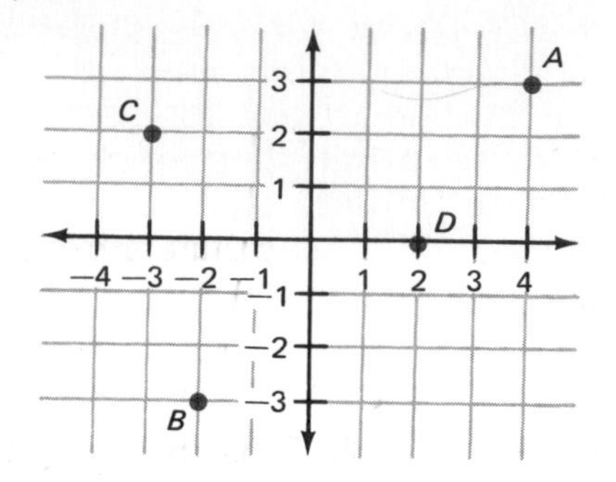

To locate or *plot* the point in the plane for any ordered real-number pair (a, b), move from the origin along the horizontal axis to the point for a. Then move up or down to match the point for b on the vertical axis. The point in the plane associated with an ordered number pair is called the **graph** for the number pair. Finding the point is called **graphing** the number pair.

EXAMPLE 2 Find the point in the plane corresponding to $(3, -4)$.

SOLUTION Find the point for 3 on the horizontal axis. Move down to match -4 on the vertical axis.

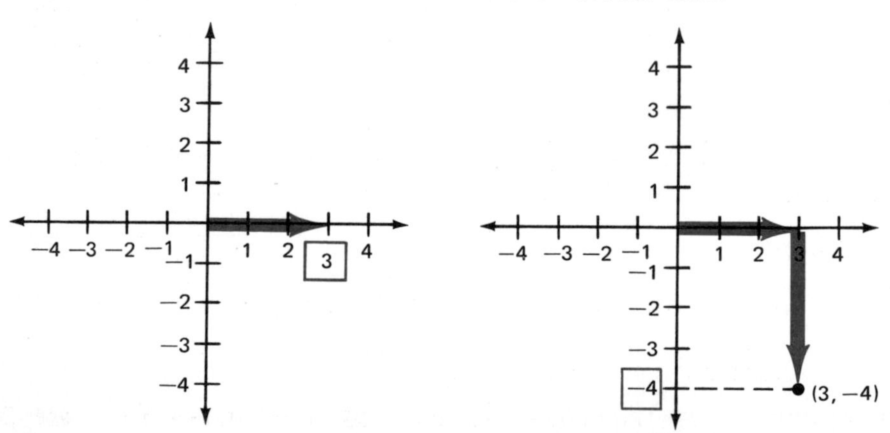

Associating a Point in a Plane with an Ordered Pair of Real Numbers

1. Move from the origin along the horizontal axis to the point for the first coordinate. It is directly below or above the point for the ordered pair.
2. Move up or down to the point for the ordered pair, referring to the vertical axis for the second coordinate.

CLASSROOM EXERCISES

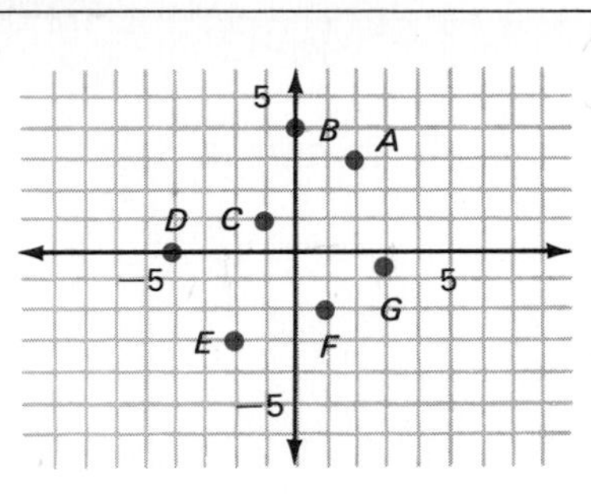

1. Give the coordinates of each point in the picture at the right.
2. Which points in the picture are in the fourth quadrant?

Plot each point in the coordinate plane.

3. $A(0, 0)$ **4.** $B(5, -5)$ **5.** $C\left(4, 3\frac{1}{2}\right)$

6. $D(-6, 2)$ **7.** $E(0, -7)$ **8.** $F(-7, -4)$

EXERCISES

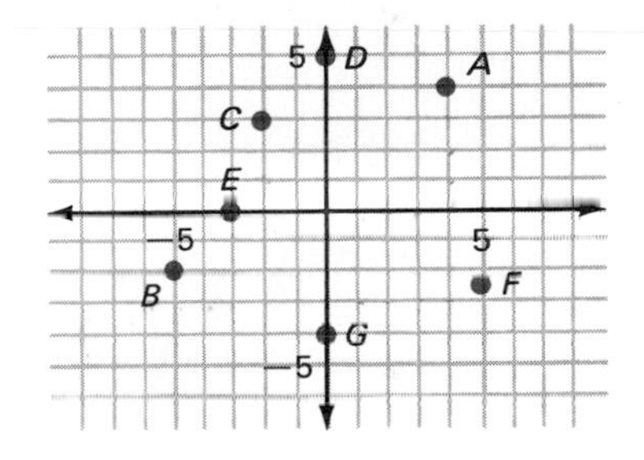

A **1.** Give the coordinates of each point in the picture. If a point is in one of the axes, name the axis.

Name the quadrant containing the point having these coordinates.

2. $(-4, 8)$ **3.** $\left(6\frac{1}{2}, -3\right)$ **4.** $(-8, -9)$

Plot each point in the coordinate plane.

5. $A(4, 7)$ **6.** $B(3, 10)$ **7.** $C(-2, -10)$ **8.** $D(-3, -3)$ **9.** $E(-3, 8)$

10. $F(-1, 4)$ **11.** $G(7, -5)$ **12.** $H(6, -2)$ **13.** $I(-9, 0)$ **14.** $J(8, 0)$

B Graph each ordered pair.

15. $A\left(5\frac{1}{2}, 4\frac{1}{2}\right)$ **16.** $B\left(-6\frac{1}{4}, 3\frac{3}{4}\right)$ **17.** $C(2.7, 8.2)$ **18.** $D(-9.3, 2.1)$ **19.** $E(0, -2.4)$

C Plot each point in the coordinate plane.

20. $A(\pi, -\pi)$ **21.** $B(-(1.5)^2, (-2.5)^2)$ **22.** $C((-2^3), -(3^2))$ **23.** $D(|-1.2|, \sqrt{1.44})$

OBJECTIVES: Identify, find solutions for, and graph linear equations in two variables. Describe the slope and intercepts of a line. Write the equation for a line.

9-2 EQUATIONS HAVING TWO VARIABLES

Each solution of an equation or inequality in one variable is just one number. Each solution of an equation or inequality in two variables is a *pair* of numbers. The solutions often are given as *ordered* pairs. When the two variables are x and y, the number for x is the first number in the ordered pair and the number for y is the second number.

EXAMPLE 1 Find three solutions of $y = 2x - 3$.

SOLUTION A solution of $y = 2x - 3$ is a pair of numbers which, when used in place of x and y, gives a true sentence.

Choose a number for x. Use 5.
Replace x by 5 in the equation.

$$\begin{aligned} y &= 2x - 3 \\ y &= 2(5) - 3 \\ &= 10 - 3 \\ &= 7 \end{aligned}$$

When 5 is used for x and 7 for y, the equation $y = 2x - 3$ becomes $7 = 2(5) - 3$, a true sentence. Therefore, as an ordered pair in which the number for x is given first and the number for y is given second, a solution for $y = 2x - 3$ is $(5, 7)$.

For other solutions, choose other numbers for x.

Use 0. Replace x by 0.

$$\begin{aligned} y &= 2x - 3 \\ y &= 2(0) - 3 \\ &= -3 \end{aligned}$$

A solution is $(0, -3)$.

Use -4. Replace x by -4.

$$\begin{aligned} y &= 2x - 3 \\ y &= 2(-4) - 3 \\ &= -11 \end{aligned}$$

A solution is $(-4, -11)$.

Three solutions for $y = 2x - 3$ are $(5, 7)$, $(0, -3)$, and $(-4, -11)$. These may be listed in table form as shown at the right.

x	y
5	7
0	-3
-4	-11

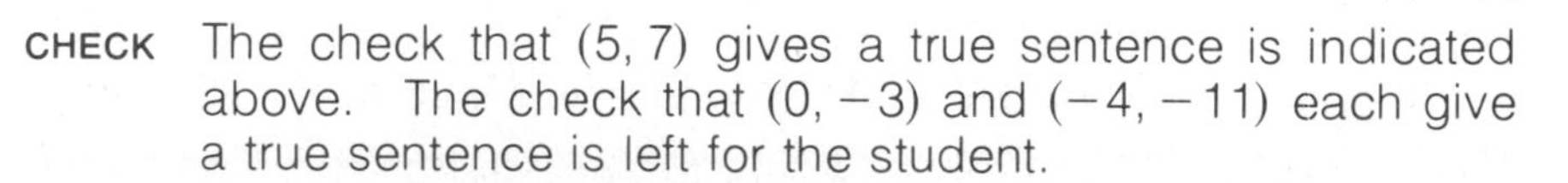

CHECK The check that $(5, 7)$ gives a true sentence is indicated above. The check that $(0, -3)$ and $(-4, -11)$ each give a true sentence is left for the student.

Solving an equation in two variables for one of the variables is a step which can simplify finding solutions.

EXAMPLE 2 Find three solutions of $2y - 3x = 6$.

SOLUTION Solve for y.

$$2y - 3x = 6$$
$$2y = 3x + 6$$
$$y = \frac{3}{2}x + 3$$

Choose numbers for x.

Use -6 for x.	Use 0 for x.	Use 4 for x.
$y = \frac{3}{2}(-6) + 3$	$y = \frac{3}{2}(0) + 3$	$y = \frac{3}{2}(4) + 3$
$= -6$	$= 3$	$= 9$

Three solutions are $(-6, -6)$, $(0, 3)$, and $(4, 9)$.

CHECK

$2y - 3x = 6$	$2y - 3x = 6$	$2y - 3x = 6$
$2(-6) - 3(-6) \stackrel{?}{=} 6$	$2(3) - 3(0) \stackrel{?}{=} 6$	$2(9) - 3(4) \stackrel{?}{=} 6$
$6 = 6$ ✓	$6 = 6$ ✓	$6 = 6$ ✓

An equation may be classified according to its *degree* which, in turn, depends upon the degree of one of its terms. For a polynomial, the **degree of a term** is the sum of the exponents of the variables in the term. The **degree of an equation**, as well as the **degree of a polynomial**, is the same as that of its highest-degree term.

To find the degree of an equation, one should first clear the equation of fractions and then clear parentheses.

First-Degree Terms	First-Degree Polynomial	First-Degree Equation
x, $3y$, $-4z$	$x + 3y$	$x + 3y = 12$
Second-Degree Terms	**Second-Degree Polynomial**	**Second-Degree Equation**
x^2, xy, $-4y^2$	$x^2 + xy - 4y^2 + 3y$	$y = x^2 + xy - 4y^2 + 3y$

EXAMPLE 3 Find three solutions of the second-degree equation $x^2 + y - 5 = 0$.

SOLUTION Solve for y.

$$x^2 + y - 5 = 0$$
$$y = 5 - x^2$$

Use 3 for x.	Use 0 for x.	Use -3 for x.
$y = 5 - x^2$	$y = 5 - x^2$	$y = 5 - x^2$
$y = 5 - 3^2$	$y = 5 - 0^2$	$y = 5 - (-3)^2$
$= -4$	$= 5$	$= -4$

Three solutions are $(3, -4)$, $(0, 5)$, and $(-3, -4)$.

CHECK The check is left for the student.

CLASSROOM EXERCISES

Find three solutions of each. Give them as ordered pairs. List them in table form.

1. $x + y = -4$ **2.** $y = 3x + 1$ **3.** $-2y + 4x = 4$

EXERCISES

A Find three solutions of each. Give them as ordered pairs. List them in table form.

1. $x + y = 3$ **2.** $x - y = 5$ **3.** $y - 2x = 1$

4. $y = 3x - 2$ **5.** $y = 4x + 5$ **6.** $y = 5x + 2$

7. $y = 3x - 8$ **8.** $y = 6x - 1$ **9.** $2y - 4x = 8$

10. $3y - 12x = 9$ **11.** $15x - 5y = 10$ **12.** $30x - 6y = 24$

B **13.** $y = -\frac{1}{2}x + 3$ **14.** $y = \frac{2}{3}x - 6$ **15.** $y = \frac{3}{4}x + \frac{1}{4}$

16. $y = -\frac{1}{3}x + \frac{5}{3}$ **17.** $2x + 5y = 8$ **18.** $-9x - 12y = -16$

19. $x^2 + y^2 = 25$ **20.** $2x^2 + y - 5 = 0$ **21.** $xy = 24$

C Find three solutions for each. Then find *one* common solution.

22. $y + 2x = 7$ and $3y = 2x + 33$ **23.** $x + 3y = 2$ and $3y = -2x - 1$

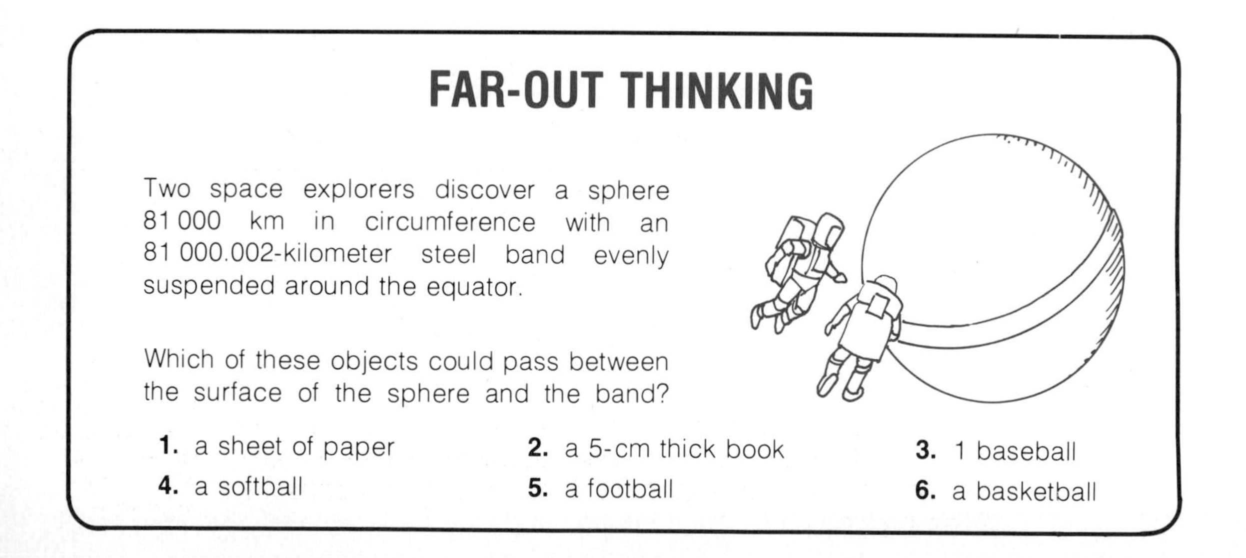

FAR-OUT THINKING

Two space explorers discover a sphere 81 000 km in circumference with an 81 000.002-kilometer steel band evenly suspended around the equator.

Which of these objects could pass between the surface of the sphere and the band?

1. a sheet of paper **2.** a 5-cm thick book **3.** 1 baseball

4. a softball **5.** a football **6.** a basketball

9-3 LINEAR EQUATIONS IN TWO VARIABLES AND THEIR GRAPHS

Each solution of an equation in two variables may be given as an ordered pair of numbers. Each ordered pair of numbers may be associated with a point in the coordinate plane. Therefore, each solution of an equation in two variables may be associated with a point in the coordinate plane. This point is the **graph** of the solution. The set of all such points is the graph of the *solution set* of the equation, or simply the **graph of the equation**.

A first-degree equation in two variables is called a **linear equation** because its graph is a line. The *standard form* for a linear equation is

$$ax + by = c$$

for which a, b, and c represent known real numbers and x and y are the variables. For an ordered pair that represents a solution of an equation in x and y, the first number refers to x in the equation and to a point in the horizontal axis in the coordinate plane. Therefore, it is called the **x-coordinate** and the horizontal axis is called the **x-axis**. The second number of the ordered pair refers to y in the equation and to a point in the vertical axis of the coordinate plane. It is called the **y-coordinate** and the vertical axis is called the **y-axis.**

Any line in the coordinate plane is the graph of some first-degree equation. We shall find equations for such lines in Section 9-6.

EXAMPLE 1 Draw the graph for the equation $3x - y = 0$.

SOLUTION First, find and graph several solutions (•).

Ⓜ

x	y
-1	-3
0	0
2	6
3	9

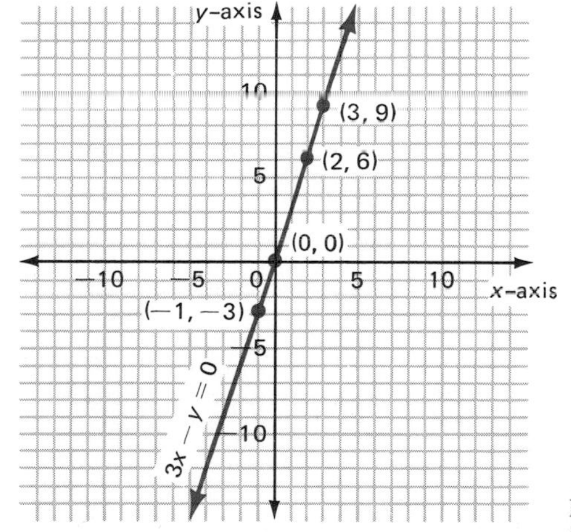

The points corresponding to the solutions are in line because $3x - 2y = 0$ is a linear equation. To complete the graph for the equation, draw the line containing these points.

Find the coordinates for some other points that appear to be in the line. Check whether these are solutions of the equation.

Two points are all that is needed to determine a line. Therefore, by finding only two number pairs that are solutions for any linear equation we are able to graph the equation. However, finding a third number-pair solution acts as a check.

EXAMPLE 2 Graph the equation $2x + y = 4$.

SOLUTION Solving for y, we have $y = -2x + 4$. Three solutions are shown in the table.

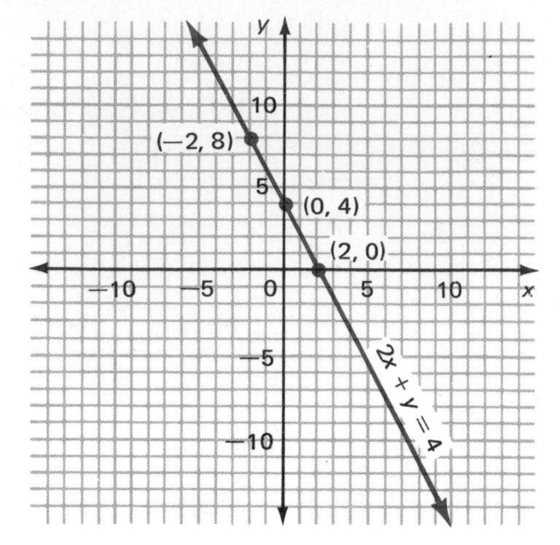

Ⓜ

x	y
−2	8
0	4
2	0

Graph the solutions. Then draw the line.

EXAMPLE 3 Graph $y = 3$.

SOLUTION You may think of this linear equation as $0x + y = 3$, or as $y = 0x + 3$.

For a solution, any number may be used for x. The only number possible for y is 3.

Ⓜ

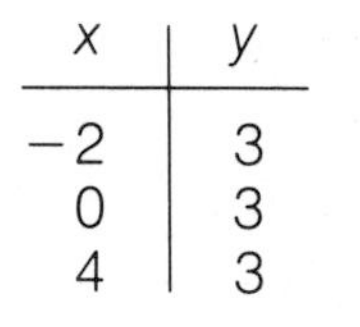

x	y
−2	3
0	3
4	3

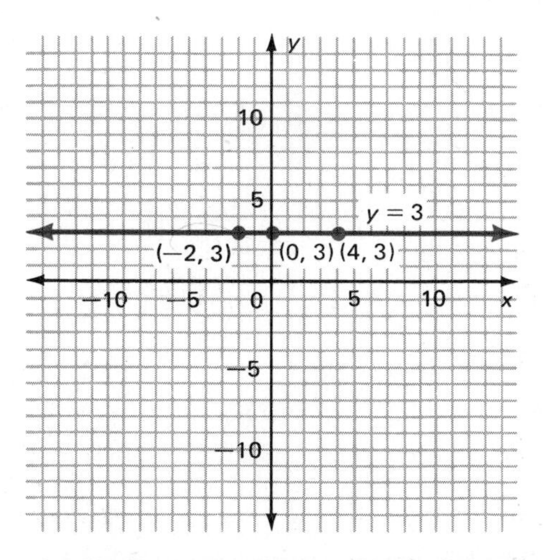

The graph is parallel to the x-axis and 3 units above it.

EXAMPLE 4 Graph $x = 2$.

SOLUTION You may think of this equation as $x + 0y = 2$.

For a solution, any number may be used for y. The only number possible for x is 2.

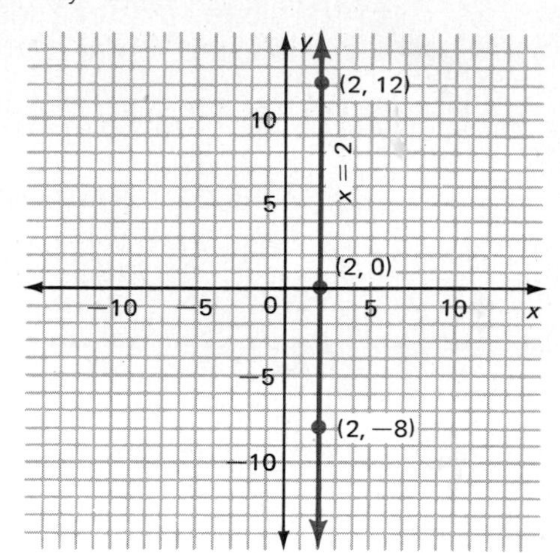

(M)

x	y
2	0
2	12
2	−8

The graph is parallel to the y-axis and 2 units to its right.

CLASSROOM EXERCISES

Find at least 3 solutions, then draw the graph for each equation.

1. $y = 2x$ **2.** $3x + y = 6$ **3.** $y = 6$ **4.** $x = 4$

EXERCISES

A Find at least 3 solutions, then draw the graph for each equation.

1. $y = 5x$ **2.** $y = 8x$ **3.** $y = -2x$ **4.** $y = -6x$

5. $5x + y = 4$ **6.** $6x + y = 8$ **7.** $-3x + y = -5$ **8.** $-8x + y = -2$

9. $y = 8$ **10.** $y = 1$ **11.** $y = -4$ **12.** $y = -9$

13. $x = 6$ **14.** $x = 10$ **15.** $x = -1$ **16.** $x = -5$

B **17.** $4x - 2y + 8 = 0$ **18.** $-3y + 6x = 12$ **19.** $10y - 25x = 15$

20. $3x - 4y = 20$ **21.** $x = 3y + 9$ **22.** $9x = 8 - 6y$

23. $-2x = 4y$ **24.** $-8y = 30$ **25.** $-12x = -80$

C **26.** $\frac{1}{2}x - \frac{3}{4}y = 0$ **27.** $\frac{1}{3}x + \frac{1}{2}y = 5$ **28.** $\frac{2}{5}y = \frac{1}{3}x + 2\frac{1}{3}$

29. $0.2x + 0.3y = 8$ **30.** $1.2x - 4.5y = -14.4$ **31.** $0.7y = 16.1x - 1.96$

9-4 THE SLOPE OF A LINE

The slope, or steepness, of a hill is important to a skier. The steeper the hill, the more expert a skier must be. The slope of a hill may be found by comparing the change in elevation to the corresponding change in horizontal distance.

EXAMPLE 1 Find the slope of this hill.

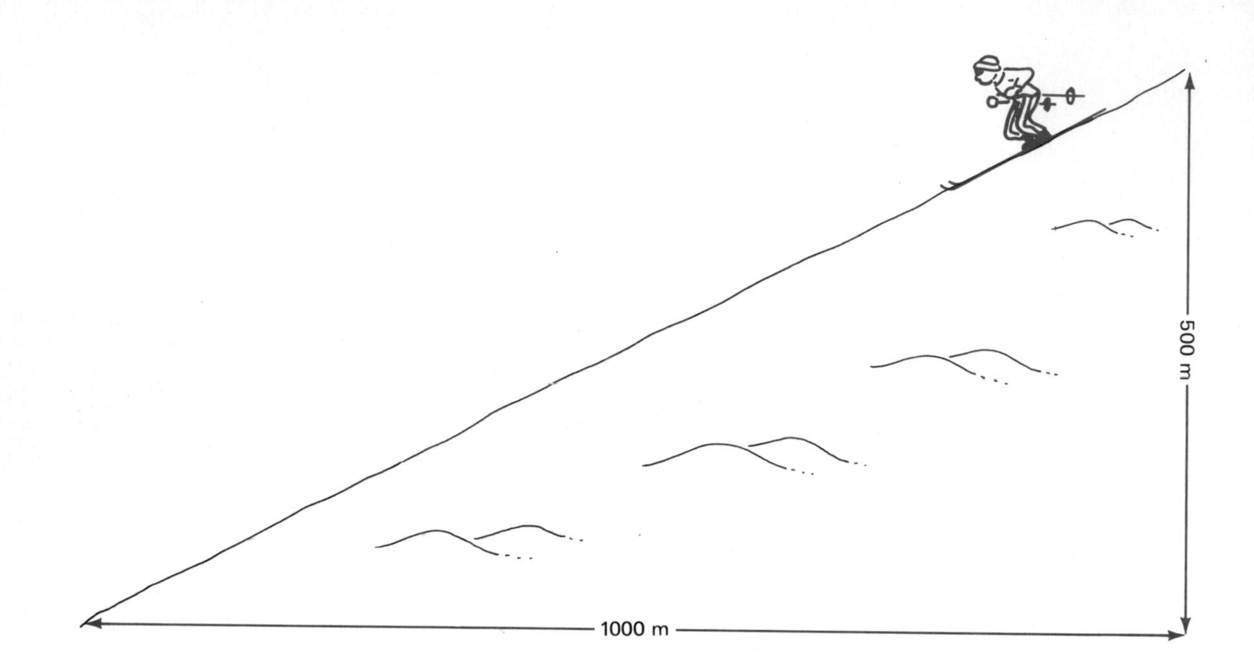

SOLUTION
$$\text{slope} = \frac{\text{change in elevation}}{\text{change in horizontal distance}}$$

$$\text{slope} = \frac{500}{1000}$$

$$\text{slope} = \frac{1}{2}$$

For a change of 1 meter in elevation there is a change of 2 meters horizontally.

This idea of slope lets us indicate the "steepness" of a line in the coordinate plane.

EXAMPLE 2 Find the slope of this line.

SOLUTION (4, 2) and (10, 5) are two points of this line. From (4, 2) to (10, 5) the "elevation" change is 5 − 2, or 3. The change in horizontal distance is 10 − 4, or 6.

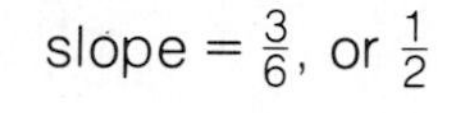

$$\text{slope} = \tfrac{3}{6}, \text{ or } \tfrac{1}{2}$$

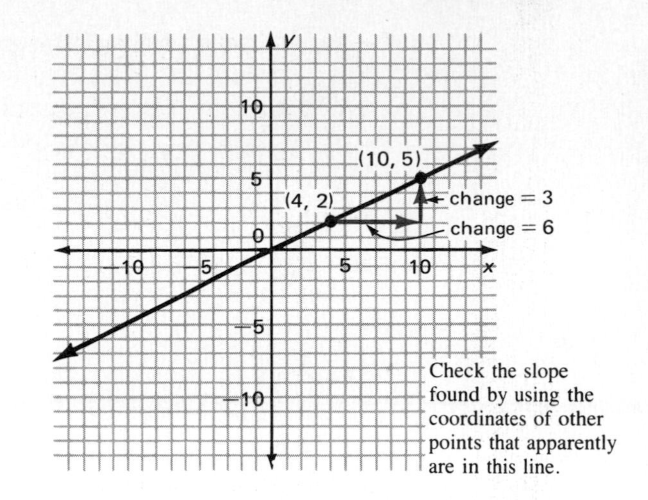

Check the slope found by using the coordinates of other points that apparently are in this line.

In general, we find the slope of a line by comparing the change in the y-coordinates to the change in the x-coordinates for any two points of the line. For two such points, (x_1, y_1) and (x_2, y_2), in a line that is not vertical,

$$\text{slope} = \frac{y_2 - y_1}{x_2 - x_1}.$$

More precisely, we compare the *difference* of the y-coordinates to the *difference* of the x-coordinates for any two points of the line.

Note that the slope also is equal to $\dfrac{y_1 - y_2}{x_1 - x_2}$. For either form, it is necessary to subtract the coordinates in the *same order*.

EXAMPLE 3 Find the slope of this line.

SOLUTION (2, 0) and (−3, 5) are two points of this line. Use (2, 0) for (x_1, y_1) and (−3, 5) for (x_2, y_2).

$$\text{slope} = \frac{y_2 - y_1}{x_2 - x_1}$$

$$= \frac{5 - 0}{-3 - 2}$$

$$\text{slope} = -1$$

or

$$\text{slope} = \frac{y_1 - y_2}{x_1 - x_2}$$

$$= \frac{0 - 5}{2 - (-3)}$$

$$\text{slope} = -1$$

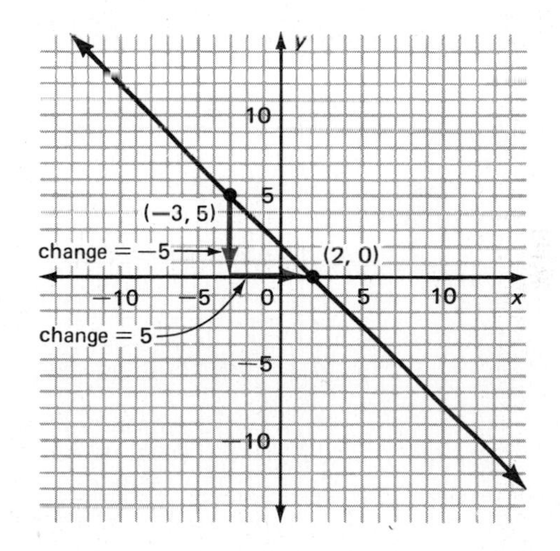

Choose other pairs of points to verify this finding.

The slope of a line that slants upward from left to right is positive (see Example 2). The slope of a line that slants downward from left to right is negative (see Example 3). For a *horizontal line*, any two points have the same y-coordinate and different x-coordinates. For such points, the numerator of the slope formula is zero and the denominator is non-zero. The slope, therefore, of any horizontal line is zero. For a *vertical line*, any two points have the same x-coordinate. Slope for such a line, as defined by the slope formula, has no meaning since the denominator would be zero. We say that a vertical line has *no slope*.

EXAMPLE 4 Find the slope of the line whose equation is $y = 2x - 5$. Draw the graph for this equation.

Ⓜ SOLUTION $y = 2x - 5$

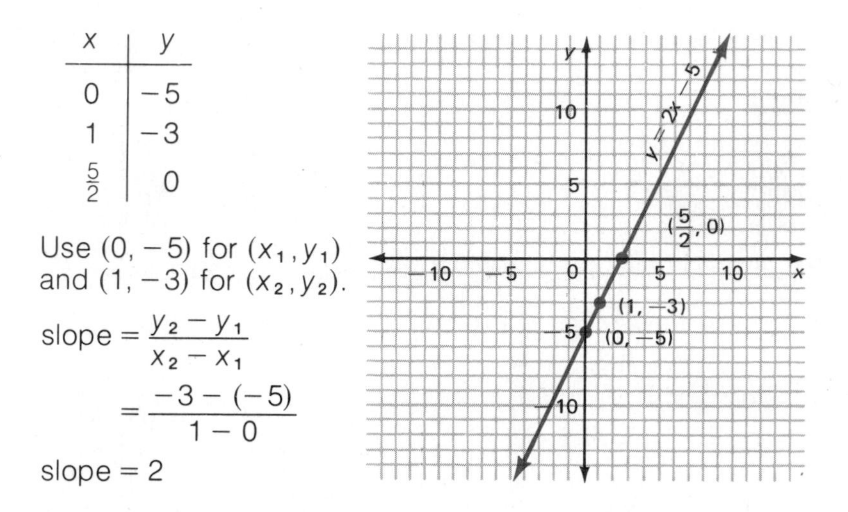

x	y
0	−5
1	−3
$\frac{5}{2}$	0

Use $(0, -5)$ for (x_1, y_1) and $(1, -3)$ for (x_2, y_2).

$$\text{slope} = \frac{y_2 - y_1}{x_2 - x_1}$$

$$= \frac{-3 - (-5)}{1 - 0}$$

$$\text{slope} = 2$$

Check the slope using other pairs of points.

FINDING THE SLOPE OF A LINE

1. Find coordinates (x_1, y_1) and (x_2, y_2) of two points of the line.
2. Compare the change in the y-coordinates to the change in the x-coordinates. If the x-coordinates are equal, the line has no slope. If $x_1 \neq x_2$,

$$\text{slope} = \frac{y_2 - y_1}{x_2 - x_1} \quad \text{or} \quad \text{slope} = \frac{y_1 - y_2}{x_1 - x_2}.$$

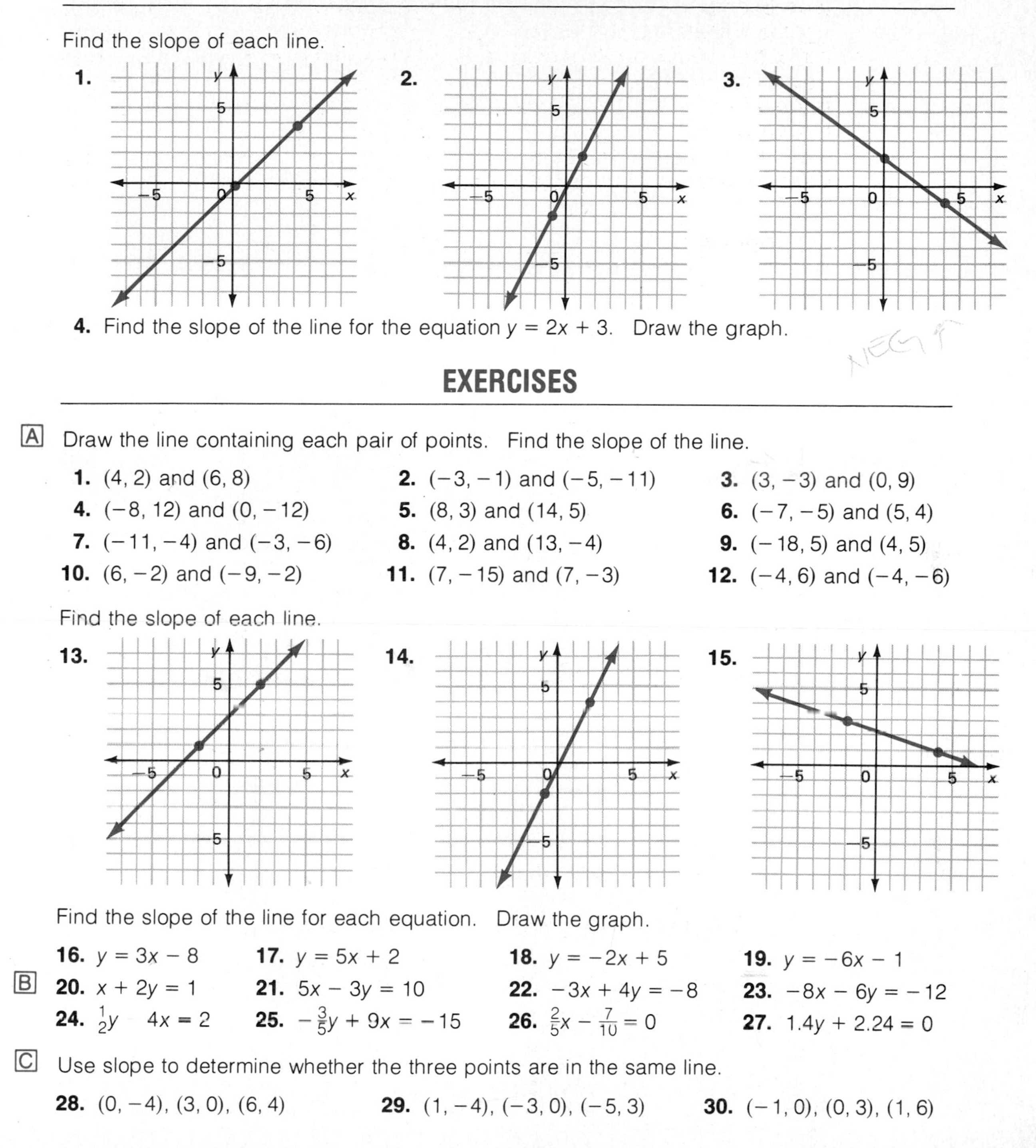

CLASSROOM EXERCISES

Find the slope of each line.

1. 2. 3.

4. Find the slope of the line for the equation $y = 2x + 3$. Draw the graph.

EXERCISES

A Draw the line containing each pair of points. Find the slope of the line.

1. (4, 2) and (6, 8) **2.** (−3, −1) and (−5, −11) **3.** (3, −3) and (0, 9)
4. (−8, 12) and (0, −12) **5.** (8, 3) and (14, 5) **6.** (−7, −5) and (5, 4)
7. (−11, −4) and (−3, −6) **8.** (4, 2) and (13, −4) **9.** (−18, 5) and (4, 5)
10. (6, −2) and (−9, −2) **11.** (7, −15) and (7, −3) **12.** (−4, 6) and (−4, −6)

Find the slope of each line.

13. **14.** **15.**

Find the slope of the line for each equation. Draw the graph.

16. $y = 3x - 8$ **17.** $y = 5x + 2$ **18.** $y = -2x + 5$ **19.** $y = -6x - 1$

B **20.** $x + 2y = 1$ **21.** $5x - 3y = 10$ **22.** $-3x + 4y = -8$ **23.** $-8x - 6y = -12$

24. $\frac{1}{2}y - 4x = 2$ **25.** $-\frac{3}{5}y + 9x = -15$ **26.** $\frac{2}{5}x - \frac{7}{10} = 0$ **27.** $1.4y + 2.24 = 0$

C Use slope to determine whether the three points are in the same line.

28. (0, −4), (3, 0), (6, 4) **29.** (1, −4), (−3, 0), (−5, 3) **30.** (−1, 0), (0, 3), (1, 6)

9-5 THE SLOPE-INTERCEPT FORM FOR LINEAR EQUATIONS

The **x-intercept** of a line is the x-coordinate of the point that the line shares with the x-axis. The **y-intercept** of a line is the y-coordinate of the point that the line shares with the y-axis.

EXAMPLE 1 Find the x-intercept and y-intercept of the line for the equation $y = 2x - 4$.

SOLUTION For $x = 0$,

$$\begin{aligned} y &= 2(0) - 4 \\ &= -4 \end{aligned}$$

The y-intercept is -4.

For $y = 0$,

$$\begin{aligned} 0 &= 2x - 4 \\ 4 &= 2x \\ 2 &= x. \end{aligned}$$

The x-intercept is 2.

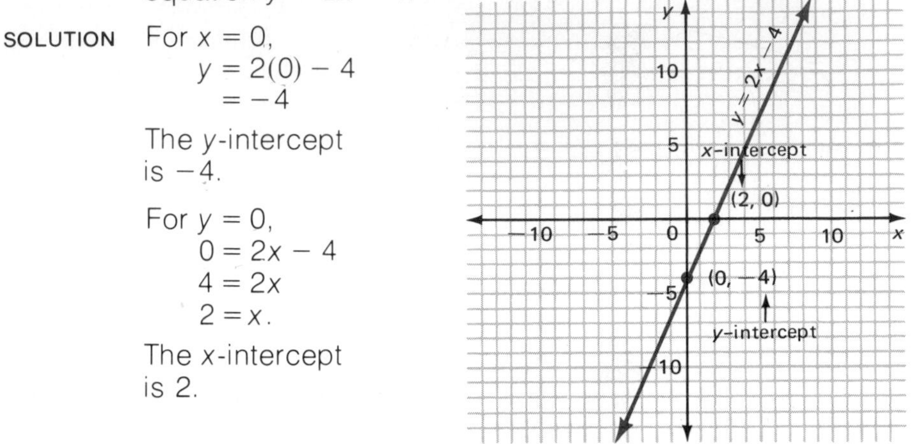

The equation for most lines may be given in *slope-intercept form*, $y = mx + b$, in which m is the coefficient of x, b is a constant, and 1 is understood to be the coefficient of y.

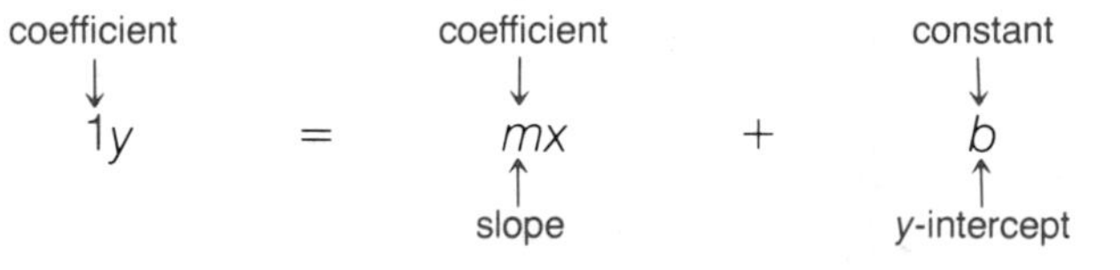

The number m is the slope of the line. The number b is the y-intercept.

EXAMPLE 2 Find the slope and y-intercept of the line for the equation $y = \frac{1}{2}x - 6$.

SOLUTION Compare $y = \frac{1}{2}x + (-6)$

and $y = mx + b$.

$$m = \frac{1}{2}, \qquad b = -6$$

The slope of the line is $\frac{1}{2}$. The y-intercept is -6.

CHECK For -6 to be the y-intercept, $(0, -6)$ must be a solution of

$$y = \frac{1}{2}x - 6.$$

$$-6 \stackrel{?}{=} \frac{1}{2}(0) - 6$$

$$-6 = -6 \checkmark$$

The x-intercept is $(12, 0)$.
To check the slope, use $(0, -6)$ for (x_1, y_1) and $(12, 0)$ for (x_2, y_2).

$$\text{slope} = \frac{y_2 - y_1}{x_2 - x_1}$$

$$\frac{1}{2} \stackrel{?}{=} \frac{0 - (-6)}{12 - 0}$$

$$\frac{1}{2} \stackrel{?}{=} \frac{6}{12}$$

$$\frac{1}{2} = \frac{1}{2} \checkmark$$

EXAMPLE 3 Find the slope and y-intercept of the line for the equation $4x + 2y = 0$.

SOLUTION First, write $4x + 2y = 0$ in the form $y = mx + b$.

$$4x + 2y = 0$$

$$2y = -4x + 0$$

$$y = \underset{\substack{\uparrow \\ m}}{-2}x + \underset{\substack{\uparrow \\ b}}{0}, \text{ or } y = -2x.$$

The slope of the line is -2.
The y-intercept is 0.

CHECK The solutions for $4x + 2y = 0$ include $(0, 0)$ and $(1, -2)$. Use $(0, 0)$ for (x_1, y_1) and $(1, -2)$ for (x_2, y_2).

To check the slope, *any* two solutions may be used.

$$\text{slope} = \frac{y_2 - y_1}{x_2 - x_1}$$

$$-2 \stackrel{?}{=} \frac{-2 - 0}{1 - 0}$$

$$-2 = -2 \checkmark$$

An equation in slope-intercept form is easily graphed. First, locate the y-intercept on the y-axis. Then use the slope to find another point of the graph.

EXAMPLE 4 Graph $y = -3x + 5$ using the slope and y-intercept.

SOLUTION The slope is -3, or $\frac{-3}{1}$. The y-intercept is 5. Locate the point for (0, 5) in the y-axis for one point of the line. Change the x-coordinate by 1 and the y-coordinate by -3 to find (1, 2), another point of the line. Then draw the line.

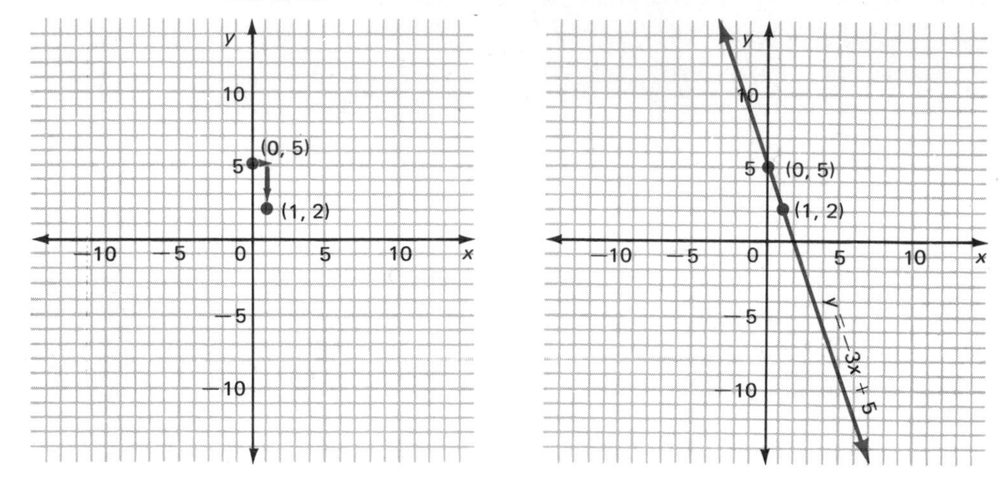

CLASSROOM EXERCISES

Find the slope and y-intercept of the line for each equation. Draw the graph for each.

1. $y = 5x$ **2.** $y = 3x + 2$ **3.** $y = \frac{1}{4}x + 3$

4. $9x + 3y = 0$ **5.** $2x + y = 3$ **6.** $-12x + 4y = 20$

EXERCISES

A Find the slope and y-intercept of the line for each equation. Draw the graph for each.

1. $y = 7x$ **2.** $y = 3x$ **3.** $y = -2x + 4$ **4.** $y = 4x + 1$

5. $y = \frac{2}{3}x - 10$ **6.** $y = -\frac{3}{5}x + 8$ **7.** $5y + 20x = 0$

8. $-3y + 18x = 0$ **9.** $6y + 3x = 0$ **10.** $-12y + 8x = 0$

11. $2y - 6x + 8 = 0$
12. $-16y - 12x - 32 = 0$
13. $2y = -8$
14. $y = 3x - 12$
15. $y = 2x + 10$
16. $y = 6x - 3$
17. $3y - 15x = 18$
18. $7y + 14x = -28$
19. $4y - 2x = -12$
20. $y = -5x + 7$
21. $y = -8x - 2$
22. $y = 3x + 4$

B Graph each equation using the slope-intercept method.

23. $y = \frac{1}{2}x - 2$
24. $2y = 3x + 8$
25. $5x - 3y = 12$
26. $5x + 2y + 10 = 0$
27. $x + y = 2y - 6$
28. $6x - 4y + 9 = 0$

Draw each line given a point in the line and the slope.

29. $(0, 5)$, $m = 2$
30. $(2, 3)$, $m = -\frac{1}{2}$
31. $(-1, 3)$, $m = -\frac{2}{5}$
32. $(-7, 0)$, $m = \frac{3}{2}$
33. $(-5, -4)$, $m = \frac{4}{3}$
34. $(-3, 3)$, $m = -5$

C Graph each pair of equations on the same set of axes.

35. $y = 3x + 2$, $y = -\frac{1}{3}x$
36. $y = 2x + 1$, $y = -\frac{1}{2}x - 3$
37. What appears to be true about the graphs in Exercises 35 and 36?

Find the slope and y-intercept of the line for each equation.

38. $3(2x - 4y) - 2(5x + 7) = 0$
39. $\frac{1}{2}(4x - 6y - 12) = \frac{2}{3}(6x + 9y - 18)$

EXPLORING EXPONENTS

Look for patterns in the table.

Row 1	64	32	16	8	4	2	?	?	?	?	?
Row 2	6	5	4	3	2	1	?	?	?	?	?

1. What occurs in Row 1 as you scan from left to right?
2. What occurs in Row 2 as you scan from left to right?
3. Copy and complete the table using the patterns you found.
4. Are there any negative numbers in Row 1? in Row 2?
5. Are there any fractions in Row 1? in Row 2?
6. Is there a zero in Row 1? in Row 2?
7. Use the pattern suggested in the table to complete these.

$2^4 = ?$ $2^3 = ?$ $2^2 = ?$ $2^1 = ?$ $2^? = 1$ $2^? = \frac{1}{2}$

9-6 FINDING AN EQUATION FOR A LINE

If you know the slope of a line and its y-intercept, you may find an equation for the line. In fact, if you know the slope and the coordinates of *any* point of the line, you may find an equation. The equation will be in slope-intercept form, $y = mx + b$.

EXAMPLE 1 Find an equation for the line with slope $\frac{2}{3}$ and y-intercept -4.

SOLUTION (M) Replace m by $\frac{2}{3}$ and b by -4 in $y = mx + b$.

$$y = mx + b$$
$$y = \tfrac{2}{3}x + (-4)$$
$$y = \tfrac{2}{3}x - 4$$

EXAMPLE 2 Find an equation for the line with slope 4 and containing the point $(2, 3)$.

SOLUTION Replace m by 4 in $y = mx + b$.

$$y = mx + b$$
$$y = 4x + b$$

Since $(2, 3)$ is a point of the line, it is a solution of the equation. Replace x by 2 and y by 3 in $y = 4x + b$.

$$3 = 4(2) + b$$
$$3 = 8 + b$$
$$-5 = b$$

CONCLUSION An equation for the line is $y = 4x - 5$.

CHECK The slope is 4. The check that $(2, 3)$ is a solution is left for the student.

If you know the coordinates of two points of a line, you may find its slope. Hence, you may write an equation for the line.

EXAMPLE 3 Find an equation for the line containing the points $(1, 2)$ and $(-2, 8)$.

SOLUTION

$$\text{slope} = \frac{y_2 - y_1}{x_2 - x_1}$$
$$= \frac{8 - 2}{-2 - 1}$$
$$\text{slope} = \frac{6}{-3}, \text{ or } -2.$$

Replace m by -2 in $y = mx + b$.

$y = mx + b$
$y = -2x + b$

Since (1, 2) and (−2, 8) are points of the line, both are solutions of the equation. Replace x and y by either pair.

Using (1, 2)	Using (−2, 8)
$y = -2x + b$	$y = -2x + b$
$2 = -2(1) + b$	$8 = -2(-2) + b$
$2 = -2 + b$	$8 = 4 + b$
$4 = b$	$4 = b$

CONCLUSION An equation for the line is $y = -2x + 4$.

CHECK The check is left for the student.

CLASSROOM EXERCISES

Find an equation for each line.

1. slope $\frac{1}{4}$, y-intercept -3
2. slope 3, containing point (1, 5)
3. containing points (3, 7) and (−4, 14)

EXERCISES

A Find an equation for each line.

1. slope -2, y-intercept 5
2. slope $\frac{3}{4}$, y-intercept -6
3. slope $-\frac{5}{12}$, y-intercept -4
4. slope 2, containing point (1, 3)
5. slope 6, containing point (−4, −8)
6. slope -4, containing point (−2, 5)
7. slope -1, containing point (−7, −1)
8. slope $\frac{1}{2}$, containing point (6, 6)
9. slope $-\frac{1}{3}$, containing point (3, −4)
10. containing points (−1, 2) and (0, 3)
11. containing points (−5, −3) and (−8, 3)
12. containing points (4, −7) and (−2, 11)
13. containing points (1, −3) and (4, 9)
14. containing points (−10, −1) and (6, 7)
15. containing points (9, −9) and (−12, −2)

B

16. slope $-\frac{1}{2}$, containing point $\left(2, \frac{1}{2}\right)$
17. slope $-\frac{2}{3}$, containing point $\left(3, \frac{1}{3}\right)$
18. slope $\frac{3}{4}$, containing point $\left(\frac{1}{3}, \frac{11}{4}\right)$
19. containing points $\left(5, \frac{9}{2}\right)$ and (2, 3)
20. containing points $\left(6, \frac{5}{2}\right)$ and $\left(5, -\frac{1}{2}\right)$
21. containing points $\left(-\frac{1}{5}, -\frac{3}{5}\right)$ and $\left(-\frac{2}{5}, -\frac{4}{5}\right)$

Find an equation for each line.

22. x-intercept 3, y-intercept -4

23. x-intercept $-2\frac{1}{2}$, y-intercept 5

24. x-intercept 100 y-intercept 0.01

25. containing points (5, 3) and (−1, 3)

26. containing points (4, 6) and (4, −5)

C **27.** slope −1, containing point $(2, b)$

28. slope b, containing point (x_1, y_1)

29. containing points (3, −5) and (a, b)

30. containing points (x_1, y_1) and (x_2, y_2)

CHECKING YOUR UNDERSTANDING

WORDS AND SYMBOLS

coordinate axes	graph of an equation	slope
coordinate plane	intercept	x-axis
coordinates	linear equation	y-axis
degree of an equation	ordered pair	x-coordinate
degree of a polynomial	origin	y-coordinate
degree of a term	quadrant	

slope-intercept form, $y = mx + b$ standard form, $ax + by = c$

CONCEPTS

- Each point of the coordinate plane corresponds to an ordered pair of real numbers and each ordered pair of real numbers corresponds to a point of the coordinate plane. [9-1]
- A linear or first-degree equation in two variables has infinitely many solutions. Each solution may be thought of as an ordered pair of numbers. Each solution has a graph in the coordinate plane. The graph of all the solutions is a line. [9-2, 9-3]
- The slope of a line indicates the steepness and the direction of slant of the line. The slope and the y-intercept of a line are unique for that line. [9-4, 9-5]

PROCESSES

- Given a point in the coordinate plane, find an ordered pair of numbers that corresponds to it. Given an ordered pair of numbers, find the corresponding point in the coordinate plane. [9-1]

  1. $B(?, ?)$ **2.** $C(?, ?)$ **3.** ?(−4, 2) **4.** ?(−5, −4)

- Given either the graph for a line or an equation for a line, find the other, as well as the slope and the intercepts. [9-2 to 9-6]

  5. For the line containing A and B, give its slope, its intercepts, and an equation.

  6. Describe the line for $2x - 3y = 5$.

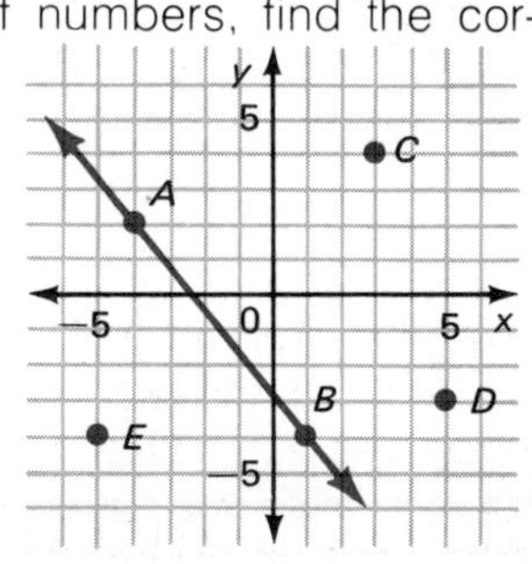

AGRICULTURAL BUSINESS AND NATURAL RESOURCES

Although the term *agriculture* suggests a farm occupation, Agricultural Business occupations involve off-farm settings as well. An occupation that requires an individual to have mathematical skills as well as agricultural skills is that of *Agricultural Accountant*. With more extensive training, an occupation as an *Agricultural Marketing Specialist* is possible. High school courses that are valuable for either career include algebra, geometry, statistics, bookkeeping, accounting, basic farm techniques, industrial relations, and nutrition.

During a typical day an *Agricultural Accountant* might provide the following services.

- Advise farmers or farm managers about tax advantages.
- Prepare income tax forms.
- Provide advice regarding the purchase of certain machinery.

An *Agricultural Marketing Specialist* might perform the following tasks.

- Compile research pertaining to sales forecasts.
- Compile research pertaining to the development of a new food product.
- Produce a chart to show the effect of new techniques of mechanization upon supply, demand, and price.

MATHEMATICAL SAMPLER

1. You are an Agricultural Accountant. You must recommend to a farmer the best crop seed based on germination rate and cost. Each type of seed is planted in a box containing 150 cm^2 of planting area. Which seed type do you recommend? Why?

Seed Type	Germination	Cost per Kilogram
1	108 cm^2	\$2.53
2	122 cm^2	\$2.75
3	136 cm^2	\$3.09

2. An Agricultural Marketing Specialist has determined that there is a market for a medium cream that is 25% butterfat. Regular milk contains about 4% butterfat. Each 1000 liters of regular milk will yield how many liters of the medium cream and how many liters of non-fat milk? Give the ratio of the amount of non-fat milk to the amount of medium cream that may be obtained from regular milk.

OBJECTIVE: Solve problems involving direct and linear variation.

9-7 PROBLEM SOLVING: DIRECT VARIATION

A relationship between two variables, x and y, sometimes may be described by a linear equation of the form $y = kx$ for which k represents a non-zero constant. For such a relationship, x and y are said to *vary directly*. When x and y vary directly and represent positive numbers only, an increase in the number used for one of the variables means the number used for the other variable also increases.

Since a direct-variation relationship may be described by a linear equation of the form $y = kx$, the graph representing it is a line, or a part of a line, with slope k and y-intercept 0. The graph contains the origin, except when 0 is not in the replacement set for one of the variables.

EXAMPLE 1 Suppose that each kilogram of scrap metal is worth 10 cents. Then, the amount of money earned collecting scrap metal varies directly with the number of kilograms collected. Find a linear equation that relates the amount of money earned collecting scrap metal to the number of kilograms collected. Draw a graph to show the direct variation.

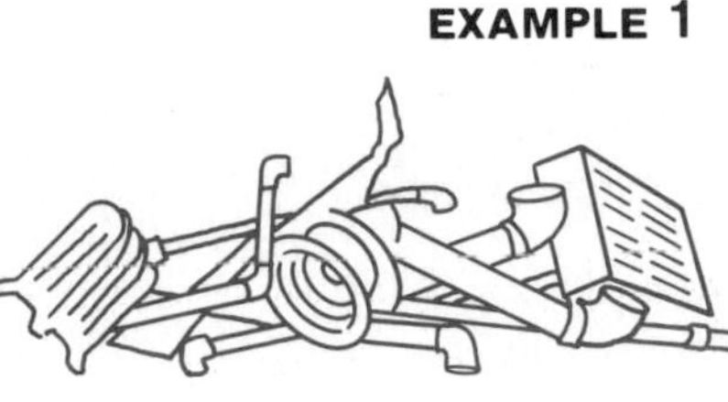

SOLUTION money earned = constant · kilograms collected

To write the mathematical form for the equation, we assign symbols to the quantities.

Use [n for the number of kilograms collected.
c for the amount earned, in cents.

Also, we try to find a value for the constant. To do this, it often is helpful to use the given information, do some mental computation, and prepare a table such as this.

Choose these.	kilograms collected (n)	0	1	2	3	8	10
Compute these.	money earned in cents (c)	0	10	20	30	80	100

$c = 10n$ and subsequent equations in the Examples are of the form $y = kx$.

$¢ = \frac{¢}{kg} \cdot kg$

From the table, we see that an equation is

$$c = 10n.$$

Ⓜ

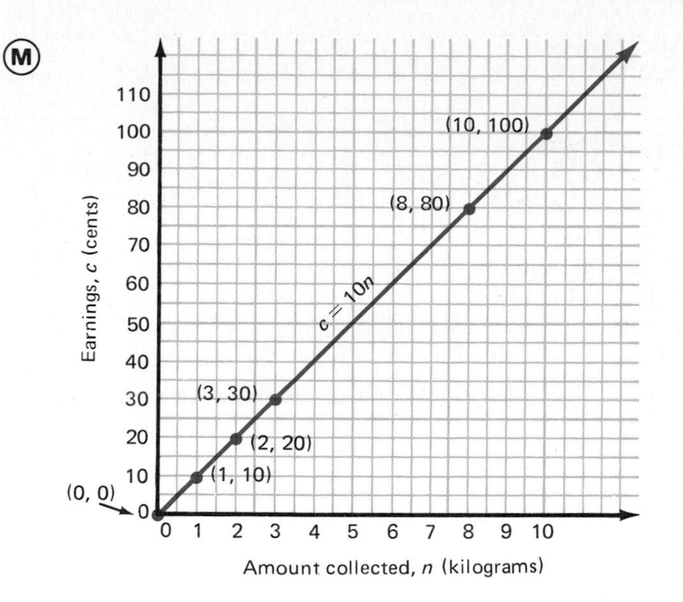

Note the difference in units for the x-axis and y-axis.

EXAMPLE 2 Some workers are paid by the hour. Their wages vary directly with the number of hours they work. Find a linear equation that relates wages to hours worked for someone who earns $5.75 an hour.

Ⓜ **SOLUTION** wages = constant · hours worked

Use h for the number of hours worked.
W for the wages earned, in dollars.

$W = 5.75h$

$\$ = k \cdot h$ suggests that the constant must represent $\frac{\$}{h}$. This helps confirm 5.75 as the constant.

$\$ = \frac{\$}{h} \cdot h$

EXAMPLE 3 Assume that x and y vary directly, and $x = 5$ when $y = 20$. Find the number for x when $y = 60$.

SOLUTION Since x and y vary directly, we may write

$y = kx.$

Find k.
Replace x by 5 and y by 20.

$20 = k \cdot 5$
$4 = k$

Rewrite $y = kx$.
Replace k by 4 in $y = kx$.

$y = 4x$

The equation that describes the direct variation is $y = 4x$.

Find x when $y = 60$. Replace y by 60 in $y = 4x$.

$y = 4x$
$60 = 4x$
$15 = x$

CONCLUSION When y is 60, x is 15.

CLASSROOM EXERCISES

1. The cost of a particular type of yarn is 5 cents a meter. Write a linear equation that relates cost in dollars to meters of yarn. Draw a graph.
2. Suppose x and y vary directly. If $x = 4$ when $y = 12$, find the value of x when $y = 42$.

EXERCISES

A

1. Each package of metal washers has a mass of 6 grams. Write an equation and draw a graph to show the relationship between the mass of the washers in grams and the number of packages.

Number of Packages	1	2	4	8	10	n
Mass of Washers	6	12	24	48	60	?

2. A recent wage settlement granted an increase of $1.25 an hour. Write a linear equation that relates total wage increase in dollars and number of hours worked. Draw a graph.
3. The shipping cost of an item is 18 cents a kilogram. Write a linear equation that relates shipping cost in dollars and the number of kilograms shipped. Draw a graph.

In each of the following, x and y vary directly.

4. If $x = 5$ when $y = 30$, find x when $y = 84$.
5. If $x = 9$ when $y = 18$, find x when $y = 62$.
6. If $y = 3$ when $x = 10.5$, find y when $x = 45.5$.
7. If $y = 4$ when $x = \frac{1}{2}$, find y when $x = 2\frac{1}{2}$.

B

8. If $x = 20$ when $y = 15$, find x when $y = 27$.
9. If $x = 30$ when $y = 18$, find y when $x = 45$.
10. If $x_1 = 7$ and $y_1 = 3$, find y_2 when $x_2 = 21$.
11. If $x_1 = 3.2$ and $y_1 = 1.2$, find x_2 when $y_2 = 4.8$

Solve.

12. Electric current (I) varies directly as the voltage (E). If $I = 7$ when $E = 110$, find the current when the voltage is 220.
13. The distance traveled in a certain time varies directly as the average speed. If the distance traveled is 110 km at an average speed of 65 km/h, how many kilometers will be traveled at 80 km/h?
14. If 30 objects cost $3.75, how much will 76 objects of the same kind cost?

C

15. Find 3 circles of different sizes (for example, use a coin, a can, and a large bottle). Measure the diameter of each circle with a ruler and measure the circumference somehow (perhaps using a string or by rolling the object along the ruler). Make a table showing diameter length and circumference. Show that diameter length and circumference are related by an equation of the form $y = kx$. Then, find k.
16. A recent Boston Marathon (a footrace of about 42 kilometers) was won in a time of 2 hours 10 minutes. Using this information and assuming that distance run varies directly with time, find the winner's time for running 100 meters. Compare this time with the best time for the 100-meter race at your school.

9-8 PROBLEM SOLVING: LINEAR VARIATION

A direct-variation relationship may be described by the linear equation

$$y = mx + b$$

when $b = 0$. When $b \neq 0$, the variation is known as *linear variation*.

EXAMPLE 1 An actress earns \$500 000 plus 5% of the box-office income for her work in a motion picture. Her income for the work and the money spent for tickets to see the motion picture vary linearly. Find a linear equation that describes this relationship.

(M) SOLUTION The income equals the sum of \$500 000 and 5% of the box-office income.

Use [I for the actress's income in dollars.
s for the number of dollars spent at box offices.

$I = 500\,000 + 0.05s$

$\$ = \$ + (\text{dimensionless}) \cdot \$$

The graph for a linear-variation relationship is a line. When the numbers involved in such a relationship are non-negative only, the graph is the part of the line that is in the first quadrant only.

EXAMPLE 2 The Harris family is driving home on their vacation. The equation $d = -90t + 500$ describes the relationship between the distance from home (d) in kilometers and the number of hours (t) spent driving. Do distance and time vary linearly? Draw a graph.

$\text{km} = \frac{\text{km}}{\text{h}} \cdot \text{h} + \text{km}$

SOLUTION Since the relationship is given by an equation of the form $y = mx + b$, the distance and time vary linearly. The graph is a portion of the line with slope -90 and y-intercept 500.

(M)

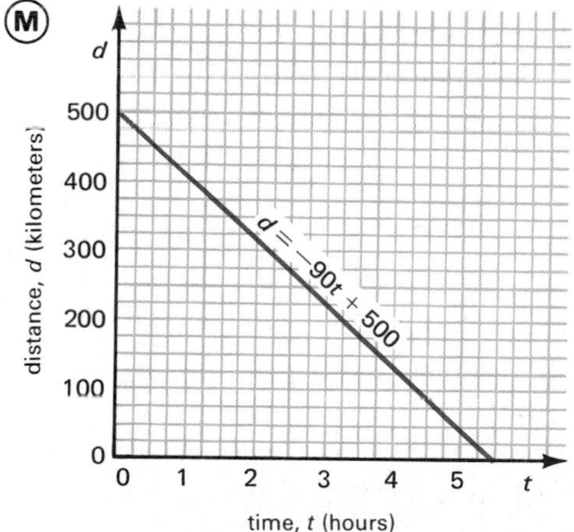

EXAMPLE 3 The charge for renting a rug-cleaning machine is \$20 for the first day and \$15 for each additional day. Find a linear equation that describes the relationship between cost and time for using the machine. Find the cost of renting the machine for 5 days.

(M) SOLUTION The total cost is the cost for the first day plus the cost for the additional days.

Use n for the number of days of rental.
Use C for the total cost in dollars.

$$C = C_{\text{first day}} + C_{\text{additional days}}$$

$$\$ = \$ + \frac{\$}{(\text{add. days})} \cdot (\text{add. days})$$

$$C = 20 + 15(n - 1)$$
$$C = 20 + 15n - 15$$
$$C = 15n + 5$$

Replace n by 5.

$$C = 15(5) + 5$$
$$C = 80$$

CONCLUSION The equation $C = 15n + 5$ gives the relationship between cost and time. The cost of renting the machine for 5 days is \$80.

EXAMPLE 4 The variables x and y vary linearly. Some of the related numbers used for x and y are shown in the table. Find a linear equation that describes the relationship between x and y.

x	y
0	5
1	8
2	11
3	14
4	17

SOLUTION We need to use only two of the number pairs to find a linear equation since two points are enough to determine a line.

Use (0, 5) and

$$y = mx + b.$$

Replace x by 0 and y by 5.

$$y = mx + b$$
$$5 = m(0) + b$$
$$5 = b$$

Use (1, 8) and

$$y = mx + 5.$$

Replace x by 1 and y by 8.

$$y = mx + 5$$
$$8 = m(1) + 5$$
$$3 = m$$

CONCLUSION The equation $y = 3x + 5$ describes the relationship between x and y for the information given in the table.

CHECK Try (4, 17).

$$y = 3x + 5$$
$$17 \stackrel{?}{=} 3(4) + 5$$
$$17 = 17 \checkmark$$

CLASSROOM EXERCISES

Solve.

1. The fee for renting a bicycle is \$8.00 the first day and \$6.00 for each additional day. Write a linear equation that describes the relationship between cost and time. Find the cost of renting a bicycle for 6 days.

x and y vary linearly. Some of their corresponding values are shown in the table. Write a linear equation that relates x and y.

2.

x	0	1	3	4	−2
y	2	6	14	18	−6

EXERCISES

A Solve.

1. Eva earns \$180 a week selling cameras. She also earns a 5% commission on her sales. Write a linear equation that relates Eva's income and her sales.
2. Dean earns \$160 a week selling sporting goods plus a 5% commission on his sales. Write a linear equation that relates Dean's income and his sales.
3. The speed of sound in air is given by the linear equation $v = 0.6t + 332$, where v represents speed in meters per second and t represents temperature in degrees Celsius. Draw a graph for this relationship.
4. A downtown parking garage charges \$1.50 for the first hour and 70¢ for each additional hour. Write a linear equation that relates cost and time. Find the cost for parking for 9 hours.

x and y vary linearly. Some of their corresponding values are shown in the table. Write a linear equation that relates x and y.

5.

x	0	1	4
y	2	12	42

6.

x	0	5	−9
y	4	39	−59

B

7. The length of a 45-centimeter spring increased 5 cm when a 20-kilogram weight was attached to it. Write a linear equation that relates the length of the spring to the number of kilograms attached to it. Find the length of the spring when a 56-kilogram weight is attached to it.
8. A long-distance telephone call from Boston to Denver costs 52¢ for the first minute and 36¢ for each additional minute. Write a linear equation that relates cost and time. Draw a graph. Find the cost for a 9-minute telephone call.

C

9. A taxi cab company charges 75¢ for the first 0.1 km and 10¢ for each additional 0.1 km. Write a linear equation that relates cost and distance. Draw a graph. What is the cost of a 6-kilometer trip?
10. A spacecraft traveling 20 000 km/h towards Mars launches a probe in the same direction. The probe's rocket engine burns for 20 minutes and accelerates the probe at a rate of 60 000 km/h². Write a linear equation that relates the probe's velocity and the time elapsed since launching. Find the speed of the probe at the time its engine stops.

OBJECTIVES: Identify a function and its ordered pairs. Use function notation. Identify and graph a linear function.

9-9 FUNCTIONS AND THEIR GRAPHS

A **function** is a set of ordered pairs, no two of which have the same first member. The pairs may be formed from two sets by a rule. The rule pairs each member of one set with exactly one member of the other set.

EXAMPLE 1 The diagram defines a function. Which two sets are used to form the function? Each arrow shows the number in the second set that corresponds to each number in the first set. Describe the function using ordered pairs.

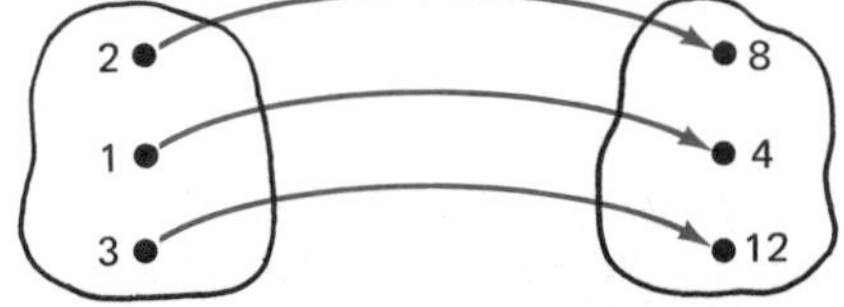

SOLUTION The first set is $\{1, 2, 3\}$. The second set is $\{4, 8, 12\}$.
The function is $\{(1, 4), (2, 8), (3, 12)\}$.

A function may be *defined* by describing the set whose members are the first members of the ordered pairs of the function, and also giving the rule for forming the ordered pairs. The set of first members of the ordered pairs is the **domain** of the function. The set of second members of the ordered pairs is the **range** of the function.

EXAMPLE 2 Give the domain and the range of the function defined below. Describe the function using ordered pairs.

By giving the domain and the rule, the range is established.

DOMAIN:	the set of counting numbers
RULE:	$x \longrightarrow 2x$ (The second member of an ordered pair of the function is twice the first member.)

SOLUTION The domain is the set of counting numbers, $\{1, 2, 3, \cdots\}$. The range is the set of *even* counting numbers, $\{2, 4, 6, \cdots\}$.
The function is $\{(1, 2), (2, 4), (3, 6), \cdots\}$.

The rule for a function may be given by using an equation in two variables. Often the variables are x and y, with x representing a member of the domain and y representing the corresponding member of the range.

The **graph of a function** is the graph of all ordered pairs of the function. The graph of a function defined by an equation in x and y is simply the graph for the equation with the requirement that the numbers for x (the first coordinates) must belong to the domain.

EXAMPLE 3 Give several ordered pairs that belong to the function defined below. Draw the graph of the function.

DOMAIN: the set of integers
RULE: $y = 2x + 1$

SOLUTION The table shows several ordered pairs that belong to the function.

Since the domain is the set of integers, the graph will have a point for each integer for x. The pairs from the table suggest the pattern for the complete graph.

x	y
-3	-5
-2	-3
0	1
1	3
2	5

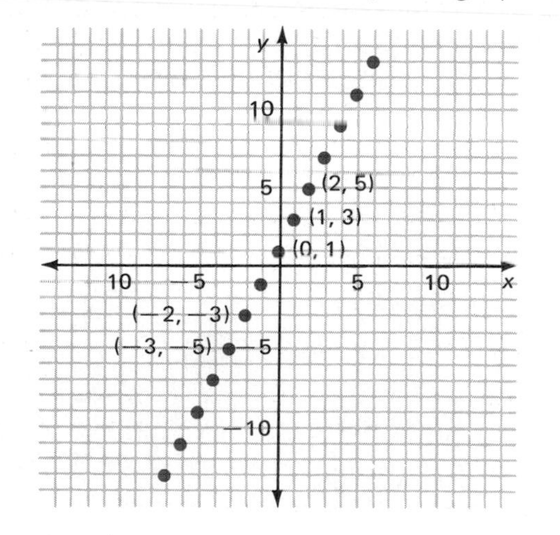

The graph continues in the same pattern and without end beyond the upper and lower edges of this picture.

Often, a function is given a special name. If the function in the preceding example is named f, we may rewrite the rule

$$y = 2x + 1 \quad \text{as}$$
$$f(x) = 2x + 1.$$

For a function named f, $f(x)$ (read "f at x" or "f of x") represents members of the range, just as y did. In fact, the table of pairs shown in Example 3 could look like this.

x	$f(x)$
-3	-5
-2	-3
0	1
1	3
2	5

$$f(x) = 2x + 1$$

$$f(-3) = 2(-3) + 1, \text{ or } -5$$
$$f(-2) = 2(-2) + 1, \text{ or } -3$$
$$f(0) = 2(0) + 1, \text{ or } 1$$
$$f(1) = 2(1) + 1, \text{ or } 3$$
$$f(2) = 2(2) + 1, \text{ or } 5$$

EXAMPLE 4 Find five ordered pairs that belong to the function g defined below. Graph the function g.

DOMAIN: the set of real numbers

RULE: $g(x) = -x + 2$

SOLUTION The table shows five ordered pairs of the function g. The domain of this function is the set of real numbers. The graph has a point for each real number associated with the x-axis. The graph is a line. The graphs of the pairs from the table suggest the line for the complete graph.

(M)

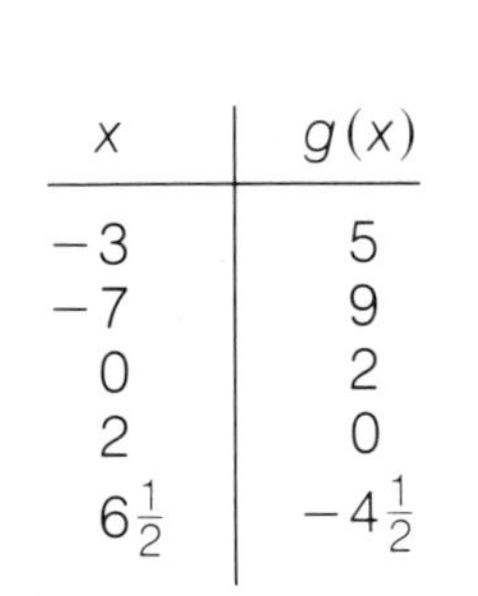

x	$g(x)$
-3	5
-7	9
0	2
2	0
$6\frac{1}{2}$	$-4\frac{1}{2}$

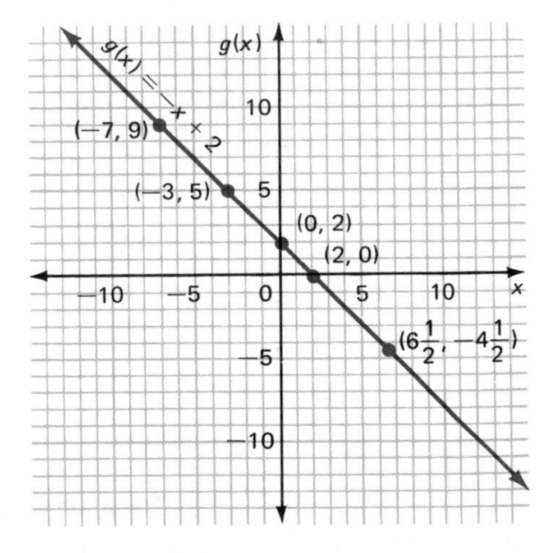

CLASSROOM EXERCISES

The diagram defines a function.

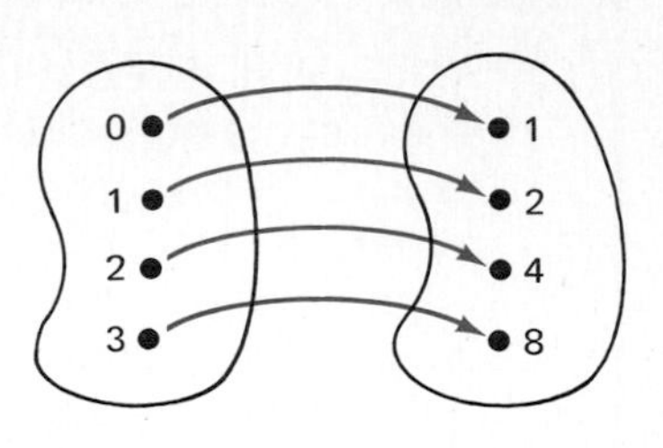

1. What is the domain of the function?
2. What is the range of the function?
3. List the ordered pairs of the function.

Give five ordered pairs of each function. Graph each function.

4. Domain: the set of integers
   Rule: $y = 2x - 1$

5. Domain: the set of real numbers
   Rule: $f(x) = 5 - x$

EXERCISES

The diagram defines a function.

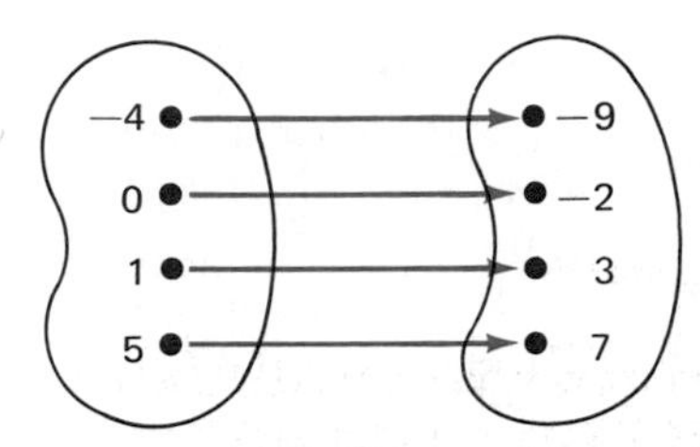

A

1. What is the domain of the function?
2. What is the range of the function?
3. List the ordered pairs of the function.
4. For $f(x) = x - 7$, find $f(0)$, $f(3)$, and $f(5)$.
5. For $h(x) = -2x - 1$, find $h(-6)$, $h(0)$, and $h(6)$.

Give five ordered pairs of each function. Graph each function.

6. Domain: the set of whole numbers
   Rule: $x \longrightarrow 6x$

7. Domain: the set of counting numbers
   Rule: $x \longrightarrow 9x$

8. Domain: the set of integers
   Rule: $y = 3x + 1$

9. Domain: the set of negative integers
   Rule: $y = -2x + 3$

10. Domain: the set of integers
    Rule: $f(x) = x + 6$

11. Domain: the set of integers
    Rule: $f(x) = -x + 4$

12. Domain: the set of real numbers
    Rule: $g(x) = 5x - 8$

13. Domain: the set of real numbers
    Rule: $g(x) = -3x + 5$

B

14. For $f(x) = 2x^2 - 3$, find $f(-5)$, $f(-3)$, $f(0)$, and $f(6)$.
15. For $g(x) = x^2 - 2x + 1$, find $g(-8)$, $g(-4)$, $g(4)$, and $g(8)$.
16. For $h(x) = |x - 4|$, find $h(-9)$, $h(-5)$, $h(2)$, and $h(6)$.
17. For $k(x) = (-x)^3 + 5$, find $k(-6)$, $k(-2)$, $k(4)$, and $k(10)$.

C Graph each function. The domain for each is the set of real numbers.

18. $f(x) = x^2$
19. $g(x) = x^2 - 3$
20. $F(x) = x^2 - 6x + 9$
21. $G(x) = |x|$
22. $k(x) = |x| - 3$
23. $p(x) = |x - 3|$

SPEAKING OF FUNCTIONS

A rule that gives the ordered pairs of a function is a "mathematical recipe." The first member of an ordered pair of the function is an ingredient (input) of the recipe. The second member of the ordered pair is the outcome (output) of the recipe.

For example, the rule $y = 3x + 1$ tells what to do with each input for x to produce each output for y.

When the rule for a function is used to describe a behavior pattern in the real world, it is good practice to use mnemonic (ni-MON-ik) or memory-aiding symbols for the variables. Such symbols suggest the ideas they represent. When this is done for a function rule that is an equation, the rule commonly is known as a formula.

For example, both rules $y = 60x$ and $d = 60t$ give the function which relates time and distance traveled at the rate 60. However, the formula $d = 60t$ is the preferred form for the rule because d suggests distance and t suggests time.

Generally, a function formula is written with the output variable as the left member. The output variable "is a function of the other variables."

For $d = 60t$, when the rate is a constant, distance is a function of time. The numbers for d vary according to the specific numbers chosen for t. For the formula, $d = rt$, distance is a function of rate and time. For a constant rate, distance is a function of time. For a constant time, distance is a function of the rate.

Identify the formula and complete the sentence, "__?__ is a function of __?__."

1. $C = \pi d$ **2.** $V = \frac{4}{3}\pi r^3$ **3.** $A = s^2$ **4.** $C = 2\pi r$

5. $A = \pi r^2$ **6.** $P = 4s$ **7.** $i = prt$ **8.** $V = lwh$

For each formula below, tell how the output changes as a result of doubling the input; tripling the input.

9. $C = \pi d$ **10.** $A = s^2$ **11.** $r = \frac{100}{t}$ **12.** $V = s^3$

Write a formula that gives

13. the diameter of a water pipe as a function of its circumference.

14. the rate of a train as a function of the time needed to travel 1500 km.

15. the wage for a 40-hour work week as a function of the hourly rate.

16. the radius of a basketball as a function of its circumference.

17. the volume of a room 8 m long and 3 m wide as a function of the height.

9-10 LINEAR FUNCTIONS

The linear equation $y = mx + b$ may be used to define a **linear function**. The ordered pairs that are solutions of the equation are the ordered pairs of the function. Hence, the graph for such a function is a line, or a part of a line, with slope m and y-intercept b.

EXAMPLE 1 Graph the function g defined below.

DOMAIN:	the set of real numbers
RULE:	$g(x) = 3x - 1$

SOLUTION The rule $g(x) = 3x - 1$ could be given as $y = 3x + (-1)$. The function g is a linear function. Its graph is a line with slope 3 and y-intercept -1.

Ⓜ

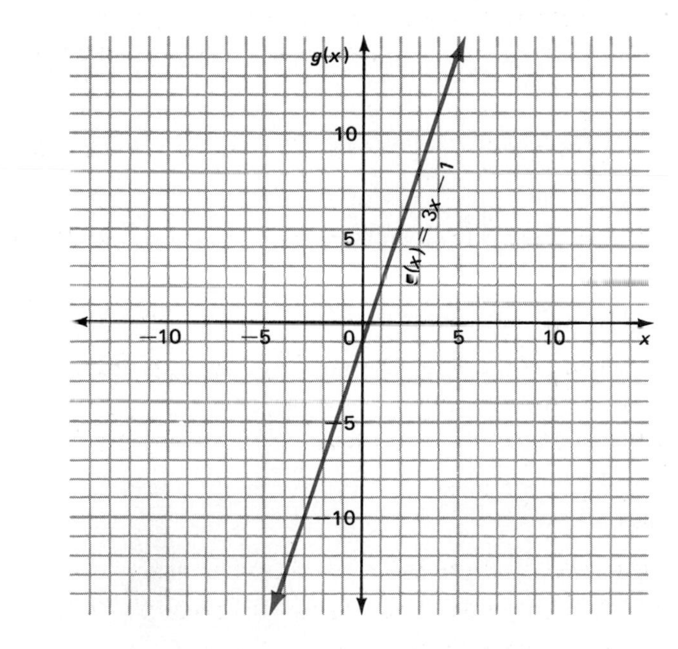

The graph of a linear function is a line if the domain is the set of real numbers. If the domain is part of the set of real numbers, the graph is part of a line.

EXAMPLE 2 Draw the graph of the function defined by the rule $y = -\frac{3}{2}x + 2$ for each of the following domains.

(M) SOLUTION

a. DOMAIN: the set of real numbers

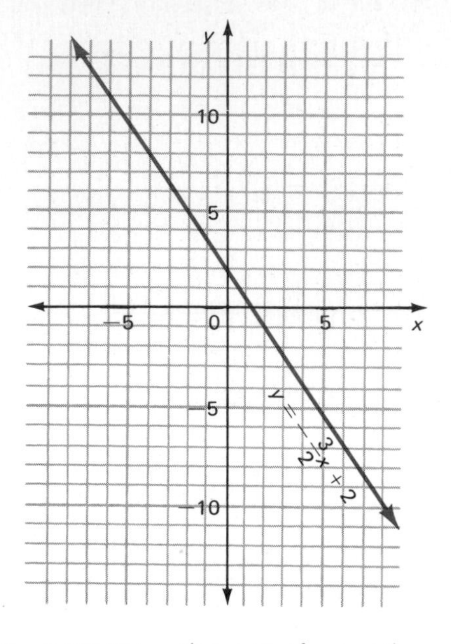

b. DOMAIN: the set of integers

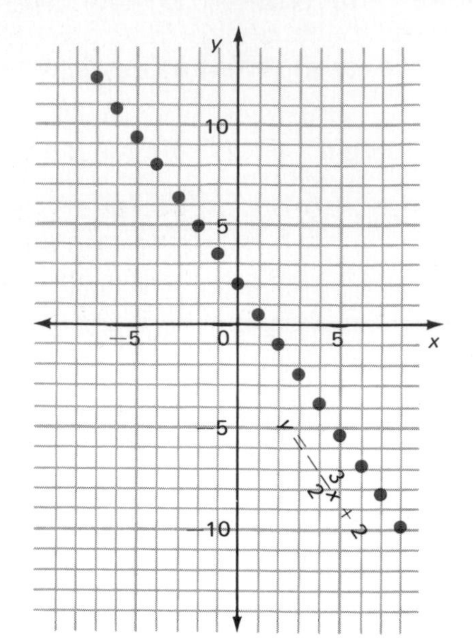

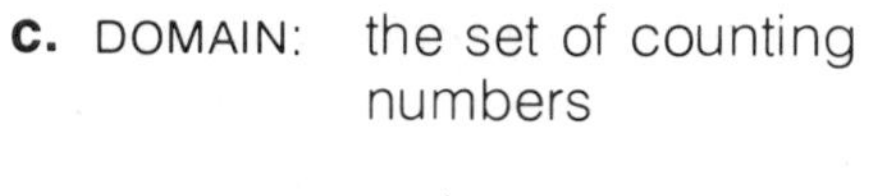
c. DOMAIN: the set of counting numbers

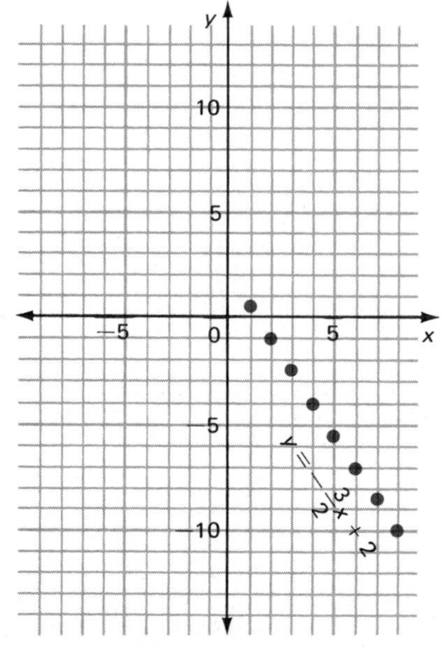

d. DOMAIN: the set of real numbers between 0 and 4 ($0 < x < 4$)

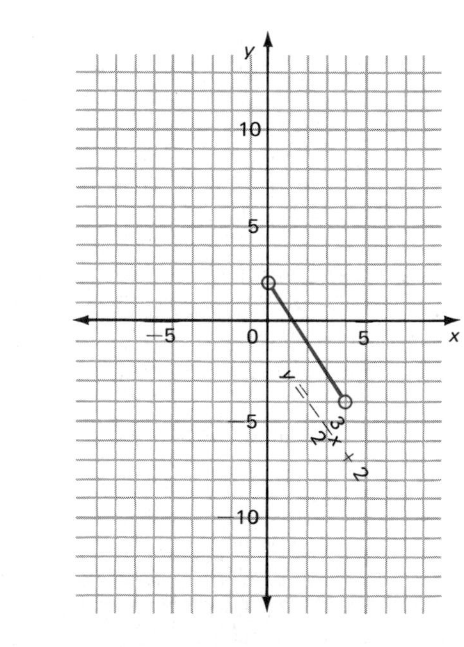

EXAMPLE 3 Graph the function f defined below. What is the range of f?

DOMAIN:	the set of non-negative real numbers ($x \geq 0$)
RULE:	$f(x) = x - 6$

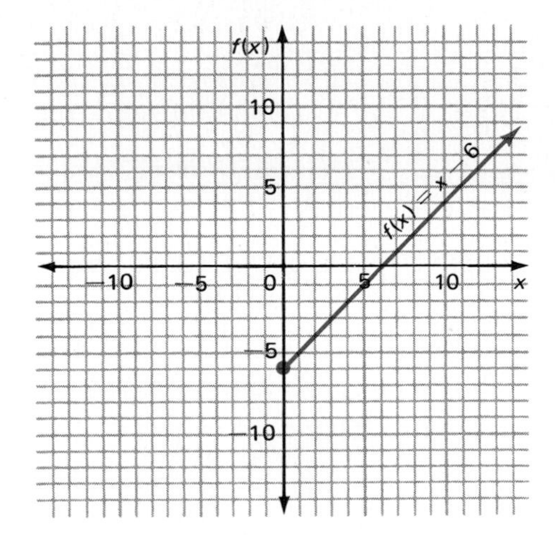

SOLUTION f is a linear function. The graph has slope 1 and y-intercept -6. The domain allows only the non-negative real numbers for x.

From the graph, we see that the range of f is the set of real numbers larger than or equal to -6.

EXAMPLE 4 Graph the function h defined below. What is the range of h?

DOMAIN:	the set of real numbers
RULE:	$h(x) = 5$

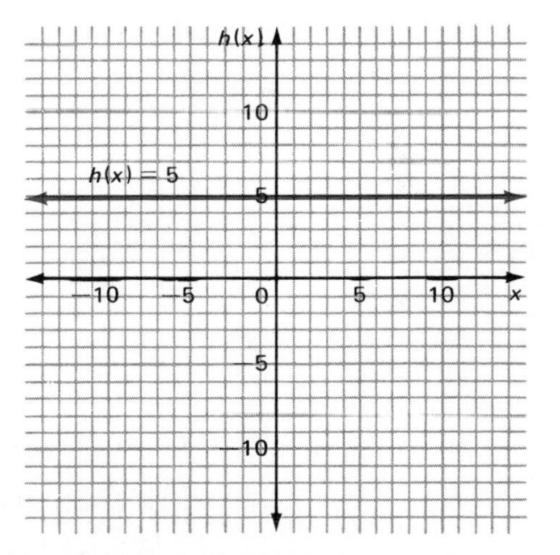

SOLUTION For the function h, every real number is paired with 5. The graph is the line with slope 0 and y-intercept 5.

The range of h is $\{5\}$.

CLASSROOM EXERCISES

Graph each function. What is the range of each?

1. DOMAIN: the set of real numbers
   RULE: $y = \frac{1}{4}x + 1$
2. DOMAIN: the set of integers
   RULE: $y = 2x - 1$
3. DOMAIN: the set of positive real numbers
   RULE: $f(x) = 2x - 1$
4. DOMAIN: the set of real numbers between 0 and 6 inclusive
   RULE: $h(x) = -3$

EXERCISES

A Graph each function.

1. DOMAIN: the set of real numbers
   RULE: $f(x) = 5x - 6$
2. DOMAIN: the set of real numbers
   RULE: $f(x) = -3x + 9$

Graph each function for each of these domains: the set of real numbers, the set of real numbers greater than zero, the set of real numbers between 0 and 5, the set of integers, and the set of counting numbers.

3. $y = 3x$
4. $y = -5x$
5. $y = \frac{1}{3}x - 4$
6. $y = -\frac{3}{4}x + 5$
7. $h(x) = 9$
8. $g(x) = -7$

Graph each function. The domain of each is the set of real numbers greater than or equal to 0. What is the range of each?

9. $f(x) = 2x - 8$
10. $k(x) = -x + 4$
11. $j(x) = 0$

B 12. Many familiar relationships are described by *step functions*. For example, consider a long-distance telephone call that costs 45 cents for 3 minutes or less and 10 cents for each additional minute or less. Complete the graph at the right to show the cost of such a call for up to 8 minutes.

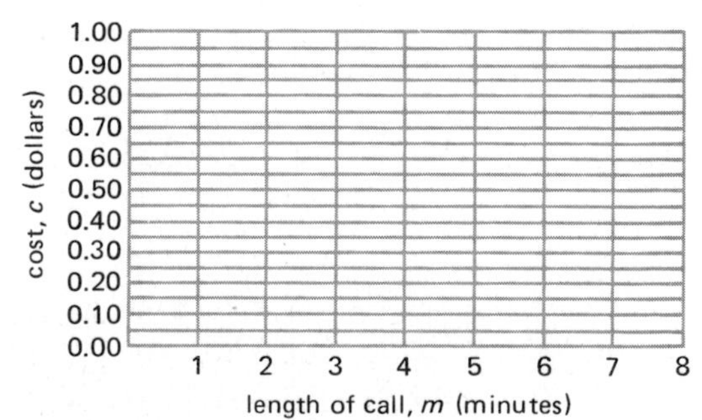

13. The parking rates for a public garage are posted as shown at the right. Draw the graph of a step function that represents the cost of parking in the garage.

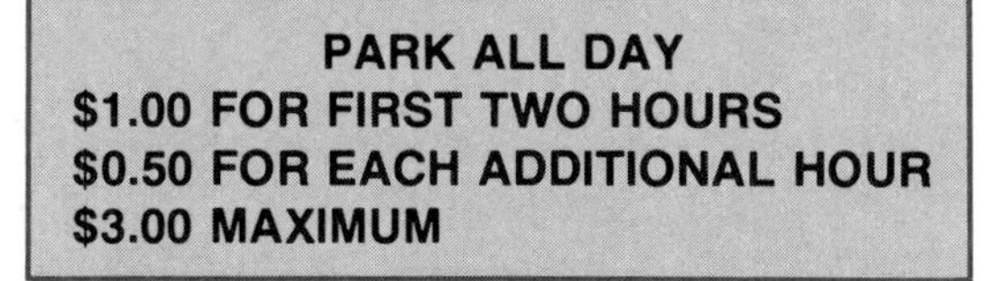

C 14. Graph the function f defined by $f(x) = |x| + 3$.
First, graph f for $x \geq 0$ ($|x| = x$). Then graph f for $x < 0$ ($|x| = -x$).

OBJECTIVES: Distinguish between a function and a relation. Draw the graph of a linear inequality in two variables.

9-11 RELATIONS, GRAPHING INEQUALITIES

A **relation** is any set of ordered pairs. These pairs may be formed from two sets by a rule as may be done for a function. For a relation, however, a member of the first set may be paired with *more than* one member of the second set. Thus, two ordered pairs of a relation may have the same first member.

Every function is a relation, but not all relations are functions.

EXAMPLE 1 Describe the relation defined by this diagram. Use ordered pairs.

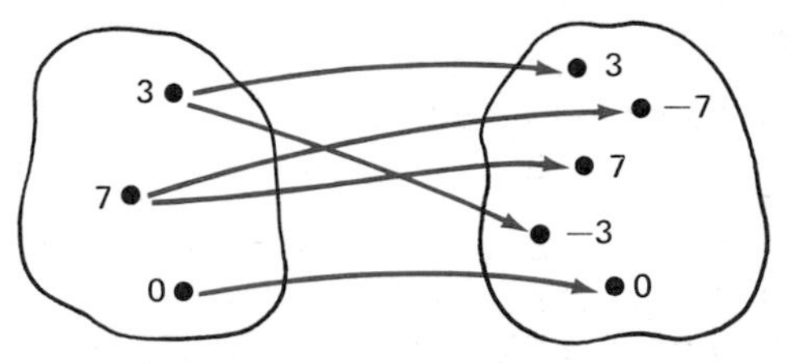

SOLUTION The relation is $\{(3, 3), (3, -3), (7, 7), (7, -7), (0, 0)\}$.

The set of first members of the ordered pairs of a relation is the *domain of the relation*. The set of second members of the ordered pairs is the *range of the relation*. The graph of the ordered pairs of a relation is the *graph of the relation*. Since a relation that is not a function has two or more ordered pairs with the same first member, the graph of the relation will have two or more points in line vertically.

EXAMPLE 2 Name four ordered pairs of this relation. Explain why the relation is not a function.

DOMAIN: the set of positive real numbers
RULE: For any positive real number x, y is a square root of x.

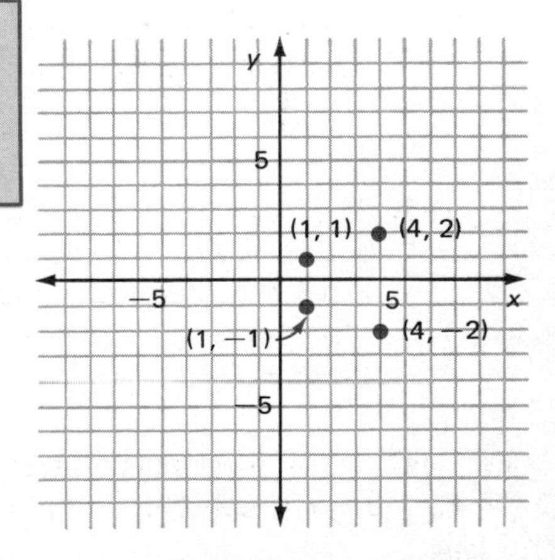

SOLUTION For $x = 1$, y could be 1 or -1.
For $x = 4$, y could be 2 or -2.
Four ordered pairs of this relation are $(1, 1)$, $(1, -1)$, $(4, 2)$, and $(4, -2)$. The relation is not a function since some of its ordered pairs have the same first member. Graphically, some points are in line vertically.

An inequality in two variables defines a relation, but not a function.

EXAMPLE 3 Draw the graph for this relation.

DOMAIN:	the set of real numbers
RULE:	$y > x$

SOLUTION The graph for $y = x$ is the *boundary* of the graph for $y > x$. It is not part of the graph, however. We show this by drawing a broken rule for the line $y = x$.

Then consider, for example, a point such as (2, 2) in the line $y = x$. Any point in the plane directly above (2, 2) has x-coordinate 2 and y-coordinate larger than 2.

In general, any point above the graph for $y = x$ has a y-coordinate larger than its x-coordinate. Therefore, these points make up the graph for $y > x$.

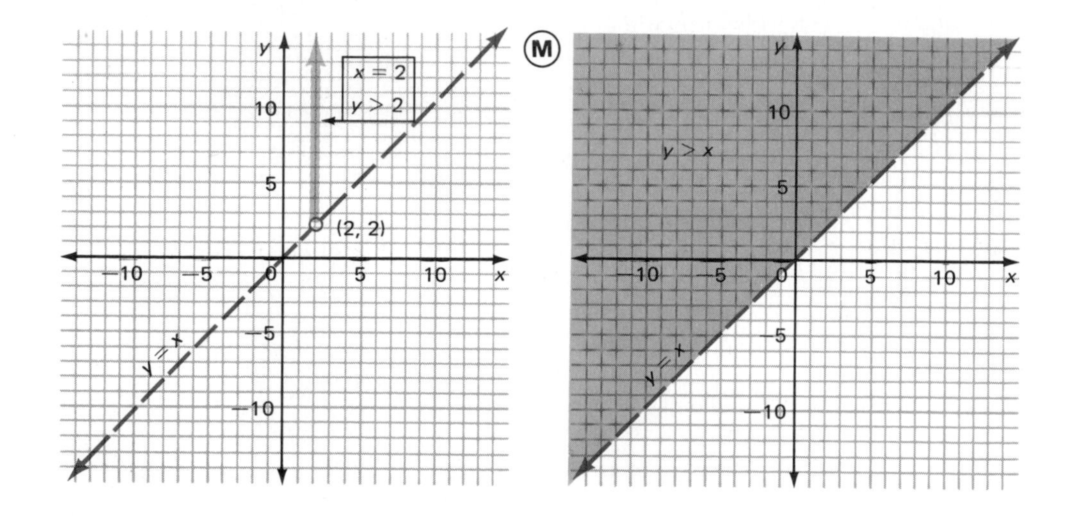

In the graph for Example 3, the broken rule indicates that the line for $y = x$ is not part of the graph for $y > x$. Had the inequality been $y \geq x$, the line $y = x$ would have been part of the graph. The graph would then show an unbroken rule (the graph of $y = x$) as its boundary.

Had the inequality in Example 3 been $y < x$ instead of $y > x$, the graph would have been the points *below* the graph for $y = x$. Had the inequality been $y \leq x$, the graph would have included the line for $y = x$.

When the boundary of the graph for an inequality is a line, the inequality is a *linear inequality*. Such an inequality may be given in the form

$$y > mx + b, \qquad y \geq mx + b, \qquad y < mx + b, \qquad y \leq mx + b,$$

or as an inequality involving the variable x only. In the latter case, the boundary is vertical.

EXAMPLE 4 Draw the graph for the relation defined by the inequality $y - 2x < 6$. The domain is the set of real numbers.

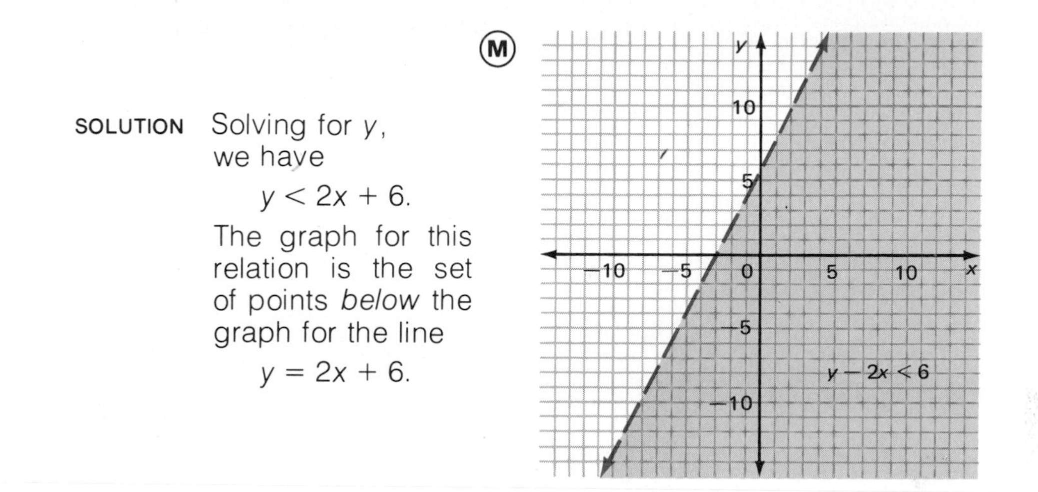

SOLUTION Solving for y, we have

$$y < 2x + 6.$$

The graph for this relation is the set of points *below* the graph for the line

$$y = 2x + 6.$$

EXAMPLE 5 Draw the graph for the relation defined by the inequality $x - y \geq 3$. The domain is the set of real numbers.

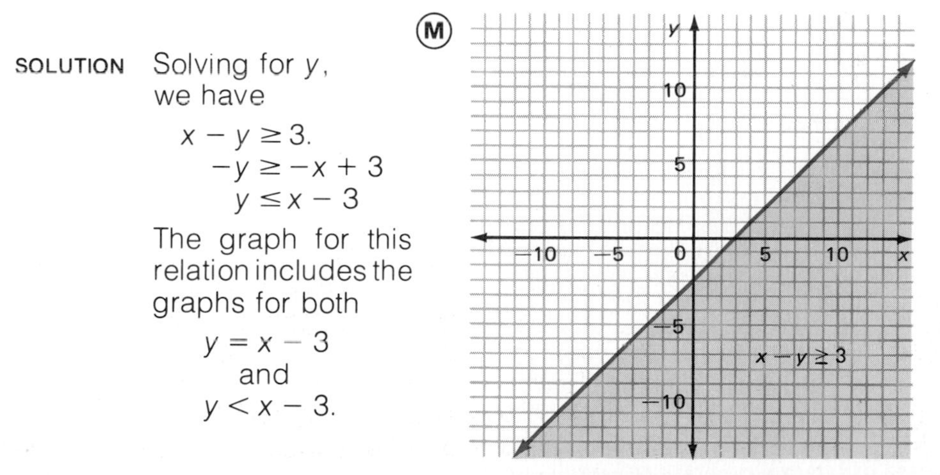

SOLUTION Solving for y, we have

$$x - y \geq 3.$$
$$-y \geq -x + 3$$
$$y \leq x - 3$$

The graph for this relation includes the graphs for both

$$y = x - 3$$
and
$$y < x - 3.$$

Note the reversal of the sense of the inequality when there is multiplication by -1.

Note that the boundary is part of the graph.

THE GRAPH FOR A LINEAR INEQUALITY

- The graph for $y < mx + b$ is the set of points below the graph for the equation $y = mx + b$.
- The graph for $y > mx + b$ is the set of points above the graph for the equation $y = mx + b$.
- The graphs for $y \le mx + b$ and $y \ge mx + b$ include the points of the line $y = mx + b$.

CLASSROOM EXERCISES

1. List the ordered pairs of the relation defined by this diagram.

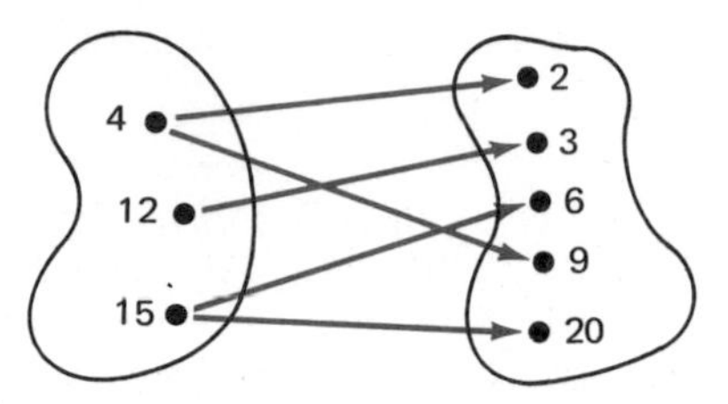

Draw the graph for the relation defined by each inequality. The domain is the set of real numbers.

2. $y \le 2x$
3. $y > 2x$
4. $y - 3x > 9$
5. $y - x \le 4$

EXERCISES

A

1. List the ordered pairs of the relation defined by this diagram.

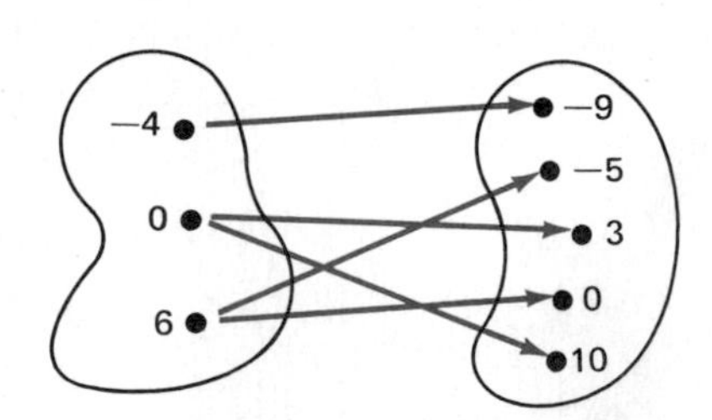

Show why the relation defined by each sentence is not a function.

2. $y > x$
3. $y > 0$
4. $x = 2$
5. $y^2 = x$

Draw the graph for the relation defined by each inequality. The domain is the set of real numbers.

6. $y > 4x$
7. $y < -3x$
8. $y \le 4x$
9. $y \ge -3x$
10. $-4x + y < 2$
11. $5x + y > -3$
12. $3x - y < 6$
13. $-2x - y > -1$
14. $4x - y \le 2$
15. $x + y \le -6$
16. $3x + y \ge 4$
17. $2x + y \le 3$

B

18. $y < \frac{2}{3}x - 6$
19. $y > -\frac{3}{4}x + 12$
20. $4x - 2y \le 8$
21. $12x - 9y \ge -24$
22. $5x - 3y - 21 \le 0$
23. $-12y - 8x + 42 \ge 0$

C

24. Graph $y < x - 3$ and $y < 2 - x$ on the same set of axes. Which part of your graph represents solutions for *both* inequalities?

CHECKING YOUR UNDERSTANDING

WORDS

direct variation
domain of a function
function
graph of a function
linear function
linear inequality
linear variation
range of a function
relation

CONCEPTS

- For two variables that vary directly and represent positive numbers only, an increase or decrease in one results in a proportional increase or decrease in the other. A direct-variation relationship is described by a linear equation of the form $y = kx$. [9-7, 9-8]

- A function is a set of ordered pairs for which each member of one set is paired by a rule with exactly one member of another set. If two ordered pairs have the same first member, they do not belong to the same function. [9-9]

- Except for a vertical line, any line in the coordinate plane, or the equation of any such line, may be used to describe a function known as a linear function. We may apply all that we know about non-vertical lines to our understanding of linear functions. [9-10]

- A relation, as a set of ordered pairs, may include two ordered pairs with the same first member. For a relation described by a linear inequality, the graph includes the set of points on one side of a line. [9-11]

PROCESSES

- Solve problems involving direct or linear variation. [9-7, 9-8]

  1. x and y vary directly.
  $x = 4$ when $y = 9$.
  Find x when $y = 45$.

  2. d and t vary linearly.
  $d = 28$ when $t = 0$.
  $d = 64$ when $t = 6$. Find t when $d = 112$.

- Given the rule for a function, find several of its ordered pairs and draw their graphs. If the function is a linear function, draw the complete graph. [9-9, 9-10]

  3. DOMAIN: The positive real numbers.
  RULE: $y = \frac{1}{2}x - 2$

- Draw the graph for a linear inequality. [9-11]

  4. $y < x + 3$

  5. $x \geq 2 - y$

CHAPTER REVIEW

1. Give the coordinates for each point as an ordered pair. [9-1]

2. Use graph paper. Graph each ordered pair. $M(7, 4)$, $N(-3, 1)$, $P(-8, -2)$, $Q(3, -3)$, $R(5, 0)$, $S(0, 9)$, $T(-6, 0)$, $U(0, -2)$, $V(0, 0)$, $W\left(3\frac{1}{2}, 2\right)$, $Z\left(-1\frac{1}{2}, -1\frac{1}{2}\right)$

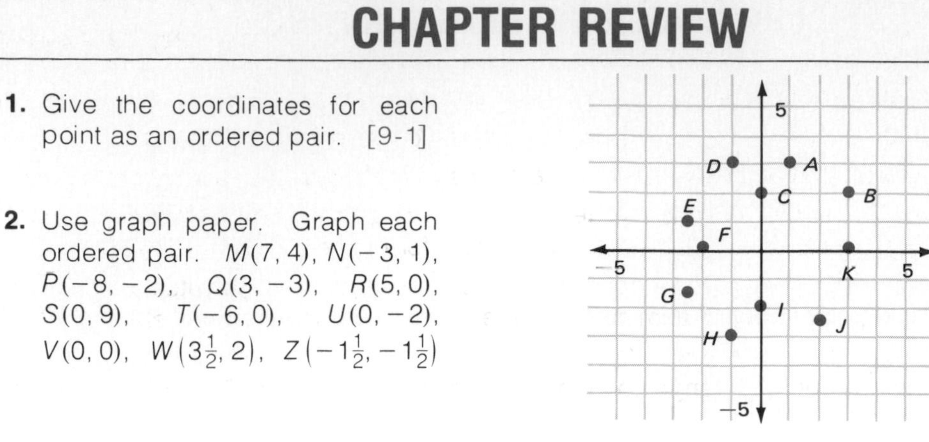

Copy and complete each table. [9-2]

3. $y = x + 4$

x	y
4	?
0	?
−4	?

4. $x + y = 4$

x	y
2	?
0	?
−2	?

5. $y = 3x - 5$

x	y
−3	?
0	?
3	?

6. $2y - 3x = 5$

x	y
1	?
0	?
−1	?

Use a table and show 3 solutions for each equation.

7. $y = -x$

8. $y = \frac{1}{2}x - 3$

9. $x - y = 2$

10. Solve $y = x^2 - 12$ for all integer values of x from -5 to 5 inclusive. Give the solutions in table form.

Graph. [9-3]

11. $y = -x$

12. $2y = 5$

13. $y = -3x - 1$

14. $4x - 3y = 12$

15. $\frac{1}{2}y - 4 + x = 0$

16. $x = y + 8$

17. $y = |x|$

18. $y = 10x - 4$

19. $\frac{2}{3}x - \frac{1}{2}y = 4$

Find the slope of the line that contains each pair of points. [9-4]

20. $(-7, 4)$ and $(2, 3)$

21. $(-5, -4)$ and $(8, -4)$

22. $(-1, 9)$ and $(-9, 1)$

23. $\left(6\frac{1}{4}, 4\right)$ and $\left(-8, -3\frac{1}{2}\right)$

Find the slope of the graph for each equation.

24. $x = 3$

25. $y = -4$

26. $2y = x + 10$

27. $3y + 4x = 24$

28. $\frac{1}{3}y + \frac{1}{2}x = \frac{5}{6}$

Find the slope and y-intercept of the graph for each equation. Draw the graph. [9-5]

29. $y = \frac{1}{3}x - 3$ **30.** $x = 4y + 10$ **31.** $3x + 4y = 8$

32. Write an equation for the line having slope 2 and y-intercept 3. [9-6]

33. Write an equation for the line having slope -2 and containing the point (3, 1).

34. Write an equation for the line containing the points $(-4, 7)$ and $(2, -8)$.

35. Write a linear equation that relates the perimeter (P) of a square to the length (s) of the side of the square. Draw a graph for this relationship. [9-7]

36. The rate for a long-distance telephone call is \$0.37 for the first 3 minutes and \$0.19 for each additional minute. Write a linear equation for this relationship. [9-8]

37. Give the domain and the range for the function defined by $y = 3x - 1$, $x \geq 0$. [9-9]

For the function f defined by $f(x) = -4x + 5$, find

38. $f(2)$ **39.** $f(-3)$ **40.** $f(0)$

41. Give 5 ordered pairs for the function defined by $f(x) = x^2 - 1$. Draw the graph.

For each domain, draw the graph for the function defined by $y = 2x + 3$. [9-10]

42. the real numbers **43.** the even integers **44.** the positive integers **45.** $-4 \leq x < 4$

Graph. [9-11]

46. $x > -5$ **47.** $y \geq \frac{1}{2}x - 2$ **48.** $3x - 2y < 6$

CAPSULE REVIEW

Write the letter of the best response.

1. Which ordered pair has its graph in the x-axis, but not in the y-axis?

a. (0, 0) **b.** (3, 0) **c.** (0, 3) **d.** (3, 3) **e.** $(-3, -3)$

2. Which ordered pair is a solution for $y = -4x + 5$?

a. (0, 0) **b.** (1, 9) **c,** (1, 1) **d.** $(-1, 1)$ **e.** (5, 0)

3. The slope of the line containing the points (2, 5) and $(-3, -5)$ is

a. $\frac{1}{2}$ **b.** 10 **c.** 0 **d.** $\frac{2}{3}$ **e.** 2

4. The y-intercept of the graph for $-2y - 5x = 10$

a. -5 **b.** 10 **c.** $-\frac{5}{2}$ **d.** $\frac{5}{2}$ **e.** 5

5. Which defines a linear function?

a. $y = x^2$ **b.** $xy = 12$ **c.** $\frac{y}{x} = 4$ **d.** $x - y = -1$ **e.** $x^2 + y^2 = 16$

6. Which is an equation for the line having slope 1 and y-intercept 0?

a. $y = 1$ **b.** $y = 0$ **c.** $y = x$ **d.** $x = 0$ **e.** $x = 1$

7. An equation for the line containing the points (2, 3) and (3, 6) is

a. $y = 2x + 3$ **b.** $y = 2x - 3$ **c.** $y = \frac{1}{3}x - 3$ **d.** $y = 3x - 3$

8. Which ordered pair is a solution for $y > -x - 2$?

a. $(3, -6)$ **b.** $(-4, 1)$ **c.** $(0, 0)$ **d.** $(1, -8)$ **e.** $(2, -4)$

9. Which does *not* define a function?

a. $y = x$ **b.** $y = x^2$ **c.** $x = y^2$ **d.** $xy = 10$ **e.** $y = 2$

CHAPTER TEST

1. Where in the coordinate plane is the point which corresponds to the ordered pair (8, 2)?

2. Which ordered pair is associated with the point that is 10 units to the left and 6 units above the origin?

3. Find a solution of $x^2 + y = 10$ for $x = 5$.

4. Give the degree of the equation $x^3 + 4x^2 + 2y = 5$.

5. Graph $x + y = 5$.

6. Graph $x = 3$.

7. Find the slope of the line that contains the points (1, 2) and (2, 5).

8. Find the slope of the line that contains the points (5, 5) and (7, 1).

9. Find the slope of the graph for $y = \frac{1}{2}x + 3$.

10. Find the y-intercept of the graph for $y = 4x - 3$.

11. Write an equation for the line having slope 3 and y-intercept 10.

12. Write an equation for the line having slope 2 and containing point (1, 1).

13. Each can of soup costs $0.35. Write an equation that relates the cost (C) and the number (n) of cans purchased.

14. The mass of a washer is 7 grams. Write an equation that relates the number (n) of grams and the number (w) of washers.

15. Fernando is paid $100 plus 8% of his sales. Write an equation that relates Fernando's income (I) and his sales (S).

16. A plumber charges $15, plus $20 an hour for a service call. Write an equation that relates the total charge (C) and the number (h) of hours.

17. The domain of a function is {4, 9} and the rule is $F(x) = x^2$. Give the range of the function.

18. The equation for a function is $g(x) = 3x + 1$. Give the value for $g(2)$.

19. Graph the function $f(x) = x - 2$ for the domain {0, 1, 2, 3, 4}.

20. Graph the function $f(x) = -x + 1$ for which the domain is the set of real numbers.

21. Is $y < x + 2$ a function?

22. Graph the relation $x + y < 4$.

Write the letter of the best response.

23. A point is 3 units to the right and 6 units below (0, 0). Its coordinates are

a. $(-3, -6)$ **b.** $(-3, 6)$ **c.** $(3, -6)$ **d.** $(6, -3)$ **e.** $(-6, 3)$

24. When 3 is used for x, the solution for $x^2 + xy = 15$ is

a. (3, 1) **b.** (3, 2) **c.** (3, 3) **d.** (3, 4) **e.** (3, 5)

25. Which line represents the graph of $y - x = 4$?

a. *a* **b.** *b* **c.** *c* **d.** *d* **e.** *e*

26. The slope of the line that contains (2, 2) and (4, 8) is

a. 2 **b.** 3 **c.** 6 **d.** -2 **e.** -3

27. The slope and y-intercept for $y = -2x + 4$ are

a. -2 and 4 **b.** -2 and -4 **c.** 2 and 4
d. 2 and 2 **e.** -2 and -2

28. Which is an equation for the line having slope 1 and containing the point (2, 3)?

a. $y = 2x + 3$ **b.** $y = 2x - 1$ **c.** $y = x - 1$ **d.** $y = x + 1$

29. Heather walks 5 kilometers an hour. Which equation relates the distance (d) and the number (h) of hours that she walks?

a. $d = 5h$ **b.** $d = \frac{h}{5}$ **c.** $d = h + 5$ **d.** $d = h - 5$ **e.** $d = 5 - h$

30. Ryan is paid \$3 plus \$2 an hour for mowing lawns. Which equation relates Ryan's earnings (E) and the number (h) of hours worked?

a. $E = 5h$ **b.** $E = 3h + 2$ **c.** $E = 2h + 3$ **d.** $E = 5h + 2$ **e.** $E = 3h + 5$

31. An equation that defines a function is $f(x) = x^2 + 1$. What does $f(3)$ equal?

a. 1 **b.** 4 **c.** 7 **d.** 10 **e.** 16

32. Which is the graph of the function defined by $g(x) = \frac{1}{2}x + 2$?

a. *a* **b.** *b* **c.** *c* **d.** *d* **e.** *e*

33. Which is the inequality for the graph?

a. $y > x + 4$ **b.** $y > x - 4$
c. $y < x + 4$ **d.** $y < x - 4$

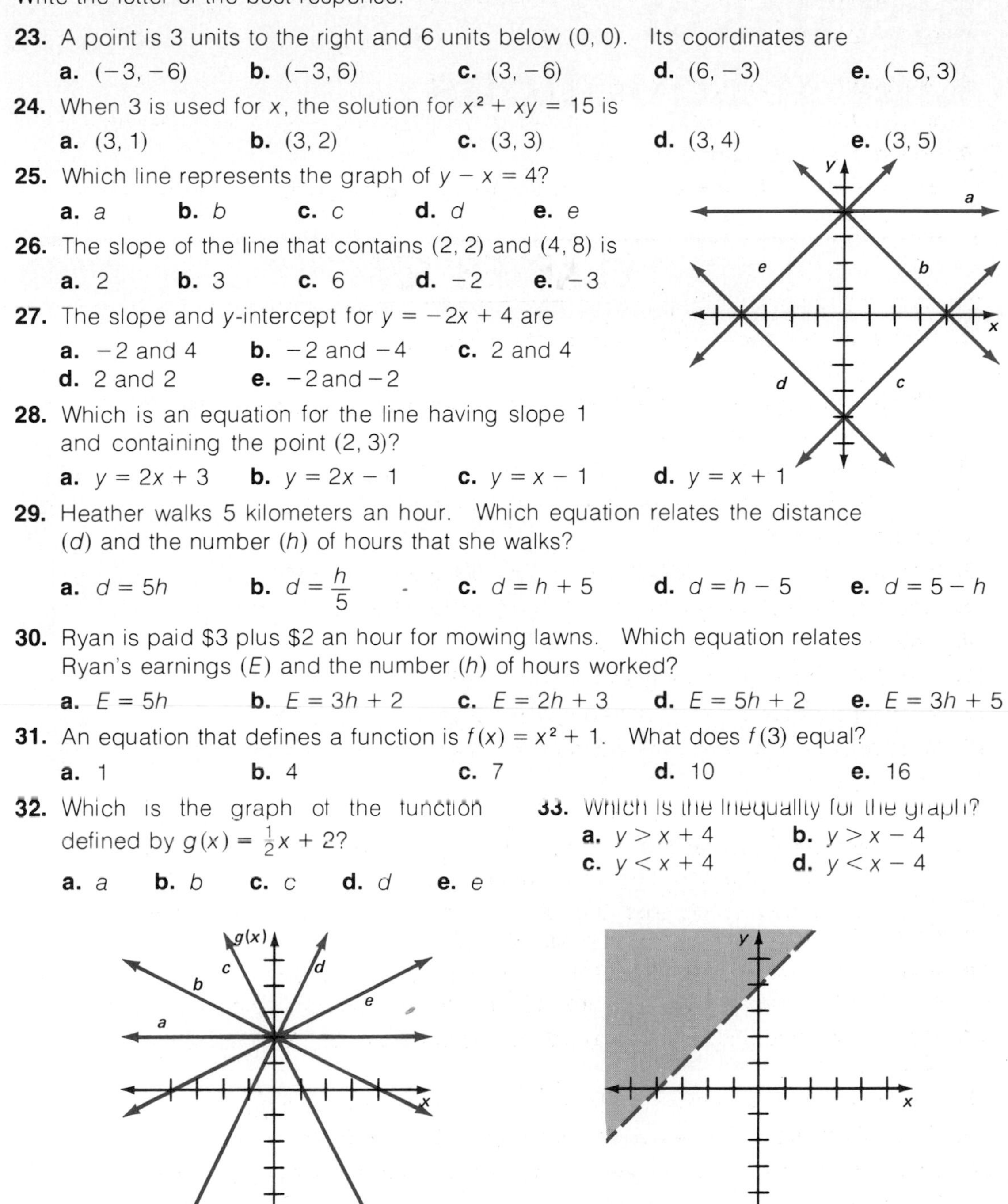

CHAPTER 10

Systems of Linear Equations

The machines used in transportation are continually changing. Highly-skilled workers who service the machines keep in touch with the changes. In some respects their schooling never ends. Those who developed good work and study habits in school have found those habits to be advantages that transfer naturally and rewardingly to their careers.

OBJECTIVES: Graph and solve systems of two linear equations.
Graph systems of two linear inequalities.

10-1 SOLVING A SYSTEM OF LINEAR EQUATIONS BY GRAPHING

A pair of linear equations in two variables is an example of a **system** of equations.

$$\begin{cases} x + y = 12 \\ x - y = 4 \end{cases}$$

The **solution** of such a system is the solution or solutions common to both equations. Graphically, each solution corresponds to a point of intersection.

EXAMPLE 1 Solve $\begin{cases} x + y = 12 \\ x - y = 4 \end{cases}$ by graphing.

Ⓜ SOLUTION $x + y = 12$ $\quad$ $x - y = 4$

x	y
0	12
12	0
6	6

x	y
0	−4
4	0
6	2

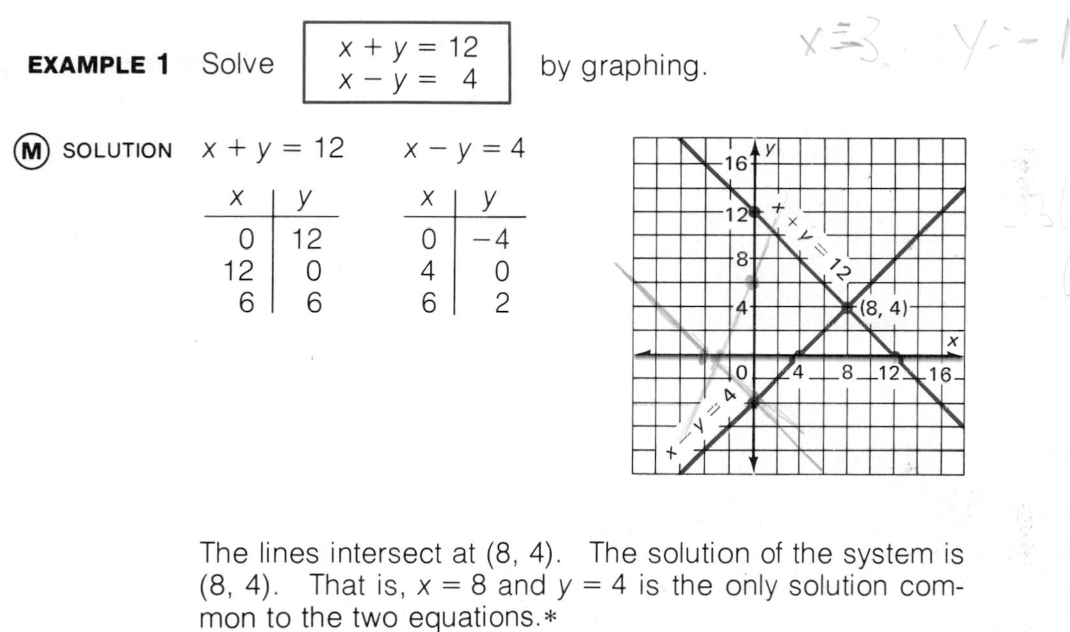

The lines intersect at (8, 4). The solution of the system is (8, 4). That is, $x = 8$ and $y = 4$ is the only solution common to the two equations.*

CHECK

$x + y = 12$ | $x - y = 4$
$8 + 4 \stackrel{?}{=} 12$ | $8 - 4 \stackrel{?}{=} 4$
$12 = 12$ ✓ | $4 = 4$ ✓

*Two equations are *consistent* if they have at least one solution in common. If they have exactly one solution in common, they are *independent*. If they have all solutions in common, they are *dependent*. If they have no solutions in common, they are *inconsistent*. The equations in Example 1 are consistent and independent.

EXAMPLE 2 Solve $\boxed{\begin{array}{l} x - y = -2 \\ x - y = -5 \end{array}}$ by graphing.

SOLUTION $x - y = -2$

x	y
0	2
−2	0
4	6

$x - y = -5$

x	y
0	5
−5	0
−3	2

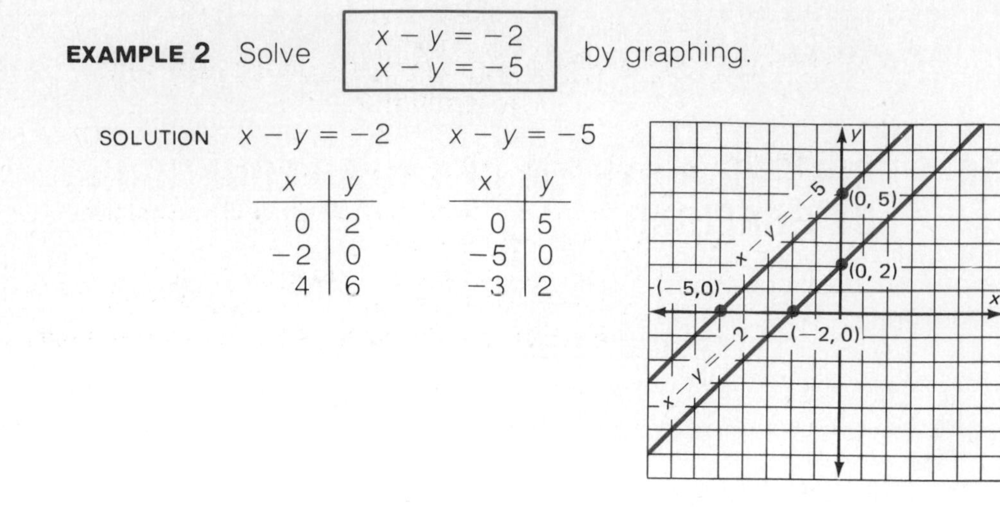

The lines appear to be parallel. That they are parallel can be confirmed by checking that their slopes are equal. The lines have no point in common. There is no solution of the system.

EXAMPLE 3 Solve $\boxed{\begin{array}{l} 2x + 3y = 6 \\ 6x + 9y = 18 \end{array}}$ by graphing.

SOLUTION $2x + 3y = 6$

x	y
0	2
3	0
−3	4

$6x + 9y = 18$

x	y
6	−2
−6	6
0	2

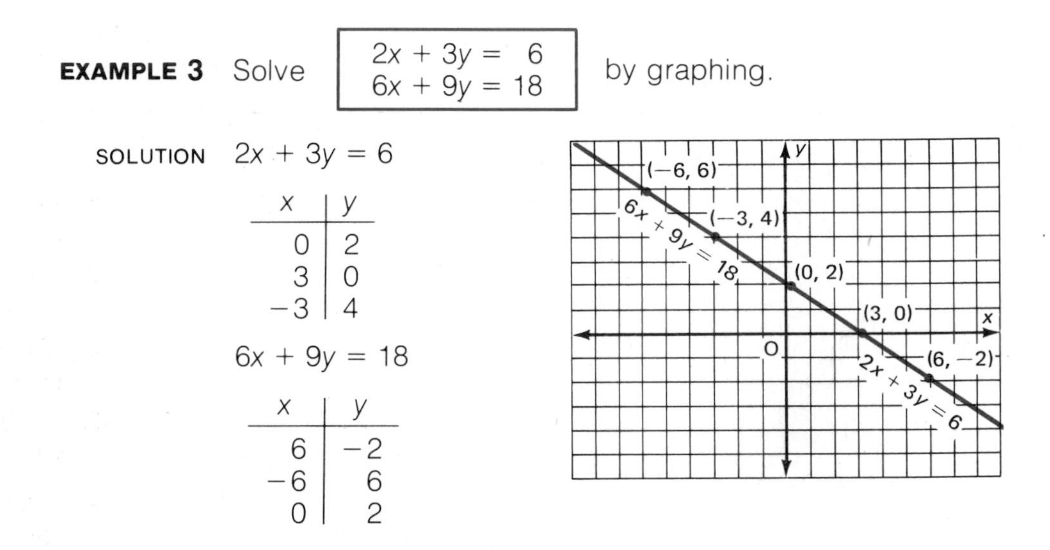

The graphs for the two equations are the same line. The solutions of the system, then, are in the ordered pairs that are solutions of either equation. The system has infinitely many solutions.

> **SOLVING A SYSTEM OF TWO LINEAR EQUATIONS BY GRAPHING**
>
> 1. Graph both equations on the same pair of axes.
> 2. If the graphs intersect in a point, read the coordinates of the point for the solution of the system.
>   If the graphs are parallel, state that there is no solution.
>   If the same graph results for both equations, state that the solutions of the system are the same as the solutions of each equation.

CLASSROOM EXERCISES

Solve by graphing. Check your solution.

1. $x + y = 5$
   $x - y = 1$
2. $x + y = -4$
   $x + y = 6$
3. $3x + 6y = 12$
   $x + 2y = 4$

EXERCISES

A Solve by graphing. Check your solution.

1. $x + y = 8$
   $x - y = 6$
2. $x - y = 3$
   $x + y = 15$
3. $x + y = -4$
   $x - y = -8$
4. $x - y = -9$
   $x + y = -1$
5. $x - y = 7$
   $x - y = 12$
6. $x + y = -9$
   $x + y = -3$
7. $y = 3x - 4$
   $y = -2x + 6$
8. $y = 2x - 1$
   $y = -x + 8$
9. $2x + y = 5$
   $8x + 4y = 20$
10. $3x - 9y = -6$
    $x - 3y = -2$
11. $x = -2$
    $y - 3 = 0$
12. $x - 5 = 0$
    $y = -3$

B

13. $3x - 2y = -9$
    $5x + y = -2$
14. $3x - 2y = -5$
    $5x + 2y = -19$
15. $6x - 4y = 8$
    $15x - 10y = 20$
16. $2x + 3y = 22$
    $x - 4y = 0$
17. $4x - 3y = 5$
    $5x - 4y = 7$
18. $-8x + 12y = 32$
    $6x - 9y = 18$

C

19. $y - 1 = 6x$
    $2x - 11 = 3y$
20. $3x = 7 - y$
    $x + 3 = -2y$
21. $14 + 3x = 2y$
    $64 - 6y = -3x$

10-2 SOLVING A LINEAR SYSTEM BY ADDITION OR SUBTRACTION

It is not always efficient and is seldom accurate to solve a system by graphing. Sometimes a pair of linear equations can be solved more easily by adding or subtracting the members of the equations. By doing this when the coefficients for one variable are opposite numbers or the same number, you obtain one equation in one variable—something you already know how to solve.

EXAMPLE 1 Solve $\begin{array}{|r|}\hline 3x + y = 7 \\ x - y = 1 \\ \hline\end{array}$

Find the ordered pair (x, y) that is a solution for both equations.

SOLUTION Solve for x by *addition*.

$$\begin{aligned} 3x + y &= 7 \\ \underline{x - y} &= \underline{1} \\ \text{Add.} \quad 4x \quad &= 8 \\ x &= 2 \end{aligned}$$

Then solve for y. Replace x by 2 in either equation.

$$\begin{aligned} 3x + y &= 7 \\ 3(2) + y &= 7 \\ 6 + y &= 7 \\ y &= 1 \end{aligned} \qquad \begin{aligned} x - y &= 1 \\ 2 - y &= 1 \\ -y &= -1 \\ y &= 1 \end{aligned}$$

The solution is (2, 1).

CHECK

$$\begin{aligned} 3x + y &= 7 \\ 3(2) + 1 &\stackrel{?}{=} 7 \\ 7 &= 7 \checkmark \end{aligned} \qquad \begin{aligned} x - y &= 1 \\ 2 - 1 &\stackrel{?}{=} 1 \\ 1 &= 1 \checkmark \end{aligned}$$

EXAMPLE 2 Solve $\begin{array}{|r|}\hline x - y = 5 \\ 2x - y = 14 \\ \hline\end{array}$

SOLUTION Solve for x by *subtraction*.

$$\begin{aligned} x - y &= 5 \\ \underline{2x - y} &= \underline{14} \\ \text{Subtract.} \quad -x \quad &= -9 \\ x &= 9 \end{aligned}$$

Then solve for y. Replace x by 9 in either equation.

$$\begin{aligned} x - y &= 5 \\ 9 - y &= 5 \\ y &= 4 \end{aligned} \qquad \begin{aligned} 2x - y &= 14 \\ 2(9) - y &= 14 \\ 18 - y &= 14 \\ y &= 4 \end{aligned}$$

The solution is (9, 4).

CHECK

$$\begin{aligned} x - y &= 5 \\ 9 - 4 &\stackrel{?}{=} 5 \\ 5 &= 5 \checkmark \end{aligned} \qquad \begin{aligned} 2x - y &= 14 \\ 2(9) - 4 &\stackrel{?}{=} 14 \\ 14 &= 14 \checkmark \end{aligned}$$

Sometimes it is necessary to first multiply the members of one equation by some number to obtain a system in which the coefficients for one variable are the same or opposite numbers.

EXAMPLE 3 Solve

$$\boxed{\begin{aligned} -3x + 4y &= 29 \\ 5x + 2y &= -5 \end{aligned}}$$

SOLUTION Solve for x by *subtraction*. To do this, first multiply the members of the second equation by 2.

$$\begin{array}{lrcr} & -3x + 4y &=& 29 \\ M_2 & 10x + 4y &=& -10 \\ \hline \text{Subtract.} & -13x &=& 39 \\ & x &=& -3 \end{array}$$

Solve for y. Replace x by -3 in either equation.

$$\begin{array}{rcl|rcl} -3x + 4y &=& 29 & 10x + 4y &=& -10 \\ -3(-3) + 4y &=& 29 & 10(-3) + 4y &=& -10 \\ 9 + 4y &=& 29 & -30 + 4y &=& -10 \\ 4y &=& 20 & 4y &=& 20 \\ y &=& 5 & y &=& 5 \end{array}$$

The solution is $(-3, 5)$.

CHECK The check is left for the student.

Sometimes it is necessary to first multiply the members of *both* equations by numbers that will provide the same or opposite coefficients for one variable.

EXAMPLE 4 Solve

$$\boxed{\begin{aligned} 2x + 3y &- 7 \\ 3x + 5y &= 12 \end{aligned}}$$

SOLUTION Solve for y by *addition*. To do this, first multiply the members of the first equation by -3. Also, multiply the members of the second equation by 2.

$$\begin{array}{lrcr} M_{-3} & -6x - 9y &=& -21 \\ M_2 & 6x + 10y &=& 24 \\ \hline & y &=& 3 \end{array}$$

Solve for x. Replacing y by 3 in either equation gives $x = -1$.

The solution is $(-1, 3)$.

CHECK The check is left for the student.

SOLVING A SYSTEM OF TWO LINEAR EQUATIONS BY ADDITION OR SUBTRACTION

1. Write both equations in standard form, $ax + by = c$.
2. If necessary, multiply both members of one or both equations by the numbers that will provide opposite or the same coefficients for one of the variables.
3. Add or subtract the members of the resulting equations to eliminate one of the variables.
4. Solve the new equation for the remaining variable.
5. Replace the variable in one of the equations involving both variables and solve for the other variable.
6. Check the solution in the original equations.

CLASSROOM EXERCISES

Solve by addition or subtraction. Check your solution.

1. $x - y = -5$; $3x + y = -3$

2. $x - 2y = 10$; $x + y = 4$

3. $4x - y = 10$; $2x + 3y = 12$

4. $2x + 3y = 20$; $3x + 2y = 15$

EXERCISES

A Solve by addition or subtraction. Check your solution.

1. $2x - y = -4$; $x + y = -2$

2. $x - y = 1$; $2x + y = -10$

3. $x - 3y = 6$; $4x + 3y = 9$

4. $4x + 7y = -14$; $6x - 7y = 84$

5. $x + 4y = 4$; $x - 2y = -2$

6. $2x + y = 12$; $3x + y = 17$

7. $3x + y = -2$; $5x + 4y = -1$

8. $6x + y = 9$; $9x + 8y = -45$

9. $-5x + 4y = 4$; $4x - 7y = 12$

10. $7x - 3y = 1$; $9x - 4y = 2$

11. $4x + 3y = 2$; $3x + 5y = -4$

12. $3x + 5y = 4$; $2x + 3y = 4$

B

13. $2x - y - 2 = 0$; $3x + 2y + 25 = 0$

14. $\frac{1}{3}x + \frac{1}{4}y = 10$; $\frac{1}{3}x - \frac{1}{2}y = 4$

15. $0.04x + 0.06y = 26$; $x + y = 500$

16. $6x - 6 = 10y$; $4 - 15y = -9x$

C Solve for x and y.

17. $x = -4y + k$; $-2y = 2k + 3x$

18. $2mx - 5ny = 12mn$; $-3mx + 7ny = 25mn$

19. $px + qy = r$; $px - qy = s$

USING GRAPHS TO SOLVE PROBLEMS

Sometimes a problem can be solved more easily by graphing than with equations.

EXAMPLE Jim can mow a lawn in $1\frac{1}{2}$ hours. Willie takes 2 hours. How long will it take both boys together to mow the lawn?

SOLUTION Distance OA represents the whole job of mowing. Distance OB represents two hours. AD shows that Jim does the job in $1\frac{1}{2}$ hours. OC shows that it takes Willie 2 hours. Point E suggests that both do the job in about 52 minutes with EF as Jim's part and EG as Willie's part.

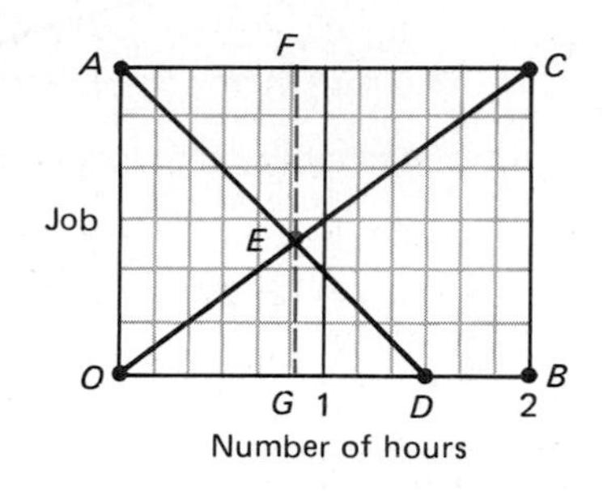

Now try these.

1. One airplane flies from St. Louis to Pittsburgh, a distance of 700 km, in 4 hours. Another flies from Pittsburgh to St. Louis in 3 hours. They leave at the same time. How soon will they pass each other? How far will they be from Pittsburgh? Find answers by copying and completing the graph shown here.

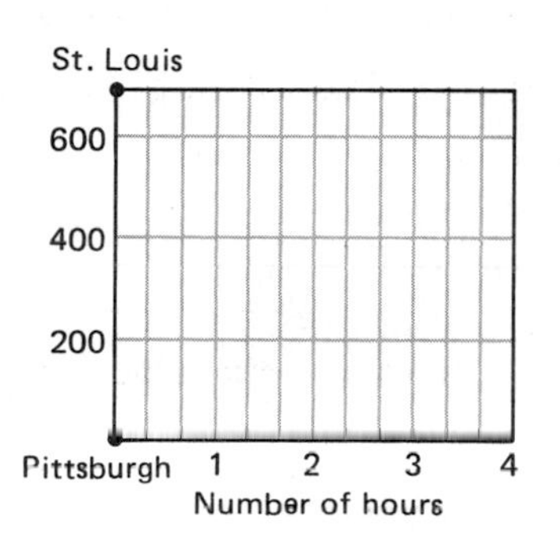

2. A bank teller can count the money from a drawer in 18 minutes. If the teller is helped by another teller, they can count it in 8 minutes. By drawing a graph, find how long it would take the second teller working alone to count the money.
3. One pump can fill a tank in 5 hours and another can fill the same tank in 4 hours. How long will it take both pumps to fill the tank?
4. One automobile traveling 56 kilometers per hour leaves Toronto at 8 A.M. Another automobile traveling 80 kilometers per hour on the same road leaves Toronto at 10 A.M. How soon will the second automobile overtake the first?
5. One pump can fill a tank in 6 hours and another pump can empty the same tank in $2\frac{1}{2}$ hours. How long will it take to empty a full tank if both pumps are working?

10-3 SOLVING A LINEAR SYSTEM BY SUBSTITUTION

A variable can be eliminated and a system solved by a process called *substitution*. One of the equations is solved for x (or y). Then x (or y) is replaced in the other equation. The new equation will involve only the other variable y (or x).

EXAMPLE 1 Solve
$$\boxed{\begin{array}{l} x + 2y = 20 \\ x = y + 2 \end{array}}$$

SOLUTION From the second equation, $x = y + 2$.
Replace x by $y + 2$ in the first equation.

$$\begin{aligned} \boxed{x} + 2y &= 20 \\ \boxed{y + 2} + 2y &= 20 \\ 3y + 2 &= 20 \\ 3y &= 18 \\ y &= 6 \end{aligned}$$

Replace y by 6 in either equation.

$$\begin{aligned} x + 2y &= 20 \\ x + 2(6) &= 20 \\ x + 12 &= 20 \\ x &= 8 \end{aligned} \qquad \Bigg| \qquad \begin{aligned} x &= y + 2 \\ x &= 6 + 2 \\ x &= 8 \end{aligned}$$

The solution is (8, 6).

CHECK

$$\begin{aligned} x + 2y &= 20 \\ 8 + 2(6) &\stackrel{?}{=} 20 \\ 20 &= 20 \ \checkmark \end{aligned} \qquad \Bigg| \qquad \begin{aligned} x &= y + 2 \\ 8 &\stackrel{?}{=} 6 + 2 \\ 8 &= 8 \ \checkmark \end{aligned}$$

EXAMPLE 2 Solve
$$\boxed{\begin{array}{l} 3x - 4y = 5 \\ x + 7y = 10 \end{array}}$$

SOLUTION Solve the second equation for x.

$$\begin{aligned} x + 7y &= 10 \\ x &= 10 - 7y \end{aligned}$$

Replace x by $10 - 7y$ in the first equation.

$$\begin{aligned} 3\boxed{x} - 4y &= 5 \\ 3\boxed{(10 - 7y)} - 4y &= 5 \\ 30 - 21y - 4y &= 5 \\ -25y &= -25 \\ y &= 1 \end{aligned}$$

Replace y by 1 in either equation.

$3x - 4y = 5$	$x + 7y = 10$
$3x - 4(1) = 5$	$x + 7(1) = 10$
$3x = 9$	$x = 3$
$x = 3$	

The solution is (3, 1).

CHECK The check is left for the student.

EXAMPLE 3 Solve

$$\begin{aligned} 5x + 3y &= -5 \\ 4x - 5y &= 33 \end{aligned}$$

SOLUTION Solve the first equation for x.

$$\begin{aligned} 5x + 3y &= -5 \\ 5x &= -3y - 5 \\ x &= -\tfrac{3}{5}y - 1 \end{aligned}$$

Replace x by $-\frac{3}{5}y - 1$ in the second equation.

$$\begin{aligned} 4\boxed{x} - 5y &= 33 \\ 4\boxed{\left(-\tfrac{3}{5}y - 1\right)} - 5y &= 33 \\ -\tfrac{12}{5}y - 4 - 5y &= 33 \\ -\tfrac{37}{5}y &= 37 \\ y &= -5 \end{aligned}$$

Replacing y by -5 in either equation gives $x = 2$.
The solution is $(2, -5)$.

CHECK The check is left for the student.

SOLVING A SYSTEM OF TWO LINEAR EQUATIONS BY SUBSTITUTION

1. Solve either equation for x (or y).
2. Replace x (or y) by the appropriate expression in the other equation.
3. Solve the resulting equation.
4. Use this number in either equation, and solve for the other variable.
5. Check the solution in both equations.

CLASSROOM EXERCISES

Solve by substitution. Check your solution.

1. $y = 2x + 4$
   $3x + y = 9$
2. $x - 2y = 11$
   $3x + 5y = -11$
3. $6x + 5y = 2$
   $5x + 3y = 4$

EXERCISES

A Solve by substitution. Check your solution.

1. $2x - 3y = 1$
   $x = y + 2$
2. $y = 2x + 3$
   $3x + 2y = 20$
3. $5x - y = 9$
   $x = y - 3$
4. $y = 2x - 2$
   $3x + 2y = -25$
5. $5x + 7y = 1$
   $x + 4y = -5$
6. $3x + 4y = 18$
   $-5x + y = -7$
7. $3x + y = -5$
   $6x + 2y = -10$
8. $x - 2y = 3$
   $-3x + 4y = -10$

B

9. $4x + 7y = 9$
   $6x + 5y = -3$
10. $8x + 5y = 2$
    $7x + 4y = 1$
11. $9x - 3y = 3$
    $6x - 2y = 2$
12. $8x - 4y = 12$
    $3y - 6x = 15$
13. $x + y = 600$
    $0.25x + 0.75y = 390$
14. $\frac{1}{3}x - \frac{1}{2}y = 11$
    $3x + y = 0$
15. $6x + 2y = 3$
    $x - y = -\frac{1}{6}$
16. $3x - 4y = 0$
    $4x - 5y - 2 = 0$

C Solve for x and y.

17. $ax - by = 0$
    $ax + 2by = c$
18. $hx + jy = k$
    $mx + ny = p$
19. $abx + acy = k$
    $bdx + cdy = j$

NUMBERS—PERFECT AND OTHERWISE

A number is classified as *deficient*, *sufficient*, or *perfect* based on the sum of its factors. If the sum of the factors is less than twice the number, the number is deficient. If the sum of the factors is greater than twice the number, the number is sufficient. Otherwise the number is perfect.

Number	Factors	Sum of Factors	Type
8	1, 2, 4, 8	15	deficient
18	1, 2, 3, 6, 9, 18	39	sufficient
28	1, 2, 4, 7, 14, 28	56	perfect

1. Classify the numbers from 1 to 10 as deficient, perfect or sufficient.
2. Classify 11 through 20.
3. There is one one-digit perfect number and one two-digit perfect number. How many three-digit perfect numbers are there?

10-4 SIMPLIFYING, THEN SOLVING A LINEAR SYSTEM

Equations in some systems will contain fractions or parentheses. These should be simplified to the standard form, $ax + by = c$. Then the system can be solved by addition or subtraction.

EXAMPLE 1 Solve

$$\frac{5x}{6} = 7 - \frac{y}{4}$$
$$4 + \frac{y}{8} = \frac{2x}{3} + 1$$

SOLUTION Simplify the first equation.

$$\frac{5}{6}x = 7 - \frac{y}{4}$$

M_{12} $$10x = 84 - 3y$$

Simplify the second equation.

$$4 + \frac{y}{8} = \frac{2x}{3} + 1$$

$$3 + \frac{y}{8} = \frac{2x}{3}$$

M_{24} $$72 + 3y = 16x$$

Write the equations in standard form, $ax + by = c$.

$$\begin{array}{rcr} 10x + 3y & = & 84 \\ 16x - 3y & = & 72 \\ \hline 26x & = & 156 \end{array}$$

Add.

$$x = 6$$

The first steps suggest that equations should be *cleared* of fractions first.

Replace x by 6 in $10x + 3y = 84$.

$$10(6) + 3y = 84$$
$$60 + 3y = 84$$
$$3y = 24$$
$$y = 8$$

The solution is (6, 8).

CHECK

$$\frac{5x}{6} = 7 - \frac{y}{4} \qquad\qquad 4 + \frac{y}{8} = \frac{2x}{3} + 1$$

$$\frac{5(6)}{6} \stackrel{?}{=} 7 - \frac{8}{4} \qquad\qquad 4 + \frac{8}{8} \stackrel{?}{=} \frac{2(6)}{3} + 1$$

$$5 = 5 \ \checkmark \qquad\qquad 5 = 5 \ \checkmark$$

As you simplify equations in some systems, you may notice that substitution will provide an easy way to solve the system.

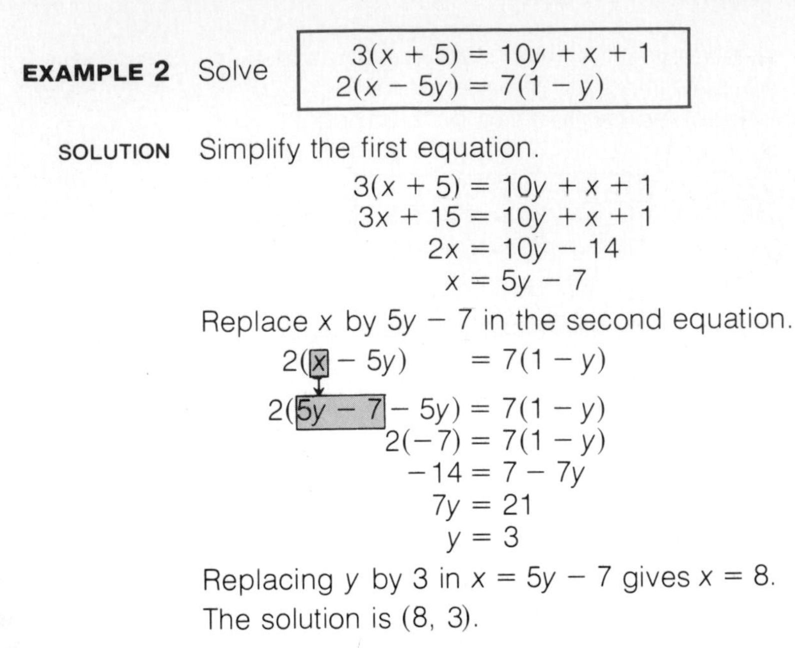

EXAMPLE 2 Solve

$$\boxed{\begin{aligned} 3(x+5) &= 10y + x + 1 \\ 2(x-5y) &= 7(1-y) \end{aligned}}$$

SOLUTION Simplify the first equation.

$$\begin{aligned} 3(x+5) &= 10y + x + 1 \\ 3x + 15 &= 10y + x + 1 \\ 2x &= 10y - 14 \\ x &= 5y - 7 \end{aligned}$$

Replace x by $5y - 7$ in the second equation.

$$\begin{aligned} 2(\boxed{x} - 5y) &= 7(1-y) \\ 2(\boxed{5y-7} - 5y) &= 7(1-y) \\ 2(-7) &= 7(1-y) \\ -14 &= 7 - 7y \\ 7y &= 21 \\ y &= 3 \end{aligned}$$

Replacing y by 3 in $x = 5y - 7$ gives $x = 8$.
The solution is (8, 3).

CHECK The check is left for the student.

CLASSROOM EXERCISES

Solve and check.

1. $\frac{x}{8} = \frac{y}{2} - 1$
   $\frac{x}{6} - \frac{y}{3} = 0$

2. $6(x + y) = 18$
   $6 - 3(2x - 3y) = 3$

3. $2x = 8(y + 1)$
   $3(x - 3y) = 15$

EXERCISES

A Solve and check.

1. $x - 2 = 3(x + y)$
   $3(x - 2) = x - y$

2. $-2(x - 6) = 4y$
   $12 = 3(3x - y)$

3. $12(x - y) + 11y = 14$
   $18x + 5(y + 1) = 0$

4. $3(x + y) = 15 - 2x$
   $y - 1 = 2(x - y)$

5. $\frac{5y}{3} = -3 - \frac{7x}{4}$
   $\frac{x}{2} - 4 = \frac{y}{3}$

6. $\frac{x}{4} = 1 - \frac{y}{5}$
   $2 - \frac{y}{9} = \frac{-2x}{9}$

7. $\frac{x}{6} = \frac{3}{2} - \frac{y}{4}$
$\frac{2x}{3} - \frac{y}{2} = 0$

8. $\frac{y}{2} = 2 - \frac{x}{4}$
$1 - \frac{x}{4} = \frac{-y}{2}$

9. $3a = 4b$
$\frac{3a + 8}{5} = \frac{3b - 1}{2}$

B 10. $\frac{2x - 1}{4} = \frac{1}{12} + \frac{y - 4}{3}$
$\frac{2(x + 3)}{5} = \frac{y - 2}{2}$

11. $4(x + y) + 5(x + 1) = -16$
$3(3x - 2y) - (2x - 3y) = 2$

12. $7(1 - 2b) - (-9a - 5b) = 0$
$3b - 2(b + 1) = 1 + 4a$

13. $\frac{1}{2}(x + y) - \frac{1}{3}(y + 5) = 3$
$2(x - 2y) = 4 - y$

C 14. $\frac{3x + 2}{3} - \frac{5y - 1}{2} = -\frac{5}{6}$
$4(x - 3y) - 2(x - 5y) = 2$

15. $16 - \frac{5x}{6} = \frac{7y - x}{5}$
$7 - 5y = \frac{2x - 3y}{3}$

16. $(x + 5)(y - 3) + 4(y - 7) = y(x - 8)$
$(x + 5)^2 - 5(4 - y) = (x + 6)(x + 1)$

17. $\frac{y + 4}{3} = \frac{x + 3}{7}$
$\frac{x}{2} - \frac{7y}{6} = \frac{19}{6}$

THE VALUE OF π

The value of π has challenged people from the earliest days. About 220 B.C., the Greeks had proved its value to be between $3\frac{10}{71}$ and $3\frac{10}{70}$ or about 3.14. By A.D. 150, π was known to be about 3.1416.

In the sixteenth century, π was calculated to 16 digits; in the seventeenth century to 72 digits; in the eighteenth century to 137 digits, and in the nineteenth century to 527 digits. All of the calculations were done without calculators or computers.

The computer has allowed this progress:

Year	1949	1954	1959	1961	1966	1967
Number of digits of π	2 036	3 093	10 000	100 000	250 000	500 000

Find a reference. Record a 50-digit approximation for π.

10-5 SYSTEMS OF LINEAR INEQUALITIES

Graphically, the solution set of a linear inequality corresponds to the set of points in the coordinate plane that are on one side of a line. The *intersection* of two or more such sets corresponds to the solution set of a *system* of two or more linear inequalities. When we say, "Graph the system", we shall mean "Graph the solution set of the system." In each of the following examples, the deeply-shaded region is the graph of the system.

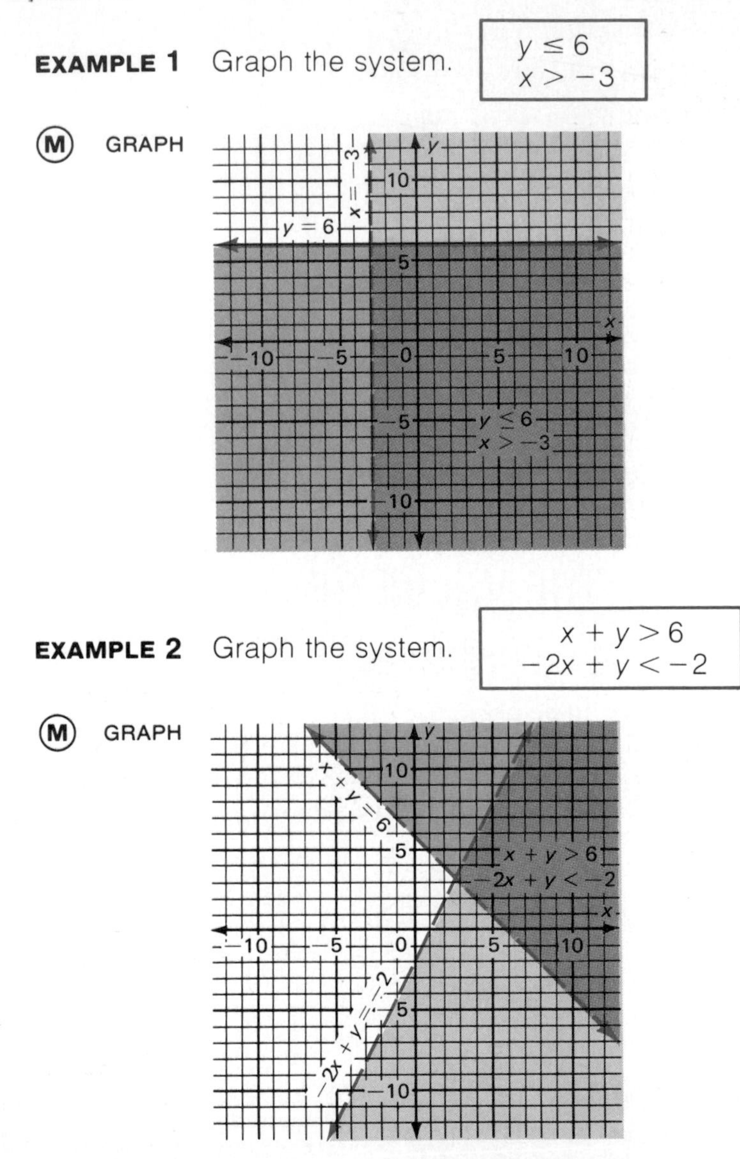

EXAMPLE 1 Graph the system. $\boxed{\begin{array}{l} y \le 6 \\ x > -3 \end{array}}$

Ⓜ GRAPH

EXAMPLE 2 Graph the system. $\boxed{\begin{array}{c} x + y > 6 \\ -2x + y < -2 \end{array}}$

Ⓜ GRAPH

EXAMPLE 3 Graph the system.

$$\begin{aligned} x + y &\geq -2 \\ x - y &> -7 \\ x &< -2 \end{aligned}$$

Ⓜ GRAPH

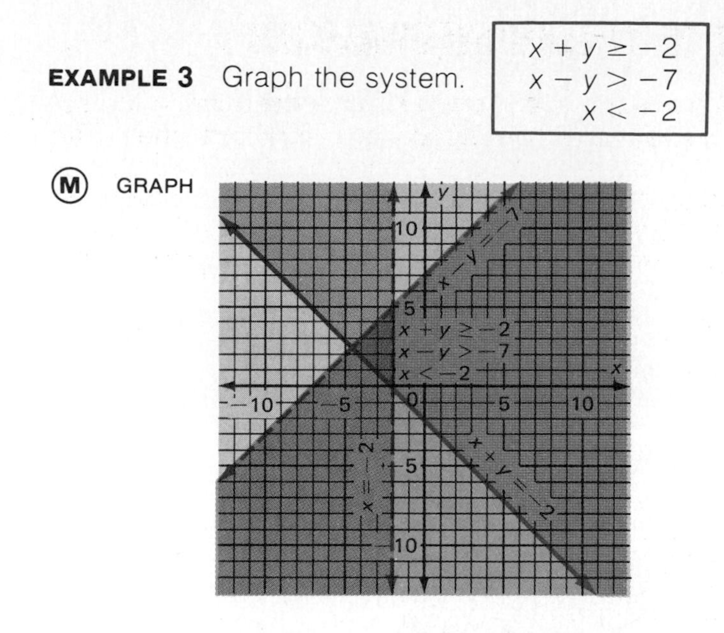

CLASSROOM EXERCISES

Graph each system.

1. $y \leq 4$
   $x > -2$

2. $x + y > 4$
   $-3x + y < -1$

3. $x + y \geq -4$
   $x - y > -8$
   $x < -1$

EXERCISES

A Graph each system.

1. $y \leq 6$
   $x > -6$

2. $y \leq 2$
   $x > -10$

3. $y > -5$
   $x \leq 5$

4. $y > -2$
   $x \leq 8$

5. $x - y > 2$
   $2x + y < 6$

6. $x - y > 1$
   $-2x + y > -4$

7. $x + y < 5$
   $4x + y > -2$

8. $x + y > -3$
   $-4x + y < 6$

9. $x + y \geq 3$
   $x - y > 0$
   $x < 6$

10. $x + y \leq 4$
    $x - y > -4$
    $y > -2$

11. $x - y \geq -2$
    $x + y > 5$
    $x < 10$

12. $x - y \geq -3$
    $x + y < 3$
    $y > -4$

B

13. $3y \leq -2x + 9$
$x - 3y < 2$

14. $5y + x \geq 15$
$3y - 2x \leq 6$

15. $2y + 3x \leq -4$
$5x + 2y > 1$

16. $x - y > y - x$
$4y - 3x > -8$

17. $2(x - 3) - 3(2y - 1) > 9$
$6\left(\frac{1}{2}x + \frac{1}{3}y\right) - 4\left(x - \frac{1}{2}y\right) > 8$

18. $2(x - 3) < -3(-x + 4)$
$5(2y - 4) > 3(4y + 2)$

C

19. $y \geq x - 3$
$y \leq 6x + 2$
$2x + 3y \leq 6$

20. $3y \geq x + 6$
$y \leq x + 8$
$y \leq -3x + 12$

21. $x \leq 5$
$y + 2 \geq 0$
$2y - x \leq 12$
$y + 2(x + 4) \geq 3$

CHECKING YOUR UNDERSTANDING

WORDS

solution of a system of linear equations or inequalities
system of linear equations or inequalities

CONCEPTS

- For a system of linear equations, there is one solution, infinitely many solutions, or no solution. When there is one solution, it corresponds to the point of intersection of the graphs of the linear equations. [10-1]

- For a system of linear inequalities, there are no solutions or infinitely many solutions. The solutions correspond to the points of intersection of the graphs of the linear inequalities. [10-5]

PROCESSES

- Solve a system of linear equations by graphing. [10-1]

1. $y = 2x - 4$
$x + y = -7$

2. $2x - y = 4$
$2y = 4x - 1$

- Solve a system of linear equations algebraically. [10-2 to 10-4]

3. $3x - y = 10$
$2x + y = 10$

4. $3y = 2x + 26$
$5x + 2y = -8$

5. $y = 3x$
$x - 2y = 10$

6. $5x + y = -15$
$x = 13 + 3y$

- Solve a system of linear inequalities by graphing. [10-5]

7. $x + y > 3$
$2x - y > 1$

8. $2x + y < 7$
$2y - x \geq 0$

OBJECTIVE: Solve problems by solving systems of linear equations.

10-6 PROBLEM SOLVING: SYSTEMS OF EQUATIONS

Some problems are solved by using one variable and one equation. Others are solved more easily by using two variables and a system of two equations. The following example is solved both ways.

EXAMPLE The difference of two numbers is 18. The sum of twice the larger and three times the smaller is 151. Find the numbers.

SOLUTION 1 (one variable) Twice the larger number plus three times the smaller number equals 151.

Use [s for the smaller number.
$s + 18$ for the larger number.

The variable may be chosen to represent the larger number.

$$2(s + 18) + 3s = 151$$
$$2s + 36 + 3s = 151$$
$$5s = 115$$
$$s = 23 \quad \text{Also, } s + 18 = 41.$$

CONCLUSION The numbers are 23 and 41.

SOLUTION 2 (two variables) The larger number less the smaller number equals 18. Twice the larger number plus three times the smaller number equals 151.

Use [s for the smaller number.
l for the larger number.

$$l - s = 18$$
$$2l + 3s = 151$$

Solve for s by *subtraction*. To do this, first multiply the members of the first equation by 2.

$$2l - 2s = 36$$
$$2l + 3s = 151$$

Subtract. $-5s = -115$

$$s = 23$$

This is an application of the idea given in the note on page 80.

Solve for l.
Replace s by 23 in $l - s = 18$.

$$l - 23 = 18$$
$$l = 41$$

CONCLUSION The numbers are 23 and 41.

Solving a problem in two different ways is one way to check your results. If the results are different, there is a mistake in your work. Had you solved the problem on the preceding page in just one of the ways shown, a check may be as follows.

CHECK The difference of 41 and 23 is 18.
Is the sum of twice 41 and three times 23 equal to 151?

$2(41) + 3(23) \stackrel{?}{=} 151$

$151 = 151$ ✓

SOLVING A PROBLEM USING TWO VARIABLES

1. Read the problem. Determine what two numbers are to be found.
2. Find two word sentences to suggest equations for the numbers.
3. Use one variable to represent one number to be found and another variable to represent the other.
4. Replace the two word sentences by two equations.
5. Solve the system of two equations.
6. Make a concluding statement.
7. Check the truth of the conclusion against the information given in the problem.

CLASSROOM EXERCISES

Solve and check. Use two variables.

1. The sum of two numbers is 30. Their difference is 12. Find the numbers.
2. The difference of two numbers is 6. The sum of 3 times the larger and twice the smaller is 78. Find the numbers.

EXERCISES

Solve and check. Use two variables.

A

1. The sum of two numbers is 50. Their difference is 22. Find the numbers.
2. The sum of two numbers is 25. Their difference is 9. Find the numbers.
3. The difference of two numbers is 16. The sum of 3 times the smaller and twice the larger is 77. Find the numbers.
4. The difference of two numbers is 24. The sum of 3 times the larger and 8 times the smaller is 160. Find the numbers.
5. The sum of two numbers is 20. The difference when 4 times the smaller is subtracted from 3 times the larger is 4. Find the numbers.

6. The sum of two numbers is 35. The difference when twice the larger is subtracted from 3 times the smaller is 15. Find the numbers.

7. The perimeter of a rectangle is 848 cm. The length exceeds the width by 200 cm. Find the dimensions of the rectangle.

8. A mother is three times as old as her son. Ten years ago the mother was seven times as old as her son. How old is each?

9. Four oranges and 6 grapefruit are selling for $2.62. Seven oranges and 5 grapefruit are selling for $2.66. Find the cost of each.

10. Clara wishes to invest $15 000, part at 6% and the remainder at 8%. The yearly income from both investments is $980. Find the amount of each investment.

B **11.** The sum of two numbers is 24. One-half of one number is 3 more than the other number. Find the numbers.

12. The difference of two numbers is 13. The smaller number is 2 more than one-fourth the larger. What are the numbers?

13. One-half the sum of two numbers is 15. One-half the difference is 8. Find the numbers.

14. One-third the sum of two numbers is 12. Twice their difference is 12. Find the numbers.

15. The length of a rectangular flower bed is to be 50% greater than the width. Its perimeter must be 30 meters. Find the length and width of the flower bed.

16. How many kilograms of candy worth 90¢ a kilogram should be mixed with 20 kg of candy worth 75¢ a kilogram to produce a mixture worth 85¢ a kilogram?

C **17.** Find two numbers such that one is 2 more than twice the other and when twice the smaller is increased by 5 the result is 5 less than twice the larger.

18. Two numbers have the properties that the larger is one-tenth more than twice the smaller and their sum is two-tenths more than the larger. Find the numbers.

19. Find two numbers such that the sum of twice the smaller and three times the larger is 34. The difference of five times the smaller and twice the larger is 9.

20. Find two numbers such that the sum of five times the larger and three times the smaller is 47. The difference of four times the larger and twice the smaller is 20.

REVERSING DIGITS

When you reverse the digits of 25, you obtain 52. When you reverse the digits of 592, you obtain 295.

1. Is there a pattern for the differences of such pairs of two-digit numbers?

2. Is there a pattern for the differences of such pairs of three-digit numbers?

10-7 PROBLEM SOLVING: MOTION PROBLEMS

The speed of a boat in moving water is affected by the speed and direction of the current. Assume that a boat can travel 40 km/h in still water. Against a 7-km/h current the boat actually travels 33 km/h. With the current, the boat travels 47 km/h.

EXAMPLE A crew rows a boat *against* a current for 6 hours. It travels 30 kilometers. The same crew rows the same distance *with* the current in 3 hours. Find the rate at which the crew would row the boat in still water. Find the rate of the current.

(M) SOLUTION

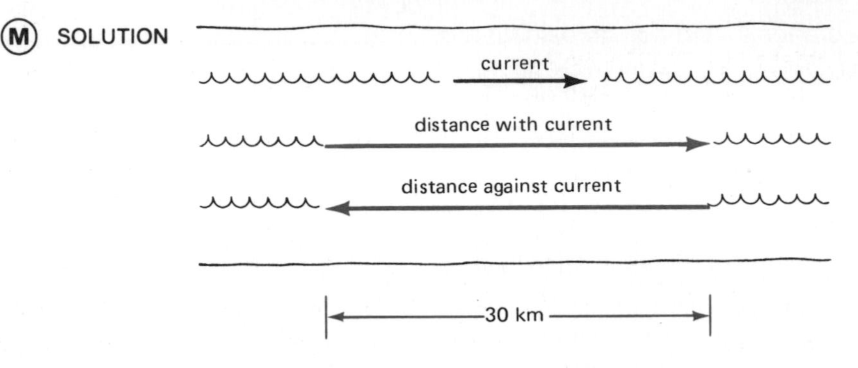

The distance traveled with the current is 30 km.
The distance traveled against the current is 30 km.

Use [s for the rate of the boat in still water in km/h.
c for the rate of the current in km/h.

$\frac{km}{h} + \frac{km}{h} = \frac{km}{h}$

$\frac{km}{h} - \frac{km}{h} = \frac{km}{h}$

	rate ·	time =	distance
With current	$s + c$	3	30
Against current	$s - c$	6	30

$\frac{km}{h} \cdot h = km$

$$(s + c)3 = 30$$
$$(s - c)6 = 30$$

Simplify the equations. Solve for s by *addition*.

D_3 $\quad s + c = 10$

D_6 $\quad s - c = 5$

Add. $\quad 2s = 15$

$s = 7.5$

Solve for c.

Replace s by 7.5 in $s + c = 10$.

$$7.5 + c = 10$$
$$c = 2.5$$

CONCLUSION The crew would row the boat 7.5 km/h in still water. The rate of the current is 2.5 km/h.

CHECK Will rowing 5 km/h for 6 hours cover the same distance as rowing 10 km/h for 3 hours?

$$5 \cdot 6 \stackrel{?}{=} 10 \cdot 3$$
$$30 = 30 \checkmark$$

CLASSROOM EXERCISES

Solve and check. Use two variables.

1. A jungle steamer travels 15 kilometers downstream (with a current) in 3 hours. The return trip upstream (against the current) takes 5 hours. Find the rate of the steamer in still water and the rate of the current.
2. An airplane flies 2240 kilometers in 8 hours against a head wind. The return trip with the wind takes 7 hours. Find the rate of the airplane in still air and the rate of the wind.

EXERCISES

A Solve and check. Use two variables.

1. A boat traveling upstream against a current takes 3 hours to go 36 kilometers. Returning downstream with the current it takes 2 hours. Find the rate of the boat in still water and the rate of the current.
2. An excursion boat traveled 24 kilometers downstream with a current in 2 hours. On the return trip against the current it took 3 hours. Find the rate of the boat in still water and the rate of the current.
3. An airplane travels 570 kilometers in 3 hours with the wind. It takes 5 hours for the return trip against the wind. Find the rate of the wind and the rate of the airplane in still air.
4. An airplane flew 3500 kilometers in 7 hours with a tail wind. The same airplane took 10 hours for the return trip against the head wind. Find the rate of the wind and the rate of the airplane in still air.
5. A boat went 14 kilometers downstream in 0.5 hour. The return trip upstream took 0.7 hour. Find the rate of the boat in still water and the rate of the current.
6. A boat takes $\frac{1}{2}$ hour to go $7\frac{1}{2}$ kilometers downstream. The return trip upstream takes $\frac{3}{4}$ hour. Find the rate of the boat in still water and the rate of the current.

B

7. A motorist made a 200-kilometer trip averaging 50 km/h on a level road and 25 km/h on a mountain road. The time spent on the mountain road was 1 hour less than the time on the level road. How many kilometers of the trip were on the mountain road?

8. It takes one airplane half the time to fly 852 kilometers with a tail wind as it takes another airplane to fly 1560 kilometers against the same wind. If both airplanes travel 408 km/h in still air, find the speed of the wind.

9. Flying with a wind at full speed, a traffic helicopter flies 31 kilometers in 10 minutes. Cruising at half speed against the same wind, the helicopter flies 18 km in 20 minutes. Find the full speed of the helicopter in still air and the speed of the wind.

10. Skip can row a boat in still water at the rate of 5 km/h. One day when the water current was 3 km/h, he left a dock, rowed downstream to a bridge, and then returned to the dock. The entire trip took 30 minutes. How far from the dock was the bridge?

C 11. A bicyclist travels 1 kilometer uphill and 2 kilometers downhill in 24 minutes. The return trip takes 30 minutes. Find the rates of bicycling uphill and bicycling downhill.

12. To reach her destination, a woman had to row across a river and then walk a certain distance along the shore. If she lands at dock A, she rows for 1 hour and walks for 2 hours for a total distance of 12 kilometers. If she lands at dock B, she rows for $1\frac{1}{2}$ hours and walks for 1 hour for a total distance of 11 kilometers. Find her rates for rowing and walking.

THREE EQUATIONS IN THREE UNKNOWNS

A system of three equations in three variables may have a solution. Remember, a solution of the system is a solution of each of the equations.

EXAMPLE Solve

$$x + y - z = 2$$
$$2x - y + 2z = 14$$
$$x + 2y + z = 2$$

SOLUTION Solving the first equation for x gives $x = 2 - y + z$. Replacing x by $2 - y + z$ in the other two equations gives this system. $-3y + 4z = 10 \quad y + 2z = 0$

Solving this system gives $y = -2$ and $z = 1$. Replacing y and z in the first equation gives $x = 5$. Thus, $x = 5$, $y = -2$, $z = 1$. A check will verify that $(5, -2, 1)$ is a solution of the system.

Solve these systems.

1. $x + 2y - z = 8$
   $2x + z = -1$
   $3x - 4y - 2z = 1$

2. $4x + 2y + z = -1$
   $x - y + 2z = 11$
   $2x + 3y - z = -13$

3. $x + y - 4z = 0$
   $3x + 4y + 2z = 6$
   $x - 3y - 2z = 9$

STOPPING DISTANCES FOR YOUR CAR

The distance it takes to stop a car depends on how fast the car is traveling.

Reaction distance is the distance your car travels between the time you realize you want to stop and the time your foot actually reaches the brake pedal. A formula for reaction distance is

$$R.D. = 0.22v$$

for which $R.D.$ represents the reaction distance in meters and v represents the speed in km/h.

Braking distance is the distance your car travels after you start applying pressure on the brake pedal. A formula for the braking distance of a certain model car is

$$B.D. = 0.00625v^2$$

for which $B.D.$ represents the braking distance in meters and v represents the speed in km/h.

Stopping distance is the total distance your car travels when you want to stop. Stopping distance is the sum of the reaction distance and the braking distance.

1. Use your calculator to find the reaction distances for speeds of 15, 30, 45, 60, 75 and 90 km/h. Use either the memory or the constant feature of your calculator, and you will have to enter the constant 0.22 only once.
2. Find braking distances for the speeds in Exercise 1
3. How do the braking distances and reaction distances change when your speed is doubled; when it is tripled; when it is quadrupled?
4. Find stopping distances for the speeds in Exercise 1.

10-8 PROBLEM SOLVING: DIGIT PROBLEMS

The symbols 0, 1, 2, 3, 4, 5, 6, 7, 8, and 9, which are used in forming numerals, are **digits**. Each digit by itself shows a number. The *place* of each digit in a numeral is also given a number. Thus, a digit in a place suggests a product.

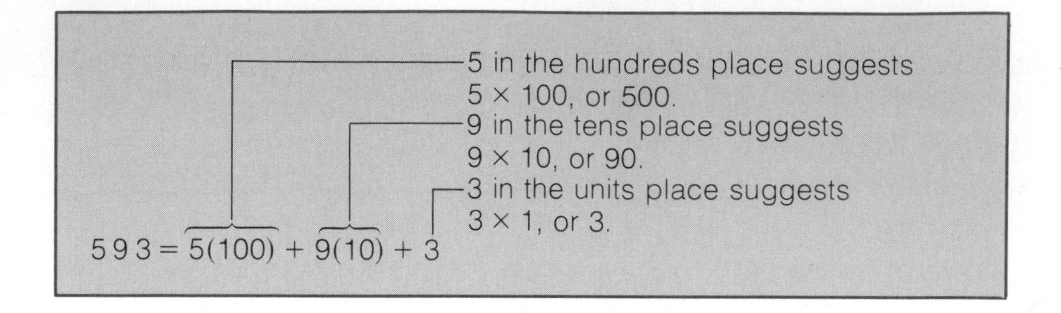

Sometimes we disregard the place number for a digit and think only of the number for that digit. Thus we say "the sum of the digits" to mean the sum of the digit numbers. For 593, the sum of the digits is $5 + 9 + 3$, or 17. The counting numbers from 10 through 99 are called two-digit numbers. Those from 100 through 999 are called three-digit numbers, and so on.

In a digit problem, you are asked to determine a number by finding each digit. For a counting number from 10 through 99, you may chose to use t for the tens digit and u for the units digit. Then the number may be shown in this way.

$$10t + u.$$

If the digits are reversed, the number they would represent may be shown in this way.

$$10u + t$$

EXAMPLE 1 The sum of the digits of a two-digit number is 10. The units digit is 1 larger than twice the tens digit. Find the number.

(two variables) Two word sentences are clearly stated above.

Use $\left[\begin{array}{l} t \text{ for the tens digit.} \\ u \text{ for the units digit.}\end{array}\right.$

Replace the word sentences.

$$t + u = 10$$
$$u = 2t + 1$$

Solve for t. Replace u by $2t + 1$ in the first equation.

$$t + u = 10$$
$$t + (2t + 1) = 10$$
$$3t + 1 = 10$$
$$3t = 9$$
$$t = 3$$

Solve for u. Replace t by 3 in $t + u = 10$.

$$3 + u = 10$$
$$u = 7$$

CONCLUSION The number is 37.

Ⓜ SOLUTION 2 (one variable) The units digit is 1 larger than twice the tens digit.

Use $\left[\begin{array}{ll} x & \text{for the units digit.} \\ 10 - x & \text{for the tens digit.} \end{array}\right.$

$$x = 2(10 - x) + 1$$
$$x = 20 - 2x + 1$$
$$3x = 21$$
$$x = 7$$

Also, $10 - x = 3$.

CONCLUSION The number is 37.

CHECK The sum of the digits 3 and 7 is 10.
7 is one larger than twice 3. ✓

EXAMPLE 2 A two-digit number is 3 larger than 4 times the sum of its digits. The units digit is 4 larger than the tens digit. Find the number.

SOLUTION Two word sentences are clearly stated above.

Use $\left[\begin{array}{ll} t & \text{for the tens digit.} \\ u & \text{for the units digit.} \\ 10t + u & \text{for the two-digit number.} \end{array}\right.$

Replace the word sentences.

$$10t + u = 4(t + u) + 3$$
$$u = t + 4$$

The first equation simplifies to $6t - 3u = 3$, or $2t - u = 1$. The second may be written $-t + u = 4$.

Solve for t by *addition*.

$$\begin{array}{r} 2t - u = 1 \\ -t + u = 4 \\ \hline t \quad\;\; = 5 \end{array}$$

Add. $t = 5$

Solve for u. Replace t by 5 in $u = t + 4$.

$$u = 5 + 4$$
$$u = 9$$

CONCLUSION The number is 59.

CHECK The check is left for the student.

EXAMPLE 3 In a two-digit number, the tens digit is 4 times the units digit. If the digits are reversed, the resulting number is 54 less than the original number. Find the number.

Ⓜ **SOLUTION** Use

- t for the tens digit.
- u for the units digit.
- $10t + u$ for the two-digit number.
- $10u + t$ for the number with its digits reversed.

$$t = 4u$$
$$10u + t = 10t + u - 54$$

Solve for u. Replace t by $4u$ in the second equation.

$$10u + 4u = 10(4u) + u - 54$$
$$14u = 41u - 54$$
$$-27u = -54$$
$$u = 2$$

Solve for t. Replace u by 2 in $t = 4u$.

$$t = 4(2)$$
$$t = 8$$

CONCLUSION The number is 82.

CHECK Is 28 equal to 82 less 54?

$28 \stackrel{?}{=} 82 - 54$

$28 = 28$ ✓

CLASSROOM EXERCISES

Solve and check.

1. The units digit of a two-digit number is twice the tens digit. The sum of the digits is 12. Find the number.
2. The units digit of a two-digit number is two greater than the tens digit. The number is 4 times the sum of its digits. Find the number.
3. In a two-digit number the units digit is twice the tens digit. If the digits are reversed, the resulting number is 9 more than the original number. Find the number.
4. The sum of the digits of a two-digit number is 8. The difference of the digits is 2. Find the number.

EXERCISES

A Solve and check.

1. The sum of the digits of a two-digit number is 11. The units digit is 3 more than the tens digit. Find the number.
2. The units digit is one less than the tens digit. If the sum of the digits is 15, find the number.

3. The units digit of a two-digit number is one more than twice the tens digit. If the sum of the digits is 13, what is the number?

4. The sum of the digits in a two-digit number is 11. The units digit is 1 less than 3 times the tens digit. Find the number.

5. A two-digit number is 4 times the sum of its digits. The tens digit is one less than the units digit. What is the number?

6. A two-digit number is 4 times the sum of its digits. The units digit exceeds the tens digit by 3. Find the number.

7. A two-digit number is 45 less than the number with its digits reversed. The sum of the digits is 9. Find the number.

8. A two-digit number is 54 greater than the number with its digits reversed. The sum of the digits is 8. Find the number.

B

9. The sum of the digits of a two-digit number is 5. If the digits are reversed, the new number is 9 less than the number. Find the number.

10. The sum of the digits of a two-digit number is 10. If 18 is added to the number, the order of the digits is reversed. Find the number.

11. The units digit of a two-digit number is 3 less than twice the tens digit. The number is 3 less than 5 times the sum of the digits. Find the number.

12. A two-digit number is 4 times the sum of the digits. Find all possible two-digit numbers that satisfy this condition.

C

13. The tens digit of a two-digit number is 3 less than twice the units digit. If 18 is subtracted from the number, the number with digits in reverse order is obtained. Find the number.

14. The tens digit of a two-digit number is 1 less than twice the units digit. If the digits are reversed, the new number is 40 more than one-fifth of the original number. Find the number.

15. A two-digit number exceeds the number obtained by reversing its digits by 18. If the original number is divided by 2, it will be 25 less than the number with digits in reverse order. Find the original number.

A PRODUCTION DECISION

A production supervisor has two machines that produce a certain valve. The first machine requires $40.00 of set-up expense and $1.15 of production expense per valve. The second machine requires $20.00 of set-up expense and $1.85 of production expense per valve.

1. Which machine should be used to produce 10 valves? 20 valves? 40 valves? more than 40 valves?
2. What is the largest valve order that should be assigned to the second machine?

CHAPTER REVIEW

Solve each system graphically. [10-1]

1. $x + y = 6$
$2x - y = 6$

2. $y = x + 4$
$y + 5 = -2x$

3. $x + 5y = 7$
$2y - x = 0$

Solve each system by addition or subtraction. [10-2]

4. $2x - y = 2$
$7x - y = 12$

5. $a - 4b = -4$
$2a - 3b = 2$

6. $2r + 3s = -12$
$3r + 2s = -13$

Solve each system by substitution. [10-3]

7. $x = y - 4$
$5x - 3y = -14$

8. $2x + 3y = -18$
$-3x + y = 16$

9. $4x + 3 = y$
$x + y = 0$

Solve each system. [10-4]

10. $2(x - 5) = y$
$-1\frac{1}{2}x = 3y$

11. $x + y = 1000$
$0.05x + 0.07y = 70$

12. $\frac{x}{3} + \frac{y}{4} = 5$
$\frac{x}{2} - \frac{y}{3} = -1$

Graph each system using the same coordinate axes. Label the solution set. [10-5]

13. $x + y > 5$
$y - x < 3$

14. $y \geq x - 1$
$y \leq -2x + 4$

15. $y + x < 4$
$y - 2x > -5$
$y > -3$

Solve. Use two variables. [10-6, 10-7]

16. The difference of the measures of two complementary angles is 10 degrees. Find the measure of each angle.

17. The perimeter of a rectangle is 54. The length is 5 greater than the width. Find the length and width.

18. An airplane flies between two cities that are 1500 kilometers apart. One way it takes 5 hours with the help of a tail wind. The return trip is made in 6 hours against the wind. Find the rate of the airplane in still air and the rate of the wind.

Solve. [10-8]

19. A two-digit number is 4 times the sum of its digits. The units digit is four more than the tens digit. Find the number.

20. A two-digit number is 9 more than the number formed when the digits are reversed. The number is 6 times the sum of its digits. Find the number.

CAPSULE REVIEW

Write the letter of the best response.

1. When the members of $2x - 3y = 7$ and $5x + 3y = 0$ are added, the result is
   a. $-3x - 6y = 7$ **b.** $7x - 6y = 7$ **c.** $3x = 7$ **d.** $-3x = -7$ **e.** $7x = 7$
2. When the members of $5x - y = 4$ and $5x + 3y = -12$ are subtracted, the result could be
   a. $2y = -8$ **b.** $2y = -16$ **c.** $4y = -8$ **d.** $4y = -16$ **e.** $10x + 4y = -16$
3. When y is replaced by $x + 5$ in $3x - 5y = 23$, the result is
   a. $3(x + 5) - 5y = 23$ **b.** $3x - x + 5 = 23$
   c. $3(x + 5) - 5(x + 5) = 23$ **d.** $3x - 5(x + 5) = 23$
4. The solution for the system $y = -x - 2$ and $y = 2x + 7$ is
   a. $(-3, 1)$ **b.** $(-2, 0)$ **c.** $(0, 7)$ **d.** $(0, -2)$ **e.** $(0, 0)$
5. The graphs of $x + y = 4$ and $x + y = -4$
   a. are the same **b.** are parallel **c.** intersect in 2 points
   d. intersect in a point and are perpendicular
   e. intersect in a point and are not perpendicular
6. The solution for the system $y = x - 1$ and $3x + 2y = -12$ is
   a. $(1, 0)$ **b.** $(-2, -3)$ **c.** $(4, 3)$ **d.** $(-6, 3)$ **e.** $(-4, 0)$
7. Which is a solution for the system $y > 2$ and $x > 5$?
   a. $(5, 2)$ **b.** $(2, 5)$ **c.** $(2, 2)$ **d.** $(5, 5)$ **e.** $(6, 6)$
8. Which is *not* a solution for the system $y \leq 2x$, $x \leq 2$, $y \geq 0$?
   a. $(0, 0)$ **b.** $(1, 2)$ **c.** $(2, 1)$ **d.** $(2, 2)$ **e.** $(1, 3)$
9. Which is a solution for the system $y > 3x + 4$ and $y \leq -2x - 1$?
   a. $(-2, 3)$ **b.** $(0, 0)$ **c.** $(1, 6)$ **d.** $(-1, -3)$ **e.** $(1, 3)$
10. t represents the tens digit and u represents the units digit of a number. The number formed when the digits are reversed is given by
   a. $10t + u$ **b.** $t + u$ **c.** tu **d.** $10u + t$ **e.** $u + 10t$

CHAPTER TEST

Solve each system by graphing.

1. $y = x + 2$
   $y = 3x - 4$
2. $x + y = 1$
   $x - y = 5$

Solve each system by addition or subtraction.

3. $2x + 3y = 7$
   $x + 3y = 5$
4. $4x - y = 3$
   $3x + 2y = 16$

Solve each system by substitution.

5. $y = x$
$2x + 4y = 3$

6. $y = x + 3$
$y + 2x = -3$

Solve each system.

7. $\frac{1}{2}x + \frac{1}{3}y = 4$
$\frac{1}{4}x - \frac{1}{2}y = -2$

8. $2(x + 2) + 3(y + 1) = 17$
$2(x - 1) + 4(y - 3) = -1$

Graph each system of inequalities. Label the solution set.

9. $y < 2$
$y > x$

10. $x + y < 4$
$x + y > 2$

Solve. Use two variables.

11. The sum of two numbers is 4. Their difference is 1. Find the two numbers.

12. The sum of a number and twice another number is 9. The sum of the number and three times the other is 13. Find the two numbers.

13. Going with the current, a motorboat travels 20 kilometers in 2 hours. Going against the current it takes 5 hours to travel the distance. Find the speed of the current.

14. Flying with the wind, an airplane takes 7 hours to fly 2240 kilometers. Flying into the wind it takes 8 hours to travel the same distance. Find the speed of the airplane in still air.

15. The sum of the digits in a 2-digit number is 12. The tens digit is 3 times as large as the units digit. Find the number.

16. The sum of the digits in a 2-digit number is 9. The units digit is 5 larger than the tens digit. Find the number.

Write the letter of the best response.

17. Use the graph. Which is the solution for the system of equations?

a. $(2, 4)$ **b.** $(4, 2)$
c. $(-1, 4)$ **d.** $\left(3, \frac{1}{2}\right)$
e. $\left(\frac{1}{2}, 3\right)$

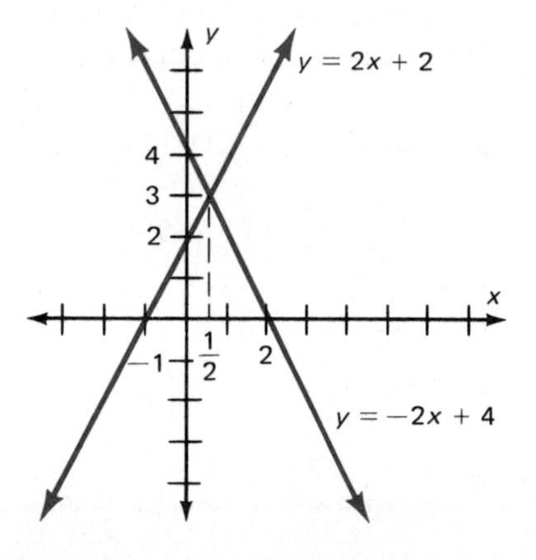

18. The solution for the system $2x + 3y = 11$ and $2x - 3y = 5$ is

a. $(0, 0)$ **b.** $\left(4, 6\frac{1}{3}\right)$ **c.** $(1, 1)$ **d.** $\left(1\frac{1}{2}, 2\frac{2}{3}\right)$ **e.** $(4, 1)$

19. The solution for the system $y = x - 2$ and $3x + y = 38$ is

a. $(8, 6)$ **b.** $(12, 10)$ **c.** $(11, 5)$ **d.** $(10, 8)$ **e.** $(9, 11)$

20. The solution for the system $3(x + y) = 12$ and $3(x + 2) + y = 16$ is

a. $(3, 1)$ **b.** $(1, 3)$ **c.** $(2, 2)$ **d.** $(4, -2)$ **e.** $(-1, 19)$

21. Which is the graph for the system $x > 4$ and $y < 4$?

a. A **b.** B

c. C **d.** D

e. $(4, 4)$

22. The sum of two numbers is 4. Their difference is 6. What are the numbers?

a. 3 and 1 **b.** 7 and -3 **c.** 5 and -1 **d.** 9 and -5 **e.** 1 and 5

23. Paddling against the current, Jessica takes 5 hours to travel 5 kilometers. Paddling with the current, she takes 1 hour to travel the 5 kilometers. What is the speed of the current?

a. 1 km/h **b.** 2 km/h **c.** 3 km/h **d.** 4 km/h **e.** 5 km/h

24. The sum of the digits in a 2-digit number is 9. The tens digit is 3 less than twice the ones digit. Which system of equations could be solved to find the number?

a. $t + u = 9$
$t = u - 3$

b. $t + u = 9$
$t = 2u - 3$

c. $t + u = 9$
$10t - 3 = 2u$

d. $t - u = 9$
$t - 3 = 2u$

e. $t + u = 9$
$t - 3 = 2u$

CHAPTER 11

Fractions and Fractional Equations

The responsibility of a family requires many thoughtful and well-informed decisions. It requires scheduling, channeling, and investment of human resources, whether the time available is for work or for leisure activities. It requires maintaining an inventory of supplies. It requires planning and management of finances. In many ways it is like running a small business.

OBJECTIVES: Add, subtract, multiply, divide and simplify fractions that contain variables.

11-1 CHANGING THE TERMS OF A FRACTION

Fractions that represent the quotient of two polynomials are **algebraic fractions**. They are sometimes called **rational expressions**.

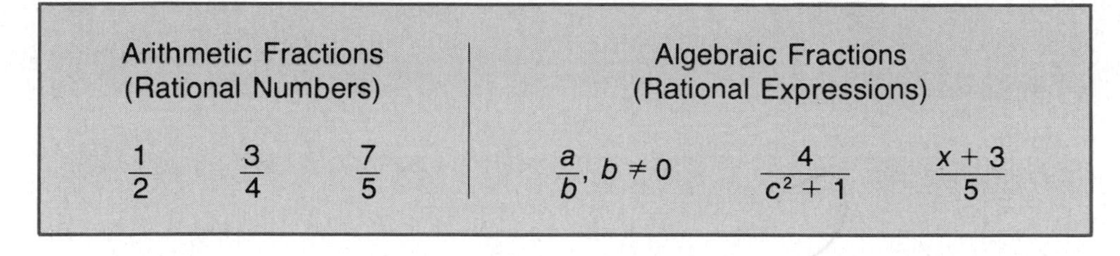

Arithmetic Fractions (Rational Numbers)			Algebraic Fractions (Rational Expressions)		
$\frac{1}{2}$	$\frac{3}{4}$	$\frac{7}{5}$	$\frac{a}{b}$, $b \neq 0$	$\frac{4}{c^2 + 1}$	$\frac{x + 3}{5}$

The numerator and denominator are the *terms* of a fraction. We multiply with fractions by multiplying their terms as follows.

This is a second use of the word "term." It is also used as in "term of a polynomial."

$$\frac{a}{b} \cdot \frac{c}{d} = \frac{ac}{bd},\ b \neq 0,\ d \neq 0$$

This rule for multiplication and the Multiplication Property of One (Section 1-5) allow us to find different fractions for the same number.

EXAMPLE 1 Replace $\frac{2}{5}$ by another fraction for the same number but with a denominator of 15.

SOLUTION
$$\frac{2}{5} = \frac{2}{5} \cdot 1$$
$$= \frac{2}{5} \cdot \frac{3}{3}$$
$$= \frac{6}{15}$$

EXAMPLE 2 Complete $\frac{x}{y} = \frac{?}{5y}$.

SOLUTION
$$\frac{x}{y} = \frac{x}{y} \cdot 1$$
$$= \frac{x}{y} \cdot \frac{5}{5}$$
$$= \frac{5x}{5y}$$

EXAMPLE 3 Complete $\frac{4a^2}{6ab} = \frac{?}{3b}$.

SOLUTION
$$\frac{4a^2}{6ab} = \frac{2a \cdot 2a}{2a \cdot 3b}$$
$$= \frac{2a}{2a} \cdot \frac{2a}{3b}$$
$$= 1 \cdot \frac{2a}{3b}, \text{ or } \frac{2a}{3b}$$

Recall that a fraction is in *lowest terms* when its numerator and denominator have no common factor involving a variable and no common integral factor except 1 and -1. A fraction is *reduced to lowest terms* when it is replaced by the fraction in lowest terms for the same number. We use the Multiplication Property of One to reduce a fraction to lowest terms. This property lets us eliminate the common factors from the numerator and denominator.

EXAMPLE 4 Reduce $\frac{12}{30}$ to lowest terms.

SOLUTION
$$\frac{12}{30} = \frac{6 \cdot 2}{6 \cdot 5} = \frac{6}{6} \cdot \frac{2}{5} = 1 \cdot \frac{2}{5}, \text{ or } \frac{2}{5}$$

EXAMPLE 5 Reduce $\frac{14ax}{21a^3}$ to lowest terms.

SOLUTION
$$\frac{14ax}{21a^3} = \frac{7a \cdot 2x}{7a \cdot 3a^2} = \frac{7a}{7a} \cdot \frac{2x}{3a^2} = 1 \cdot \frac{2x}{3a^2}, \text{ or } \frac{2x}{3a^2}$$

Once you understand how the Multiplication Property of One allows you to eliminate common factors from the numerator and denominator, you may use a shorter method to reduce a fraction to lowest terms.

EXAMPLE 6 Reduce $\frac{4y}{2y^2 + 2y}$ to lowest terms.

SOLUTION
$$\frac{4y}{2y^2 + 2y} = \frac{2y \cdot 2}{2y(y+1)} = \frac{2y}{2y} \cdot \frac{2}{y+1} = 1 \cdot \frac{2}{y+1}, \text{ or } \frac{2}{y+1}$$

Ⓜ SHORTER METHOD
$$\frac{4y}{2y^2 + 2y} = \frac{\overset{2 \cdot 1}{\cancel{4y}}}{\underset{1 \cdot 1}{\cancel{2y}}(y+1)} = \frac{2}{y+1}$$

EXAMPLE 7 Reduce $\frac{a^2 - 2a - 24}{5a - 30}$ to lowest terms.

Ⓜ SOLUTION
$$\frac{a^2 - 2a - 24}{5a - 30} = \frac{(a+4)\overset{1}{\cancel{(a-6)}}}{5\underset{1}{\cancel{(a-6)}}} = \frac{a+4}{5}$$

CLASSROOM EXERCISES

Find the missing term.

1. $\frac{5}{-8} = \frac{-10}{?}$
2. $\frac{12}{42} = \frac{?}{7}$
3. $\frac{m}{n} = \frac{?}{an}$
4. $\frac{?}{cd} = \frac{15}{5cd}$

Reduce to lowest terms.

5. $\frac{18a^3}{14a^2}$
6. $\frac{3(x+y)}{4(x+y)}$
7. $\frac{2x+3y}{4x+6y}$
8. $\frac{4a-4b}{-8}$

EXERCISES

A Find the missing term.

1. $\frac{9}{27} = \frac{18}{?}$
2. $\frac{8}{3} = \frac{?}{6}$
3. $\frac{?}{9} = \frac{4}{18}$
4. $\frac{?}{7} = \frac{42}{21}$
5. $\frac{4}{6a} = \frac{8}{?}$
6. $\frac{5}{10a} = \frac{20}{?}$
7. $\frac{?}{12x} = \frac{5}{4x}$
8. $\frac{?}{21x} = \frac{5}{7x}$
9. $\frac{7}{x+y} = \frac{?}{2x+2y}$
10. $\frac{6}{a+b} = \frac{?}{3a+3b}$
11. $\frac{x+4}{x-1} = \frac{?}{(x-1)(x+2)}$
12. $\frac{m+2}{m-1} = \frac{?}{(m-1)(m-3)}$
13. $\frac{3b+5}{b-4} = \frac{?}{b^2-7b+12}$
14. $\frac{4x+5}{x-2} = \frac{?}{x^2-5x+6}$

Reduce to lowest terms.

15. $\frac{14}{35}$
16. $\frac{12}{20}$
17. $\frac{3a}{6a}$
18. $\frac{4b}{8b}$
19. $\frac{b^2c}{bc^2}$
20. $\frac{a^2c}{ac^2}$
21. $\frac{xy}{x^2y^2}$
22. $\frac{r^3s^3}{rs}$
23. $\frac{39x^4y^6}{52x^2y^2}$
24. $\frac{90b^3c^2}{30a^2b^2}$
25. $\frac{-rst^4}{r^2st^4}$
26. $\frac{-abc^3}{a^2bc^3}$
27. $\frac{5x+5}{6x+6}$
28. $\frac{4x+4}{7x+7}$
29. $\frac{4x-28}{6x-42}$
30. $\frac{8x-32}{16x-64}$
31. $\frac{(x+1)(x-1)}{x-1}$
32. $\frac{(x+2)(x-3)}{x-3}$
33. $\frac{(x+1)(x-1)}{2x-2}$

B

34. $\frac{5b^2+15b}{b^2+3b}$
35. $\frac{4a^2+12a}{a^2+3a}$
36. $\frac{2m^3-6m^2+2m}{m^2-3m+1}$
37. $\frac{2x^3-12x^2+2x}{x^2-6x+1}$
38. $\frac{x^2-1}{x^2-2x+1}$
39. $\frac{a^2-1}{a^2+2a+1}$
40. $\frac{6x^2+11x+4}{2x^2-9x-5}$
41. $\frac{6x^2+5x+1}{6x^2-7x-3}$
42. $\frac{r^2-rs}{r^2+rs}$
43. $\frac{(a+b)^2(a-b)}{a^2-b^2}$
44. $\frac{2a^2-ab-b^2}{2a^2+ab-b^2}$
45. $\frac{6x^2-13x-5}{4x^2-12x+15}$

C

46. $\frac{(a+b)^2+(a+b)-2}{a+b+2}$
47. $\frac{(a+b)^2-(x+y)^2}{a+b-x-y}$
48. Find the values for x for which the fraction $\frac{x^2-13x+42}{x^2-8x+12}$ has no meaning.

11-2 MULTIPLYING WITH FRACTIONS

As indicated in Section 11-1, algebraic fractions are multiplied using the same rule that is used for arithmetic fractions. The product of two fractions equals the product of the numerators divided by the product of the denominators. It is good practice to reduce a product to lowest terms.

$$\frac{a}{b} \cdot \frac{c}{d} = \frac{a \cdot c}{b \cdot d},\ b \neq 0,\ d \neq 0$$

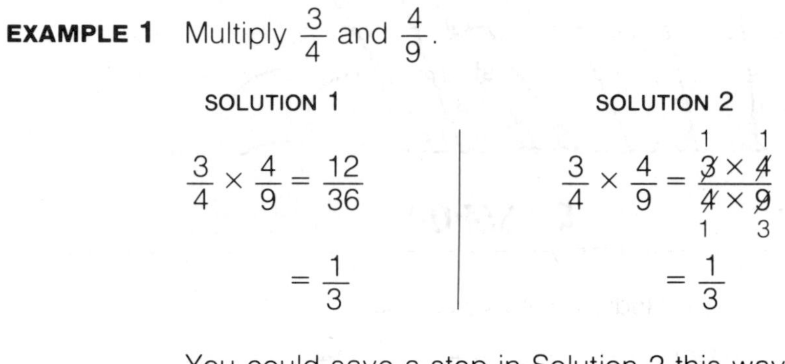

EXAMPLE 1 Multiply $\frac{3}{4}$ and $\frac{4}{9}$.

SOLUTION 1

$$\frac{3}{4} \times \frac{4}{9} = \frac{12}{36} = \frac{1}{3}$$

SOLUTION 2

$$\frac{3}{4} \times \frac{4}{9} = \frac{\overset{1}{\cancel{3}} \times \overset{1}{\cancel{4}}}{\underset{1}{\cancel{4}} \times \underset{3}{\cancel{9}}} = \frac{1}{3}$$

You could save a step in Solution 2 this way.

Ⓜ
$$\frac{\overset{1}{\cancel{3}}}{\underset{1}{\cancel{4}}} \times \frac{\overset{1}{\cancel{4}}}{\underset{3}{\cancel{9}}} = \frac{1}{3}$$

EXAMPLE 2 Multiply $\frac{7ab^2}{3}$ and $\frac{15}{14a^2}$.

Ⓜ SOLUTION
$$\frac{\overset{1 \cdot 1}{\cancel{7}\cancel{a}b^2}}{\underset{1}{\cancel{3}}} \cdot \frac{\overset{5}{\cancel{15}}}{\underset{2 \cdot a}{\cancel{14}\cancel{a^2}}} = \frac{5b^2}{2a}$$

Factoring the numerators and denominators before multiplying can simplify finding the product as shown in Example 3.

EXAMPLE 3 Multiply $\dfrac{4x^2 - 25y^2}{3x - 2y}$ and $\dfrac{9x^2 - 12xy + 4y^2}{2x^2 - 5xy}$.

Ⓜ SOLUTION

$$\frac{4x^2 - 25y^2}{3x - 2y} \cdot \frac{9x^2 - 12xy + 4y^2}{2x^2 - 5xy}$$

$$= \frac{(2x + 5y)\overset{1}{\cancel{(2x - 5y)}}}{\underset{1}{\cancel{(3x - 2y)}}} \cdot \frac{\overset{1}{\cancel{(3x - 2y)}}(3x - 2y)}{x\underset{1}{\cancel{(2x - 5y)}}}$$

$$= \frac{(2x + 5y)(3x - 2y)}{x}, \text{ or } \frac{6x^2 + 11xy - 10y^2}{x}$$

MULTIPLYING WITH FRACTIONS

1. Multiply the numerators to find the numerator of the product.
2. Multiply the denominators to find the denominator of the product.
3. Reduce the product to lowest terms. This step may precede Steps 1 and 2.

CLASSROOM EXERCISES

Simplify each product. Reduce to lowest terms.

1. $\frac{3}{5} \cdot \frac{10}{21}$ **2.** $\frac{6m}{15mn^2} \cdot \frac{n}{8m^2}$ **3.** $\frac{x + 2y}{7} \cdot \frac{14}{3x + 6y}$ **4.** $\frac{4a^2 - 6ab}{2a + 3b} \cdot \frac{4a^2 + 12ab + 9b^2}{4a^2 - 9b^2}$

EXERCISES

Ⓐ Simplify each product. Reduce to lowest terms.

1. $\frac{a}{6} \cdot \frac{3b^7}{2}$ **2.** $\frac{x}{3} \cdot \frac{4y^5}{5}$ **3.** $\frac{x^2y^2}{m^3n} \cdot \frac{n}{x^3}$ **4.** $\frac{c^2d^2}{a^2b} \cdot \frac{b}{c}$

5. $\frac{2c}{n} \cdot \frac{7}{6c}$ **6.** $\frac{4r}{9} \cdot \frac{9}{12r}$ **7.** $\frac{a^2}{b^3} \cdot \frac{a^2}{b} \cdot \frac{b}{c}$ **8.** $\frac{x^2}{y^2} \cdot \frac{x^2}{y} \cdot \frac{y}{z}$

9. $\frac{2c^3}{15d^6} \cdot 2cd$ **10.** $\frac{30c^5}{10d^4} \cdot 7cd$ **11.** $\frac{2a^5}{3b^4} \cdot \frac{10b^4}{8c^5}$ **12.** $\frac{3m^3}{4n^4} \cdot \frac{12n^4}{6r^2}$

13. $\frac{x + y}{8} \cdot \frac{10}{x^2 - y^2}$ **14.** $\frac{a + b}{6} \cdot \frac{8}{a^2 - b^2}$ **15.** $\frac{a + 3}{a - 5} \cdot \frac{2a - 10}{3a + 9}$

16. $\frac{x + 4}{x - 5} \cdot \frac{2x - 10}{3x + 12}$ **17.** $\frac{2a}{3b} \cdot \frac{b^2 - b}{2ab - 2a}$ **18.** $\frac{3a}{4b} \cdot \frac{b^2 - b}{3ab - 3a}$

19. $\frac{x^2-1}{x^2-2x} \cdot \frac{3x-6}{4x+4}$

20. $\frac{a^2-1}{a^2-2a} \cdot \frac{4a-8}{3a+3}$

21. $\frac{3x+3b}{4x^2} \cdot -\frac{2x^2}{x^2-b^2}$

22. $\frac{5x+5b}{4x^2} \cdot \frac{2x^2}{x^2-b^2}$

23. $\frac{x^2-4}{(x-2)^2} \cdot \frac{7x-14}{3x+6}$

24. $\frac{a^2-4}{(a-3)^2} \cdot \frac{5a-15}{3(a+2)}$

25. $\frac{(x-y)^2}{3} \cdot \frac{6}{(x-y)^3}$

26. $\frac{(A-B)^2}{3} \cdot \frac{9}{(A-B)^3}$

27. $\frac{3x-12}{4x+20} \cdot \frac{x^2+5x}{x^2-4x}$

28. $\frac{4x-12}{3x+15} \cdot \frac{x^2+5x}{x^2-3x}$

29. $\frac{a^2-6a+5}{a+1} \cdot \frac{a+1}{a-5}$

30. $\frac{x^2-5x+6}{x+1} \cdot \frac{x+1}{x-3}$

B

31. $\frac{m^2-64}{3} \cdot \frac{24}{m^2-15+56}$

32. $\frac{m^2-81}{8} \cdot \frac{32}{m^2-16m+63}$

33. $\frac{1-c^2}{b^3} \cdot \frac{b^2}{1-2c+c^2}$

34. $\frac{1-a^2}{b^2} \cdot \frac{b^2}{1+2a+a^2}$

35. $\frac{b^2+6b+9}{3} \cdot \frac{4b+16}{b^2+7b+12}$

36. $\frac{2m^2+6}{15y^2} \cdot \frac{21y^4}{3m^2+9}$

37. $\frac{3x^2+9}{15y^2} \cdot \frac{35y^3}{2x^2+6}$

38. $\frac{x^2+4}{x^2-4} \cdot \frac{(x^2-4)^2}{x^4-16}$

39. $\frac{1}{3x+2} \cdot (6x^2-11x-10)$

40. $\frac{-2}{2x+5} \cdot (6x+13x-5)$

41. $\frac{x^2-4x-21}{x^2+x-6} \cdot \frac{x^2-6x+8}{x^2-2x-35}$

C

42. $\frac{m-5}{2m-1} \cdot \frac{2m-1}{2m+1} \cdot \frac{4m^2-9}{2m^2-13m+15}$

43. $\frac{3a^2-27a+60}{2a^2-72} \cdot \frac{3a^2-17a-6}{a^3-25a}$

44. $\frac{2b^2+bx-3x^2}{b^2-3bx-18x^2} \cdot \frac{2bx^2+6x^3}{3b^2-2bx-x^2}$

45. $\frac{3a^2-2ax-x^2}{4a^2-5ax+x^2} \cdot \frac{4a^2+11ax-3x^2}{3a^2+10ax+3x^2}$

ADDITION MADE SIMPLE

Carl Friedrich Gauss (1777-1855) astonished his teacher when, at age 7, he mentally found the sum of the first 100 counting numbers. The following suggests the method he used.

Simplify. 1 + 2 + 3 + 4 + 5 + 6 + 7 + 8 + 9 + 10

Write	1	2	3	4	5	6	7	8	9	10	We have 10 sums of 11, or 110.
	10	9	8	7	6	5	4	3	2	1	However, each number from
Add	11	11	11	11	11	11	11	11	11	11	1 to 10 has been used twice.

Therefore, $1+2+3+4+5+6+7+8+9+10 = \frac{110}{2}$, or 55.

1. Try the method above to find the sum of the counting numbers from 1 to 100. Can you do this mentally?
2. What is the sum of the first 1000 counting numbers? of the first 10 000? of the first 100 000?
3. Predict the sum of the first one million counting numbers. Then find the sum and compare.

11-3 DIVIDING WITH FRACTIONS

The fractions $\frac{c}{d}$ and $\frac{d}{c}$ are *reciprocals*. The product of reciprocals is 1.

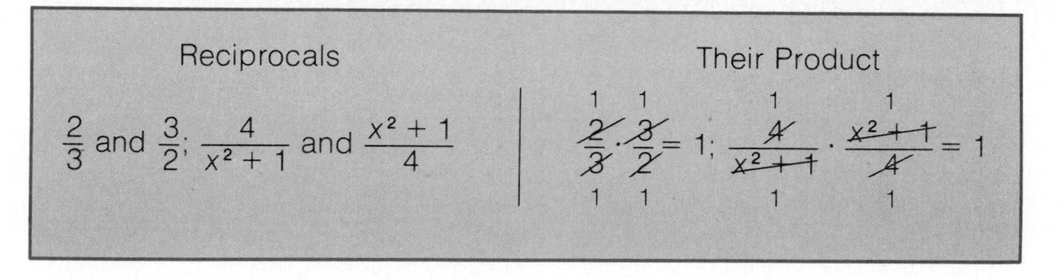

Reciprocals	Their Product
$\frac{2}{3}$ and $\frac{3}{2}$; $\frac{4}{x^2+1}$ and $\frac{x^2+1}{4}$	$\frac{\overset{1}{\cancel{2}}}{\underset{1}{\cancel{3}}} \cdot \frac{\overset{1}{\cancel{3}}}{\underset{1}{\cancel{2}}} = 1$; $\frac{\overset{1}{\cancel{4}}}{\underset{1}{\cancel{x^2+1}}} \cdot \frac{\overset{1}{\cancel{x^2+1}}}{\underset{1}{\cancel{4}}} = 1$

We use reciprocals to help us find quotients. The quotient of two fractions is equal to the product of the first fraction and the reciprocal of the second.

$$\frac{a}{b} \div \frac{c}{d} = \frac{a}{b} \cdot \frac{d}{c},\ b \neq 0,\ c \neq 0,\ d \neq 0$$

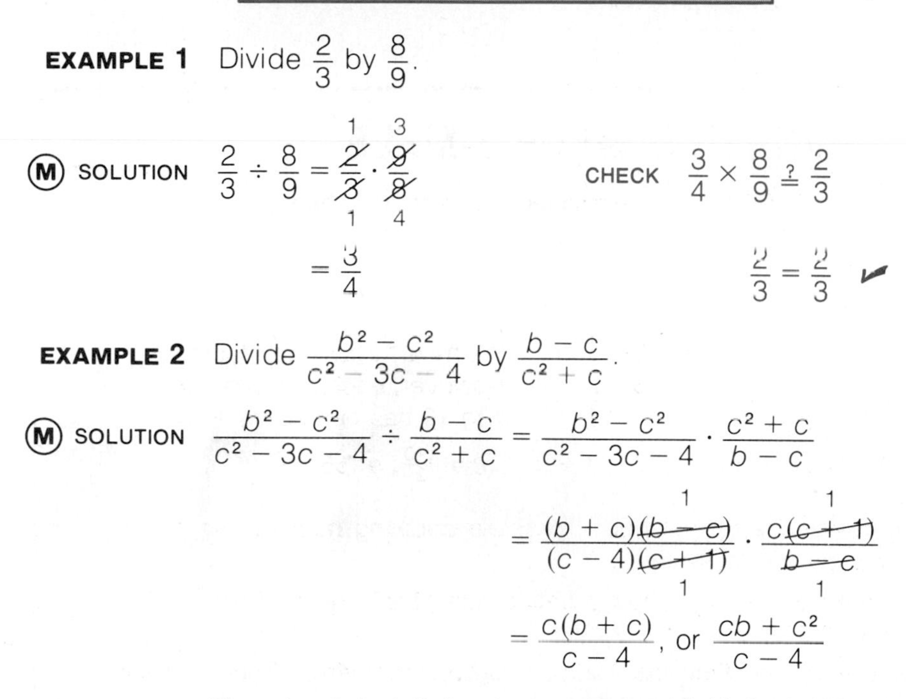

EXAMPLE 1 Divide $\frac{2}{3}$ by $\frac{8}{9}$.

Ⓜ **SOLUTION**

$$\frac{2}{3} \div \frac{8}{9} = \frac{\overset{1}{\cancel{2}}}{\underset{1}{\cancel{3}}} \cdot \frac{\overset{3}{\cancel{9}}}{\underset{4}{\cancel{8}}}$$

$$= \frac{3}{4}$$

CHECK

$$\frac{3}{4} \times \frac{8}{9} \stackrel{?}{=} \frac{2}{3}$$

$$\frac{2}{3} = \frac{2}{3} \checkmark$$

EXAMPLE 2 Divide $\frac{b^2 - c^2}{c^2 - 3c - 4}$ by $\frac{b - c}{c^2 + c}$.

Ⓜ **SOLUTION**

$$\frac{b^2 - c^2}{c^2 - 3c - 4} \div \frac{b - c}{c^2 + c} = \frac{b^2 - c^2}{c^2 - 3c - 4} \cdot \frac{c^2 + c}{b - c}$$

$$= \frac{(b + c)\overset{1}{\cancel{(b - c)}}}{(c - 4)\underset{1}{\cancel{(c + 1)}}} \cdot \frac{c\overset{1}{\cancel{(c + 1)}}}{\underset{1}{\cancel{b - c}}}$$

$$= \frac{c(b + c)}{c - 4}, \text{ or } \frac{cb + c^2}{c - 4}$$

CHECK The check is left for the student. Multiply the quotient by the divisor. The result should equal the dividend.

DIVIDING WITH FRACTIONS

1. To divide by a number, multiply by its reciprocal.
2. Reduce the quotient to lowest terms.

CLASSROOM EXERCISES

Simplify each quotient. Reduce to lowest terms.

1. $\frac{7}{8} \div \frac{1}{2}$ **2.** $c \div \frac{c}{b}$ **3.** $\frac{m^2}{n^2} \div \frac{2mn}{n^2}$ **4.** $\frac{b^2 - 9}{4b} \div (b - 3)$

EXERCISES

[A] Simplify each quotient. Reduce to lowest terms.

1. $\frac{1}{x^2} \div \frac{1}{x^3}$ **2.** $\frac{2}{u^2} \div \frac{2}{u^3}$ **3.** $\frac{3x - 6}{8} \div \frac{1}{24}$ **4.** $\frac{2x - 8}{6} \div \frac{1}{18}$

5. $\frac{(m - 1)^2}{4} \div (m - 1)$ **6.** $\frac{(r - s)^2}{3} \div (r - s)$ **7.** $1 \div \frac{x - y}{xy}$ **8.** $1 \div \frac{a - b}{a + b}$

9. $\frac{ab}{(a - b)^2} \div \frac{1}{a - b}$ **10.** $\frac{rs}{(r^2 - s^2)} \div \frac{1}{2r - 2s}$ **11.** $\frac{9 - y^2}{15} \div \frac{3 - y}{5}$

12. $\frac{9 - a^2}{16} \div \frac{3 - a}{4}$ **13.** $\frac{c^2 - 9}{c^2 + 3c} \div \frac{c - 3}{c}$ **14.** $\frac{c^2 - 25}{c^2 + 5c} \div \frac{c + 5}{c}$

15. $\frac{a - x}{y} \div \frac{a^2 - x^2}{xy}$ **16.** $\frac{a - y}{y} \div \frac{a^2 - y^2}{xy}$ **17.** $\frac{(a - 3b)^2}{a^2 - 9b^2} \div \frac{a - 3b}{a + 3b}$

18. $\frac{(r - 2s)^2}{r^2 - 4s^2} \div \frac{r - 2s}{r + 2s}$ **19.** $\frac{x^2 + 7x + 6}{x^2 + 6x + 5} \div \frac{x^3 + 6x^2}{x^2 + 5x}$

20. $\frac{a^2 + 4a + 3}{a^2 + 6a + 5} \div \frac{a^3 + 3a^2}{a^2}$ **21.** $\frac{x^2 - 7x + 10}{x^2 + 3x} \div \frac{x^2 - 9x + 20}{4x + 12}$

[B] **22.** $\frac{a^2 - b^2}{a^2 + 4ab + 3b^2} \div \frac{a^2 + ab - 2b^2}{a^2 + ab - 6b^2}$ **23.** $\frac{2x^2 - x - 3}{6x^2 - 13x + 6} \div \frac{x + 1}{3x^2 - 2x}$

24. $\frac{20 + x - x^2}{x^2 + 7x + 12} \div \frac{(x + 5)^2}{(x + 3)^2}$ **25.** $\frac{3a^2 - 14a + 8}{2a^2 - 3a - 20} \div \frac{6 - 25a + 24a^2}{15 - 34a - 16a^2}$

26. $\frac{2a^2 - 5a - 3}{3a^2 - 10a - 8} \div \frac{9 - a^2}{12 + a - a^2}$ **27.** $\frac{c^2 + 2c^3}{9 - c^2} \div \frac{c - 4c^3}{3c + c^2}$

[C] **28.** $\frac{a + b}{a - b} \cdot \frac{a - 2b}{a + 2b} \div \frac{a + b}{a + 2b}$ **29.** $\frac{a + b}{a - b} \div \frac{a - 2b}{a + 2b} \cdot \frac{3a + 6b}{4a + 4b}$

30. $\frac{x^2 - x}{x^2 - 2x - 3} \cdot \frac{x^2 + 2x + 1}{x^2 + 4x} \div \frac{x^2 - 3x - 4}{x^2 - 16}$ **31.** $\frac{a^2 - ac - 2c^2}{10a + 5c} \cdot \frac{4a^2 - c^2}{3a - 6c} \div \frac{a^2 - c^2}{15a - 15c}$

11-4 ADDING AND SUBTRACTING WITH FRACTIONS

For fractions having the same denominator, we add their numerators to help us find their sum. We subtract their numerators to help us find their difference.

$$\frac{a}{b} + \frac{c}{b} = \frac{a+c}{b},\ b \neq 0$$

$$\frac{a}{b} - \frac{c}{b} = \frac{a-c}{b},\ b \neq 0$$

The rule for adding fractions may be proved true as follows.

$$\frac{a}{b} + \frac{c}{b} = \frac{1}{b}a + \frac{1}{b}c$$
$$= \frac{1}{b}(a + c)$$
$$= \frac{a+c}{b}$$

EXAMPLE 1 Add $\frac{3}{5}$ and $\frac{7}{5}$.

Ⓜ SOLUTION $\frac{3}{5} + \frac{7}{5} = \frac{3+7}{5}$

$= \frac{10}{5}$, or 2

EXAMPLE 2 Add $\frac{4}{b}$ and $\frac{3}{b}$.

Ⓜ SOLUTION $\frac{4}{b} + \frac{3}{b} = \frac{7}{b}$

EXAMPLE 3 Subtract $\frac{4a}{3b}$ from $\frac{a}{3b}$.

Ⓜ SOLUTION $\frac{a}{3b} - \frac{4a}{3b} = \frac{a - 4a}{3b}$

$= \frac{^-3a}{3b}$

$= \frac{^-a}{b}$

This may be given as $-\frac{a}{b}$. See Section 11-5.

To add or subtract fractions with different denominators, first we replace fractions with other fractions for the same numbers so that all denominators are the same. It usually saves time if this denominator is the *least common denominator* (L.C.D.).

$$\frac{a}{b} + \frac{c}{d} = \frac{ad}{bd} + \frac{bc}{bd} = \frac{ad+bc}{bd}$$

$$\frac{a}{b} - \frac{c}{d} = \frac{ad}{bd} - \frac{bc}{bd} = \frac{ad-bc}{bd} \quad b \neq 0, d \neq 0$$

EXAMPLE 4 Add $\frac{x}{6}$ and $\frac{2x}{9}$.

SOLUTION The smallest number that can be divided by 6 and 9 is 18. 18 is the L.C.D. We replace each fraction by another fraction having 18 as its denominator.

Note that the L.C.D. is no different from the L.C.M. of the denominators that was introduced in Section 8-1. In Section 8-1, however, we were clearing equations of fractions. That is, we were eliminating denominators. Here, since we are "combining" fractions, we must retain a denominator.

Ⓜ
$$\frac{x}{6} + \frac{2x}{9} = \frac{x}{6} \cdot \frac{3}{3} + \frac{2x}{9} \cdot \frac{2}{2}$$
$$= \frac{3x}{18} + \frac{4x}{18}$$
$$= \frac{3x + 4x}{18}$$
$$= \frac{7x}{18}$$

EXAMPLE 5 Add 4 and $\frac{a}{b}$.

SOLUTION The L.C.D. of $\frac{4}{1}$ and $\frac{a}{b}$ is b.

Ⓜ
$$4 + \frac{a}{b} = \frac{4}{1} \cdot \frac{b}{b} + \frac{a}{b}$$
$$= \frac{4b}{b} + \frac{a}{b}$$
$$= \frac{4b + a}{b}$$

EXAMPLE 6 Add $\frac{3}{a - b}$ and $\frac{4}{a + 2b}$.

SOLUTION The L.C.D. is $(a - b)(a + 2b)$.

Ⓜ
$$\frac{3}{a - b} + \frac{4}{a + 2b} = \frac{3}{a - b} \cdot \frac{a + 2b}{a + 2b} + \frac{4}{a + 2b} \cdot \frac{a - b}{a - b}$$
$$= \frac{3(a + 2b)}{(a - b)(a + 2b)} + \frac{4(a - b)}{(a - b)(a + 2b)}$$
$$= \frac{3(a + 2b) + 4(a - b)}{(a - b)(a + 2b)}$$
$$= \frac{3a + 6b + 4a - 4b}{(a - b)(a + 2b)}$$
$$= \frac{7a + 2b}{(a - b)(a + 2b)}, \text{ or } \frac{7a + 2b}{a^2 + ab - 2b^2}$$

Factoring the denominators before adding may simplify finding the L.C.D. as shown in Example 7.

EXAMPLE 7 Add $\frac{2x}{x^2 - 4}$ and $\frac{5}{x - 2}$.

SOLUTION Since $x - 2$ is a factor of $x^2 - 4$, the L.C.D. is $(x + 2)(x - 2)$.

Ⓜ
$$\frac{2x}{x^2 - 4} + \frac{5}{x - 2} = \frac{2x}{(x + 2)(x - 2)} + \frac{5}{x - 2} \cdot \frac{x + 2}{x + 2}$$
$$= \frac{2x + 5(x + 2)}{(x + 2)(x - 2)}$$
$$= \frac{7x + 10}{(x + 2)(x - 2)} \text{ or } \frac{7x + 10}{x^2 - 4}$$

EXAMPLE 8 Simplify $\frac{1}{3a - 6} + \frac{1}{6a} - \frac{1}{2a + 4}$.

Ⓜ SOLUTION

$$\frac{1}{3a - 6} + \frac{1}{6a} - \frac{1}{2a + 4}$$
$$= \frac{1}{3(a - 2)} + \frac{1}{6a} - \frac{1}{2(a + 2)} \quad \text{The L.C.D. is } 6a(a - 2)(a + 2).$$
$$= \frac{2a(a + 2)}{6a(a - 2)(a + 2)} + \frac{(a - 2)(a + 2)}{6a(a - 2)(a + 2)} - \frac{3a(a - 2)}{6a(a - 2)(a + 2)}$$
$$= \frac{2a^2 + 4a + a^2 - 4 - 3a^2 + 6a}{6a(a - 2)(a + 2)}$$
$$= \frac{10a - 4}{6a(a - 2)(a + 2)}$$
$$= \frac{\overset{1}{\cancel{2}}(5a - 2)}{\underset{3}{\cancel{6}}a(a - 2)(a + 2)}$$
$$= \frac{5a - 2}{3a(a - 2)(a + 2)}, \text{ or } \frac{5a - 2}{3a^3 - 12a}$$

ADDING OR SUBTRACTING WITH FRACTIONS

1. If necessary, replace fractions with other fractions for the same numbers so that all denominators are the same. It is best to use the least common denominator.
2. Add or subtract the numerators. Write the result above the common denominator.
3. Reduce to lowest terms.

CLASSROOM EXERCISES

Add or subtract as indicated. Then reduce to lowest terms.

1. $\frac{5}{x} - \frac{3}{x}$
2. $5 - \frac{x}{y}$
3. $\frac{4x^2}{2x-1} - \frac{1}{2x-1}$
4. $\frac{2}{x-y} + \frac{3}{x+2y}$

EXERCISES

A Add or subtract as indicated. Then reduce to lowest terms.

1. $\frac{3}{x} + \frac{4}{x}$
2. $\frac{5}{y} + \frac{3}{y}$
3. $\frac{a}{4} + \frac{2a}{3}$
4. $\frac{2b}{5} - \frac{b}{3}$
5. $\frac{4y}{15} - \frac{y}{15}$
6. $\frac{3x}{12} - \frac{x}{12}$
7. $\frac{7}{y+2} - \frac{2}{y+2}$
8. $\frac{8}{x^2y} - \frac{2}{x^2y}$
9. $\frac{1}{a^3} + \frac{2}{a^2} + \frac{3}{a}$
10. $\frac{4+y}{2} + \frac{2-y}{3}$
11. $\frac{5+c}{3} + \frac{3-c}{2}$
12. $\frac{a+3b}{4} - \frac{2a+b}{5}$
13. $\frac{x+2b}{5} - \frac{3x+b}{4}$
14. $\frac{x^2-xy}{10} - \frac{x^2-xy}{12}$
15. $\frac{a^2-ab}{8} - \frac{a^2-ab}{10}$
16. $\frac{x-2}{3} + \frac{3}{x-2}$
17. $\frac{b-1}{2} + \frac{3}{b-1}$
18. $\frac{1}{x+2} - \frac{2}{x-3}$
19. $\frac{1}{x+3} - \frac{2}{x-2}$
20. $\frac{b}{a+b} - \frac{a}{a-b}$
21. $\frac{y}{x+y} - \frac{x}{x-y}$
22. $\frac{x}{x-5} + \frac{2x}{x+5}$
23. $\frac{a}{a-3} + \frac{2a}{a+4}$
24. $\frac{2}{x+y} + \frac{4}{x-y}$
25. $\frac{3}{x+y} + \frac{1}{x-y}$
26. $\frac{r}{r-s} + \frac{s}{r+s}$
27. $\frac{3a}{a^2-4} + \frac{4}{a-2}$
28. $\frac{4x}{x+1} - \frac{3x^2}{x^2-1}$
29. $\frac{1}{6a-12} - \frac{4}{a-2}$

B

30. $\frac{3a-2b}{ab} - \frac{3b-a}{b^2}$
31. $\frac{a+b-1}{a} - \frac{2a-b+1}{2a}$
32. $\frac{3x^2-4x+4}{6x^2} - \frac{x+2}{3x}$
33. $\frac{2a-5}{14a^2} - \frac{4-a}{7a} + \frac{3a-2}{2a}$
34. $\frac{2p+1}{3p} - \frac{p-5}{2p} + \frac{p+4}{30p^2}$
35. $\frac{a}{a+1} + \frac{a^2}{a^2-1}$
36. $\frac{a^2+b^2}{a^2-b^2} + \frac{2a}{a+b}$
37. $\frac{x}{1-x} - \frac{x}{1+x}$
38. $\frac{c-2}{5c-5} - \frac{c+1}{6c+18}$

C

39. $\frac{2m-4}{9m^2-9m} - \frac{5}{6m-6}$
40. $\frac{5x}{x^2+x} + \frac{2x-4}{x^2-1}$
41. $\frac{x}{x^2-6x+8} - \frac{x}{x^2-16}$
42. $\frac{a-4b}{a^2-7ab+12b^2} - \frac{a-3b}{a^2-ab-12b^2}$
43. $\frac{4}{x^2-16} - \frac{2}{x^2-8x+16}$

HEALTH

There are hundreds of health-related occupations. Some involve caring for the sick and injured. Others are preventive in nature. Others are business-oriented. Although some health occupations provide on-the-job training, most require a two-year or a four-year college degree. Almost all require an interest in and an aptitude for mathematics, science, and psychology. All require that a person care about the health of others.

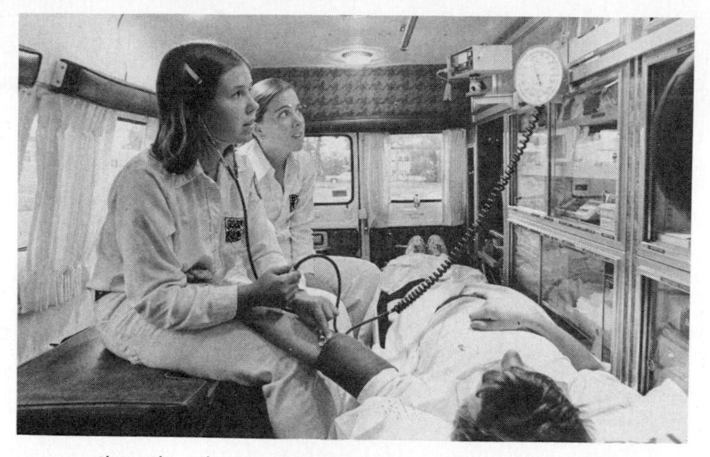

A health occupation that has attracted above-average interest in recent years is that of *paramedic*. The paramedic may work in a variety of settings, from a doctor's office to an emergency vehicle. Typical paramedic duties, always performed under the supervision of a doctor, include:

- Determining the pulse and respiration rates of an accident victim.
- Administering oxygen to a patient.
- Administering dextrose solution intravenously.
- Giving immediate first aid for body fractures.
- Taking an electrocardiogram (ECG or EKG).
- Administering a general physical examination.

MATHEMATICAL SAMPLER

1. As a paramedic, you have 150 mL of 5% dextrose solution. The doctor's instructions require that you administer a 3% solution. How many milliliters of distilled water should you add to the 5% solution to give a 3% solution?
2. The paramedical team must get an accident victim to the hospital within 30 minutes. They must travel 27 km on a freeway and 12 km in city traffic. They know from experience that they can go about $\frac{2}{3}$ as fast in the city as on the freeway. Find the minimum average freeway speed so that they are likely to arrive at the hospital on time.

11-5 POSITIVE AND NEGATIVE NUMERATORS AND DENOMINATORS

For any fraction, there are three other fractions whose numerators have the same absolute value and whose denominators have the same absolute value.

$$\frac{a}{b} = \frac{-a}{-b} \quad \Big| \quad \frac{a}{b} = -\frac{-a}{b} \quad \Big| \quad \frac{a}{b} = -\frac{a}{-b}$$

$$-\frac{a}{b} = -\frac{-a}{-b} \quad \Big| \quad -\frac{a}{b} = \frac{-a}{b} \quad \Big| \quad -\frac{a}{b} = \frac{a}{-b}$$

That these fractions name the same number can be verified using the Properties of One and Negative One.

EXAMPLE 1 Represent $\frac{1}{2}$ four ways so that all numerators have the same absolute value and all denominators have the same absolute value.

SOLUTION $\frac{1}{2} = \frac{-1}{-2} \quad \Big| \quad \frac{1}{2} = -\frac{-1}{2} \quad \Big| \quad \frac{1}{2} = -\frac{1}{-2}$

EXAMPLE 2 Represent $-\frac{x}{2}$ four ways so that all numerators have the same absolute value and all denominators have the same absolute value.

SOLUTION $-\frac{x}{2} = -\frac{-x}{-2} \quad \Big| \quad -\frac{x}{2} = \frac{-x}{2} \quad \Big| \quad -\frac{x}{2} = \frac{x}{-2}$

EXAMPLE 3 Replace $\frac{a-b}{c-d}$ by a fraction for the same number but with denominator $d - c$.

SOLUTION Since $c - d = -(d - c)$, we may write

$$\frac{a-b}{c-d} = \frac{-(a-b)}{-(c-d)} = \frac{b-a}{d-c}$$

or

$$\frac{a-b}{c-d} = -\frac{a-b}{-(c-d)} = -\frac{a-b}{d-c}$$

Replacing a fraction by another fraction for the same number, but with the opposite denominator, may help to simplify an expression.

EXAMPLE 4 Simplify $\frac{2y}{4-y}+\frac{5y}{y-4}$. Simplify $\frac{5}{r-2s}-\frac{3}{2s-r}$.

Ⓜ SOLUTION

$$\frac{2y}{4-y}+\frac{5y}{y-4}$$
$$=\frac{2y}{4-y}+\frac{-5y}{4-y}$$
$$=\frac{-3y}{4-y},$$
$$\text{or } -\frac{3y}{4-y}, \text{ or } \frac{3y}{y-4}$$

$$\frac{5}{r-2s}-\frac{3}{2s-r}$$ Ⓜ
$$=\frac{5}{r-2s}+\frac{3}{-(2s-r)}$$
$$=\frac{5}{r-2s}+\frac{3}{r-2s}$$
$$=\frac{8}{r-2s}$$

EXAMPLE 5 Reduce $\frac{x^2-6x}{24+2x-x^2}$ to lowest terms.

SOLUTION 1

Ⓜ
$$\frac{x^2-6x}{24+2x-x^2}=-\frac{x^2-6x}{x^2-2x-24}$$
$$=-\frac{x\cancel{(x-6)}^{1}}{\cancel{(x-6)}_{1}(x+4)}$$
$$=-\frac{x}{x+4}$$

SOLUTION 2

$$\frac{x^2-6x}{24+2x-x^2}=\frac{x(x-6)}{(6-x)(4+x)}$$ Ⓜ
$$=\frac{x\cancel{(x-6)}^{1}}{\cancel{-(x-6)}_{-1}(x+4)}$$
$$=-\frac{x}{x+4}$$

EXAMPLE 6 Simplify $\frac{x+3}{x+1}+\frac{x+2}{1-x}+\frac{x^2+3}{x^2-1}$.

Ⓜ SOLUTION

$$\frac{x+3}{x+1}+\frac{x+2}{1-x}+\frac{x^2+3}{x^2-1}$$
$$=\frac{x+3}{x+1}-\frac{x+2}{x-1}+\frac{x^2+3}{(x+1)(x-1)}$$
$$=\frac{(x+3)(x-1)-(x+1)(x+2)+x^2+3}{(x+1)(x-1)}$$
$$=\frac{x^2-x-2}{(x+1)(x-1)}$$
$$=\frac{(x-2)\cancel{(x+1)}^{1}}{\cancel{(x+1)}_{1}(x-1)}$$
$$=\frac{x-2}{x-1}$$

CLASSROOM EXERCISES

Simplify.

1. $\frac{a^2 - 3a}{15 - 2a - a^2}$
2. $\frac{4p}{5 - p} - \frac{3}{p - 5}$
3. $\frac{x - 3}{x^2 - 25} + \frac{6}{x + 5} + \frac{3}{5 - x}$

EXERCISES

A Simplify.

1. $\frac{y^2 - 9}{6 + y - y^2}$
2. $\frac{x^2 - 4x}{8 + 2x - x^2}$
3. $\frac{6 + x}{-6 - 7x - x^2}$
4. $\frac{3 - x}{12 - x - x^2}$
5. $\frac{4y}{5 - y} + \frac{5y}{y - 5}$
6. $\frac{6x}{x - 7} + \frac{2x}{7 - x}$
7. $\frac{4z}{z - 3} + \frac{2z}{3 - z}$
8. $\frac{8m}{m - 2} + \frac{3m}{2 - m}$
9. $\frac{3}{2x - 3} - \frac{4}{3 - 2x}$
10. $\frac{5}{p - 3q} - \frac{4}{3q - p}$
11. $\frac{3}{2x - 3} + \frac{5}{3 - 2x}$
12. $\frac{4x}{2x - 5} - \frac{3x}{5 - 2x}$
13. $\frac{6x}{4x - 2} + \frac{3y}{2 - 4x}$

B Find the missing term.

14. $\frac{a - 3}{a - 2} = -\frac{?}{2 - a}$
15. $\frac{c - d}{x - y} = -\frac{c - d}{?}$
16. $\frac{4 - a}{x - y} = +\frac{?}{y - x}$
17. $\frac{4}{a - b} = +\frac{?}{b - a}$
18. $-\frac{a^2 - 2b}{a^2 - b^2} = +\frac{?}{a^2 - b^2}$
19. $\frac{a^2 + b^2}{a^2 - b^2} = -\frac{?}{a^2 - b^2}$

Simplify.

20. $\frac{x^2 - 4x + 3}{3 - x}$
21. $\frac{x^2 - x - 12}{4 + 47x - 12x^2}$
22. $\frac{1 - x^2}{3x^2 - 6x + 3}$
23. $\frac{(n - m)^2}{m^2 + 2mn - 3n^2}$
24. $\frac{4a - 4b}{b^2 - a^2}$
25. $\frac{x^2 - 6x + 9}{9 - x^2}$

C

26. $\frac{a^2 + 5a + 1}{a^2 - a - 20} + \frac{a + 3}{5 - a}$
27. $\frac{abx^2 - aby^2}{x^2 + 2xy + y^2} \div \frac{x^2 - 2xy + y^2}{y^2 - xy}$

PATTERNS

Find the patterns.

1. Multiply 37 037 037 by 3, 6, 9, 12, and 18.
2. Multiply 12 345 679 by 8.
3. Multiply 98 765 432 by 9.
4. Write the standard name for 11^4; for 101^4; for 111^3.

11-6 MIXED EXPRESSIONS

A numerical sum involving an integer and a fraction may be represented by a numeral in *mixed form*.

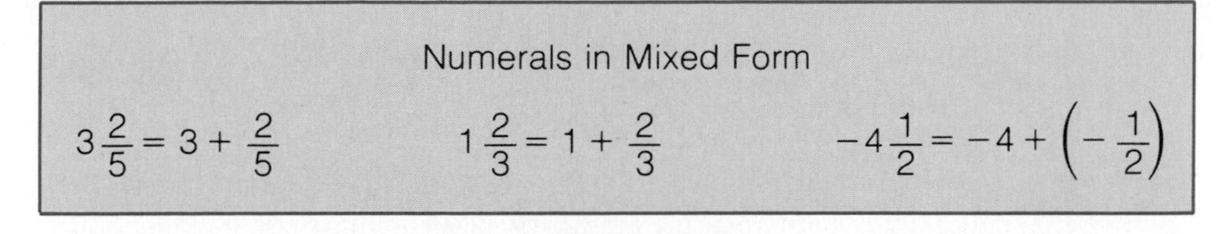

An algebraic expression involving a sum in which one term is a fraction may be called a *mixed expression*.

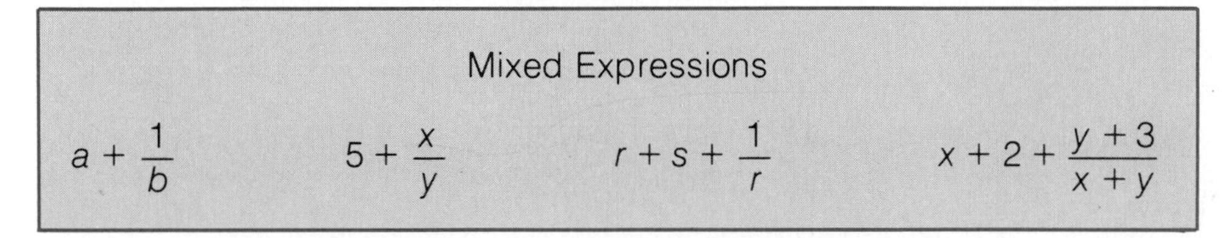

In earlier work in mathematics, you probably learned how to replace numerals in mixed form by fractions and some fractions by numerals in mixed form. Similarly, you may replace mixed expressions by fractions and some fractions by mixed expressions.

EXAMPLE 1 Replace $4\frac{3}{5}$ by a fraction. Replace $\frac{14}{3}$ by a numeral in mixed form.

Ⓜ **SOLUTION**

$$4\frac{3}{5} = \frac{4}{1} + \frac{3}{5}$$
$$= \frac{20}{5} + \frac{3}{5}$$
$$= \frac{23}{5}$$

$$3\overline{)14}\ \text{quotient } 4;\quad 12;\quad \text{remainder } 2$$

$$\frac{14}{3} = 4\frac{2}{3}$$

EXAMPLE 2 Replace $a + \frac{b}{c}$ by a fraction.

Ⓜ **SOLUTION**

$$a + \frac{b}{c} = \frac{ac}{c} + \frac{b}{c}$$
$$= \frac{ac + b}{c}$$

EXAMPLE 3 Replace $x + 3 - \frac{2x}{x-1}$ by a fraction.

Ⓜ SOLUTION

$$x + 3 - \frac{2x}{x-1} = \frac{x+3}{1} - \frac{2x}{x-1}$$
$$= \frac{(x+3)(x-1)}{x-1} - \frac{2x}{x-1}$$
$$= \frac{(x+3)(x-1) - 2x}{x-1}$$
$$= \frac{x^2 + 2x - 3 - 2x}{x-1}$$
$$= \frac{x^2 - 3}{x-1}$$

EXAMPLE 4 Replace $\frac{12x^2 - 8x + 3}{4x}$ by a mixed expression.

Ⓜ SOLUTION 1

$$\begin{array}{r} 3x \quad - 2 \\ 4x\overline{)12x^2 - 8x + 3} \\ \underline{12x^2 - 8x} \\ 3 \end{array}$$

$$\frac{12x^2 - 8x + 3}{4x} = 3x - 2 + \frac{3}{4x}$$

Ⓜ SOLUTION 2

$$\frac{12x^2 - 8x + 3}{4x}$$
$$= \frac{12x^2}{4x} - \frac{8x}{4x} + \frac{3}{4x}$$
$$= 3x - 2 + \frac{3}{4x}$$

EXAMPLE 5 Replace $\frac{2x^2 + 2x - 7}{2x - 4}$ by a mixed expression.

Ⓜ SOLUTION

$$\begin{array}{r} x \quad + 3 \\ 2x - 4\overline{)2x^2 + 2x - 7} \\ \underline{2x^2 - 4x} \\ 6x - 7 \\ \underline{6x - 12} \\ 5 \end{array}$$

$$\frac{2x^2 + 2x - 7}{2x - 4} = x + 3 + \frac{5}{2x - 4}$$

CHECK

$$(2x - 4)\left(x + 3 + \frac{5}{2x-4}\right) \stackrel{?}{=} 2x^2 + 2x - 7$$
$$(2x - 4)(x + 3) + 5 \stackrel{?}{=} 2x^2 + 2x - 7$$
$$2x^2 + 2x - 7 = 2x^2 + 2x - 7 \quad ✓$$

CLASSROOM EXERCISES

Replace each mixed expression by a fraction.

1. $8\frac{3}{4}$
2. $\frac{c}{d} - 1$
3. $2a - 3 + \frac{3}{a}$
4. $1 - \frac{4}{a + b}$

Replace each fraction by a mixed expression.

5. $\frac{17}{5}$
6. $\frac{a + b}{a}$
7. $\frac{6x^2 + 4x - 7}{2x}$
8. $\frac{3y^2 - 2y - 8}{3y + 4}$

EXERCISES

A Replace each mixed expression by a fraction.

1. $y + \frac{5}{y}$
2. $x + \frac{3}{x}$
3. $a + \frac{2}{a + 1}$
4. $x + \frac{2x}{x + 1}$
5. $6 + \frac{x + y}{x - y}$
6. $8 + \frac{z + 3}{z - 3}$
7. $\frac{4}{x + 2} + 3$
8. $\frac{6}{h - 3} + 2$
9. $x - 2 + \frac{1}{x + 2}$
10. $4m^2 - 2m + 3 + \frac{1}{3m}$
11. $7x^2 + 3x + 4 - \frac{1}{2x}$

Replace each fraction by a mixed expression.

12. $\frac{r + t}{r}$
13. $\frac{4 - x}{x}$
14. $\frac{5 - y}{y}$
15. $\frac{x^2 + x + 1}{x}$
16. $\frac{x^2 + x + 3}{x}$
17. $\frac{ab + ac + 2}{a}$
18. $\frac{mn + mr + 3}{m}$
19. $\frac{15x^2 - 20x + 2}{5x}$
20. $\frac{12c^2 - 8c + 3}{2c}$
21. $\frac{6x^2 - 7x + 6}{3x - 2}$
22. $\frac{5x^2 + 5x + 6}{x + 4}$
23. $\frac{y^2 - 8y + 6}{y - 3}$

B Replace each mixed expression by a fraction.

24. $a - b + \frac{b^2}{a + b}$
25. $2x - y + \frac{y^2}{x + y}$
26. $t - 3 + \frac{5t - 6}{t - 2}$
27. $n - 3 + \frac{5n - 6}{n - 2}$
28. $n - 8 + \frac{6n}{n - 2}$
29. $x + 4 - \frac{4x}{x - 2}$

Replace each fraction by a mixed expression.

30. $\frac{4a^2 + 10a + 6}{4a + 2}$
31. $\frac{2x^2 + 3x + 2}{x + 2}$
32. $\frac{5a^2 - 7a + 1}{a - 1}$

C

33. $\frac{8x^3 - 27}{2x - 3}$
34. $\frac{x^3 + bx^2 - b^2x - 2b^3}{x + b}$
35. $\frac{3x^2 + 4xy - 4y^2 + 2}{x + 2y}$

11-7 COMPLEX FRACTIONS

A **complex fraction** is one that has a fraction in either the numerator or the denominator or both.

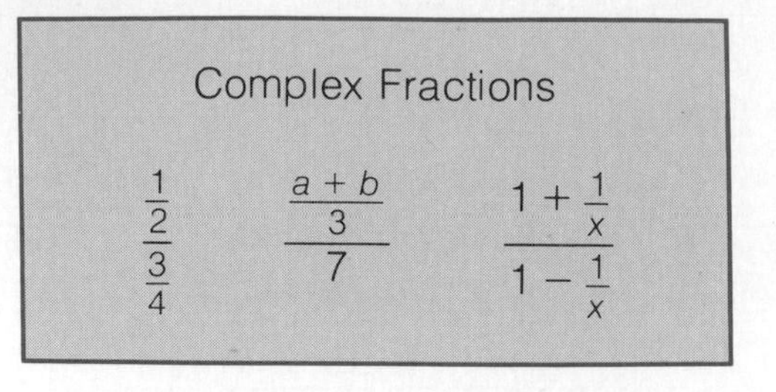

There are two ways we can simplify complex fractions.

- Multiply both numerator and denominator of the fraction by the least common denominator of all fractions appearing in the numerator and denominator.
- Divide the numerator by the denominator.

EXAMPLE 1 Simplify $\dfrac{\frac{a^2-b^2}{6}}{\frac{a+b}{3}}$.

SOLUTION 1 The L.C.D. of $\dfrac{a^2-b^2}{6}$ and $\dfrac{a+b}{3}$ is 6.

Ⓜ

$$\frac{\frac{a^2-b^2}{6}}{\frac{a+b}{3}} = \frac{\frac{a^2-b^2}{\not{6}_{1}}\cdot\overset{1}{\not{6}}}{\frac{a+b}{\underset{1}{\not{3}}}\cdot\underset{2}{\not{6}}}$$

$$= \frac{a^2-b^2}{2(a+b)}$$

$$= \frac{\overset{1}{\cancel{(a+b)}}(a-b)}{2\underset{1}{\cancel{(a+b)}}}$$

$$= \frac{a-b}{2}$$

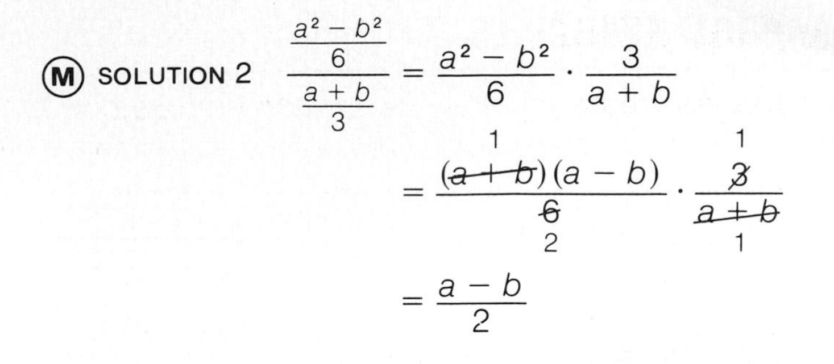

Ⓜ SOLUTION 2

$$\frac{\frac{a^2-b^2}{6}}{\frac{a+b}{3}} = \frac{a^2-b^2}{6} \cdot \frac{3}{a+b}$$

$$= \frac{\overset{1}{\cancel{(a+b)}}(a-b)}{\underset{2}{\cancel{6}}} \cdot \frac{\overset{1}{\cancel{3}}}{\underset{1}{\cancel{a+b}}}$$

$$= \frac{a-b}{2}$$

CHECK

$$\frac{a-b}{2} \cdot \frac{a+b}{3} \stackrel{?}{=} \frac{a^2-b^2}{6}$$

$$\frac{a^2-b^2}{6} = \frac{a^2-b^2}{6} \quad ✓$$

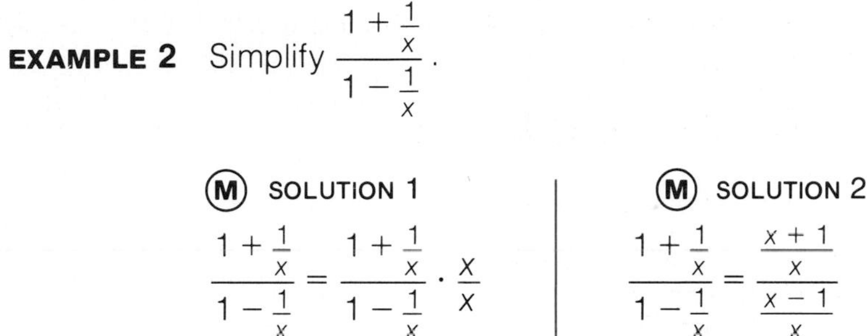

EXAMPLE 2 Simplify $\dfrac{1+\frac{1}{x}}{1-\frac{1}{x}}$.

Ⓜ SOLUTION 1

$$\frac{1+\frac{1}{x}}{1-\frac{1}{x}} = \frac{1+\frac{1}{x}}{1-\frac{1}{x}} \cdot \frac{x}{x}$$

$$= \frac{x+1}{x-1}$$

Ⓜ SOLUTION 2

$$\frac{1+\frac{1}{x}}{1-\frac{1}{x}} = \frac{\frac{x+1}{x}}{\frac{x-1}{x}}$$

$$= \frac{x+1}{\underset{1}{\cancel{x}}} \cdot \frac{\overset{1}{\cancel{x}}}{x-1}$$

$$= \frac{x+1}{x-1}$$

CHECK

$$\frac{x+1}{x-1} \cdot \left(1-\frac{1}{x}\right) \stackrel{?}{=} 1+\frac{1}{x}$$

$$\frac{x+1}{x-1} \cdot \frac{x-1}{x} \stackrel{?}{=} \frac{x+1}{x}$$

$$\frac{x+1}{x} = \frac{x+1}{x} \quad ✓$$

CLASSROOM EXERCISES

Simplify. Use two methods.

1. $\dfrac{6+\frac{1}{4}}{9-\frac{3}{4}}$

2. $\dfrac{\frac{x+y}{x-y}}{\frac{x-y}{x+y}}$

3. $\dfrac{\frac{x^2+3x+2}{8}}{\frac{x+2}{4}}$

EXERCISES

A Simplify. Use two methods.

1. $\dfrac{2\frac{2}{3}}{\frac{4}{5}}$

2. $\dfrac{3\frac{1}{2}}{\frac{3}{2}}$

3. $\dfrac{\frac{a}{b}+1}{\frac{a}{b}-1}$

4. $\dfrac{\frac{x}{y}-1}{\frac{x}{y}+1}$

5. $\dfrac{a}{1-\frac{1}{a}}$

6. $\dfrac{b}{1-\frac{2}{b}}$

7. $\dfrac{\frac{x^2+y^2}{3}}{\frac{x+y}{5}}$

8. $\dfrac{\frac{a^2-b^2}{2}}{\frac{a+b}{3}}$

9. $\dfrac{\frac{4}{a+b}}{a-b}$

10. $\dfrac{2}{\frac{m-n}{m+n}}$

11. $\dfrac{\frac{x+3y}{2y}}{\frac{2x-y}{4y^2}}$

12. $\dfrac{\frac{x+4y}{6x}}{\frac{x-2y}{12x^2}}$

13. $\dfrac{\frac{6x^2y^2}{10z}}{\frac{3xy^2}{5z}}$

14. $\dfrac{\frac{14a^2b^3}{5c}}{\frac{7a^2b}{10c}}$

15. $\dfrac{\frac{x+3}{x-3}}{\frac{3x+9}{x^2-9}}$

16. $\dfrac{\frac{x+2}{x-4}}{\frac{2x+4}{x^2-16}}$

B

17. $\dfrac{m+\frac{m}{n}}{\frac{1}{n}+\frac{1}{n^2}}$

18. $\dfrac{a+\frac{a}{b}}{\frac{1}{b}+\frac{1}{b^2}}$

19. $\dfrac{\frac{m+n}{m-n}}{\frac{m-n}{m+n}}$

20. $\dfrac{\frac{x^2}{3}-3}{\frac{x}{6}-\frac{1}{2}}$

21. $\dfrac{b-\frac{36}{b}}{b+6}$

22. $\dfrac{a-2-\frac{3}{a}}{1+\frac{1}{a}}$

23. $\dfrac{1-\frac{2}{c}-\frac{3}{c^2}}{1+\frac{1}{c}}$

24. $\dfrac{\frac{2x}{a-3b}}{\frac{2xy}{2a-6b}}$

C

25. $\dfrac{x+2-\frac{12}{x+3}}{x-5+\frac{16}{x+3}}$

26. $\dfrac{\frac{a^2+b^2}{a^2-b^2}}{\frac{a-b}{a+b}-\frac{a+b}{a-b}}$

27. $\dfrac{\frac{1}{a}-\frac{1}{b+c}}{\frac{1}{a}+\frac{1}{b+c}}+\dfrac{\frac{1}{b}-\frac{1}{a+c}}{\frac{1}{b}+\frac{1}{a+c}}$

28. $1-\dfrac{1}{1-\frac{1}{y-2}}$

CHECKING YOUR UNDERSTANDING

WORDS AND SYMBOLS

algebraic fraction
complex fraction
least common denominator (L.C.D.)
mixed expression
rational expression
reduce to lowest terms

CONCEPTS

- The rules for adding, subtracting, multiplying, dividing, or reducing algebraic fractions are the same as for arithmetic fractions. [11-1 to 11-4]
- For any fraction, there are three other fractions whose numerators have the same absolute value and whose denominators have the same absolute value. [11-5]

PROCESSES

- Reduce a fraction to lowest terms. [11-1, 11-5]

1. $\frac{6xy^2}{21x^2}$ **2.** $\frac{4a}{6a + 2ab}$ **3.** $\frac{5xy - x}{25y^2 - 1}$ **4.** $\frac{x - y}{y - x}$ **5.** $\frac{x^2 + x - 12}{12 - 4x}$

- Add, subtract, multiply, or divide algebraic fractions. [11-2 to 11-4]

6. $\frac{4x}{6a} - \frac{3y}{6a}$ **7.** $\frac{5x}{12} + \frac{2x}{3}$ **8.** $\frac{7}{a - b} - \frac{3}{a + b}$ **9.** $\frac{2x - 3}{4 - x^2} + \frac{x + y}{x - 2}$

10. $\left(\frac{3ax}{5}\right)\left(\frac{10a}{9x}\right)$ **11.** $\frac{5b}{x^2 - y^2} \cdot \frac{x + y}{10b^2}$ **12.** $\frac{6r^2s}{5t} \div \frac{2rs^4}{15t^3}$ **13.** $\frac{4m^2 - 9n^2}{x^2 - x - 6} \div \frac{2m + 3n}{x + 2}$

- Give different fractions for a number so that the numerators have the same absolute value and the denominators have the same absolute value. [11-5]

14. $\frac{a}{b - c} = -\frac{?}{?}$ **15.** $\frac{-x^2 + 1}{y - 2} = \frac{?}{2 - y}$ **16.** $-\frac{-4 + c}{-d - 6} = \frac{?}{?}$

- Write a mixed expression for a fraction or a fraction for a mixed expression. [11-6]

17. $x + \frac{3}{x}$ **18.** $x - 3 + \frac{1}{x + 4}$ **19.** $\frac{8x^3 + 5}{2x^2}$

- Simplify a complex fraction. [11-7]

20. $\frac{\frac{1}{x}}{\frac{1}{y}}$ **21.** $\frac{\frac{4x^2 - 9}{6}}{\frac{2x - 3}{2}}$ **22.** $\frac{\frac{a^2}{3} - \frac{1}{3}}{\frac{a}{2} + \frac{1}{2}}$

OBJECTIVES: Solve fractional equations and systems of fractional equations.

11-8 SOLVING FRACTIONAL EQUATIONS

In a **fractional equation**, the variable appears in a denominator. A fractional equation is solved in the same manner as any other equation containing fractions.

EXAMPLE 1 $\frac{x}{8} = 2$ is not a fractional equation because it has no variable in a denominator.

$\frac{8}{x} = 2$ is a fractional equation. Solve both equations.

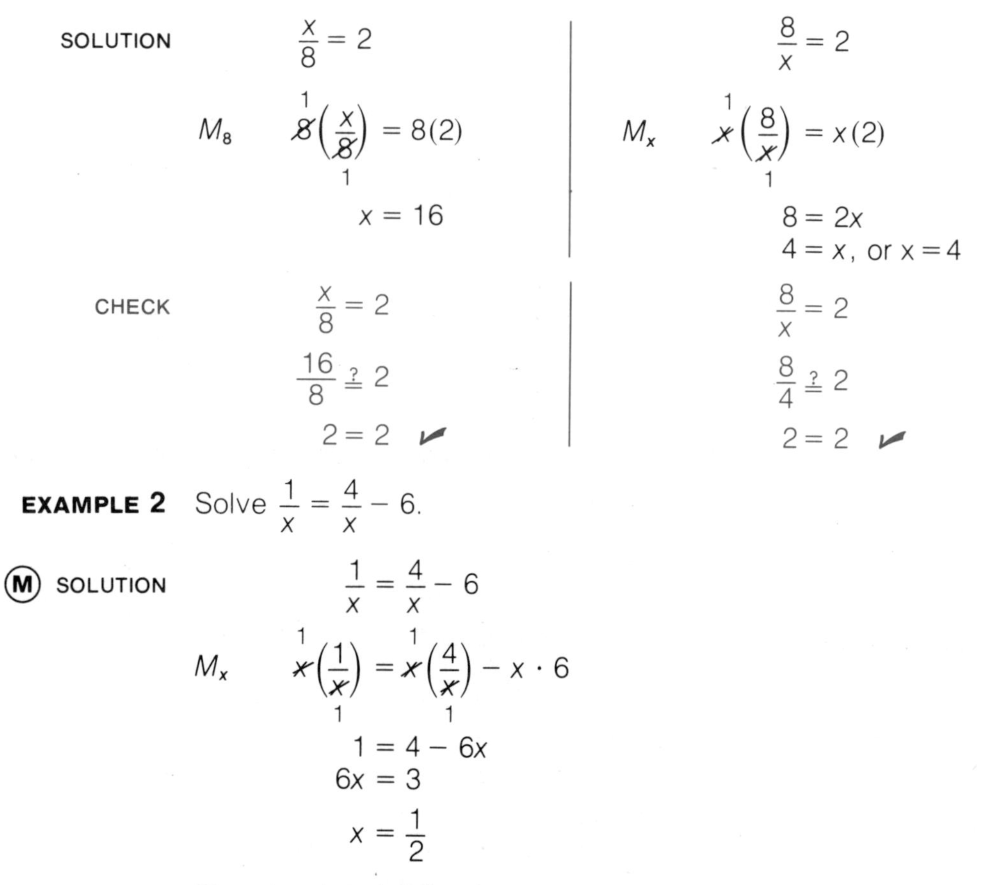

SOLUTION

$$\frac{x}{8} = 2$$

$$M_8 \quad \overset{1}{\cancel{8}}\left(\frac{x}{\underset{1}{\cancel{8}}}\right) = 8(2)$$

$$x = 16$$

$$\frac{8}{x} = 2$$

$$M_x \quad \overset{1}{\cancel{x}}\left(\frac{8}{\underset{1}{\cancel{x}}}\right) = x(2)$$

$$8 = 2x$$

$$4 = x, \text{ or } x = 4$$

CHECK

$$\frac{x}{8} = 2$$

$$\frac{16}{8} \stackrel{?}{=} 2$$

$$2 = 2 \checkmark$$

$$\frac{8}{x} = 2$$

$$\frac{8}{4} \stackrel{?}{=} 2$$

$$2 = 2 \checkmark$$

EXAMPLE 2 Solve $\frac{1}{x} = \frac{4}{x} - 6$.

(M) SOLUTION

$$\frac{1}{x} = \frac{4}{x} - 6$$

$$M_x \quad \overset{1}{\cancel{x}}\left(\frac{1}{\underset{1}{\cancel{x}}}\right) = \overset{1}{\cancel{x}}\left(\frac{4}{\underset{1}{\cancel{x}}}\right) - x \cdot 6$$

$$1 = 4 - 6x$$

$$6x = 3$$

$$x = \frac{1}{2}$$

CHECK The check is left for the student.

Keep in mind that to solve a fractional equation your first step should be to clear the equation of fractions by multiplying both members by the L.C.D.

EXAMPLE 3 Solve the fractional equation $\frac{21}{2y} - 4 = \frac{9}{y}$.

Ⓜ **SOLUTION** The L.C.D. is $2y$.

$$\frac{21}{2y} - 4 = \frac{9}{y}$$

$$\overset{1}{\cancel{2y}}\left(\frac{21}{\underset{1}{\cancel{2y}}}\right) - 2y(4) = 2\overset{1}{\cancel{y}}\left(\frac{9}{\underset{1}{\cancel{y}}}\right)$$

$$21 - 8y = 18$$

$$-8y = -3$$

$$y = \frac{3}{8}$$

CHECK

$$\frac{21}{2y} - 4 = \frac{9}{y}$$

$$\frac{21}{2\left(\frac{3}{8}\right)} - 4 \stackrel{?}{=} \frac{9}{\frac{3}{8}}$$

$$\frac{21}{\frac{3}{4}} - 4 \stackrel{?}{=} 9\left(\frac{8}{3}\right)$$

$$21\left(\frac{4}{3}\right) - 4 \stackrel{?}{=} 24$$

$$24 = 24 \checkmark$$

Sometimes a fractional equation will lead to an equation that may be solved by factoring.

EXAMPLE 4 Solve $x - \frac{15}{x} = 2$.

Ⓜ **SOLUTION**

$$x - \frac{15}{x} = 2$$

M_x

$$x^2 - 15 = 2x$$

$$x^2 - 2x - 15 = 0$$

$$(x - 5)(x + 3) = 0$$

$$x - 5 = 0 \quad \text{or} \quad x + 3 = 0$$

$$x = 5 \quad \Big| \quad x = -3$$

CHECK The check is left for the student.

CLASSROOM EXERCISES

Solve and check.

1. $\frac{3x}{4} = \frac{9}{2}$
2. $\frac{x-3}{3} = \frac{x}{4}$
3. $\frac{x+6}{2} - \frac{x-1}{3} = 5$
4. $\frac{18}{3x} = 2$
5. $\frac{-3}{x} = 4 - \frac{2}{x}$
6. $\frac{x-2}{x} = \frac{14}{3x} - \frac{1}{3}$

EXERCISES

A Solve and check.

1. $\frac{2x}{3} = 6$
2. $\frac{7x}{8} = 14$
3. $\frac{2x-3}{3} = 13$
4. $\frac{3x-3}{4} = 3$
5. $\frac{5}{c} = 3$
6. $\frac{3}{h} = -1$
7. $4 - \frac{1}{y} = 0$
8. $\frac{1}{y} + 6 = -2$
9. $\frac{x}{5} - \frac{x}{3} = 5$
10. $\frac{x}{3} - \frac{x}{7} = 21$
11. $\frac{3}{p} + \frac{1}{5} = 5$
12. $\frac{2}{b} + \frac{4}{b} - 3 = 0$
13. $\frac{2x-1}{2} = \frac{4x-1}{7}$
14. $\frac{2x-1}{5} = \frac{3x-1}{8}$
15. $\frac{21}{2y} - 4 = \frac{9}{y}$
16. $\frac{4}{2x} + 7 = \frac{6}{x}$
17. $5 + \frac{8}{2x} = \frac{4}{x} + 6$
18. $7 - \frac{4}{x} = \frac{12}{2x} - 3$

B

19. $\frac{x}{x+2} = \frac{3}{5}$
20. $\frac{2}{3n} = \frac{2}{n+4}$
21. $\frac{5}{x+1} = 7$
22. $\frac{n-1}{n+1} = 2$
23. $\frac{3y}{y+2} - \frac{5}{7} = 4$
24. $\frac{x}{x-4} + \frac{3}{4} = 5$
25. $\frac{y}{2y+4} + 6 = 11$
26. $5 + \frac{x}{3x+2} = 6$
27. $\frac{r-1}{r+1} + 2 = -\frac{3}{5}$
28. $\frac{x+5}{x-2} + \frac{2}{3} = 2$
29. $\frac{x+3}{x-1} + \frac{5}{7} = 1$
30. $\frac{3}{4} + \frac{x-2}{x+4} = 3$

C

31. $\frac{4a}{2a+6} + \frac{3}{a+3} = 4$
32. $\frac{5}{3x-9} + \frac{3}{x-3} = 3$
33. $-2 + \frac{4}{3x+12} = \frac{6}{x+4}$
34. $\frac{-8}{5x-10} + \frac{4x}{3x-6} = \frac{2}{x-2}$
35. $\frac{2x-1}{2} - \frac{x+2}{2x+5} = \frac{6x-5}{6}$
36. $\frac{8x+9}{4} + \frac{x+3}{x+2} = \frac{6x+10}{3}$
37. $\frac{x+4}{(x-1)(x-2)} + \frac{5}{(1-x)(x-3)} + \frac{4-x}{(2-x)(3-x)} = 0$
38. $\frac{1}{x+1} + \frac{2}{x^3+1} = \frac{3}{x^2-x+1}$

11-9 FRACTIONAL EQUATIONS HAVING POLYNOMIAL DENOMINATORS

A denominator cannot be zero. Therefore, a variable cannot represent a number that would result in zero as a denominator.

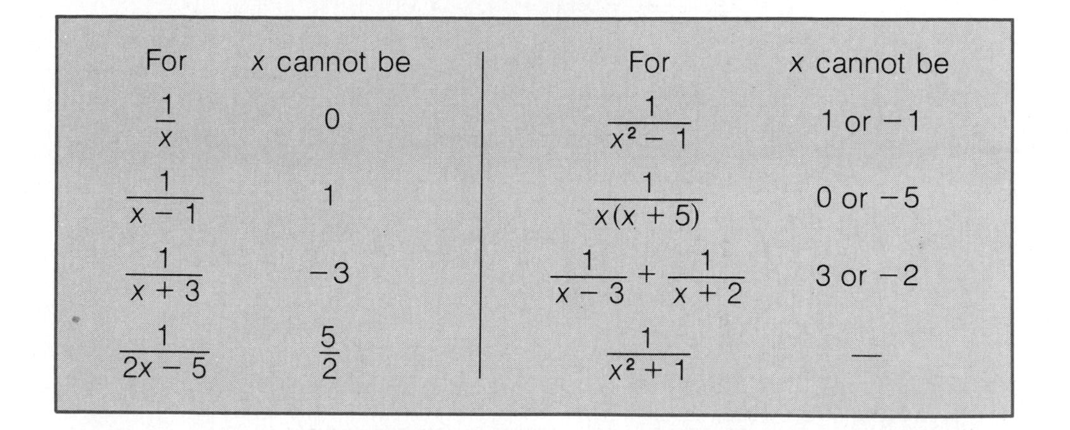

For	x cannot be	For	x cannot be
$\frac{1}{x}$	0	$\frac{1}{x^2 - 1}$	1 or -1
$\frac{1}{x - 1}$	1	$\frac{1}{x(x + 5)}$	0 or -5
$\frac{1}{x + 3}$	-3	$\frac{1}{x - 3} + \frac{1}{x + 2}$	3 or -2
$\frac{1}{2x - 5}$	$\frac{5}{2}$	$\frac{1}{x^2 + 1}$	—

Sometimes a "solution" for a fractional equation, when substituted in the equation, produces a zero as a denominator. To avoid this result, you should *check* each "solution."

EXAMPLE 1 Solve $\frac{1}{x - 1} + \frac{1}{x} = \frac{1}{x(x - 1)}$.

SOLUTION The L.C.D. is $x(x - 1)$.

Ⓜ $$x(\cancel{x - 1})\frac{1}{\cancel{x - 1}} + \cancel{x}(x - 1)\frac{1}{\cancel{x}} = \cancel{x}(\cancel{x - 1})\frac{1}{\cancel{x}(\cancel{x - 1})}$$

The first step is to clear fractions by multiplying by the L.C.D.

$$x + x - 1 = 1$$
$$2x - 1 = 1$$
$$2x = 2$$
$$x = 1$$

CHECK Replacing x by 1 gives zero in two denominators.

The question: Does $\frac{1}{1 - 1} + \frac{1}{1} = \frac{1}{1(1 - 1)}$? is meaningless.

CONCLUSION There is no solution for $\frac{1}{x - 1} + \frac{1}{x} = \frac{1}{x(x - 1)}$.

EXAMPLE 2 Solve $\frac{x+3}{x-1} - \frac{3}{x} = 1$.

SOLUTION The L.C.D. is $x(x-1)$.

$$\frac{x+3}{x-1} - \frac{3}{x} = 1$$

Ⓜ $$x\,\overset{1}{\cancel{(x-1)}}\,\frac{x+3}{\underset{1}{\cancel{x-1}}} - \overset{1}{\cancel{x}}(x-1)\frac{3}{\underset{1}{\cancel{x}}} = x(x-1)$$

$$x^2 + 3x - 3x + 3 = x^2 - x$$
$$x^2 - x^2 + 3x - 3x + x = -3$$
$$x = -3$$

CHECK The check that -3 *is* a solution is left for the student.

It can be helpful to state, *before* you solve an equation, the numbers that cannot be solutions.

EXAMPLE 3 Solve $\frac{2x+3}{x+2} - \frac{3x-8}{x-2} = \frac{4}{(x+2)(x-2)}$.

SOLUTION -2 and 2 cannot be solutions.

The L.C.D. is $(x+2)(x-2)$.

Ⓜ $$\overset{1}{\cancel{(x+2)}}(x-2)\frac{2x+3}{\underset{1}{\cancel{x+2}}} - (x+2)\cancel{(x-2)}\frac{3x-8}{\underset{1}{\cancel{x-2}}}$$

$$= \overset{1}{\cancel{(x+2)}}\,\overset{1}{\cancel{(x-2)}}\,\frac{4}{\underset{1}{\cancel{(x+2)}}\,\underset{1}{\cancel{(x-2)}}}$$

$$(x-2)(2x+3) - (x+2)(3x-8) = 4$$
$$2x^2 - x - 6 - 3x^2 + 2x + 16 = 4$$
$$-x^2 + x + 6 = 0$$
$$x^2 - x - 6 = 0$$
$$(x-3)(x+2) = 0$$

$x - 3 = 0$ or $x + 2 = 0$,

$x = 3$ | $x = -2$

But -2 is not a solution.

CHECK The check that 3 *is* a solution is left for the student.

SOLVING AN EQUATION HAVING ONE ... NOMINATORS

1. Clear the equation of fractions, if any, by multiplying both m... L.C.D. of all fractions in the equation.
2. Clear the equation of parentheses.
3. Clear the equation of decimals, if any, by multiplying both members by ... appropriate power of 10.

If it is a first-degree equation,

4. Collect all terms containing the variable so they are in the left member. Collect all other terms in the right member.
5. Simplify both members.
6. Divide each member by the coefficient of the variable.
7. Check your result by replacing the variable in the original equation.

If it is a second-degree equation,

4. Collect the terms so they are in the left member. The right member should be zero.
5. Simplify the left member.
6. Factor the left member.
7. Set each factor containing the variable equal to zero and solve each resulting equation.
8. Check your results by replacing the variable in the original equation.

CLASSROOM EXERCISES

Solve and check.

1. $\frac{5x}{x+1} = 4$ **2.** $\frac{5}{3a} = \frac{a-5}{a^2-4a}$ **3.** $\frac{r-1}{r+1} - \frac{2r}{r-1} = -1$

4. $\frac{3}{x+1} - \frac{x}{x-1} = \frac{3-x^2}{(x+1)(x-1)}$ **5.** $\frac{2x+1}{x-1} - \frac{3x}{x+2} = \frac{5x-2}{x^2+x-2}$

EXERCISES

A Before solving each equation, give the values that cannot replace the variables as solutions. Then solve and check.

1. $\frac{5}{y-1} = 4$ **2.** $\frac{6}{a+1} = 3$ **3.** $\frac{1}{y} = \frac{2}{y+2}$

4. $\frac{3}{x} = \frac{1}{x+1}$ **5.** $\frac{12x}{x+3} = 48$ **6.** $\frac{8x}{x+1} = 15$

7. x

8. $r - \frac{3}{2} = \frac{7}{r}$

9. $\frac{y-2}{4y-8} = 0$

10. $\frac{}{-1} = \frac{2}{y^2 - y}$

11. $\frac{2}{3x+4} = \frac{1}{2x+1}$

12. $\frac{2}{3x+4} = \frac{3}{4x+1}$

$\frac{}{x} - 3 = \frac{5}{2x+3}$

14. $\frac{1}{x^2 - x} = \frac{3}{x} - 1$

15. $\frac{4}{a} - \frac{3}{3a+1} = -2$

17. $\frac{4}{p+4} - \frac{5}{p} = \frac{9p-10}{p^2+4p}$

18. $\frac{3y}{y-1} - \frac{4}{y+1} = \frac{4}{y^2-1}$

19. $\frac{y-5}{y-3} - 1 = \frac{2}{y}$

20. $\frac{x-3}{x-5} - 1 = \frac{3}{x}$

21. $\frac{14}{x-2} + \frac{12}{x+2} = 9$

22. $\frac{4}{x-3} + \frac{6}{x+3} = \frac{2}{3}$

23. $\frac{4}{y} + \frac{2}{y^2+3y} = \frac{5}{y+3}$

24. $\frac{6}{y+1} + \frac{4}{y-1} = \frac{3}{y^2-1}$

25. $\frac{4}{x-3} - \frac{4}{x} = \frac{1}{15}$

26. $\frac{60}{x+3} - \frac{60}{x} + 1 = 0$

27. $\frac{y+2}{y-3} + \frac{y+3}{y+2} = \frac{2y^2+7}{y^2-y-6}$

28. $\frac{x}{x-2} + \frac{2}{x+2} = \frac{x^2+4}{x^2-4}$

C 29. $\frac{3}{x} + \frac{5}{2x} = \frac{x+27}{x+2}$

30. $\frac{2x-5}{x^2+3x+2} + \frac{x-6}{x^2-4} = \frac{3x+1}{x^2-x-2}$

31. $\frac{x-2}{x^2-x-6} = \frac{1}{x^2-4} + \frac{3}{2x+4}$

32. $\frac{2x}{2x-3} = \frac{23-32x}{4x^2-9} + \frac{3x}{2x+3}$

THE IMPOSSIBLE RECTANGLE

For each rectangle shown, the perimeter is numerically equal to the area.

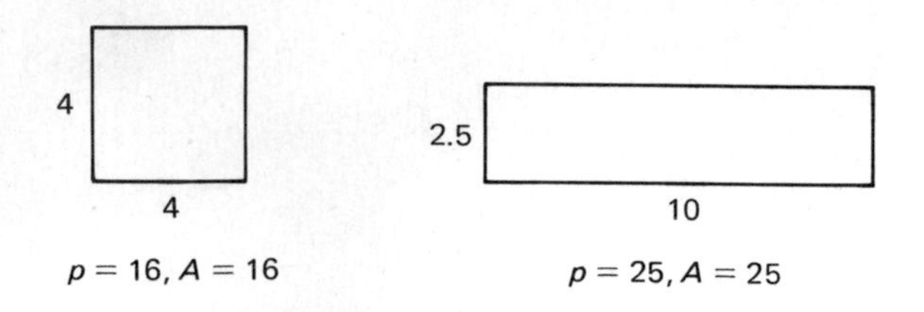

$p = 16, A = 16$ $\qquad$ $p = 25, A = 25$

1. Find other rectangles for which the perimeter is numerically equal to the area.
2. For certain widths it is impossible for the perimeter and area of a rectangle to be numerically equal. Find such a width.
3. There is only one equilateral triangle for which the perimeter is numerically equal to the area. Find the length of one side of this triangle.

11-10 LITERAL EQUATIONS AND FORMULAS CONTAINING FRACTIONS

In a *literal equation*, we represent with variables some numbers that will be known in any particular situation for which the equation can be used.

In literal equations or formulas, letters from the beginning of the alphabet usually are used for expected known numbers. Letters near the end of the alphabet are used for unknowns to be determined.

EXAMPLE 1 Solve $\frac{y}{a} - \frac{3}{b} = 5$ for y.

SOLUTION We think of a and b as numbers that will be known for particular situations. The L.C.D. is ab.

Ⓜ

$$\frac{y}{a} - \frac{3}{b} = 5$$

M_{ab}

$$\overset{1}{\cancel{a}}b\left(\frac{y}{\underset{1}{\cancel{a}}}\right) - a\overset{1}{\cancel{b}}\left(\frac{3}{\underset{1}{\cancel{b}}}\right) = 5ab$$

$$by - 3a = 5ab$$

$$by = 5ab + 3a$$

D_b

$$y = \frac{5ab + 3a}{b}$$

CHECK

$$\frac{y}{a} - \frac{3}{b} = 5$$

$$\frac{\frac{5ab + 3a}{b}}{a} - \frac{3}{b} \stackrel{?}{=} 5$$

$$\frac{a(5b + 3)}{b} \cdot \frac{1}{a} - \frac{3}{b} \stackrel{?}{=} 5$$

$$\frac{5b + 3 - 3}{b} \stackrel{?}{=} 5$$

$$\frac{5b}{b} \stackrel{?}{=} 5$$

$$5 = 5 \checkmark$$

The solution of a literal equation may involve fractions even though the equation itself does not. Therefore, you need to know how to work with fractions to check your result.

EXAMPLE 2 Solve $ax + b = c$ for x.

Ⓜ SOLUTION

$$ax + b = c$$
$$ax = c - b$$
$$x = \frac{c-b}{a}$$

CHECK

$$ax + b = c$$
$$a\left(\frac{c-b}{a}\right) + b \stackrel{?}{=} c$$
$$c - b + b \stackrel{?}{=} c$$
$$c = c \checkmark$$

Sometimes factoring will help in solving a literal equation.

EXAMPLE 3 Solve $\frac{ax - a^2}{bx - b^2} = 1$ for x.

Ⓜ SOLUTION

$$\frac{ax - a^2}{bx - b^2} = 1$$

$M_{(bx - b^2)}$ $$\overset{1}{\cancel{(bx - b^2)}}\,\frac{ax - a^2}{\underset{1}{\cancel{bx - b^2}}} = bx - b^2$$

$$ax - a^2 = bx - b^2$$
$$ax - bx = a^2 - b^2$$
$$x(a - b) = (a + b)(a - b)$$

$D_{(a - b)}$ $$x = \frac{(a + b)\overset{1}{\cancel{(a - b)}}}{\underset{1}{\cancel{(a - b)}}}$$

$$x = a + b$$

CHECK The check is left for the student.

A formula is a literal equation. A formula may be solved for any one of its variables in terms of the other variables.

EXAMPLE 4 The formula $A = p + prt$ gives the number of dollars, A, that an investment of p dollars is worth in t years at the simple interest rate r. Solve this formula for p.

Ⓜ SOLUTION

$$A = p + prt$$
$$A = p(1 + rt)$$

$D_{(1 + rt)}$ $$\frac{A}{1 + rt} = p$$

$$p = \frac{A}{1 + rt}$$

CHECK

$$A = p + prt$$
$$A \stackrel{?}{=} \frac{A}{1 + rt} + \left(\frac{A}{1 + rt}\right)rt$$
$$A \stackrel{?}{=} \left(\frac{A}{1 + rt}\right)(1 + rt)$$
$$A = A \checkmark$$

CLASSROOM EXERCISES

Solve for x. Then check.

1. $mx + b = 1$
2. $a(x + 3) - b = 7$
3. $ax - bx = ab$
4. $\frac{px}{3} - q = \frac{qx}{6} + p$
5. $\frac{c}{b} - \frac{c^2}{bx} = \frac{2b - 3c}{x} + 1$
6. $g = \frac{T + xf}{x}$

EXERCISES

A Solve for x or y. Then check.

1. $cy + d = e$
2. $ax - f = g$
3. $(a - b)x = 2(a - b)$
4. $ax - bx = 2a - 2b$
5. $\frac{x}{c} + \frac{2}{d} = 3$
6. $\frac{y}{e} - \frac{3}{f} = 5$
7. $\frac{r}{x} = \frac{p}{q}$
8. $\frac{a - b}{cx} = d$
9. $\frac{p - q}{kx} = t$
10. $(b - 3)x = b^2 - 6b + 9$
11. $(a + 2)x = a^2 + 4a + 4$
12. $ax - d = bx + c$
13. $ax - 2a = bx - 2b$
14. $d(a - x) = x(c - d)$
15. $a(b - y) = y(c - a)$

Solve for the variable indicated.

16. $V = lwh$ for h
17. $V = \frac{1}{3}\pi r^2 h$ for h
18. $A = p + prt$ for t
19. $T = \frac{1}{a} + t$ for a
20. $F = \frac{W}{R + 1}$ for W
21. $M = \frac{t}{g - b}$ for t

B Solve for x. Then check.

22. $\frac{x - 1}{x + 1} = \frac{m - n}{m + n}$
23. $\frac{3x}{c - d} - 2 = \frac{5x}{c}$
24. $\frac{1}{5(x - c)} = \frac{1}{4(c - d)}$
25. $\frac{2a}{x} + \frac{1}{2x} = \frac{4a + 1}{4a}$
26. $\frac{1}{a} + \frac{1}{b} + \frac{1}{c} = \frac{1}{x}$
27. $\frac{x}{b} + \frac{b}{a} = \frac{a}{b} + \frac{x}{a}$

Solve for the variable indicated.

28. $P = l + 2w + 2h$ for h
29. $s = \frac{n}{2}(a + l)$ for l
30. $a = S(1 - r)$ for r

C Solve for x. Then check.

31. $\frac{a}{b} - 1 = \frac{a^2}{bx} + \frac{2b - 3a}{x}$
32. $\frac{2}{a} - \frac{b}{ax} = \frac{x - b}{x}$
33. $w = \frac{1}{x} + \frac{1}{y} + \frac{1}{z}$

11-11 SYSTEMS WITH FRACTIONAL EQUATIONS

A system of equations can involve fractions. Such a system may be solved by the methods you studied in Chapter 10. Your first step, remember, should be to clear the equations of fractions.

EXAMPLE 1 Solve

$$\frac{1}{x} + \frac{2}{y} = \frac{7}{5xy}$$
$$\frac{5}{x} + \frac{2}{y} = \frac{3}{xy}$$

SOLUTION First, clear fractions. Multiply the members of the first equation by $5xy$ to obtain $5y + 10x = 7$. Multiply the members of the second equation by xy to obtain $5y + 2x = 3$.

(M)

Solve for x by *subtraction*.

$$\begin{aligned} 5y + 10x &= 7 \\ 5y + 2x &= 3 \\ \text{Subtract.} \quad 8x &= 4 \\ x &= \tfrac{1}{2} \end{aligned}$$

Solve for y. Replace x by $\frac{1}{2}$ in $5y + 2x = 3$.

$$\begin{aligned} 5y + 2\left(\tfrac{1}{2}\right) &= 3 \\ 5y + 1 &= 3 \\ 5y &= 2 \\ y &= \tfrac{2}{5} \end{aligned}$$

The solution is $\left(\frac{1}{2}, \frac{2}{5}\right)$.

CHECK The check is left for the student.

EXAMPLE 2 Solve

$$\frac{x}{x+1} + \frac{2}{y-1} = 1$$
$$\frac{y}{y+1} - \frac{1}{x-1} = 1$$

SOLUTION Clear the first equation of fractions. To do this, multiply both members by $(x + 1)(y - 1)$.

$$\begin{aligned} x(y-1) + 2(x+1) &= (x+1)(y-1) \\ xy - x + 2x + 2 &= xy + y - x - 1 \\ 2x + 3 &= y \end{aligned}$$

Clear the second equation of fractions. Multiply both members by $(y + 1)(x - 1)$.

$$\begin{aligned} y(x-1) - (y+1) &= (y+1)(x-1) \\ xy - y - y - 1 &= xy - y + x - 1 \\ -y &= x, \text{ or } x = -y \end{aligned}$$

Replace x by $-y$ in $2\boxed{x} + 3 = y$

$$2(\boxed{-y}) + 3 = y$$
$$-2y + 3 = y$$
$$3 = 3y$$
$$1 = y$$

Replace y by 1 in $x = -y$.

$$x = -1$$

The solution is $(-1, 1)$.

CHECK Replacing x and y by these values in the first equation gives zeros for the denominators.

CONCLUSION There is *no solution* of the system.

CLASSROOM EXERCISES

Solve and check.

1. $\frac{x}{3} + \frac{y}{2} = 3$
   $4x - 3y = 24$

2. $\frac{a+1}{b-1} = \frac{4}{3}$
   $\frac{2a-3}{b+1} = 1$

3. $\frac{5}{x+y} - 2 = \frac{3}{x+y}$
   $\frac{3}{x-y} + 2 = \frac{17}{x-y}$

EXERCISES

A Solve and check.

1. $\frac{x}{8} - \frac{y}{5} = \frac{1}{2}$
   $15x + 16y = 140$

2. $7m + 2n = 126$
   $\frac{m}{7} - \frac{n}{2} = -5$

3. $\frac{1}{2y} + \frac{1}{5x} = \frac{0}{5xy}$
   $\frac{1}{3y} - \frac{1}{5x} = \frac{1}{15xy}$

4. $\frac{1}{y} + \frac{2}{x} = \frac{3}{xy}$
   $\frac{4}{y} + \frac{1}{x} = -\frac{2}{xy}$

5. $\frac{7}{2y} + \frac{1}{x} = \frac{9}{2xy}$
   $\frac{3x}{xy} + 1 = \frac{11}{8y}$

6. $\frac{3}{5y} + \frac{1}{5x} = \frac{1}{xy}$
   $\frac{x}{y} + \frac{3}{2} = \frac{4}{y}$

7. $\frac{9x}{4y} + \frac{7}{4} = \frac{1}{y}$
   $2 - \frac{y}{x} = \frac{6}{x}$

8. $\frac{3}{y} + \frac{11}{3x} = \frac{17}{xy}$
   $\frac{x}{10y} + \frac{4}{15} = \frac{1}{y}$

9. $\frac{3x}{y} + 4 = \frac{8}{y}$
   $\frac{3}{2} + \frac{y}{2x} = \frac{1}{x}$

10. $\frac{2x}{5y} - \frac{1}{2} = \frac{1}{y}$
    $\frac{2}{5} - \frac{y}{x} = \frac{-2}{x}$

11. $\frac{1}{2b} + \frac{1}{4a} = 0$
    $-\frac{a}{6b} - \frac{1}{3} = \frac{1}{4b}$

12. $\frac{x}{4y} + 1 = \frac{7}{2y}$
    $\frac{1}{2} - \frac{y}{x} = \frac{1}{x}$

B

13. $\frac{x+1}{y-2} = \frac{4}{5}$
$\frac{2x+2}{y-1} = \frac{4}{3}$

14. $\frac{x+1}{y+5} = \frac{6}{5}$
$\frac{x+1}{y+1} = \frac{5}{4}$

15. $\frac{4a-7}{5} - \frac{5b+3}{7} + 7 = 0$
$a + 3 = 4 - \frac{5b-4}{7}$

16. $\frac{x-1}{y} = \frac{4}{5}$
$\frac{1}{x+y} + \frac{1}{x-y} = \frac{x+y+8}{x^2-y^2}$

17. $2 + \frac{11}{x-y} = \frac{5x}{x-y}$
$\frac{3x}{x+y} - 2 = \frac{2x-1}{x+y}$

C Solve for x and y in terms of the other variables.

18. $\frac{1}{x} + \frac{1}{y} = \frac{2m}{xy}$
$\frac{2}{x} - \frac{3}{y} = \frac{3n}{xy}$

19. $\frac{b}{a+y} - \frac{a}{b-x} = 0$
$\frac{a}{b-y} - \frac{b}{a+x} = 0$

20. $mx + ny = 2m^2$
$nx + my = 2n^2$

CHECKING YOUR UNDERSTANDING

WORDS

fractional equation

literal equation

CONCEPTS

- A number that produces zero as a denominator when it replaces a variable in an equation cannot be a solution of the equation. [11-9]
- A literal equation or formula is solved for one variable by treating the other variables as known numbers. [11-10]

PROCESSES

- Solve a fractional equation. [11-8, 11-9]

1. $\frac{5}{x} - \frac{1}{2} = \frac{8}{3x}$

2. $\frac{3}{x-1} - \frac{1}{x} = \frac{4}{x-1}$

3. $\frac{x-2}{x-3} - \frac{x-1}{x+2} = \frac{2x-1}{x^2-x-6}$

- Solve a literal equation for a given variable. [11-10]

4. $bx - ax = a$ (for x)

5. $S = \frac{a}{1-r}$ (for r)

- Solve a system of fractional equations. [11-11]

6. $\frac{3}{x} - \frac{2}{y} = \frac{-7}{xy}$
$\frac{2}{x} + \frac{3}{y} = \frac{4}{xy}$

7. $\frac{2}{x} + \frac{y}{1-y} = -1$
$\frac{4x}{x+2} - \frac{1}{y} = 4$

OBJECTIVE: Solve problems using fractional equations.

11-12 PROBLEM SOLVING: USING FRACTIONAL EQUATIONS

To solve some problems, we must know how to solve fractional equations.

EXAMPLE 1 The sum of two numbers is 60. The sum divided by the smaller number is four times the sum divided by the larger number. Find the numbers.

(M) SOLUTION 1 The sum, 60, divided by the smaller number is 4 times 60 divided by the larger number.

Use $\left[\begin{array}{ll} x & \text{for the smaller number.} \\ 60 - x & \text{for the larger number.} \end{array}\right.$

$$\frac{60}{x} = 4\left(\frac{60}{60 - x}\right)$$

$$\begin{aligned} M_{x(60-x)} \qquad 60(60 - x) &= 4x(60) \\ 3600 - 60x &= 240x \\ 3600 &= 300x \\ 12 &= x. \quad \text{Also, } 60 - x = 48. \end{aligned}$$

CONCLUSION The numbers are 12 and 48.

SOLUTION 2 The sum of two numbers is 60. 60 divided by the smaller number is 4 times 60 divided by the larger number.

Use $\left[\begin{array}{ll} s & \text{for the smaller number.} \\ l & \text{for the larger number.} \end{array}\right.$

$$s + l = 60 \quad \text{and} \quad \frac{60}{s} = 4 \cdot \frac{60}{l}$$

Clear the second equation of fractions.
Solve it for l.

$$\begin{aligned} 60l &= 240s \\ l &= 4s \end{aligned}$$

Replace l by $4s$ in $s + l = 60$.

$$\begin{aligned} s + 4s &= 60 \\ 5s &= 60 \\ s &= 12 \end{aligned}$$

Replace s by 12 in $l = 4s$.

$$\begin{aligned} l &= 4 \cdot 12 \\ l &= 48 \end{aligned}$$

CONCLUSION The numbers are 12 and 48.

CHECK The check that 60 divided by 12 equals 4 times 60 divided by 48, is left for the student.

EXAMPLE 2 The numerator of each of two fractions is 1. The denominator of one of the fractions is three times the denominator of the other. The difference of the fractions is $\frac{1}{3}$. Find the fractions.

Ⓜ **SOLUTION** The difference of the fractions is $\frac{1}{3}$.

Use $\left[\begin{array}{ll} x & \text{for the denominator of one fraction.} \\ 3x & \text{for the denominator of the other fraction.}\end{array}\right.$

There are two cases.

$$\frac{1}{x} - \frac{1}{3x} = \frac{1}{3} \quad \text{or} \quad \frac{1}{3x} - \frac{1}{x} = \frac{1}{3}$$

M_{3x} $\quad 3 - 1 = x$	M_{3x} $\quad 1 - 3 = x$
$2 = x$	$-2 = x$
Also, $6 = 3x$.	Also, $-6, = 3x$.

CONCLUSION The fractions are $\frac{1}{2}$ and $\frac{1}{6}$ or $-\frac{1}{2}$ and $-\frac{1}{6}$.

CHECK Is the difference of the fractions $\frac{1}{3}$?

$\frac{1}{2} - \frac{1}{6} \stackrel{?}{=} \frac{1}{3}$	$-\frac{1}{6} - \left(-\frac{1}{2}\right) \stackrel{?}{=} \frac{1}{3}$
$\frac{1}{3} = \frac{1}{3}$ ✓	$\frac{1}{3} = \frac{1}{3}$ ✓

EXAMPLE 3 Eric can shovel the snow from a walk in 20 minutes. If he works with Glen, they can clean the walk in 12 minutes. How long would it take Glen to shovel the snow from the walk working alone?

SOLUTION The part of the walk cleaned by Glen plus the part cleaned by Eric equals the whole walk.

Use t for the number of minutes it would take Glen to clean the walk alone.

Since Eric can clean the whole walk in 20 minutes, his rate is $\frac{1}{20}$ of the walk per minute.

$\frac{(\text{walk})}{(\text{min})} = \frac{\text{walk}}{\text{min}}$

Since Glen can clean the whole walk in t minutes, his rate is $\frac{1}{t}$ of the walk per minute.

$\frac{(\text{walk})}{(\text{min})} = \frac{\text{walk}}{\text{min}}$

(M)

	rate	· time	= work
Glen	$\frac{1}{t}$	12	$\frac{12}{t}$
Eric	$\frac{1}{20}$	12	$\frac{12}{20}$ or $\frac{3}{5}$

$\frac{\text{walk}}{\text{min}} \cdot \text{min} = \text{walk}$

$\frac{\text{walk}}{\text{min}} \cdot \text{min} = \text{walk}$

$$work_G + work_E = work_{total}$$

$$\frac{12}{t} + \frac{3}{5} = 1$$

walk + walk = walk

$$M_{5t} \quad 60 + 3t = 5t$$

$$60 = 2t$$

$$30 = t$$

CONCLUSION Glen could clean the walk by himself in 30 minutes.

CHECK If Glen can shovel the snow from the walk by himself in 30 minutes, he can clean $\frac{1}{30}$ of the walk in 1 minute. Eric can clean $\frac{1}{20}$ of the walk in 1 minute. Working together, can they clean the walk in 12 minutes?

$$\frac{1}{30}(12) + \frac{1}{20}(12) \stackrel{?}{=} 1$$

$$\frac{2}{5} + \frac{3}{5} \stackrel{?}{=} 1$$

$$1 = 1 \checkmark$$

CLASSROOM EXERCISES

Solve and check. Do each exercise two ways. Use one variable. Then use two variables.

1. The sum of two numbers is 12. When the larger is divided by the smaller, the quotient is 5. Find the numbers.
2. The denominator of a fraction exceeds the numerator by 3. If 4 is added to both the numerator and denominator, the result equals $\frac{6}{7}$. Find the fraction.
3. If 1 is added to the numerator and denominator of a fraction, the result equals $\frac{2}{3}$. If 1 is subtracted from the numerator and denominator of the fraction, the result equals $\frac{1}{2}$. Find the fraction.

EXERCISES

A Solve and check.

1. A number exceeds its reciprocal by $3\frac{3}{4}$. Find the number.
2. A number plus three times its reciprocal equals $9\frac{1}{3}$. Find the number.

3. The numerator of a certain fraction exceeds the denominator by 3. In lowest terms, the fraction equals $\frac{4}{3}$. Find the fraction.

4. The denominator of a fraction is 2 greater than the numerator. In lowest terms the fraction equals $\frac{4}{5}$. Find the fraction.

5. The denominator of a fraction exceeds the numerator by 3. When 1 is added to both the numerator and the denominator, the result equals $\frac{3}{4}$. Find the fraction.

6. One number is 21 more than another number. When the larger is divided by the smaller, the quotient is 5 and the remainder is 1. Find the numbers.

7. One number is 19 more than another number. When the larger is divided by the smaller, the quotient is 2 and the remainder is 1. Find the numbers.

8. Gerry can paint a house in 6 days. If she works with Kurt they can paint it in 4 days. How long would it take Kurt to paint it alone?

9. Margo can clean, wash, and wax her car in $3\frac{1}{2}$ hours. If she works with Karen they can do it in 2 hours. How long would it take Karen working alone?

10. The sum of two numbers is 24. When their difference is divided by their sum, the quotient is $\frac{1}{3}$. Find the numbers.

11. The sum of two numbers is 54. When their difference is divided by their sum, the quotient is $\frac{1}{9}$. Find the numbers.

12. If 7 is subtracted from 13 times the numerator of a certain fraction to give a new numerator, the resulting fraction equals 5. If 1 is subtracted from the denominator, the resulting fraction equals $\frac{1}{2}$. Find the fraction.

13. The denominator of a fraction is 3 less than 3 times the numerator. When 1 is subtracted from the numerator and 3 is added to the denominator, the result equals $\frac{1}{6}$. Find the fraction.

[B] 14. The sum of two fractions is $\frac{7}{10}$. The smaller fraction equals $\frac{4}{5}$ the larger. Find the fractions.

15. The denominator of a certain fraction exceeds the numerator by 1. The reciprocal of the fraction exceeds the fraction by $\frac{7}{12}$. Find the fraction.

16. A train runs between two cities 240 kilometers apart. If the speed of the train would increase by 12 kilometers per hour, the running time would decrease by one hour. Find the present speed of the train.

17. Two pipes together can fill a swimming pool in 4 hours and 48 minutes. How long does it take each pipe alone to fill the pool if the difference of their times is 4 hours?

18. One pipe can fill a tank in 5 hours. Another can empty it in 9 hours. If both pipes are left open, how long does it take to fill the tank?

[C] 19. A group of boys walked 6 km each way on a hike. They walked 2 km/h more slowly on their return. They spent a total of $2\frac{1}{2}$ hours walking. Find their rates, going and returning.

20. One machine can dig a basement in five days. A second machine can do the same work in six days. The excavation was begun by the first machine, but the machine broke down after 3 days. How many days are needed by the second machine to complete the work?

21. A tank can be filled by one pipe in 8 hours and emptied by another in 12 hours. Both pipes are turned on when the tank is half full. How many hours will it take to fill the tank?

11-13 PROBLEM SOLVING: WIND AND RIVER PROBLEMS

When we travel against a current, whether in the air or in water, we go slower. When we travel with the current, we go faster. Traveling a certain distance against the current takes more time than traveling the same distance with the current.

In solving problems related to wind and river currents, we use the distance, rate, and time formula, $d = rt$.

EXAMPLE 1 A boat travels 30 km/h in still water. At that rate, it can go 72 kilometers downstream in the same time it takes to go 48 kilometers upstream. How fast is the current?

Ⓜ **SOLUTION** The time for traveling downstream equals the time for traveling upstream.

Use r for the rate of the current.
$30 + r$ for the rate traveling downstream.
$30 - r$ for the rate traveling upstream.

$$\frac{km}{h} + \frac{km}{h} = \frac{km}{h}$$
$$\frac{km}{h} - \frac{km}{h} = \frac{km}{h}$$

Since $d = rt$, use $t = \frac{d}{r}$.

	distance	÷ rate	= time
Downstream	72	$30 + r$	$\frac{72}{30 + r}$
Upstream	48	$30 - r$	$\frac{48}{30 - r}$

$$\frac{km}{\frac{km}{h}} = h$$

$$t_{downstream} = t_{upstream}$$
$$\frac{72}{30 + r} = \frac{48}{30 - r}$$

$h - h$

$$72(30 - r) = 48(30 + r)$$
D_{24}
$$3(30 - r) = 2(30 + r)$$
$$90 - 3r = 60 + 2r$$
$$30 = 5r$$
$$6 = r$$

CONCLUSION The rate of the current is 6 km/h.

CHECK If the rate of the current is 6 km/h, the boat goes downstream at 36 km/h and upstream at 24 km/h. Is the time it takes to go 72 km downstream equal to the time it takes to go 48 km upstream?

$$\frac{72}{36} \stackrel{?}{=} \frac{48}{24}$$
$$2 = 2 \checkmark$$

EXAMPLE 2 The current in a river travels at 4 km/h. At what still-water speed must a boat be rowed to go 5 km down the river and 5 km back in 3 hours?

$\frac{km}{h} + \frac{km}{h} = \frac{km}{h}$

$\frac{km}{h} - \frac{km}{h} = \frac{km}{h}$

Ⓜ **SOLUTION** The time for the trip downstream plus the time for the trip upstream is 3 hours.

Use
- r for the rate of the boat in still water.
- $r + 4$ for the rate traveling downstream.
- $r - 4$ for the rate traveling upstream.

$\frac{km}{\frac{km}{h}} = h$

	distance ÷	rate =	time
Downstream	5	$r + 4$	$\frac{5}{r+4}$
Upstream	5	$r - 4$	$\frac{5}{r-4}$

h + h = h

$$t_{downstream} + t_{upstream} = 3$$

$$\frac{5}{r+4} + \frac{5}{r-4} = 3$$

$$5(r - 4) + 5(r + 4) = 3(r + 4)(r - 4)$$

$$5r - 20 + 5r + 20 = 3(r^2 - 16)$$

$$10r = 3r^2 - 48$$

$$0 = 3r^2 - 10r - 48$$

$$0 = (3r + 8)(r - 6)$$

Therefore, $3r + 8 = 0$ or $r - 6 = 0$

$3r = -8$ | $r = 6$

$r = -\frac{8}{3}$

CONCLUSION Since the rate should be positive, the boat should be rowed at a still-water speed of 6 km/h.

CHECK If the still-water speed is 6 km/h, the boat travels 5 km downstream at 10 km/h and 5 km upstream at 2 km/h. Is the total time for the trip equal to 3 hours?

$$\frac{5}{10} + \frac{5}{2} \stackrel{?}{=} 3$$

$$\frac{1}{2} + \frac{5}{2} \stackrel{?}{=} 3$$

$$3 = 3 \checkmark$$

EXAMPLE 3 On a trip, an airplane that travels 200 km/h in still air flew with a steady tail wind of 20 km/h. Returning, it flew against a head wind of 20 km/h and took 15 minutes longer. How much time did it take flying each way? How far did it travel each way?

(M) SOLUTION The distance going equals the distance returning.

Use t for the number of hours flying with the tail wind.

	rate	time	distance
Going	220	t	$220t$
Returning	180	$t + \frac{1}{4}$	$180(t + \frac{1}{4})$

$\frac{km}{h} \cdot h = km$

$h + h = h, \frac{km}{h} \cdot h = km$

$$d_{going} = d_{returning}$$
$$220t = 180(t + \tfrac{1}{4})$$
$$220t = 180t + \tfrac{180}{4}$$
$$40t = 45$$
$$t = \tfrac{9}{8}$$

$km = km$

Also, $t + \frac{1}{4} = \frac{11}{8}$

CONCLUSION 1 The airplane traveled for $1\frac{1}{8}$ hours with the tail wind. It traveled for $1\frac{3}{8}$ hours against the head wind.

Use $d = rt$ to find the distance the airplane traveled with the tail wind.

$$d = rt$$
$$d = 220\left(\tfrac{9}{8}\right)$$
$$= 247\tfrac{1}{2}, \text{ or } 247.5$$

$km = \frac{km}{h} \cdot h$

CONCLUSION 2 The airplane traveled 247.5 kilometers each way.

CHECK Does the airplane travel 247.5 km by returning at the rate of 180 km/h for $1\frac{3}{8}$ hours?

$$d = rt$$
$$247.5 \stackrel{?}{=} 180\left(\tfrac{11}{8}\right)$$
$$247.5 = 247.5 \checkmark$$

CLASSROOM EXERCISES

Solve and check.

1. An airplane that normally flies at 500 km per hour traveled 1200 km with a tail wind. It returned against the wind, taking 1 hour longer. Find the rate of the wind.
2. A rowing crew can row 5 km downstream in the same time it can row 3 km upstream. The speed of the current is 3 km/h. Find the rowing rate of the crew in still water.

EXERCISES

A Solve and check.

1. A boat traveled 6 km with a 2 km/h current. Then it returned against the current. The entire trip took 2 hours 15 minutes. Find the rate of the boat in still water.
2. Betsy normally flies her airplane at the rate of 200 km/h in still air. One day she traveled 480 km with a tail wind. She returned against the wind and the entire trip took 5 hours. Find the rate of the wind.
3. A boat goes 24 km upstream in the same time that it takes to go 36 km downstream. The current is flowing at 3 km/h. Find the rate of the boat in still water.
4. A boat travels 20 kilometers per hour in still water. It can go 50 kilometers upstream in the same time it takes to go 85 kilometers downstream. How fast is the current?
5. A group of girls rowed 7 km downstream in an hour. They needed $2\frac{1}{2}$ hours to return. Find their rate of rowing in still water. Find the rate of the current.
6. An airplane can go 200 km with the wind in 20 minutes. The return trip against the wind requires 25 minutes. Find the rate of the wind and the rate of the airplane in still air.

B

7. Jim can row in still water at twice the rate of the current in the river near his home. It takes him 2 hours less time to row 2 km up the river than it does to row 9 km down the river. Find the rate of the current.
8. The rate of an airplane in still air is 420 km/h. It can fly 600 km with the wind in the same time that it can go 520 km against the wind. Find the rate of the wind.
9. An airplane flew 200 km with a 60-kilometer per hour tail wind. Then it returned against the wind. The entire trip took 45 minutes. Find the rate of the airplane in still air.
10. The rate of one airplane in still air is 352 km/h. It can travel 832 km with the wind in the same time that it travels 576 km against the wind. Find the rate of the wind.

C

11. Carl knows that in still water he can swim twice as fast as the rate of the current of the stream that passes his cottage. He swims one kilometer upstream and then back in 40 minutes. Find the rate of the current.
12. Two boats on a lake race on a 4-kilometer oval path. The sum of the rates at which they travel is 200 km/h. Find the rate of each if the faster boat gains one lap in 40 minutes.

11-14 PROBLEM SOLVING: DIRECT AND INVERSE VARIATION

When two variables x and y vary directly, their relationship may be described by a linear equation $y = kx$ for which k represents a non-zero constant. The relationship when $x \neq 0$ also may be described by the fractional equation $\frac{y}{x} = k$.

Direct Variation
$y = kx,\ k \neq 0$ or $\frac{y}{x} = k,\ k \neq 0,\ x \neq 0$

The second equation tells us that when x and y vary directly, their *quotient* is constant.

EXAMPLE 1 The amount of money Tina saves varies directly with the amount she earns. When she earns \$5, she saves \$3. Write an equation to show this direct variation.

SOLUTION $\frac{\text{dollars saved}}{\text{dollars earned}} = \text{constant}$

Use [s for the number of dollars Tina saves.
e for the number of dollars Tina earns.

Replace s by 3 and e by 5 in $\frac{s}{c} = k$. $\frac{3}{5} = k$.

Replace k by $\frac{3}{5}$ in $\frac{s}{e} = k$. $\frac{s}{e} = \frac{3}{5}$, or $s = \frac{3}{5}c$.

When two variables are related in such a way that their *product* is constant, the variables are said to **vary inversely**. When the variables represent *positive* numbers, an increase in the number used for one of the variables means the number used for the other variable must decrease. An equation of the form $xy = k$, k a constant, or the fractional equation $y = \frac{k}{x}$, may be used to describe inverse variation.

Inverse Variation
$xy = k,\ x \neq 0,\ k \neq 0$ or $y = \frac{k}{x},\ x \neq 0,\ k \neq 0$

EXAMPLE 2 The label on a paint can says that the paint should cover 20 square meters. Find the length and width of a rectangular region whose area is 20 square meters.

SOLUTION Since length · width = Area, length and width vary inversely. In the formula, $l \cdot w = A$, replace A by 20 and find ordered number pairs (l, w) such that $l \cdot w = 20$.

$m \cdot m = m^2$

l	1	2	4	5	8	20
w	20	10	5	4	$2\frac{1}{2}$	1

For positive numbers for l and w, the graph of $lw = 20$ looks like this.

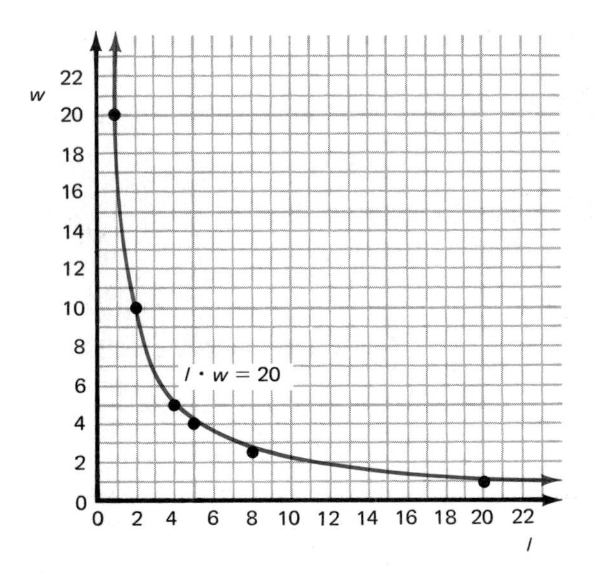

CONCLUSION Any ordered number pair corresponding to a point of the graph gives the length and width of a rectangular region that has an area of 20 square meters.

When y and x vary directly, their quotient is constant and they are said to be *directly proportional* to each other. If (x_1, y_1) and (x_2, y_2) are solutions of the equation

$$\frac{y}{x} = k,$$

then $\frac{y_1}{x_1} = \frac{y_2}{x_2}$. This relationship may also be written $\frac{x_1}{y_1} = \frac{x_2}{y_2}$ or $\frac{x_1}{x_2} = \frac{y_1}{y_2}$.

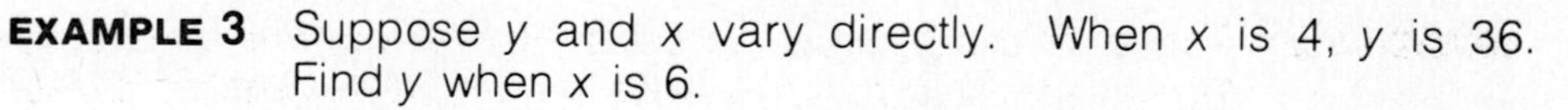

EXAMPLE 3 Suppose y and x vary directly. When x is 4, y is 36. Find y when x is 6.

SOLUTION 1

Ⓜ $\frac{y_1}{x_1} = \frac{y_2}{x_2}$

$\frac{36}{4} = \frac{y}{6}$

$9 = \frac{y}{6}$

$54 = y$

SOLUTION 2

Ⓜ $\frac{x_1}{y_1} = \frac{x_2}{y_2}$

$\frac{4}{36} = \frac{6}{y}$

$4y = 216$

$y = 54$

SOLUTION 3

Ⓜ $\frac{x_1}{x_2} = \frac{y_1}{y_2}$

$\frac{4}{6} = \frac{36}{y}$

$4y = 216$

$y = 54$

When y and x vary inversely, their product is constant and they are said to be *inversely proportional* to each other. If (x_1, y_1) and (x_2, y_2) satisfy the equation

$$xy = k,$$

then $x_1y_1 = x_2y_2$ and $\frac{x_1}{x_2} = \frac{y_2}{y_1}$.

EXAMPLE 4 x and y vary inversely. $x = 3$ when $y = 4$. Find x when $y = 6$.

SOLUTION 1

Ⓜ $x_1y_1 = x_2y_2$

$3 \cdot 4 = x \cdot 6$

$12 = 6x$

$2 = x$

SOLUTION 2

Ⓜ $\frac{x_1}{x_2} = \frac{y_2}{y_1}$

$\frac{3}{x} = \frac{6}{4}$

$6x = 12$

$x = 2$

CLASSROOM EXERCISES

1. x and y vary directly. $y = 40$ when $x = 8$. Find x when $y = 120$.
2. x and y vary inversely. $y = 15$ when $x = 4$. Find y when $x = 6$.
3. Ten pipes, each 6 centimeters in diameter, can fill a pool with water in 24 hours. How long will it take to fill the pool using only 8 of these pipes?
4. If 60 men can do a piece of work in 42 days, how long will it take 45 men to do the same work?

EXERCISES

A x and y vary directly.

1. $y = 72$ when $x = 12$. Find x when $y = 6$.
2. $y = 4$ when $x = 9$. Find y when $x = 18$.
3. $y = 4$ when $x = 10$. Find y when $x = 20$.

C is directly proportional to n.

4. $C = 22$ when $n = 2$. Find C when $n = 3$.

5. $C = 44$ when $n = 4$. Find C when $n = 5$.

x and y vary inversely.

6. $x = 2$ when $y = 10$. Find y when $x = 4$.

7. $x = 3$ when $y = 12$. Find y when $x = 6$.

8. $x = 2.1$ when $y = 1.1$. Find y when $x = 1.1$.

x and y are inversely proportional.

9. $x = \frac{1}{4}$ when $y = \frac{1}{3}$. Find x when $y = \frac{1}{2}$.

10. $x = 2\frac{1}{2}$ when $y = \frac{4}{15}$. Find x when $y = \frac{1}{3}$.

Solve.

11. The cost of a bus ticket varies directly as the number of kilometers traveled. A ticket for 200 kilometers costs $9.50. Find the cost for 300 kilometers.

12. A car uses 10 liters of gasoline to travel 88 kilometers. How much gasoline will the car use to travel 220 km?

13. Jennifer drove 4 hours at a rate of 80 km/h. How long would traveling the same distance take Jennifer if she drove at 75 km/h?

14. While traveling from Toronto to Montreal, John drove 3 hours at a rate of 100 km/h. How long would traveling the same distance take John if he drove at 90 km/h?

15. Jim has a mass of 45 kilograms. Mary has a mass of 30 kilograms. How far from the seesaw support must Jim sit to balance Mary, who sits 6 meters from the support?

16. Abel's mass is 28 kilograms. Hannah's mass is 42 kilograms. How far from the seesaw support must Abel sit to balance Hannah, who sits 2 meters from the support?

17. The number of hours required to make a 150-kilometer trip is inversely proportional to the rate of travel. Jennie normally requires $2\frac{1}{2}$ hours for the trip. Last week, however, she needed $3\frac{1}{3}$ hours. What is Jennie's usual rate of travel? What was her rate last week?

18. Carol won the election for president of the freshman class by a 6 to 5 margin. The losing candidate received 330 votes. How many votes did Carol receive?

19. There are 5.6 kilograms of nitrogen in 112 kilograms of one brand of plant food. How many kilograms of nitrogen are there in 500 kg of that brand of plant food?

20. The number of centimeters that a rubber band will stretch is directly proportional to the force causing it to stretch. If a rubber band stretches 5 centimeters under a force of $4\frac{1}{2}$ newtons, how many centimeters will it stretch under a force of 9 newtons?

B **21.** The number of meters through which a parachutist falls before the parachute begins to open is directly proportional to the square of the number of seconds spent falling. A fall covers 19.5 meters in 2 seconds. How far does the parachutist fall in 5 seconds?

C **22.** The *resistance* of a wire to the passage of electricity varies directly as the length of the wire and inversely as the square of the diameter of a cross section of the wire. One kilometer of wire has a cross-section diameter of 0.927 cm and a resistance of 0.420 ohms. Another wire, made from the same metal, has a cross-section diameter of 1.06 cm. Find the resistance of 450 m of this wire.

CHAPTER REVIEW

Simplify. [11-1]

1. $\frac{2x + 3y}{4x + 6y}$
2. $\frac{r^2 - s^2}{r + s}$
3. $\frac{x^2 - 7x + 6}{x - 6}$

Find the missing term.

4. $\frac{m + 3}{m - 1} = \frac{?}{(m - 1)(m - 2)}$
5. $\frac{3x + 1}{x - 2} = \frac{?}{x^2 - 2x}$
6. $\frac{2x - 1}{x + 1} = \frac{?}{x^2 + 5x + 4}$

Simplify each product. [11-2]

7. $\frac{5x + 5y}{4a^2} \cdot \frac{2a^2}{x + y}$
8. $\frac{x^2 - 6x + 8}{x + 5} \cdot \frac{x^2 + 5x}{x - 4}$
9. $\frac{8a^2 + 4a - 21}{a + 7} \cdot \frac{a^2 + 7a}{a^2 - 3a}$

Simplify each quotient. [11-3]

10. $\frac{a^2 - b^2}{3a} \div \frac{a + b}{a^2}$
11. $\frac{a^2 - 2a - 15}{a + 3} \div \frac{a - 5}{(a + 3)^2}$
12. $\frac{x^2 - 25}{x^2 - 5x} \div \frac{x}{x + 5}$

Simplify. [11-4, 11-5]

13. $\frac{9y}{x} + \frac{y}{3x}$
14. $\frac{3}{a + 2} + \frac{5}{a - 2}$
15. $\frac{-1}{x + 3} + \frac{-2}{x} + \frac{3}{2x + 6}$
16. $\frac{3}{1 - x} + \frac{2}{x - 1}$
17. $\frac{5x}{3x - 2} - \frac{2x - 1}{2 - 3x}$
18. $\frac{n^2 - 3n}{-9 + 6n - n^2}$

Find the missing term.

19. $\frac{4}{x - 5} = \frac{?}{5 - x}$
20. $\frac{x - 2}{x + 3} = -\frac{?}{3 + x}$
21. $\frac{a + b}{-a + b} = \frac{-(a + b)}{?}$

Write as a fraction. [11-6]

22. $m + \frac{3}{m} + 1$
23. $x - 3 + \frac{1}{x - 2}$
24. $b^2 + 3b - \frac{2}{b}$

Write as a mixed expression.

25. $\frac{b + s}{s}$
26. $\frac{a - b + 2}{a - b}$
27. $\frac{20a^2 - 12a + 3}{4a}$

Simplify. [11-7]

28. $\frac{\frac{a^2b^2}{2}}{\frac{a^2b^2}{4}}$
29. $\frac{\frac{a^2 - b^2}{2}}{\frac{a - b}{4}}$
30. $\frac{\frac{a^2}{3} - \frac{1}{3}}{\frac{a}{2} + \frac{1}{2}}$

Solve. [11-8]

31. $\frac{2x - 1}{10} = \frac{x - 2}{2}$
32. $\frac{x - 7}{4} = \frac{2(x - 6)}{12}$
33. $\frac{y}{5} = \frac{2y - 9}{3} - 11$

Identify the numbers that may not replace the variable as solutions. Then solve. [11-9]

34. $\frac{a}{a-3} = \frac{2}{3}$ **35.** $\frac{1}{x+1} + \frac{1}{x-1} = \frac{1}{x^2-1}$ **36.** $\frac{5x-7}{3} + \frac{x-11}{x-5} = 4$

Solve as indicated. [11-10]

37. $b = \frac{m}{n-p}$ for n **38.** $v = \frac{m}{m+n}$ for m **39.** $I = \frac{n-z}{P}$ for n

Solve each system. [11-11]

40. $\frac{x}{6} - \frac{3y}{5} = -1, \frac{x}{2} - 9y = 1$ **41.** $\frac{a}{2} = \frac{2b}{3}, \frac{a}{4} - \frac{b}{3} = -1$ **42.** $\frac{5}{x} - \frac{3}{y} = \frac{3}{2}, \frac{1}{x} + \frac{1}{y} = \frac{5}{6}$

Solve. [11-12 to 11-14]

43. The length of a rectangle is 3 meters greater than the width. When the width is divided by the length, the quotient is $\frac{4}{5}$. Find the length and width.

44. A rower went 5 kilometers downstream in $1\frac{1}{2}$ hours. The return trip took 2 hours. Find the rowing rate in still water and the rate of the stream.

45. The number of liters of fuel used on a trip is directly proportional to the number of kilometers traveled. For one trip, 7 liters of fuel are used for 112 kilometers. Find the number of liters needed for 475 kilometers.

CAPSULE REVIEW

Write the letter of the best response.

1. $\frac{m^2-16}{4+3m-m^2} =$

a. $\frac{m+4}{m+1}$ **b.** $\frac{-m+4}{m+1}$ **c.** $-\frac{m+4}{m+1}$ **d.** $\frac{m+4}{-m+1}$ **e.** $-\frac{m+4}{1-m}$

2. $\frac{5}{a+b} = \frac{?}{3a+3b}$

a. 3 **b.** 5 **c.** 15 **d.** $5(a+b)$ **e.** $15(a+b)$

3. $-\frac{-1}{2-x} = \frac{?}{x-2}$

a. 1 **b.** -1 **c.** 2 **d.** -2 **e.** $2-x$

4. Which is the solution for $\frac{x+1}{x-1} + \frac{1}{x} = 1$?

a. 0 **b.** $\frac{1}{3}$ **c.** $\frac{2}{3}$ **d.** 1 **e.** no solution

5. $I = \frac{E}{R+r}$ solved for R gives $R =$

a. $\frac{I-E}{r}$. **b.** $\frac{E-I}{r}$. **c.** $\frac{E-r}{I}$. **d.** $\frac{I-r}{E}$. **e.** $\frac{E-Ir}{I}$.

6. The solution for the system $x - y = 1, \frac{y}{x-1} = 0$ is

a. (1, 2). **b.** (2, 1). **c.** (0, −1). **d.** (−1, 0). **e.** no solution

7. Which does *not* represent direct variation?

a. $x = 3y$ **b.** $x = \frac{y}{3}$ **c.** $\frac{x}{y} = 3$ **d.** $\frac{3}{x} = y$ **e.** $\frac{x}{3} = y$

8. Which does *not* represent inverse variation?

a. $\frac{5}{x} = y$ **b.** $\frac{6}{y} = x$ **c.** $xy = 7$ **d.** $y = \frac{x}{2}$ **e.** $\frac{1}{y} = x$

9. $a + \frac{1}{a} =$

a. $\frac{a^2 + 1}{a}$ **b.** $a^2 + 1$ **c.** $a^2 + \frac{1}{a}$ **d.** $\frac{1}{a^2}$ **e.** $\frac{a + 1}{a}$

CHAPTER TEST

Simplify.

1. $\frac{5xy}{15x^2}$ **2.** $\frac{5r}{8} \cdot \frac{3}{2s}$ **3.** $\frac{a}{b} \cdot \frac{b^2}{a^3}$ **4.** $\frac{2a}{3} + \frac{a}{6}$

5. Write the reciprocal of $\frac{c}{3}$.

6. Complete $\frac{3a}{4b} = \frac{?}{8ab}$.

7. Divide $\frac{2a}{3b}$ by $\frac{4r}{s}$.

8. Subtract $\frac{2}{y}$ from $\frac{x}{y^2}$.

9. Represent $\frac{2}{b - a}$ as a fraction with denominator $a - b$.

10. Write $5 + \frac{a}{b}$ as a fraction.

11. Write $\frac{4x + 5y}{x}$ as a mixed expression.

Simplify.

12. $\frac{5}{2 - x} + \frac{3}{x - 2}$ **13.** $\frac{\frac{2a}{3}}{\frac{6}{6b}}$ **14.** $\frac{\frac{(x + y)^2}{2}}{\frac{x + y}{3}}$

Solve for x.

15. $\frac{12}{x} = 4$ **16.** $\frac{10}{x} + \frac{3}{2} = \frac{3}{x}$ **17.** $\frac{2}{x - 2} = x - 3$

18. $\frac{1}{x} + \frac{x - 4}{x - 1} = \frac{-3}{x^2 - x}$ **19.** $ax + b = c$ **20.** $\frac{s}{x} = \frac{a}{1 + x}$

Solve each system.

21. $\frac{x}{2} + \frac{2y}{3} = 4, \quad \frac{3x}{8} - \frac{y}{6} = 1$

22. $\frac{2}{x} + \frac{6}{y} = \frac{12}{xy}, \quad \frac{6}{x} - \frac{6}{y} = \frac{12}{xy}$

Solve.

23. The numerators of two fractions are each 3.
The denominator of one fraction is twice the denominator of the other.
The sum of the fractions is $\frac{9}{8}$. Find the fractions.

24. The denominators of two fractions are alike. Their numerators are 5 and 4. The sum of the fractions is 3. Find the fractions.

25. Nicole's boat goes 10 km/h in still water. It takes the same time to go 10 kilometers against the current as it takes it to go 30 kilometers with the current. Find the speed of the current.

26. Alfredo flew in a plane that goes 550 km/h in still air. It took him 0.5 hour to make a trip flying with the wind. It took 0.6 hour to make the return trip flying against the wind. Find the speed of the wind.

27. a and b vary directly. $a = 12$ when $b = 8$. Find a when $b = 32$.

28. x and y vary inversely. $x = 50$ when $y = 2$. Find x when $y = 4$.

Write the letter of the best response.

29. $\frac{3ab^2}{6a^2b} =$

a. $\frac{b}{2a}$ **b.** $\frac{b^2}{2ab}$ **c.** $\frac{ab}{2a^2}$ **d.** $\frac{b}{3a}$ **e.** $\frac{b^3}{3a^3}$

30. The product of $\frac{2x}{3y}$ and $\frac{1}{4y}$ is

a. $\frac{2x+1}{7y}$. **b.** $\frac{2x+1}{12y}$. **c.** $\frac{x}{6y^2}$. **d.** $\frac{2x}{7y}$. **e.** $\frac{2x+1}{12y^2}$.

31. $\frac{3r}{5s}$ divided by $\frac{r}{10s^2}$ is equal to

a. $\frac{3r^2}{50s^2}$. **b.** $\frac{6rs+r}{10s^2}$. **c.** $15s$. **d.** $\frac{1}{6s}$. **e.** $6s$.

32. $\frac{a}{b} + \frac{3}{2b} =$

a. $\frac{a+3}{3b}$ **b.** $\frac{2a+3}{2b}$ **c.** $\frac{a+3}{2b}$ **d.** $\frac{ab+3}{2b^2}$ **e.** $\frac{2ab+3}{2b^2}$

33. How may $\frac{r}{t-s}$ be written as a fraction with denominator $s - t$?

a. $\frac{r}{s-t}$ **b.** $\frac{-rt}{s-t}$ **c.** $\frac{rs}{s-t}$ **d.** $\frac{-r}{s-t}$ **e.** $\frac{2s-2t+r}{s-t}$

34. How may $a + \frac{5}{a}$ be written as a fraction?

a. $\frac{5a}{a^2}$ **b.** $\frac{6a}{a^2}$ **c.** $\frac{a^2+5}{a}$ **d.** $\frac{2a+5}{a}$ **e.** $\frac{a^2+5a}{a^2}$

35. $\frac{\frac{x}{y}}{\frac{2x}{y^2}} =$

a. $\frac{2x^2}{y^3}$ **b.** $\frac{2}{y}$ **c.** $\frac{y}{2}$ **d.** $\frac{y^3}{2x^2}$ **e.** $\frac{1}{xy}$

36. The solution for $\frac{8}{x} = 6$ is

a. $\frac{3}{4}$. **b.** $\frac{4}{3}$. **c.** 2. **d.** $1\frac{1}{6}$ **e.** -2.

37. The solution for $\frac{5}{x+1} + \frac{7}{x+1} = 2$ is

a. 2. **b.** 3. **c.** 4. **d.** 5. **e.** 6.

38. What does x equal when $\frac{r+s}{x} = t$?

a. $r+s-t$ **b.** $r+s+t$ **c.** $\frac{t}{r+s}$ **d.** $\frac{r-s}{t}$ **e.** $\frac{r+s}{t}$

39. Which is the solution for this system? $\boxed{\frac{x}{2} + \frac{y}{3} = \frac{7}{6}, \quad \frac{x}{8} - \frac{y}{4} = \frac{5}{8}}$

a. $(3, -1)$ **b.** $\left(\frac{1}{3}, 3\right)$ **c.** $\left(4, -2\frac{1}{2}\right)$ **d.** $\left(-1\frac{1}{3}, 5\frac{1}{2}\right)$ **e.** $(7, 1)$

40. The numerators of two fractions are each 3. Their denominators differ by 2. The sum of the fractions is $\frac{36}{35}$. Which equation gives the denominator of the larger fraction?

a. $\frac{3}{x} + \frac{3}{x+2} = \frac{36}{35}$ **b.** $\frac{x}{3} + \frac{x+2}{3} = \frac{36}{35}$ **c.** $\frac{3}{x} - \frac{3}{x-2} = \frac{36}{35}$ **d.** $\frac{x}{3} - \frac{x+2}{3} = \frac{36}{35}$

41. A boat goes 12 km/h in still water. It takes the same time to go 2.7 kilometers against the current as it takes it to go 4.5 kilometers with the current. What is the speed of the current?

a. 2 km/h **b.** 3 km/h **c.** 4 km/h **d.** 5 km/h **e.** 6 km/h

42. For which of these equations do x and y vary inversely?

a. $\frac{x}{y} = 3$ **b.** $x = 3y$ **c.** $y = 3x$ **d.** $\frac{y}{x} = 3$ **e.** $xy = 3$

CUMULATIVE REVIEW

Give the words(s) to complete each sentence.

1. $y = mx + b$ is called the ___?___ form of a linear equation.

2. The degree of the equation $y = 6x^3 - 5x^2 + 4x + 2$ is ___?___.

3. The sentence $-5x + 6y < -12$ is called a(n) ___?___.

4. The graph for $y = 0$ is the ___?___.

5. $\dfrac{\frac{-x}{5}}{\frac{-3}{y}}$ is called a ___?___.

Briefly answer each question. Refer to the concept suggested.

6. Is $(4, 3) = (3, 4)$? Why?

7. How many solutions does $4x + 2y = 12$ have? Explain.

8. $\frac{2x}{3}$ can be rewritten as $\frac{10x}{15}$. Why?

9. Is $\frac{x-y}{a-b}$ equal to $\frac{y-x}{b-a}$? Why?

10. How many solutions does the system $\boxed{\begin{array}{l} 2x + 3y = 12 \\ 4x + 6y = 18 \end{array}}$ have? Explain.

11. Give the coordinates for each point as an ordered pair.

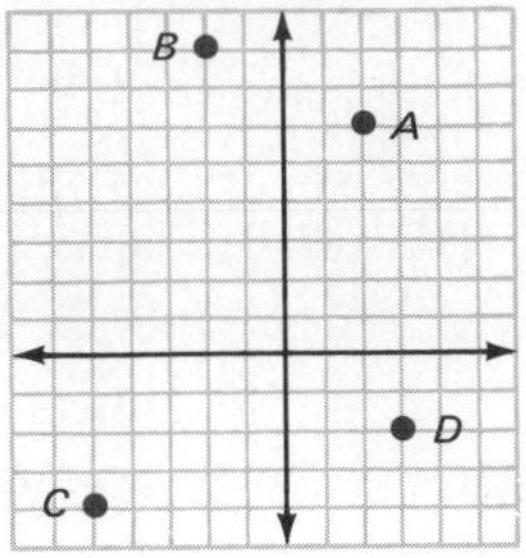

12. Use a table to show three solutions for the equation $2x - y = 4$.

Graph.

13. $|z| > 3$ **14.** $y > 3x - 5$ **15.** $6x - 3y \leq 9$

16. $-4x + 8y = 20$ **17.** $y = -3x + 2$

18. Graph the compound sentence $y < 5x - 4$ and $y > -2x + 3$.

19. Find 5 solutions for $y = |x|$. Draw the graph.

20. Find the slope of the line that contains the points $(3, -8)$ and $(-4, 6)$.

21. Find the slope of the graph for the equation $5x - 8y = -10$.

22. Find the slope and y-intercept of $6x - 2y = -12$. Graph the equation.

23. Write an equation for the line having slope $-\frac{1}{3}$ and y-intercept -2.

24. Write an equation for the line having slope 2 and containing the point $(-4, -3)$.

25. Write an equation for the line containing the points $(5, -3)$ and $(-3, -1)$.

26. Find a linear equation that relates the number (n) of nickels to the value (c) of the nickels in cents. Draw a graph for this relationship.

27. The Ace Taxi Company charges $1.75 for the first kilometer and $0.30 for each additional kilometer. Write a linear equation for this relationship.

Solve each system graphically.

28. $x + y = -4$
$-2x + y = 6$

29. $x + y > -3$
$y - x > 7$

30. Solve the system by addition or subtraction.
$5x - 2y = 8$
$-7x - 2y = 14$

31. Solve the system by substitution.
$y = x - 3$
$6x - 3y = 10$

32. Solve the system by any method.
$-5x + 4y = 23$
$3x - 5y = -19$

33. For the function $f(x) = \frac{1}{2}x - 7$, find $f(-8)$.

34. Graph the function defined by $y = 3x - 2$ for the domain of real numbers.

Simplify.

35. $\frac{-5yz}{6} \cdot \frac{9z}{10y^2}$

36. $\frac{a^2 - b^2}{6c + 6d} \div \frac{5a - 5b}{c^2 - d^2}$

37. $\frac{3x - 5}{x^2 - 9} + \frac{2x - 1}{x + 3}$

38. $\dfrac{\frac{16x^2 - 25}{9}}{\frac{4x + 5}{12}}$

39. $\dfrac{5y}{4x} + \dfrac{7y}{3x}$ **40.** $\dfrac{-2x}{3y - 3z} - \dfrac{5x}{2y - 2z}$ **41.** $2x - 7 - \dfrac{3}{x - 5}$ **42.** $\dfrac{4a - 12}{a^2 - a - 6}$

Factor.

43. $x^2 - 10x - 24$ **44.** $8x^2 + 18x + 9$ **45.** Find a square root of $4h^2 + 2h + \frac{1}{4}$.

(2h + 1/2)

Solve.

46. $3(x + 4) + 8 = -\left(\frac{x}{2} + 1\right)$ **47.** $\dfrac{4}{x} + \dfrac{5}{2} = \dfrac{4x + 5}{2x} - \dfrac{2x - 3}{5x}$

48. $\dfrac{x - 1}{x + 3} - \dfrac{x + 2}{x - 4} = \dfrac{-5x + 18}{x^2 - x - 12}$ **49.** Solve $xa - 6 = 2ay$ for a.

50. The sum of two numbers is 43. Their difference is 11. Find the numbers.

51. The width of a rectangle is 7 less than its length. The perimeter is 150. Find the length and width of the rectangle.

52. An airplane flies a distance of 4200 kilometers in 7 hours with the aid of a tail wind. The return trip takes 10 hours against a head wind. Find the rate of the plane in still air and the rate of the wind.

53. In a 2-digit number, the units digit is 1 more than twice the tens digit. The number is 7 more than 3 times the sum of its digits. Find the number.

54. A two-digit number is two more than twice the number formed when its digits are reversed. The number is four less than eight times the sum of its digits. Find the number.

Write the letter of the best response.

55. The slope of the graph for the equation $-5y + 2x = -6$ is

a. $\frac{2}{5}$. **b.** $\frac{5}{2}$. **c.** $-\frac{2}{5}$. **d.** $-\frac{5}{2}$.

56. The common denominator for $\dfrac{-5}{4a - 4b} + \dfrac{6}{3a + 3b}$ is

a. $12a - 12b$. **b.** $12a + 12b$. **c.** $12a^2 - 12b^2$. **d.** $12b^2 - 12a^2$.

57. Which ordered pair is a solution of $x < -3$ and $y > -4$?

a. $(0, -5)$ **b.** $(-6, -2)$ **c.** $(-9, -6)$ **d.** $(-1, -1)$

58. Which of these is *not* equal to $\dfrac{x - y}{y - x}$?

a. $-\dfrac{x - y}{x - y}$ **b.** $\dfrac{y - x}{x - y}$ **c.** -1 **d.** $-\dfrac{y - x}{x - y}$

59. Which of these is the simplified form for $\dfrac{a}{a + b} - \dfrac{a}{a - b}$?

a. $\dfrac{-a^2 - b^2}{a^2 - b^2}$ **b.** $\dfrac{1}{a - b}$ **c.** $\dfrac{-2ab}{a^2 - b^2}$ **d.** 1

60. Which of these does not equal $\left(\frac{1}{3}x + \frac{2}{3}y\right)^2$?

a. $\left[\frac{1}{3}(x + 2y)\right]^2$ **b.** $\frac{1}{3}(x^2 + 4xy + 4y^2)$ **c.** $\frac{1}{9}x^2 + \frac{4}{9}xy + \frac{4}{9}y^2$ **d.** $\left[\frac{1}{3}(x + 2y)\right] \cdot \left[\frac{1}{3}(x + 2y)\right]$

CHAPTER 12

Radical Expressions

A bit of skill and understanding of mathematics can contribute to success with and enjoyment of personal leisure-time activities. Whether it be a parlor competition over a playing board, the challenge of a hand-held electronic game, a puzzle to be solved, or a creation to be assembled, such as the piece of electronic sculpture above, a logical process of thought that is typical of mathematical thinking can be an asset.

OBJECTIVES: Define radicals. Identify rational numbers and irrational numbers. Identify square root and find approximate square root.

12-1 SQUARES AND SQUARE ROOTS

When a number is used two times as a factor, the product is the *second power*, or *square* of the number. The number is a **square root** of the product.

EXAMPLE 1 Square $4x^3$.

SOLUTION $(4x^3)^2 = (4x^3)(4x^3)$
$= 16x^6$

EXAMPLE 2 Find a square root of 36.

SOLUTION $36 = 6 \cdot 6$
6 is a square root of 36.
$36 = (-6)(-6)$
-6 is also a square root of 36.

Every positive number has two square roots, one positive and one negative. We use the **radical sign**, $\sqrt{}$, to indicate the *positive* square root. We use $-\sqrt{}$ to indicate the *negative* square root. We use $\pm\sqrt{}$ to indicate both square roots. The number shown below the radical sign is the **radicand**. The radical sign and the radicand together form a **radical**.

Although 9 has two square roots, it is not correct to write $\sqrt{9} = \pm 3$. $\sqrt{9}$ indicates only 3, the positive square root of 9. $-\sqrt{9}$ indicates -3, the negative square root of 9. The positive square root of a number is called the *principal square root* of the number.

EXAMPLE 3 Simplify $\sqrt{16}$; $-\sqrt{16}$; $\pm\sqrt{16}$.

(M) SOLUTION $\sqrt{16} = 4$ | $-\sqrt{16} = -4$ | $\pm\sqrt{16} = \pm 4$

The square of any real number is positive or zero. For $\sqrt{a}$ to represent a real number such that $\sqrt{a} \cdot \sqrt{a} = a$, it must be true that a is positive or zero. In this book we assume that for variables in a radicand, the only replacements possible are *non-negative* numbers that give *non-negative* radicands. In particular, we may write $\sqrt{x^2} = x$.

EXAMPLE 4 Simplify $\sqrt{16x^2}$.

SOLUTION $16x^2 = (4x)(4x)$
Thus, $\sqrt{16x^2} = 4x$.

EXAMPLE 5 Simplify $-\sqrt{81c^6}$.

SOLUTION $81c^6 = (9c^3)(9c^3)$

Thus, $\sqrt{81c^6} = 9c^3$

and $-\sqrt{81c^6} = -9c^3$.

CLASSROOM EXERCISES

1. Square $\frac{2x}{7y^2}$. **2.** Find the second power of $5y^3$. **3.** Find a square root of 64.

EXERCISES

A Square.

1. $9c$ **2.** $12d$ **3.** $6h$ **4.** $15k$ **5.** $-8m$ **6.** $-19n$

7. $\frac{3c}{5d^2}$ **8.** $\frac{8m}{11n^2}$ **9.** $\frac{7h}{12k^2}$ **10.** $\frac{18p}{25r^2}$ **11.** $-\frac{4x}{9y^2}$ **12.** $-\frac{13w}{16z^2}$

Find the second power.

13. $7z^3$ **14.** $17a^3$ **15.** $21x^4$ **16.** $23y^4$ **17.** $-14h^2$ **18.** $-22k^2$

Find a square root.

19. 81 **20.** 121 **21.** 256 **22.** 576 **23.** 484 **24.** 289

B Square.

25. $-x^2y^3z$ **26.** $20r^2s^3$ **27.** $0.1m^3n^2$ **28.** $0.3a^2b^3$

29. $\frac{7a^5b^6}{8y^3}$ **30.** $\frac{5x^3y^5}{9mn}$ **31.** $\frac{-4mn^2}{11s^4t^5}$ **32.** $\frac{-3a^3c}{2b^2d^4}$

Find the indicated root.

33. $\sqrt{x^2}$ **34.** $\sqrt{y^6}$ **35.** $-\sqrt{a^4}$ **36.** $\sqrt{100x^6y^8}$

37. $\sqrt{289m^{10}n^{12}}$ **38.** $-\sqrt{0.49m^4n^6}$ **39.** $-\sqrt{1.44a^{10}b^{16}}$ **40.** $-\sqrt{0.0016x^{16}y^{36}}$

C Simplify.

41. $\sqrt{9(a+b)^2}$ **42.** $\sqrt{(2x-5)^2}$ **43.** $\sqrt{x^2+6x+9}$

44. $\sqrt{x^2-4x+4}$ **45.** $\sqrt{4x^2+4x+1}$ **46.** $\sqrt{4x^2+16x+16}$

47. $\sqrt{9x^2+18x+9}$ **48.** $\sqrt{9x^2-12x+4}$ **49.** $\sqrt{a^2x^2+2abx+b^2}$

12-2 RATIONAL NUMBERS, IRRATIONAL NUMBERS, AND DECIMALS.

A rational number is one that can be expressed in the form $\frac{a}{b}$ for which a and b are integers and $b \neq 0$.

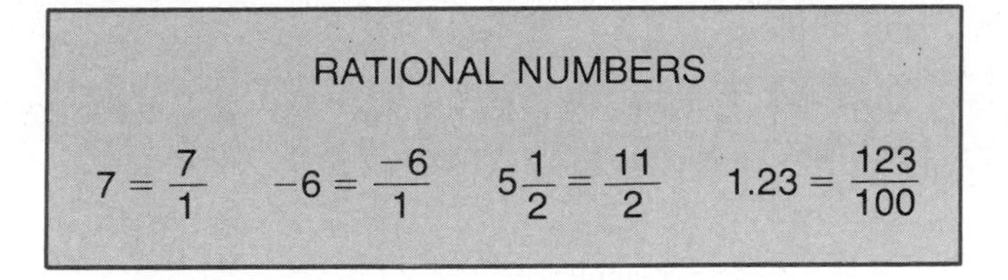

The symbol $\frac{a}{b}$ also represents the quotient $a \div b$. We use this idea to help us represent a rational number by a decimal.

EXAMPLE 1 Find a decimal for $\frac{-7}{8}$.

SOLUTION $\frac{-7}{8} = -\frac{7}{8}$

For $\frac{7}{8}$, divide $8\overline{)7.000}$.

```
    0.875
 8)7.000
   6 4
     60
     56
      40
      40
       0
```

CONCLUSION $\frac{-7}{8} = -0.875$

CHECK $8(-0.875) \stackrel{?}{=} -7$

$-7 = -7$ ✓

In Example 1, we were able to complete the division process and represent the rational number by a *terminating* or *finite* decimal. For some rational numbers we may obtain *infinite* decimals whose digits follow a repeating pattern.

EXAMPLE 2 Find a decimal for $\frac{5}{11}$.

SOLUTION

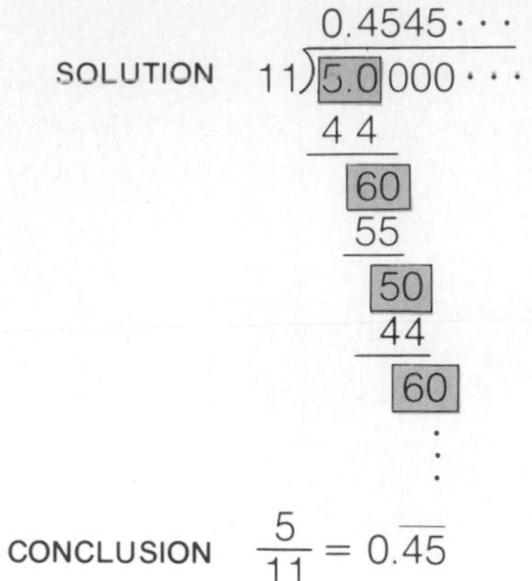

The pattern in the division process suggests that we cannot complete the process. It also suggests that 4s and 5s repeat endlessly as digits in the quotient. We indicate an infinite decimal whose digits follow a repeating pattern by showing a bar over the repeating digits.

CONCLUSION $\frac{5}{11} = 0.\overline{45}$

CHECK Use the process suggested by Example 5.

It can be proved that any rational number may be represented by a finite decimal or by an infinite decimal whose digits follow a repeating pattern. Also, any finite decimal or any infinite decimal whose digits follow a repeating pattern represents a rational number.

Actually, any finite decimal may be represented by an infinite repeating decimal. For example, $0.5 = 0.5\overline{0}$.

EXAMPLE 3 Express 2.375 in $\frac{a}{b}$ form.

SOLUTION
$$2.375 = \frac{2375}{1000} = \frac{19}{8}$$

CHECK $19 \div 8 \stackrel{?}{=} 2.375$
$2.375 = 2.375$ ✓

The following suggests a way to replace an infinite decimal whose digits follow a repeating pattern by the $\frac{a}{b}$ form for the rational number.

EXAMPLE 4 Express $0.\overline{6}$ in $\frac{a}{b}$ form.

Ⓜ SOLUTION Use $\left[\begin{array}{r} x \text{ for } 0.\overline{6} \\ 10x \text{ for } 6.\overline{6} \end{array}\right.$

$$10x = 6.\overline{6}$$
$$x = 0.\overline{6}$$

Subtract. $9x = 6$

$$x = \frac{6}{9}, \text{ or } \frac{2}{3}$$

CHECK Dividing 2 by 3 shows $\frac{2}{3} = 0.\overline{6}$. ✓

EXAMPLE 5 Express $2.\overline{63}$ and $2.6\overline{3}$ in $\frac{a}{b}$ form.

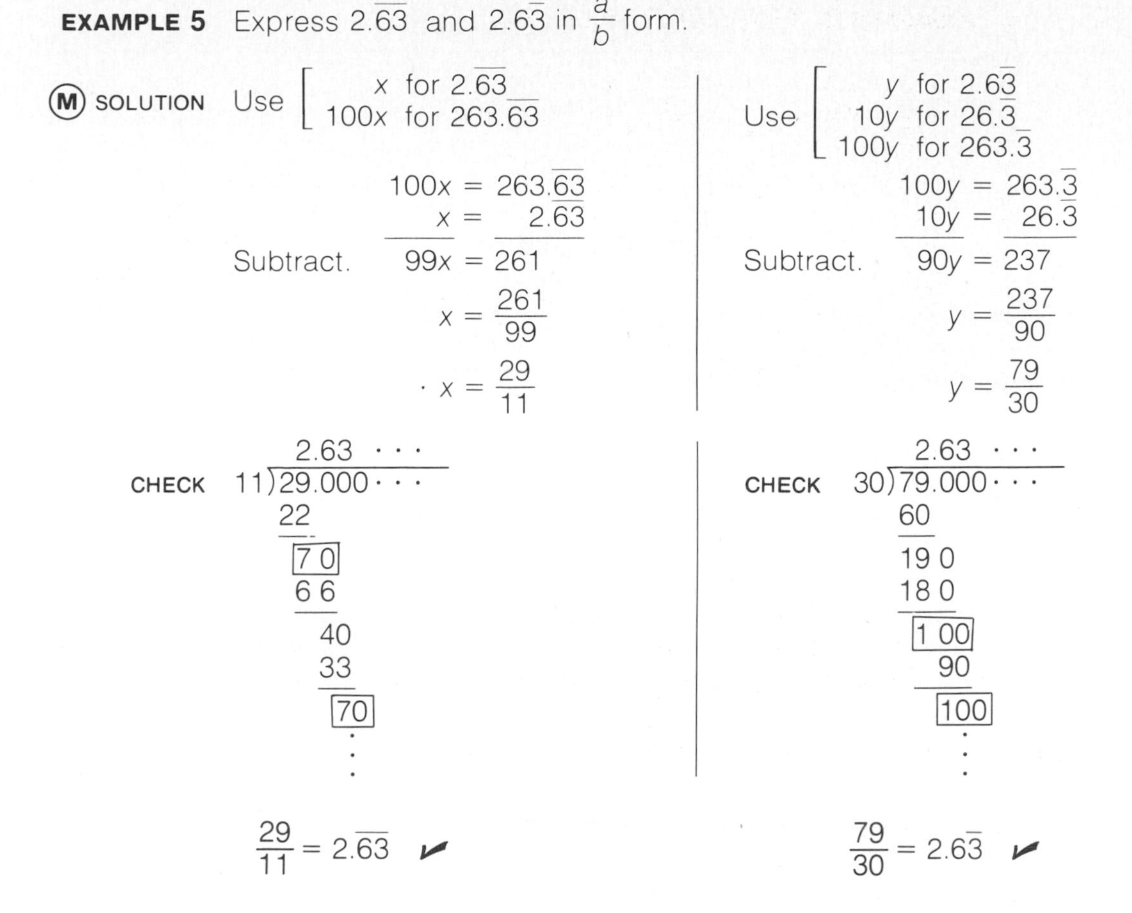

Ⓜ SOLUTION

Use $\left[\begin{array}{l} x \text{ for } 2.\overline{63} \\ 100x \text{ for } 263.\overline{63} \end{array}\right.$

$$\begin{aligned} 100x &= 263.\overline{63} \\ x &= 2.\overline{63} \end{aligned}$$

Subtract. $99x = 261$

$$x = \frac{261}{99}$$

$$x = \frac{29}{11}$$

CHECK $11\overline{)29.000\cdots}$ quotient $2.63\cdots$

$$\begin{array}{l} 22 \\ \boxed{7\,0} \\ 6\,6 \\ \quad 40 \\ \quad 33 \\ \quad \boxed{70} \\ \quad \vdots \end{array}$$

$$\frac{29}{11} = 2.\overline{63} \quad ✓$$

Use $\left[\begin{array}{l} y \text{ for } 2.6\overline{3} \\ 10y \text{ for } 26.\overline{3} \\ 100y \text{ for } 263.\overline{3} \end{array}\right.$

$$\begin{aligned} 100y &= 263.\overline{3} \\ 10y &= 26.\overline{3} \end{aligned}$$

Subtract. $90y = 237$

$$y = \frac{237}{90}$$

$$y = \frac{79}{30}$$

CHECK $30\overline{)79.000\cdots}$ quotient $2.63\cdots$

$$\begin{array}{l} 60 \\ 19\,0 \\ 18\,0 \\ \boxed{1\,00} \\ \quad 90 \\ \quad \boxed{100} \\ \quad \vdots \end{array}$$

$$\frac{79}{30} = 2.6\overline{3} \quad ✓$$

A real number that *cannot* be expressed in the form $\frac{a}{b}$ for which a and b are integers and $b \neq 0$ is an **irrational number**. An example is $\sqrt{2}$, or the square root of *any* counting number that is itself not the square of some counting number. It has also been proved that the number π is irrational ($\pi = 3.1415926\cdots$). Infinite decimals such as

$$0.232232223\cdots \quad \text{and}$$
$$7.101100111000\cdots,$$

whose digits do not follow a repeating pattern, represent irrational numbers. For computations that involve irrational numbers, we use finite decimal approximations for the numbers, such as 3.14 for π.

Do not misinterpret this statement. If there is *no* pattern, or if there is a pattern that never repeats, the decimal represents an irrational number.

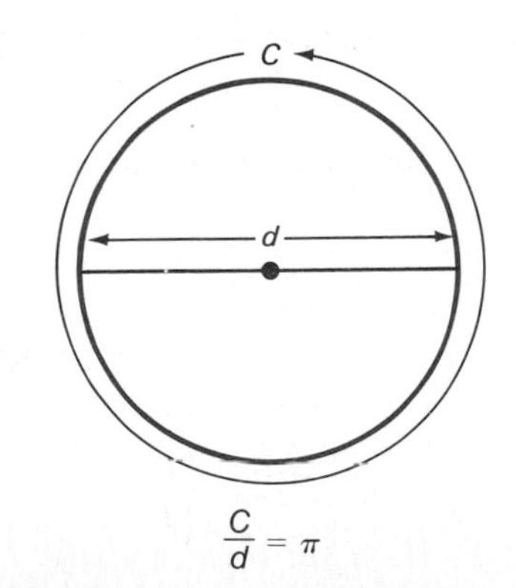

$\frac{C}{d} = \pi$

CLASSROOM EXERCISES

Express each as a decimal.

1. $\frac{1}{4}$ **2.** $-\frac{3}{8}$ **3.** $\frac{5}{9}$ **4.** $\frac{9}{11}$

Express each in $\frac{a}{b}$ form.

5. 0.75 **6.** 3.875 **7.** $0.\overline{7}$ **8.** $-3.\overline{45}$

EXERCISES

A Express each as a decimal.

1. $\frac{3}{4}$ **2.** $\frac{5}{8}$ **3.** $\frac{11}{16}$ **4.** $\frac{19}{25}$ **5.** $-\frac{5}{6}$ **6.** $-\frac{33}{40}$ **7.** $\frac{1}{3}$

8. $\frac{11}{15}$ **9.** $\frac{13}{18}$ **10.** $\frac{1}{11}$ **11.** $\frac{6}{11}$ **12.** $\frac{5}{22}$ **13.** $\frac{3}{22}$ **14.** $\frac{5}{13}$

Express each in $\frac{a}{b}$ form.

15. 0.95 **16.** 0.84 **17.** 0.20 **18.** 0.45 **19.** -5.625

20. -9.125 **21.** $0.\overline{2}$ **22.** $0.\overline{4}$ **23.** $0.\overline{5}$ **24.** $0.\overline{1}$

25. $4.\overline{63}$ **26.** $9.\overline{18}$ **27.** $-0.4\overline{2}$ **28.** $-0.\overline{65}$ **29.** $0.3\overline{8}$

B Write each sum in $\frac{a}{b}$ form. Reduce to lowest terms.

30. $0.\overline{3} + \frac{1}{9}$ **31.** $0.\overline{54} + \frac{2}{9}$ **32.** $0.\overline{2} + 0.\overline{4}$

Write each product in both $\frac{a}{b}$ form and decimal form.

33. $0.7\overline{3} \cdot \frac{5}{11}$ **34.** $0.\overline{27} \cdot \frac{5}{6}$ **35.** $0.\overline{3} \cdot \frac{1}{5}$

Write each product in $\frac{a}{b}$ form. Reduce to lowest terms.

36. $0.7\overline{3} \cdot \frac{1}{5}$ **37.** $0.\overline{24} \cdot \frac{1}{8}$ **38.** $1.\overline{54} \cdot \frac{5}{8}$

C **39.** Express $0.\overline{9}$ in $\frac{a}{b}$ form. Explain your result.

40. Suppose $\frac{1}{n}$ may be represented by a decimal whose digits follow an infinite repeating pattern. Explain why the smallest number of digits needed to represent the pattern is always less than n. (For example, the pattern for $\frac{1}{3}$, $0.\overline{3}$, needs 1 digit. The pattern for $\frac{1}{7}$, $0.\overline{142857}$, needs 6 digits.)

Which of the following are true? Explain.

41. The sum of two irrational numbers is an irrational number.

42. The sum of two irrational numbers is a rational number.

43. The product of two irrational numbers is an irrational number.

12-3 APPROXIMATING SQUARE ROOTS

It can be proved that unless a square root of a whole number is an integer, the number must be irrational. A decimal for such a square root can show only an approximation.

EXAMPLE 1 Approximate the square root of 39.

SOLUTION The square root of 36 is 6. The square root of 49 is 7. The square root of 39 is between 6 and 7 and probably closer to 6. Thus, 6.2 or 6.3 are reasonable approximations for $\sqrt{39}$.

To find an approximation for the square root of a number, use a calculator or a table of squares and square roots. The table on the next page gives approximate square roots to three decimal places.

EXAMPLE 2 Use the table on the next page to approximate $\sqrt{7}$.

SOLUTION Find 7 in column n.
Find $\sqrt{7}$ in column $\sqrt{n}$.
$\sqrt{7} \doteq 2.646$
The numbers 2.6 and 2.65 are also approximate square roots of 7, but 2.646 is more precise.

The number of decimal places to use in an approximation of a square root depends upon the intended use of the approximate square root. For most practical applications, one decimal place should suffice.

CLASSROOM EXERCISES

1. Approximate the square root of 54.
2. Use the table on the next page to approximate $\sqrt{21}$.

EXERCISES

A Approximate the square root.

1. 3 **2.** 5 **3.** 90 **4.** 12 **5.** 48 **6.** 72 **7.** 109 **8.** 162

Use the table on the next page to approximate each of these.

9. $\sqrt{10}$ **10.** $\sqrt{20}$ **11.** $\sqrt{19}$ **12.** $\sqrt{58}$ **13.** $\sqrt{17}$ **14.** $\sqrt{65}$ **15.** $\sqrt{77}$ **16.** $\sqrt{51}$

B Use the formula $c = \sqrt{a^2 + b^2}$ and the table. Approximate c.

17. $a = 5, b = 8$ **18.** $a = 12, b = 12$ **19.** $a = 8, b = 15$

Table of Squares and Square Roots

n	n^2	$\sqrt{n}$	$\sqrt{10n}$	n	n^2	$\sqrt{n}$	$\sqrt{10n}$
				50	2 500	7.071	22.361
1	1	1.000	3.162	51	2 601	7.141	22.583
2	4	1.414	4.472	52	2 704	7.211	22.804
3	9	1.732	5.477	53	2 809	7.280	23.022
4	16	2.000	6.325	54	2 916	7.348	23.238
5	25	2.236	7.071	55	3 025	7.416	23.452
6	36	2.449	7.746	56	3 136	7.483	23.664
7	49	2.646	8.367	57	3 249	7.550	23.875
8	64	2.828	8.944	58	3 364	7.616	24.083
9	81	3.000	9.487	59	3 481	7.681	24.290
10	100	3.162	10.000	60	3 600	7.746	24.495
11	121	3.317	10.488	61	3 721	7.810	24.698
12	144	3.464	10.954	62	3 844	7.874	24.900
13	169	3.606	11.402	63	3 969	7.937	25.100
14	196	3.742	11.832	64	4 096	8.000	25.298
15	225	3.873	12.247	65	4 225	8.062	25.495
16	256	4.000	12.649	66	4 356	8.124	25.690
17	289	4.123	13.038	67	4 489	8.185	25.884
18	324	4.243	13.416	68	4 624	8.246	26.077
19	361	4.359	13.784	69	4 761	8.307	26.268
20	400	4.472	14.142	70	4 900	8.367	26.458
21	441	4.583	14.491	71	5 041	8.426	26.646
22	484	4.690	14.832	72	5 184	8.485	26.833
23	529	4.796	15.166	73	5 329	8.544	27.019
24	576	4.899	15.492	74	5 476	8.602	27.203
25	625	5.000	15.811	75	5 625	8.660	27.386
26	676	5.099	16.125	76	5 776	8.718	27.568
27	729	5.196	16.432	77	5 929	8.775	27.749
28	784	5.292	16.733	78	6 084	8.832	27.928
29	841	5.385	17.029	79	6 241	8.888	28.107
30	900	5.477	17.321	80	6 400	8.944	28.284
31	961	5.568	17.607	81	6 561	9.000	28.460
32	1 024	5.657	17.889	82	6 724	9.055	28.636
33	1 089	5.745	18.166	83	6 889	9.110	28.810
34	1 156	5.831	18.439	84	7 056	9.165	28.983
35	1 225	5.916	18.708	85	7 225	9.220	29.155
36	1 296	6.000	18.974	86	7 396	9.274	29.326
37	1 369	6.083	19.235	87	7 569	9.327	29.496
38	1 444	6.164	19.494	88	7 744	9.381	29.665
39	1 521	6.245	19.748	89	7 921	9.434	29.833
40	1 600	6.325	20.000	90	8 100	9.487	30.000
41	1 681	6.403	20.248	91	8 281	9.539	30.166
42	1 764	6.481	20.494	92	8 464	9.592	30.332
43	1 849	6.557	20.736	93	8 649	9.644	30.496
44	1 936	6.633	20.976	94	8 836	9.695	30.659
45	2 025	6.708	21.213	95	9 025	9.747	30.822
46	2 116	6.782	21.448	96	9 216	9.798	30.984
47	2 209	6.856	21.679	97	9 409	9.849	31.145
48	2 304	6.928	21.909	98	9 604	9.899	31.305
49	2 401	7.000	22.136	99	9 801	9.950	31.464
50	2 500	7.071	22.361	100	10 000	10.000	31.623

Use the formula $a = \sqrt{b} - \sqrt{c}$. Approximate a.

20. $b = 57$, $c = 19$ **21.** $b = 83$, $c = 40$ **22.** $b = 64$, $c = 36$

C Which of the following are true for all positive numbers a and b? Use the Table of Squares and Square Roots to help you decide.

23. $\sqrt{a \cdot b} \stackrel{?}{=} \sqrt{a} \cdot \sqrt{b}$ **24.** $\sqrt{\frac{a}{b}} \stackrel{?}{=} \frac{\sqrt{a}}{\sqrt{b}}$ **25.** $\sqrt{a} - \sqrt{b} \stackrel{?}{=} \sqrt{a - b}$

Use Exercises 23 and 24, and the Table of Squares and Square Roots. Approximate each of these by a decimal.

26. $\sqrt{513}$ **27.** $\sqrt{284}$ **28.** $\sqrt{\frac{3}{4}}$ **29.** $\sqrt{\frac{13}{20}}$

CHECKING YOUR UNDERSTANDING

WORDS AND SYMBOLS

infinite decimal, $0.\overline{6}$
irrational number
radical, $\sqrt{a}$
radical sign, $\sqrt{\ }$
radicand, $\sqrt{ⓐ}$
square root of a number

CONCEPTS

- Every positive number has two square roots, one positive and one negative. [12-1]
- Every rational number may be represented by a finite decimal or by an infinite decimal whose digits follow a repeating pattern. [12-2]
- Any irrational number may be approximated by a finite decimal. [12-3]

PROCESSES

- Find squares and square roots. [12-1]

1. $(-10x)^2 = ?$ **2.** $\sqrt{225} = ?$ **3.** $-\sqrt{49r^6} = ?$

- Use a table to find an approximation for a square root. [12-3]

4. $\sqrt{15}$ **5.** $\sqrt{32}$ **6.** $\sqrt{640}$

- Express a rational number in both decimal and $\frac{a}{b}$ form. [12-2]

7. $\frac{7}{8} = ?$ **8.** $\frac{1}{6} = ?$ **9.** $2.375 = ?$ **10.** $0.\overline{36} = ?$

OBJECTIVES: Add, subtract, multiply, divide, and simplify radical expressions. Solve equations containing radicals.

12-4 SIMPLIFYING RADICALS

A radical is in its simplest form when

1. the radicand contains no square of an algebraic expression,
2. the radicand has no integral factor, except 1, that is the square of another integer, and
3. the radicand contains no fraction.

We use two important properties to help us simplify radicals.

Multiplication Property of Square Roots	Division Property of Square Roots
The square root of a product and the product of the square roots are equal. $\sqrt{ab} = \sqrt{a}\sqrt{b}$	The square root of a quotient and the quotient of the square roots are equal. $\sqrt{\frac{a}{b}} = \frac{\sqrt{a}}{\sqrt{b}}, b \neq 0$

EXAMPLE 1 Simplify $\sqrt{36}$.

SOLUTION 1

Since $36 = 6 \cdot 6$,
$\sqrt{36} = 6$.

SOLUTION 2

Since $36 = 4 \cdot 9$, $\sqrt{36} = \sqrt{4} \cdot \sqrt{9}$
$= 2 \cdot 3$
$= 6$

EXAMPLE 2 Simplify $3\sqrt{32}$.

(M) SOLUTION

$$\begin{aligned} 3\sqrt{32} &= 3\sqrt{16 \cdot 2} \\ &= 3\sqrt{16} \cdot \sqrt{2} \\ &= 3 \cdot 4 \cdot \sqrt{2} \\ &= 12\sqrt{2} \end{aligned}$$

A radical such as $\sqrt{ab^2}$ may be simplified to $\sqrt{a}b$, or $b\sqrt{a}$. The simpler form shall always be shown as $b\sqrt{a}$ with b to the left of the radical sign. Otherwise, as $\sqrt{a}b$, b could be seen incorrectly as part of the radicand.

Remember, we assume that the only replacements possible for a variable in a radicand are non-negative numbers that give non-negative radicands.

EXAMPLE 3 Simplify $\sqrt{98a^3}$.

Ⓜ SOLUTION
$$\sqrt{98a^3} = \sqrt{49a^2 \cdot 2a}$$
$$= \sqrt{49a^2}\sqrt{2a}$$
$$= 7a\sqrt{2a}$$

EXAMPLE 4 Simplify $\sqrt{\frac{4}{9}}$.

SOLUTION 1

Ⓜ
$$\sqrt{\frac{4}{9}} = \sqrt{\frac{2}{3} \cdot \frac{2}{3}}$$
$$= \frac{2}{3}$$

SOLUTION 2

$$\sqrt{\frac{4}{9}} = \frac{\sqrt{4}}{\sqrt{9}}$$ Ⓜ
$$= \frac{2}{3}$$

The Multiplication Property of One may help us simplify a radical that involves a fraction. It allows us to replace the fraction by one whose denominator is a square.

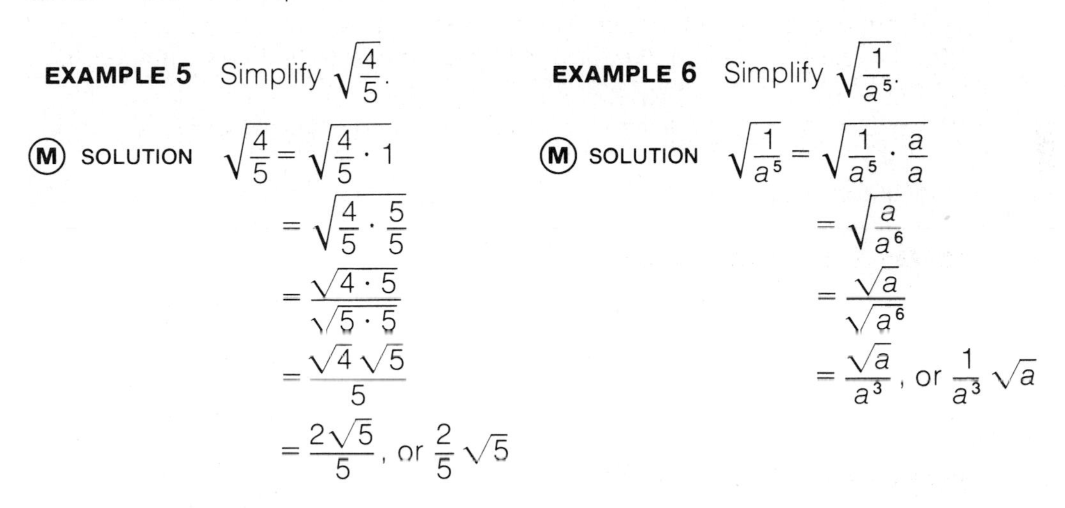

EXAMPLE 5 Simplify $\sqrt{\frac{4}{5}}$.

Ⓜ SOLUTION
$$\sqrt{\frac{4}{5}} = \sqrt{\frac{4}{5} \cdot 1}$$
$$= \sqrt{\frac{4}{5} \cdot \frac{5}{5}}$$
$$= \frac{\sqrt{4 \cdot 5}}{\sqrt{5 \cdot 5}}$$
$$= \frac{\sqrt{4}\sqrt{5}}{5}$$
$$= \frac{2\sqrt{5}}{5}, \text{ or } \frac{2}{5}\sqrt{5}$$

EXAMPLE 6 Simplify $\sqrt{\frac{1}{a^5}}$.

Ⓜ SOLUTION
$$\sqrt{\frac{1}{a^5}} = \sqrt{\frac{1}{a^5} \cdot \frac{a}{a}}$$
$$= \sqrt{\frac{a}{a^6}}$$
$$= \frac{\sqrt{a}}{\sqrt{a^6}}$$
$$= \frac{\sqrt{a}}{a^3}, \text{ or } \frac{1}{a^3}\sqrt{a}$$

EXAMPLE 7 Find a decimal approximation for $\sqrt{\frac{4}{5}}$.
Use the table on page 454.

SOLUTION From Example 5, $\sqrt{\frac{4}{5}} = \frac{2}{5}\sqrt{5}$.

From the table of square roots, $\sqrt{5} \doteq 2.236$.

Therefore, $\sqrt{\frac{4}{5}} \doteq \frac{2}{5}(2.236)$, or 0.894.

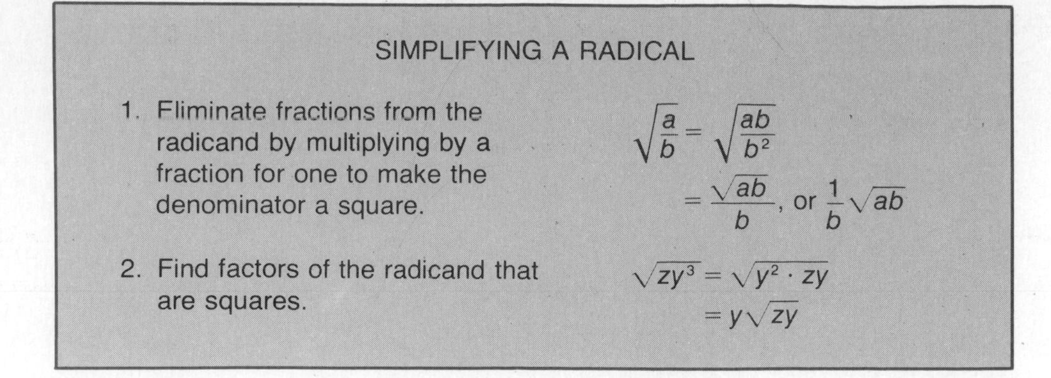

SIMPLIFYING A RADICAL

1. Eliminate fractions from the radicand by multiplying by a fraction for one to make the denominator a square. $\sqrt{\frac{a}{b}} = \sqrt{\frac{ab}{b^2}} = \frac{\sqrt{ab}}{b}$, or $\frac{1}{b}\sqrt{ab}$

2. Find factors of the radicand that are squares. $\sqrt{zy^3} = \sqrt{y^2 \cdot zy} = y\sqrt{zy}$

CLASSROOM EXERCISES

Simplify.

1. $\sqrt{49}$ **2.** $4\sqrt{18}$ **3.** $\sqrt{72x^3}$ **4.** $\sqrt{\frac{16}{25}}$ **5.** $\sqrt{\frac{3}{5}}$ **6.** $\sqrt{\frac{1}{x^5}}$

EXERCISES

A Simplify.

1. $\sqrt{81}$ **2.** $\sqrt{100}$ **3.** $\sqrt{64}$ **4.** $\sqrt{144}$ **5.** $5\sqrt{12}$ **6.** $6\sqrt{20}$

7. $9\sqrt{45}$ **8.** $12\sqrt{27}$ **9.** $\sqrt{50z^3}$ **10.** $\sqrt{128b^3}$ **11.** $\sqrt{48k^5}$ **12.** $\sqrt{108m^5}$

13. $\sqrt{\frac{36}{49}}$ **14.** $\sqrt{\frac{144}{625}}$ **15.** $\sqrt{\frac{5}{6}}$ **16.** $\sqrt{\frac{7}{10}}$ **17.** $\sqrt{\frac{3}{17}}$ **18.** $\sqrt{\frac{11}{15}}$

19. $\sqrt{\frac{9}{10}}$ **20.** $\sqrt{\frac{25}{42}}$ **21.** $\sqrt{\frac{16}{21}}$ **22.** $\sqrt{\frac{49}{65}}$ **23.** $8\sqrt{40}$ **24.** $12\sqrt{72}$

25. $15\sqrt{75}$ **26.** $10\sqrt{28}$ **27.** $\sqrt{125a^7}$ **28.** $\sqrt{80c^5}$ **29.** $\sqrt{180y^{11}}$ **30.** $\sqrt{96x^{13}}$

31. $\sqrt{\frac{1}{x^3}}$ **32.** $\sqrt{\frac{1}{y^3}}$ **33.** $\sqrt{\frac{1}{a^{11}}}$ **34.** $\sqrt{\frac{1}{b^9}}$ **35.** $\sqrt{\frac{1}{m^9}}$ **36.** $\sqrt{\frac{1}{n^7}}$

B **37.** $\sqrt{40x^6y^4}$ **38.** $\sqrt{135a^6b^8}$ **39.** $\sqrt{60h^5k^4}$ **40.** $\sqrt{90m^7n^6}$

41. $\sqrt{280y^5z^6}$ **42.** $\sqrt{270g^8h^9}$ **43.** $\sqrt{500x^7y^9}$ **44.** $\sqrt{216x^{11}y^{13}}$

45. $\sqrt{\frac{x^5z^4}{36y^2}}$ **46.** $\sqrt{\frac{3a^2b}{4b^3}}$ **47.** $\sqrt{\frac{10uv^2}{8u}}$ **48.** $\sqrt{\frac{8m^2n}{2n^2}}$

C **49.** $\sqrt{0.09x^4y^6}$ **50.** $-\sqrt{2.89x^2y^9z^4}$ **51.** $\sqrt{0.0004h^2}$ **52.** $\sqrt{0.5r^3}$

12-5 ADDING AND SUBTRACTING WITH RADICALS

You may simplify sums and differences that involve radicals if the radicands are the same. To do so, add or subtract the coefficients of the radicals.

EXAMPLE 1 Simplify $6\sqrt{2} + 3\sqrt{2} - 7\sqrt{2}$.

Ⓜ SOLUTION
$$6\sqrt{2} + 3\sqrt{2} - 7\sqrt{2} = (6 + 3 - 7)\sqrt{2}$$
$$= 2\sqrt{2}$$

This is identical to simplifying an expression like $6a + 3a - 7a$.

EXAMPLE 2 Simplify $2\sqrt{3} + 4\sqrt{4} + 6\sqrt{3} - 6\sqrt{5}$.

Ⓜ SOLUTION
$$2\sqrt{3} + 4\sqrt{5} + 6\sqrt{3} - 6\sqrt{5} = 2\sqrt{3} + 6\sqrt{3} + 4\sqrt{5} - 6\sqrt{5}$$
$$= (2 + 6)\sqrt{3} + (4 - 6)\sqrt{5}$$
$$= 8\sqrt{3} - 2\sqrt{5}$$

EXAMPLE 3 Simplify $3\sqrt{8} - \sqrt{50} + 6\sqrt{32}$.

Ⓜ SOLUTION
$$3\sqrt{8} - \sqrt{50} + 6\sqrt{32} = 3\sqrt{4 \cdot 2} - \sqrt{25 \cdot 2} + 6\sqrt{16 \cdot 2}$$
$$= 3\sqrt{4}\sqrt{2} - \sqrt{25}\sqrt{2} + 6\sqrt{16}\sqrt{2}$$
$$= 3 \cdot 2\sqrt{2} - 5\sqrt{2} + 6 \cdot 4\sqrt{2}$$
$$= 6\sqrt{2} - 5\sqrt{2} + 24\sqrt{2}$$
$$= 25\sqrt{2}$$

EXAMPLE 4 Simplify $\sqrt{18} + \sqrt{20} - \sqrt{\frac{1}{2}} + \sqrt{125}$.

Ⓜ SOLUTION
$$\sqrt{18} + \sqrt{20} - \sqrt{\frac{1}{2}} + \sqrt{125} = \sqrt{9}\sqrt{2} + \sqrt{4}\sqrt{5} - \sqrt{\frac{2}{4}} + \sqrt{25}\sqrt{5}$$
$$= 3\sqrt{2} + 2\sqrt{5} - \frac{1}{2}\sqrt{2} + 5\sqrt{5}$$
$$= \frac{5}{2}\sqrt{2} + 7\sqrt{5}$$

CLASSROOM EXERCISES

Simplify.

1. $8\sqrt{2} + 4\sqrt{2} - 3\sqrt{2}$
2. $9\sqrt{3} + 2\sqrt{2} - 4\sqrt{3} + 5\sqrt{2}$
3. $2\sqrt{48} - \sqrt{75} + 5\sqrt{12}$
4. $\sqrt{\frac{1}{2}} - \sqrt{24} + \sqrt{98} + \sqrt{54}$

EXERCISES

A Simplify.

1. $4\sqrt{3}+2\sqrt{3}+5\sqrt{3}$
2. $5\sqrt{5}+2\sqrt{5}+7\sqrt{5}$
3. $3\sqrt{6}-4\sqrt{6}-\sqrt{6}$
4. $5\sqrt{10}-4\sqrt{10}-6\sqrt{10}$
5. $9\sqrt{11}-8\sqrt{11}+\sqrt{11}$
6. $\sqrt{13}+9\sqrt{13}-3\sqrt{13}$
7. $2\sqrt{7}-3\sqrt{2}+5\sqrt{7}+\sqrt{2}$
8. $5\sqrt{11}+3\sqrt{3}-6\sqrt{11}+\sqrt{3}$
9. $8\sqrt{5}+9\sqrt{13}-11\sqrt{5}-5\sqrt{13}$
10. $21\sqrt{19}-40\sqrt{31}-25\sqrt{19}+16\sqrt{31}$
11. $8\sqrt{6}+9\sqrt{10}-3\sqrt{10}-12\sqrt{6}$
12. $19\sqrt{26}-14\sqrt{14}-16\sqrt{26}+21\sqrt{14}$
13. $5\sqrt{27}-\sqrt{108}+2\sqrt{75}$
14. $\sqrt{98}-4\sqrt{8}+3\sqrt{128}$
15. $3\sqrt{32}-6\sqrt{8}+4\sqrt{72}$
16. $9\sqrt{12}+3\sqrt{48}-4\sqrt{300}$
17. $3\sqrt{54}-3\sqrt{96}+2\sqrt{150}$
18. $7\sqrt{24}+3\sqrt{54}-4\sqrt{216}$
19. $\sqrt{80}-\sqrt{27}+\sqrt{\frac{1}{3}}-\sqrt{20}$
20. $\sqrt{96}-\sqrt{50}+\sqrt{24}-\sqrt{\frac{1}{2}}$
21. $\sqrt{98}-\sqrt{\frac{1}{5}}-\sqrt{162}+\sqrt{125}$
22. $\sqrt{\frac{1}{6}}+\sqrt{192}-\sqrt{150}-\sqrt{75}$
23. $\sqrt{180}-\sqrt{54}-\sqrt{45}+\sqrt{\frac{1}{6}}$
24. $\sqrt{72}+\sqrt{108}-\sqrt{200}-\sqrt{\frac{1}{3}}$

B

25. $10\sqrt{\frac{1}{5}}-2\sqrt{\frac{9}{20}}$
26. $\sqrt{3\frac{3}{4}}+\sqrt{28}$
27. $\sqrt{4\frac{1}{6}}+\sqrt{24}$
28. $\sqrt{72}-\sqrt{1\frac{1}{8}}$
29. $\sqrt{54}-\sqrt{2\frac{2}{3}}$
30. $3\sqrt{\frac{1}{6}}+\sqrt{12}-5\sqrt{\frac{3}{2}}$
31. $3\sqrt{\frac{5}{2}}+\sqrt{20}-5\sqrt{\frac{1}{10}}$
32. $2\sqrt{\frac{1}{2}}-6\sqrt{\frac{1}{8}}-10\sqrt{\frac{4}{5}}$
33. $7\sqrt{4x}+3\sqrt{y}-\sqrt{9x}-3\sqrt{16y}$
34. $4\sqrt{4y}-\sqrt{x}+9\sqrt{y}-\sqrt{9x}$
35. $6\sqrt{a^3}+\sqrt{25a^3}-\sqrt{b^2}+\sqrt{a^3}$
36. $2a\sqrt{25a}+a\sqrt{4a}-3a\sqrt{9a}+\sqrt{16a^3}$

C

37. $5\sqrt{3y}-\sqrt{27x}+\sqrt{12y}-4\sqrt{48x}$
38. $3\sqrt{2y^3}-\sqrt{8y^3}-\frac{2}{3}\sqrt{72y^3}$
39. $5\sqrt{12a^3}-2\sqrt{3a^3}+\frac{1}{3}\sqrt{27a^3}$
40. $x\sqrt{8y}+3\sqrt{2x^2y}-4x\sqrt{32y}$
41. $b\sqrt{27a}-6\sqrt{3ab^2}+\frac{5}{9}\sqrt{108ab^2}$
42. $7\sqrt{3x^3}+3\sqrt{12x^3}-2x\sqrt{75x}$

QUICK CHANGE

A box contains $1.15 in coins, but does not contain change for a dollar, half dollar, quarter, dime, or nickel. What coins are in the box?

12-6 MULTIPLYING WITH RADICALS

You may simplify products that involve radicals by multiplying their radicands.

$$\sqrt{a}\sqrt{b} = \sqrt{ab}$$

EXAMPLE 1 Multiply $\sqrt{6}$ and $\sqrt{5}$.

Ⓜ **SOLUTION** $\sqrt{6} \cdot \sqrt{5} = \sqrt{6 \cdot 5}$
$= \sqrt{30}$

EXAMPLE 2 Multiply $3\sqrt{2}$ and $4\sqrt{6}$.

Ⓜ **SOLUTION** $3\sqrt{2} \cdot 4\sqrt{6} = 12\sqrt{2 \cdot 6}$
$= 12\sqrt{12}$
$= 12\sqrt{4}\sqrt{3}$
$= 24\sqrt{3}$

EXAMPLE 3 Multiply $\sqrt{2}$ and $4 - \sqrt{2}$.

SOLUTION Use the Distributive Property.

Ⓜ $\sqrt{2}(4 - \sqrt{2}) = 4\sqrt{2} - \sqrt{4}$
$= 4\sqrt{2} - 2$

EXAMPLE 4 Multiply $3 + \sqrt{2}$ and $1 - \sqrt{2}$.

Ⓜ **SOLUTION** $(3 + \sqrt{2})(1 - \sqrt{2}) = (3 + \sqrt{2}) \cdot 1 - (3 + \sqrt{2}) \cdot \sqrt{2}$
$= 3 + \sqrt{2} - 3\sqrt{2} - \sqrt{4}$
$= 3 + \sqrt{2} - 3\sqrt{2} - 2$
$= 1 + (1 - 3)\sqrt{2}$
$= 1 - 2\sqrt{2}$

CLASSROOM EXERCISES

Simplify each product.

1. $\sqrt{7} \cdot \sqrt{2}$

2. $2\sqrt{3} \cdot 4\sqrt{6}$

3. $\sqrt{3} \cdot (6 - \sqrt{3})$

4. $(4 + \sqrt{2}) \cdot (2 - \sqrt{2})$

EXERCISES

Simplify each product.

A

1. $\sqrt{5} \cdot \sqrt{7}$ **2.** $\sqrt{3} \cdot \sqrt{11}$ **3.** $\sqrt{3} \cdot \sqrt{13}$

4. $\sqrt{6} \cdot \sqrt{17}$ **5.** $\sqrt{10} \cdot \sqrt{19}$ **6.** $\sqrt{14} \cdot \sqrt{3}$

7. $5\sqrt{2} \cdot 7\sqrt{6}$ **8.** $2\sqrt{3} \cdot 4\sqrt{15}$ **9.** $8\sqrt{8} \cdot 3\sqrt{5}$

10. $9\sqrt{10} \cdot 5\sqrt{5}$ **11.** $3\sqrt{14} \cdot 6\sqrt{7}$ **12.** $4\sqrt{10} \cdot 11\sqrt{6}$

13. $\sqrt{5} \cdot (9 - \sqrt{5})$ **14.** $\sqrt{6} \cdot (12 - \sqrt{6})$ **15.** $\sqrt{2} \cdot (3 + \sqrt{2})$

16. $\sqrt{3} \cdot (5 + \sqrt{3})$ **17.** $\sqrt{14} \cdot (8 - \sqrt{14})$ **18.** $\sqrt{10} \cdot (15 + \sqrt{10})$

19. $(2 + \sqrt{3})(3 - \sqrt{3})$ **20.** $(8 + \sqrt{5})(4 - \sqrt{5})$ **21.** $(-9 + \sqrt{2})(-6 - \sqrt{2})$

22. $(-8 + \sqrt{7})(-3 - \sqrt{7})$ **23.** $(-12 + \sqrt{11})(4 - \sqrt{11})$ **24.** $(7 - \sqrt{15})(-5 + \sqrt{15})$

B

25. $\sqrt{\frac{5}{9}} \cdot \sqrt{\frac{2}{3}}$ **26.** $\sqrt{\frac{3}{4}} \cdot \sqrt{\frac{5}{7}}$ **27.** $\sqrt{15} \cdot \sqrt{2} \cdot \sqrt{32}$

28. $3\sqrt{5} \cdot \sqrt{18} \cdot \sqrt{27}$ **29.** $\sqrt{\frac{1}{2}} \cdot \sqrt{\frac{3}{8}} \cdot \sqrt{\frac{4}{6}}$ **30.** $\sqrt{3}(\sqrt{7} - \sqrt{8})$

31. $\sqrt{6}(\sqrt{7} + \sqrt{18})$ **32.** $3\sqrt{5}(\sqrt{2} - 2\sqrt{12})$ **33.** $2\sqrt{7}(\sqrt{8} - \sqrt{21})$

34. $(\sqrt{3} + \sqrt{2})(\sqrt{3} + \sqrt{2})$ **35.** $(2\sqrt{5} - \sqrt{2})^2$ **36.** $(3\sqrt{5} - 2)^2$

37. $(2\sqrt{7} + 3)(2\sqrt{7} + 3)$ **38.** $(\sqrt{a} + \sqrt{b})^2$ **39.** $(2\sqrt{x} - 3\sqrt{y})^2$

40. $3\sqrt{2x} \cdot 5\sqrt{3x}$ **41.** $-2\sqrt{7y} \cdot 5\sqrt{2y}$ **42.** $y^2\sqrt{xy} \cdot 2x\sqrt{y}$

43. $-3a\sqrt{ab} \cdot 2a\sqrt{ab}$ **44.** $3x\sqrt{x^2y} \cdot 2y\sqrt{xy^2}$ **45.** $5m^2\sqrt{n^3} \cdot 2m\sqrt{n}$

46. $(2x\sqrt{y} - 3\sqrt{x})^2$ **47.** $(3a^2\sqrt{b} + \sqrt{c})^2$ **48.** $2\sqrt{x} \cdot 3\sqrt{x^3} \cdot 3\sqrt{x^5}$

C

49. $(\sqrt{a} + \sqrt{b})^3$ **50.** $(\sqrt{x+1} - x)^3$ **51.** $(\sqrt{x+1} - \sqrt{x})^3$

52. $2x\sqrt{3}(3\sqrt{5x^3} - 2x\sqrt{20x} - \sqrt{45x^3})$ **53.** $5\sqrt{2x}(8x\sqrt{2x} - 2\sqrt{8x^3} + 3x\sqrt{32x})$

IRRATIONAL LENGTHS

The diagram at the right suggests how to construct a line segment that has length $\sqrt{2}$.

Show how you could construct line segments having these lengths.

1. $\sqrt{3}$ **2.** $\sqrt{5}$ **3.** $\sqrt{6}$ **4.** $\sqrt{8}$ **5.** $\sqrt{12}$ **6.** $\sqrt{13}$

12-7 DIVIDING WITH RADICALS; RATIONALIZING DENOMINATORS

In Section 12-4, we studied how to simplify a radical whose radicand is a fraction. It also is useful to know how to simplify a fraction whose demoninator includes a radical. We use the Multiplication Property of One to replace such a fraction by one for which a radicand in the denominator is a square. The process is called *rationalizing the denominator*.

EXAMPLE 1 Rationalize the denominator for $\frac{2}{\sqrt{3}}$.

SOLUTION

$$\frac{2}{\sqrt{3}} = \frac{2}{\sqrt{3}} \cdot 1$$
$$= \frac{2}{\sqrt{3}} \cdot \frac{\sqrt{3}}{\sqrt{3}}$$
$$= \frac{2\sqrt{3}}{3}, \text{ or } \frac{2}{3}\sqrt{3}$$

EXAMPLE 2 Find a decimal approximation for $\frac{2}{\sqrt{3}}$.

Use the table on page 454.

SOLUTION 1 From the table, $\sqrt{3} \doteq 1.732$.

$$\frac{2}{\sqrt{3}} \doteq \frac{2}{1.732}$$
$$\doteq 1.155$$

SOLUTION 2 From Example 1, $\frac{2}{\sqrt{3}} = \frac{2\sqrt{3}}{3}$.

Using 1.732 as an approximation for $\sqrt{3}$,

$$\frac{2\sqrt{3}}{3} \doteq \frac{2(1.732)}{3}$$
$$= \frac{3.464}{3}$$
$$\doteq 1.155$$

The ease of performing the indicated division makes the second solution preferable.

EXAMPLE 3 Rationalize the denominator for $\dfrac{2\sqrt{5b^3}}{\sqrt{18}}$.

Ⓜ SOLUTION

$$\frac{2\sqrt{5b^3}}{\sqrt{18}} = \frac{2\sqrt{5b^3}}{\sqrt{18}} \cdot \frac{\sqrt{2}}{\sqrt{2}}$$
$$= \frac{2\sqrt{10b^3}}{\sqrt{36}}$$
$$= \frac{2\sqrt{b^2}\sqrt{10b}}{6}$$
$$= \frac{\overset{1}{\cancel{2}}b\sqrt{10b}}{\underset{3}{\cancel{6}}}$$
$$= \frac{b\sqrt{10b}}{3}$$

Sometimes a denominator may be a sum whose addends include radicals. To rationalize the denominator, use the fact that the product of the sum and the difference of two numbers is the difference of their squares.

EXAMPLE 4 Rationalize the denominator for $\dfrac{4-\sqrt{2}}{2+\sqrt{2}}$.

$a - \sqrt{b}$ is the **conjugate** of $a + \sqrt{b}$. The two are conjugates of each other.

Ⓜ SOLUTION

$$\frac{4-\sqrt{2}}{2+\sqrt{2}} = \frac{4-\sqrt{2}}{2+\sqrt{2}} \cdot \frac{2-\sqrt{2}}{2-\sqrt{2}}$$
$$= \frac{(4-\sqrt{2})2-(4-\sqrt{2})\sqrt{2}}{2^2-(\sqrt{2})^2}$$
$$= \frac{8-2\sqrt{2}-4\sqrt{2}+2}{4-2}$$
$$= \frac{10-6\sqrt{2}}{2}$$
$$= 5-3\sqrt{2}$$

CLASSROOM EXERCISES

Rationalize the denominator and simplify.

1. $\dfrac{4}{\sqrt{5}}$
2. $\dfrac{4\sqrt{5}}{\sqrt{8}}$
3. $\dfrac{\sqrt{18x^3}}{\sqrt{10}}$
4. $\dfrac{2-\sqrt{3}}{3+\sqrt{3}}$

EXERCISES

A Rationalize the denominator and simplify.

1. $\frac{4}{\sqrt{7}}$
2. $\frac{5}{\sqrt{6}}$
3. $\frac{3}{\sqrt{10}}$
4. $\frac{2}{\sqrt{11}}$
5. $\frac{7}{\sqrt{14}}$
6. $\frac{13}{\sqrt{26}}$
7. $\frac{5\sqrt{6}}{\sqrt{20}}$
8. $\frac{3\sqrt{5}}{\sqrt{18}}$
9. $\frac{9\sqrt{3}}{\sqrt{24}}$
10. $\frac{6\sqrt{2}}{\sqrt{75}}$
11. $\frac{14\sqrt{7}}{\sqrt{98}}$
12. $\frac{8\sqrt{15}}{\sqrt{32}}$
13. $\frac{\sqrt{24y^3}}{\sqrt{15}}$
14. $\frac{\sqrt{8a^3}}{\sqrt{5}}$
15. $\frac{\sqrt{45z^3}}{\sqrt{30}}$
16. $\frac{\sqrt{27c^3}}{\sqrt{14}}$
17. $\frac{\sqrt{12k^5}}{\sqrt{6}}$
18. $\frac{\sqrt{20h^5}}{\sqrt{35}}$
19. $\frac{1-\sqrt{3}}{2+\sqrt{3}}$
20. $\frac{3+\sqrt{3}}{2-\sqrt{3}}$
21. $\frac{2+\sqrt{5}}{2-\sqrt{5}}$
22. $\frac{4-\sqrt{5}}{4+\sqrt{5}}$
23. $\frac{5-\sqrt{2}}{3+\sqrt{2}}$
24. $\frac{2+\sqrt{2}}{3-\sqrt{2}}$

B

25. $\frac{\sqrt{x^3}}{\sqrt{xy}}$
26. $\frac{\sqrt{a^5}}{\sqrt{ab}}$
27. $\frac{\sqrt{15x}}{\sqrt{5x}}$
28. $\frac{\sqrt{18y}}{\sqrt{3y}}$
29. $\sqrt{\frac{18a^2b^3}{24ab^5}}$
30. $\sqrt{\frac{12x^3y}{32xy}}$
31. $\sqrt{\frac{45rs}{6s^3}}$
32. $\sqrt{\frac{24a}{50a^3b^5}}$
33. $\frac{x-4}{\sqrt{x}+2}$
34. $\frac{\sqrt{a}+\sqrt{b}}{\sqrt{a}-\sqrt{b}}$
35. $\frac{3\sqrt{x}-1}{\sqrt{x}+1}$
36. $\frac{2\sqrt{x}-1}{\sqrt{x}+4}$
37. $\frac{\sqrt{24}-\sqrt{6}}{\sqrt{2}}$
38. $\frac{\sqrt{125}-2\sqrt{10}}{\sqrt{5}}$
39. $\frac{15\sqrt{15}+10\sqrt{60}}{5\sqrt{3}}$

C Rationalize the binomial denominator and simplify.

40. $\frac{3\sqrt{5}+2\sqrt{3}}{2\sqrt{5}-5\sqrt{3}}$
41. $\frac{2\sqrt{12}+\sqrt{18}}{3\sqrt{3}-\sqrt{2}}$
42. $\frac{3\sqrt{6}+\sqrt{2}}{\sqrt{6}-2\sqrt{2}}$
43. $\frac{3\sqrt{2}+3}{\sqrt{2}-5\sqrt{3}}$
44. $\frac{2\sqrt{5}+3\sqrt{12}}{4\sqrt{5}-\sqrt{2}}$
45. $\frac{2\sqrt{18}+\sqrt{28}}{\sqrt{2}+3\sqrt{7}}$

1.4142136

CAN THE RADICAND BE NEGATIVE?

$\sqrt{x}$ does *not* represent a real number for any value for x that is negative. Your calculator works only with real numbers. What happens on your calculator when you enter a negative number and then press $\boxed{\sqrt{x}}$?

12-8 SOLVING EQUATIONS CONTAINING RADICALS

An equation may contain a radical. It is a **radical equation** when the radicand includes a variable.

RADICAL EQUATIONS

$\sqrt{x} = 3$ $\quad 2\sqrt{c} = 16$ $\quad \sqrt{2x - 1} = 5$

$4 + \sqrt{t} = 6$ $\quad \sqrt{\frac{c}{5}} - 7 = 0$ $\quad 3 + 3\sqrt{x + 1} = 6$

An equation such as $2x - \sqrt{5} = 0$ is *not* a radical equation.

To solve a radical equation, show the radical as one member of the equation. Then use the Squaring Property. This property allows us to square both members of an equation.

THE SQUARING PROPERTY

If a and b are expressions for the same real number (that is, if $a = b$), then

$$a^2 = b^2.$$

From $a^2 = b^2$, it does not necessarily follow that $a = b$.

EXAMPLE 1 Solve $\sqrt{x} = 7$.

Ⓜ SOLUTION

$$\sqrt{x} = 7$$
$$(\sqrt{x})^2 = 7^2$$
$$x = 49$$

CHECK

$$\sqrt{x} = 7$$
$$\sqrt{49} \stackrel{?}{=} 7$$
$$7 = 7 \checkmark$$

Squaring both members of an equation may yield an equation that has more solutions than the original equation. For example, there are more solutions for $x^2 = 9$ than there are for $x = 3$. For this reason it is very important that you always check your "solution" in the original equation.

EXAMPLE 2 Solve $2 + \sqrt{x} = 4$.

Ⓜ SOLUTION

$$2 + \sqrt{x} = 4$$
$$\sqrt{x} = 2$$
$$(\sqrt{x})^2 = 2^2$$
$$x = 4$$

CHECK

$$2 + \sqrt{x} = 4$$
$$2 + \sqrt{4} \stackrel{?}{=} 4$$
$$4 = 4 \checkmark$$

EXAMPLE 3 Solve $\sqrt{x+4} - 3 = 2$.

Ⓜ **SOLUTION**

$$\sqrt{x+4} - 3 = 2$$
$$\sqrt{x+4} = 5$$
$$(\sqrt{x+4})^2 = 5^2$$
$$x + 4 = 25$$
$$x = 21$$

CHECK

$$\sqrt{x+4} - 3 = 2$$
$$\sqrt{21+4} - 3 \stackrel{?}{=} 2$$
$$2 = 2 \checkmark$$

EXAMPLE 4 Solve $\sqrt{x} = -5$.

Ⓜ **SOLUTION**

$$\sqrt{x} = -5$$
$$(\sqrt{x})^2 = (-5)^2$$
$$x = 25$$

CHECK

$$\sqrt{x} = -5$$
$$\sqrt{25} \stackrel{?}{=} -5$$
$$5 \neq -5$$

The equation $\sqrt{x} = -5$ has no solution.

> SOLVING A RADICAL EQUATION
>
> 1. Collect all terms that do not contain the radical so they are in one member and the radical *is* the other member.
> 2. Square both members of the equation and solve.
> 3. Check your results by replacing the variables in the original equation.

CLASSROOM EXERCISES

Solve and check.

1. $\sqrt{x} = 5$
2. $4 + \sqrt{x} = 8$
3. $\sqrt{x+7} - 4 = 7$
4. $\sqrt{x} = -3$

EXERCISES

A Solve and check.

1. $\sqrt{x} = 2$
2. $\sqrt{x} = 8$
3. $\sqrt{x} = 15$
4. $\sqrt{x} = 21$
5. $\sqrt{x} = 24$
6. $\sqrt{x} = 9$
7. $2 + \sqrt{x} = 5$
8. $5 + \sqrt{x} = 7$
9. $\sqrt{x} - 4 = 10$
10. $\sqrt{x} - 9 = 7$
11. $\sqrt{x+8} - 9 = 7$
12. $\sqrt{x+2} + 11 = 21$
13. $\sqrt{x} = -1$
14. $\sqrt{x} = -12$
15. $-\sqrt{x} = -12$
16. $-\sqrt{x} = -5$

B

17. $7 = \sqrt{2x+3}$
18. $\sqrt{3y-5} = 4$
19. $3\sqrt{b+1} = 4$
20. $5\sqrt{x+2} = 8$
21. $3 + 4\sqrt{y} = 9$
22. $7 + 5\sqrt{b} = 19$
23. $\sqrt{5x-12} - 8 = 3$
24. $\sqrt{2c-7} - 5 = 9$
25. $9 = \frac{3}{4}\sqrt{x}$

26. $9 = \frac{1}{\sqrt{x}}$ **27.** $3 = \frac{1}{2\sqrt{x}}$ **28.** $\frac{1}{2}\sqrt{y} - 48 = 2$

C **29.** $4\sqrt{2x + 2} - 9 = 2\sqrt{2x + 2}$ **30.** $5\sqrt{3x - 1} - 4 = 3\sqrt{3x - 1}$

31. $\sqrt{2x + 6} - \sqrt{5x} = 0$ **32.** $\sqrt{4x - 3} - \sqrt{3x + 4} = 0$ **33.** $\sqrt{x^2 - 4} = x + 2$

CHECKING YOUR UNDERSTANDING

WORDS AND SYMBOLS

Multiplication Property of Square Roots Division Property of Square Roots
radical equation rationalize a denominator The Squaring Property

CONCEPTS

- Radicals whose radicands include squares as factors may be simplified. Radicals whose radicands include fractions should be simplified. [12-4]
- Sums or differences that involve radicals with the same radicand may be simplified. [12-5]
- Radicals involving fractions in the radicands, and fractions involving radicals in the denominator may be simplified using the Multiplication Property of One. [12-4, 12-7]
- A radical may be eliminated from an equation by squaring both members. [12-8]

PROCESSES

- Simplify a radical. Rationalize a denominator. [12-4, 12-7]

1. $\sqrt{52}$ **2.** $3\sqrt{50}$ **3.** $\sqrt{200x^3}$ **4.** $\sqrt{\frac{9}{10a^3}}$ **5.** $\frac{5}{\sqrt{3}}$

- Add, subtract, multiply, or divide using expressions involving radicals. Simplify the results. [12-5 to 12-7]

6. $5\sqrt{3} - 2\sqrt{3}$ **7.** $5\sqrt{2} + 3 + 2\sqrt{2}$ **8.** $\sqrt{\frac{1}{2}} + 6\sqrt{3} - 2\sqrt{32}$

9. $\sqrt{6}\sqrt{12}$ **10.** $(1 - \sqrt{2})(2 + \sqrt{2})$ **11.** $\frac{6 - \sqrt{3}}{5 + \sqrt{3}}$

- Solve an equation containing a radical. [12-8]

12. $\sqrt{x} + 1 = 4$ **13.** $6 = 7 + \sqrt{2x - 3}$ **14.** $\sqrt{x + 12} = 2$

CHAPTER REVIEW

Write the correct response. [12-1]

1. The square of a positive number is (positive, negative).
2. The square of a negative number is (positive, negative).

Give the missing number.

3. A positive number has ___?___ square roots.
4. A negative number has ___?___ square roots.

Square.

5. -9 6. $\sqrt{9}$ 7. $3a$ 8. $\sqrt{a^3}$ 9. $\frac{5x}{4y}$ 10. $-2x^3y$

Express as a decimal. [12-2]

11. $\frac{3}{8}$ 12. $\frac{-5}{6}$ 13. $\frac{15}{13}$

Express in $\frac{a}{b}$ form.

14. 2.875 15. $0.\overline{81}$ 16. $0.\overline{23}$

Use the table on p. 454. Find a decimal approximation for each square root. [12-3]

17. $\sqrt{51}$ 18. $\sqrt{70}$ 19. $\sqrt{26}$

Approximate to one decimal place.

20. $\sqrt{135}$ 21. $\sqrt{4.57}$ 22. $\sqrt{0.825}$

Simplify. [12-4]

23. $\sqrt{20}$ 24. $\sqrt{\frac{1}{3}}$ 25. $\sqrt{108}$ 26. $3\sqrt{18}$ 27. $5\sqrt{45}$

28. $\sqrt{9x^2}$ 29. $\sqrt{x^4y^6}$ 30. $\sqrt{9x^7y^3}$ 31. $\sqrt{3a^4b^2c^2}$ 32. $\sqrt{72r^5}$

Simplify. [12-5]

33. $\sqrt{12} + \sqrt{27}$
34. $\sqrt{28} + \sqrt{7} - \sqrt{63}$
35. $\sqrt{18} - \sqrt{5} + \sqrt{20} - \sqrt{50}$
36. $\sqrt{75} - 2\sqrt{5} + \sqrt{108}$
37. $6\sqrt{\frac{1}{3}} + 5\sqrt{\frac{1}{5}} + \sqrt{3}$
38. $2\sqrt{\frac{1}{2}} + 3\sqrt{\frac{1}{5}} + \sqrt{50}$

Simplify. [12-6]

39. $\sqrt{5}\sqrt{3\frac{1}{5}}$ **40.** $\sqrt{6}\sqrt{8}$ **41.** $\sqrt{5}\sqrt{75}$

42. $\sqrt{3}(2-\sqrt{3})$ **43.** $(2+\sqrt{3})(2-\sqrt{3})$ **44.** $(\sqrt{5}+\sqrt{2})(\sqrt{5}-\sqrt{2})$

Rationalize the denominator. [12-7]

45. $\frac{4\sqrt{3}}{\sqrt{8}}$ **46.** $\frac{9\sqrt{2x}}{\sqrt{3}}$ **47.** $\frac{5-\sqrt{5}}{5+\sqrt{5}}$

Solve. [12-8]

48. $\sqrt{x}+2=7$ **49.** $\sqrt{\frac{x}{3}}-4=0$ **50.** $\sqrt{5y-6}=3$ **51.** $2\sqrt{x}-7=-5$

CAPSULE REVIEW

Write the letter of the best response.

1. Which is an irrational number?

a. $\sqrt{5}$ **b.** $7\frac{3}{4}$ **c.** $0.6\overline{1}$ **d.** 0.01 **e.** $\sqrt{36}$

2. For the expression $4\sqrt{5xy}$, which is the radicand?

a. $5xy$ **b.** 5 **c.** xy **d.** $\sqrt{5xy}$ **e.** 4

3. An approximation for $\sqrt{20}$ to the nearest tenth is

a. 4.0 **b.** 4.4 **c.** 4.47 **d.** 4.5 **e.** 4.472

4. $\sqrt{72}=$

a. $6\sqrt{2}$ **b.** $6+\sqrt{2}$ **c.** $36\sqrt{2}$ **d.** $6-\sqrt{2}$ **e.** 6

5. $2\sqrt{18x^5}=$

a. $18\sqrt{2x^5}$ **b.** $6x^4\sqrt{2x}$ **c.** $6x^2\sqrt{2x}$ **d.** $6x^4\sqrt{x}$ **e.** $36x^5$

6. $5\sqrt{3}-\sqrt{48}=$

a. $-11\sqrt{3}$ **b.** $\sqrt{3}$ **c.** $9\sqrt{3}$ **d.** -11 **e.** $\sqrt{27}$

7. $(2+\sqrt{3})(4-\sqrt{3})=$

a. 6 **b.** 5 **c.** $5-2\sqrt{3}$ **d.** $11-2\sqrt{3}$ **e.** $5+2\sqrt{3}$

8. $\frac{2-\sqrt{5}}{\sqrt{5}}=$

a. $\frac{2\sqrt{5}-5}{5}$ **b.** $-\frac{3}{5}$ **c.** $2\sqrt{5}-1$ **d.** 1 **e.** $\frac{7\sqrt{5}}{5}$

9. The solution for $\sqrt{x+4}=-1$ is

a. -3 **b.** -5 **c.** 0 **d.** 6 **e.** no real number

10. $c=\sqrt{a^2+b^2}$ For $a=36$ and $b=15$, $c=$

a. 51 **b.** 39 **c.** 1521 **d.** 7.1 **e.** 2601

CHAPTER TEST

1. Use symbols to write "the fourth power of x."
2. Give the radicand for the symbol $\sqrt{25}$.
3. Write $\frac{5}{8}$ in decimal form.
4. Write $0.\overline{4}$ in $\frac{a}{b}$ form.
5. Use the table on page 454 to find a decimal approximation for $\sqrt{17}$.
6. Approximate to one decimal place. $\sqrt{66}$
7. Simplify. $\sqrt{18}$
8. Simplify. $\sqrt{\frac{3}{5}}$
9. Simplify. $\sqrt{5} + 6\sqrt{5} - 2\sqrt{5}$
10. Simplify. $\sqrt{12} + \sqrt{27}$
11. Multiply $2\sqrt{3}$ and $\sqrt{2}$.
12. Multiply $\sqrt{5}$ and $2 + \sqrt{5}$
13. Rationalize the denominator. $\frac{3}{\sqrt{2}}$
14. Rationalize the denominator. $\frac{14\sqrt{2}}{\sqrt{7}}$
15. Solve. $\sqrt{x} = 9$
16. Solve. $\sqrt{x+2} = 6$

Write the letter of the best response.

17. The square of $4a^4$ equals
    a. $2a^2$. **b.** $2a^4$. **c.** $16a^4$. **d.** $16a^8$. **e.** $16a^{16}$.
18. Which of these is an irrational number?
    a. 5 **b.** $\frac{4}{5}$ **c.** $0.\overline{3}$ **d.** $\sqrt{8}$ **e.** $\sqrt{9}$
19. $\sqrt{69} \doteq$
    a. 4.1 **b.** 8.3 **c.** 12.5 **d.** 16.7 **e.** 34.5
20. $\sqrt{72} =$
    a. $9\sqrt{8}$ **b.** $6\sqrt{2}$ **c.** $4\sqrt{18}$ **d.** $3\sqrt{8}$ **e.** $2\sqrt{18}$
21. $\sqrt{20} + \sqrt{45} =$
    a. $5\sqrt{5}$ **b.** $7\sqrt{5}$ **c.** $11\sqrt{5}$ **d.** $13\sqrt{5}$ **e.** $\sqrt{65}$
22. $(3\sqrt{5})(\sqrt{2}) =$
    a. $\sqrt{30}$ **b.** $5\sqrt{6}$ **c.** $6\sqrt{10}$ **d.** $6\sqrt{5}$ **e.** $3\sqrt{10}$
23. $\frac{12\sqrt{5}}{\sqrt{6}} =$
    a. $2\sqrt{5}$ **b.** $\sqrt{10}$ **c.** $2\sqrt{30}$ **d.** 60 **e.** $6\sqrt{5}$
24. Which is a solution for $\sqrt{x-8} = 10$?
    a. 2 **b.** 18 **c.** 58 **d.** 92 **e.** 108

CHAPTER 13
Quadratic Equations

Important sources of information for people concerned with consumer interests are the consumers themselves. Data gathered from consumers are compiled in the form of statistical tables, charts, and graphs. These aids provide the basis for decisions and courses of action that affect consumers directly. This cycle generally benefits both the consumers and those who provide consumer services.

13-1 SOLVING INCOMPLETE QUADRATIC EQUATIONS

A **quadratic equation** in one variable is one that contains the second power of the variable but no greater power. If a quadratic equation also contains the first power of the variable, it is a **complete** quadratic equation. If it does not contain the first power of the variable, it is an **incomplete** quadratic equation.

QUADRATIC EQUATIONS

Complete		Incomplete
$x^2 + 2x + 1 = 0$	$3x^2 + x = 2$	$x^2 - 4 = 0$
$x^2 - 2\sqrt{2}x + 2 = 0$	$x^2 = \frac{5}{6}x + 1$	$3x^2 = 27$

To solve an incomplete quadratic equation, solve for x^2 and then find square roots.

EXAMPLE 1 Solve $x^2 - 9 = 0$.

(M) SOLUTION

$$x^2 - 9 = 0$$
$$x^2 = 9$$
$$x = \pm 3$$
$$x = 3 \text{ or } x = -3$$

CHECK

$$x^2 - 9 = 0 \qquad\qquad x^2 - 9 = 0$$
$$3^2 - 9 \stackrel{?}{=} 0 \qquad\qquad (-3)^2 - 9 \stackrel{?}{=} 0$$
$$0 = 0 \checkmark \qquad\qquad 0 = 0 \checkmark$$

EXAMPLE 2 Solve $x^2 - 18 = 0$.

(M) SOLUTION

$$x^2 - 18 = 0$$
$$x^2 = 18$$
$$x = \pm\sqrt{18}$$
$$x = \pm 3\sqrt{2}$$
$$x = 3\sqrt{2} \text{ or } x = -3\sqrt{2}$$

CHECK

$$x^2 - 18 = 0$$
$$(3\sqrt{2})^2 - 18 \stackrel{?}{=} 0$$
$$9(2) - 18 \stackrel{?}{=} 0$$
$$0 = 0 \checkmark$$

The check for $x = -3\sqrt{2}$ is left for the student.

EXAMPLE 3 Solve $3x(x-4)-x(x+3)=3(6-5x)$.

(M) SOLUTION

$$3x(x-4)-x(x+3)=3(6-5x)$$
$$3x^2-12x-x^2-3x=18-15x$$
$$2x^2=18$$
$$x^2=9$$
$$x=\pm 3$$

$x=3$ or $x=-3$

CHECK The check is left for the student.

> **Solving an Incomplete Quadratic Equation in x**
>
> 1. Solve the equation for x^2.
> 2. Find square roots of both members.
> 3. Check by replacing the variable in the original equation.

CLASSROOM EXERCISES

Solve. Give irrational solutions in simplest form.

1. $x^2-25=0$ **2.** $3x^2-24=0$ **3.** $2x(3x-4)=2(3-4x)$

EXERCISES

A Solve and check. Give irrational solutions in simplest form.

1. $x^2-49=0$ **2.** $y^2-36=0$ **3.** $m^2-81=0$

4. $h^2-100=0$ **5.** $z^2-32=0$ **6.** $a^2-75=0$

7. $b^2-500=0$ **8.** $c^2-150=0$ **9.** $5c^2=125$

10. $4x^2=4$ **11.** $4p^2=144$ **12.** $2a^2=98$

13. $6z^2=72$ **14.** $3y^2=60$ **15.** $\frac{1}{2}x^2=\frac{2}{9}$

16. $x(2x+3)=3x+50$ **17.** $x(3x+5)=15+5x$

18. $(x+2)(x+2)=2(11+2x)$ **19.** $(x-2)(x-2)=4(4-x)$

20. $(3x+4)(3x+4)=4(6x+13)$ **21.** $(3x-2)(3x-2)=4(19-3x)$

B **22.** $\frac{3x^2}{4}-3=6$ **23.** $\frac{x^2-3}{2}=\frac{2x^2}{9}+1$ **24.** $\frac{2x+5}{2}-x=\frac{x^2}{3}$

25. $8x-\frac{2}{3}=\frac{x(24-x)}{3}$ **26.** $\frac{x^2-4}{2}=\frac{x^2-2}{4}$ **27.** $x(4x+3)-2x=3-(1-x)$

Solve for x.

C **28.** $ax^2=b$ **29.** $x(x+a)=ax+c$ **30.** $\frac{2x}{3p}=\frac{x}{6p}+\frac{5}{x}$ **31.** $\frac{x^2-a}{b}=\frac{x^2-b}{a}$

13-2 COMPLETING THE SQUARE

One method for solving complete quadratic equations involves *completing the square*. To use this method, you must know how to square a binomial, find a square root of a perfect-square trinomial, and form a perfect-square trinomial when two of its terms are given.

EXAMPLE 1 Square $x + 3$.

Ⓜ SOLUTION

$$(x + 3)^2 = (x + 3)(x + 3)$$
$$= x^2 + 3x + 3x + 9$$
$$= x^2 + 6x + 9$$

EXAMPLE 2 Square $x + a$. Square $x - a$.

Ⓜ SOLUTION $(x + a)^2 = x^2 + 2ax + a^2$ | $(x - a)^2 = x^2 - 2ax + a^2$

In each of the above examples, look at the coefficient of x in the middle term of the trinomial. One-half the coefficient is a square root of the third term. The third term is always *added* to the first two. These are the clues to use for finding perfect-square trinomials.

EXAMPLE 3 Is $x^2 - 16x + 64$ a perfect-square trinomial? If it is, find a square root.

SOLUTION The coefficient of x is 16. One-half of 16 is 8 which is also a square root of 64. Therefore, $x^2 - 16x + 64$ is a perfect square.

$$x^2 - 16x + 64 = (x - 8)^2$$

$x - 8$ is a square root of $x^2 - 16x + 64$.

EXAMPLE 4 What third term must be added for this to be a perfect-square trinomial? $x^2 + 8x + ?$

SOLUTION The coefficient of x is 8. One-half of 8 is 4. Four should be a square root of the third term for the trinomial to be a perfect square. Thus, the third term should be 16. $x^2 + 8x + 16$ is a perfect-square trinomial.

$$x^2 + 8x + 16 = (x + 4)^2$$

EXAMPLE 5 Find the term that must be added to make this a perfect-square trinomial. $x^2 - 12x + ?$

SOLUTION One-half of 12 is 6. $6^2 = 36$.
$x^2 - 12x + 36$ is a perfect-square trinomial.

$$x^2 - 12x + 36 = (x - 6)^2$$

EXAMPLE 6 Add to complete the square. $x^2 + \frac{2}{3}x + ?$

SOLUTION One-half of $\frac{2}{3}$ is $\frac{1}{3}$. $\left(\frac{1}{3}\right)^2 = \frac{1}{9}$. $x^2 + \frac{2}{3}x + \frac{1}{9}$ is a perfect square.

$$x^2 + \frac{2}{3}x + \frac{1}{9} = \left(x + \frac{1}{3}\right)^2$$

Completing a Perfect-Square Trinomial in x

1. Find one-half the coefficient of x.
2. Add its square as the third term of the trinomial.

CLASSROOM EXERCISES

Square each of the following.

1. $x - 5$ **2.** $x + b$ **3.** $x + \frac{1}{3}$

Find the missing term to complete a perfect-square trinomial.

4. $x^2 - 10x + ?$ **5.** $x^2 + 6x + ?$ **6.** $x^2 - \frac{1}{2}x + ?$

7. Find a square root of $x^2 - 12x + 36$.

EXERCISES

A Square each of the following.

1. $x - 8$ **2.** $x - 12$ **3.** $x + 9$ **4.** $x + 15$

5. $x + \frac{2}{5}$ **6.** $x + \frac{3}{8}$ **7.** $x + h$ **8.** $x + z$

Find a square root of each.

9. $m^2 - 10m + 25$ **10.** $x^2 - 22x + 121$ **11.** $k^2 + 14k + 49$

12. $x^2 + 28x + 196$ **13.** $x^2 + \frac{2}{3}x + \frac{1}{9}$ **14.** $a^2 + \frac{12}{5}a + \frac{36}{25}$

Find the missing term to complete a perfect-square trinomial.

15. $r^2 + 20r + ?$ **16.** $x^2 + 30x + ?$ **17.** $y^2 - 18y + ?$

18. $a^2 - 16a + ?$ **19.** $x^2 + 5x + ?$ **20.** $p^2 + 11p + ?$

21. $y^2 - 13y + ?$ **22.** $z^2 - 9z + ?$ **23.** $x^2 + \frac{1}{3}x + ?$

24. $y^2 + \frac{1}{5}y + ?$ **25.** $z^2 - \frac{5}{3}z + ?$ **26.** $a^2 - \frac{3}{2}a + ?$

B **27.** $m^2 - 2mn + ?$ **28.** $a^2 - 6ab + ?$ **29.** $t + 4\sqrt{t} + ?$

30. $b + 10\sqrt{b} + ?$ **31.** $a^2 + ab + ?$ **32.** $r^2 + \frac{1}{2}rs + ?$

33. $b^2 + \frac{2}{3}bc + ?$ **34.** $x^2 + 2x\sqrt{2y} + ?$

35. $x^2 + 2x(a + b) + ?$ **36.** $(x + y)^4 + 2y(x + y)^2 + ?$

37. $(a + b)^4 + 6(a + b)^2 + ?$ **38.** $(a + b)^2 + 2\sqrt{2}(a + b) + ?$

C **39.** $a^2 + 2a(b + c)^2 + ?$ **40.** $(x + y)^4 + 9(x + y)^2 + ?$

41. $(x + y)^2 + \frac{\sqrt{3}}{4}(x + y) + ?$ **42.** $9x^2 + 24x + ?$

43. $25x^2 - 10x + ?$ **44.** $9x^2 - 12x + ?$

FINDING SQUARE ROOTS

Consider some number, n, and a divisor, d.

If $d = \sqrt{n}$, then $\frac{n}{d} = d$. If $d < \sqrt{n}$, then $d < \frac{n}{d}$. If $d > \sqrt{n}$, then $d > \frac{n}{d}$.

In the latter two cases, both n and the mean (average) of the divisor and quotient are *between* the divisor and the quotient. This fact provides a simple approach to finding a square root of a number.

EXAMPLE Find the positive square root of 2052.

SOLUTION $45^2 = 2025$, $46^2 = 2116$

Therefore, $45^2 < 2052 < 46^2$. Use 45 as the first divisor.

$\frac{2052}{45} = 45.6$ $45 < \sqrt{2052} < 45.6$ $\frac{45 + 45.6}{2} = 45.3$

Use 45.3 as the second divisor.

$\frac{2052}{45.3} = 45.298$ $45.298 < \sqrt{2052} < 45.3$ $\frac{45.298 + 45.3}{2} = 45.299$

The process is continued until the desired precision is reached. Here, we say $2052 \doteq 45.3$.

Use the above method to find approximate square roots of these numbers.

1. 29 **2.** 67 **3.** 53 **4.** 159 **5.** 483

13-3 SOLVING QUADRATIC EQUATIONS BY COMPLETING THE SQUARE

To solve a quadratic equation by completing the square, we make one member a perfect square so that we can find a square root.

EXAMPLE 1 Solve $x^2 - 6x + 8 = 0$.

SOLUTION $x^2 - 6x + 8 = 0$

$x^2 - 6x = -8$

Complete the square. Be sure to add the same number to both members of the equation.

$x^2 - 6x + 9 = -8 + 9$

$(x - 3)^2 = 1$

Find square roots.

$x - 3 = \pm 1$

$x - 3 = 1$ or $x - 3 = -1$

$x = 4$ | $x = 2$

CHECK

$x^2 - 6x + 8 = 0$	$x^2 - 6x + 8 = 0$
$4^2 - 6(4) + 8 \stackrel{?}{=} 0$	$2^2 - 6(2) + 8 \stackrel{?}{=} 0$
$0 = 0$ ✓	$0 = 0$ ✓

In Section 7-11, we solved equations by factoring. Now we have a second method for solving quadratic equations. Of the two, factoring is faster when factors are found easily. The advantage of completing the square is that this same process *always* provides the real-number solutions of any quadratic equation.

EXAMPLE 2 Solve $x^2 - 3x - 18 = 0$.

Ⓜ SOLUTION 1

$x^2 - 3x - 18 = 0$

$x^2 - 3x = 18$

Complete the square.

$x^2 - 3x + \frac{9}{4} = 18 + \frac{9}{4}$

$\left(x - \frac{3}{2}\right)^2 = \frac{81}{4}$

$x - \frac{3}{2} = \pm \frac{9}{2}$

$x - \frac{3}{2} = \frac{9}{2}$ or $x - \frac{3}{2} = -\frac{9}{2}$

$x = 6$ | $x = -3$

Ⓜ SOLUTION 2

$x^2 - 3x - 18 = 0$

$(x - 6)(x + 3) = 0$

$x - 6 = 0$ or $x + 3 = 0$

$x = 6$ | $x = -3$

CHECK The check is left for the student.

EXAMPLE 3 Solve $6x^2 + 5x - 4 = 0$ by completing a square.

SOLUTION

$$6x^2 + 5x - 4 = 0$$
$$6x^2 + 5x = 4$$

We know how to complete a square when the coefficient of the x^2 term is 1. Therefore, divide both members by 6.

D_6 $\quad x^2 + \frac{5}{6}x = \frac{4}{6}$

Complete the square.

$$x^2 + \frac{5}{6}x + \frac{25}{144} = \frac{4}{6} + \frac{25}{144}$$
$$\left(x + \frac{5}{12}\right)^2 = \frac{121}{144}$$
$$x + \frac{5}{12} = \pm\frac{11}{12}$$

$x + \frac{5}{12} = \frac{11}{12}$ or $x + \frac{5}{12} = -\frac{11}{12}$

$x = \frac{6}{12}$ | $x = -\frac{16}{12}$

$x = \frac{1}{2}$ | $x = -\frac{4}{3}$

CHECK The check is left for the student.

In Example 3, if we had recognized the factors of $6x^2 + 5x - 4$ as being $2x - 1$ and $3x + 4$, we could have solved the equation quickly by factoring. There are equations, however, which we simply cannot solve by factoring. For such equations, completing the square will still provide the solutions.

EXAMPLE 4 Solve $3x^2 + 7x + 3 = 0$.

(M) SOLUTION

$$3x^2 + 7x + 3 = 0$$
$$3x^2 + 7x = -3$$

D_3 $\quad x^2 + \frac{7}{3}x = -1$

$$x^2 + \frac{7}{3}x + \frac{49}{36} = -1 + \frac{49}{36}$$
$$\left(x + \frac{7}{6}\right)^2 = \frac{13}{36}$$
$$x + \frac{7}{6} = \pm\frac{\sqrt{13}}{6}$$

$x + \frac{7}{6} = \frac{\sqrt{13}}{6}$ or $x + \frac{7}{6} = -\frac{\sqrt{13}}{6}$

$x = -\frac{7}{6} + \frac{\sqrt{13}}{6}$ | $x = -\frac{7}{6} - \frac{\sqrt{13}}{6}$

$x = \frac{-7 + \sqrt{13}}{6}$ | $x = \frac{-7 - \sqrt{13}}{6}$

You may wish to try a check for one of these solutions before studying the Check on the next page.

CHECK (Example 4) Replace x by $\frac{-7+\sqrt{13}}{6}$ in $3x^2 + 7x + 3 = 0$.

$$3\left(\frac{-7+\sqrt{13}}{6}\right)^2 + 7\left(\frac{-7+\sqrt{13}}{6}\right) + 3 \stackrel{?}{=} 0$$
$$\frac{3(49-14\sqrt{13}+13)}{36} + \frac{-49+7\sqrt{13}}{6} + 3 \stackrel{?}{=} 0$$
$$\frac{62-14\sqrt{13}}{12} + \frac{-98+14\sqrt{13}}{12} + 3 \stackrel{?}{=} 0$$
$$\frac{-36}{12} + 3 \stackrel{?}{=} 0$$
$$0 = 0 \checkmark$$

The check for $x = \frac{-7-\sqrt{13}}{6}$ is left for the student.

EXAMPLE 5 Solve $\frac{x-2}{x+2} - \frac{x+2}{x-1} = \frac{x^2-32}{x^2+x-2}$.

Ⓜ SOLUTION

$$\frac{x-2}{x+2} - \frac{x+2}{x-1} = \frac{x^2-32}{x^2+x-2}$$
$$\frac{x-2}{x+2} - \frac{x+2}{x-1} = \frac{x^2-32}{(x+2)(x-1)}$$

Multiply both members by $(x+2)(x-1)$.

$$(x-1)(x-2) - (x+2)^2 = x^2 - 32$$
$$(x^2-3x+2) - (x^2+4x+4) = x^2 - 32$$
$$x^2 - 3x + 2 - x^2 - 4x - 4 = x^2 - 32$$
$$-x^2 - 7x = -30$$
$$M_{-1} \qquad x^2 + 7x = 30$$
$$x^2 + 7x + \tfrac{49}{4} = 30 + \tfrac{49}{4}$$
$$\left(x + \tfrac{7}{2}\right)^2 = \tfrac{169}{4}$$

$x + \frac{7}{2} = \frac{13}{2}$ or $x + \frac{7}{2} = -\frac{13}{2}$

$x = \frac{6}{2}$ | $x = -\frac{20}{2}$

$x = 3$ | $x = -10$

CHECK The check is left for the student.

SOLVING A QUADRATIC EQUATION BY COMPLETING THE SQUARE

1. Write the equation in the form $x^2 + bx = c$.
2. Add the square of one-half b to each member. This completes the square in the left member.
3. Find square roots of both members.
4. Solve the two resulting equations.
5. Check by replacing the variable in the original equation.

CLASSROOM EXERCISES

Solve by completing the square. Then check.

1. $m^2 + 2m - 24 = 0$ **2.** $2x^2 - 7x - 15 = 0$ **3.** $4x^2 + 2x - 1 = 0$

EXERCISES

A Solve by completing the square. Then check.

1. $x^2 + 4x - 5 = 0$ **2.** $x^2 + 10x + 24 = 0$ **3.** $y^2 - 6y - 27 = 0$

4. $y^2 - 10y - 24 = 0$ **5.** $x^2 - 20x - 96 = 0$ **6.** $y^2 - 8y - 48 = 0$

7. $x^2 - 11x + 28 = 0$ **8.** $x^2 - 7x + 6 = 0$ **9.** $y^2 - 3y - 40 = 0$

10. $y^2 - y - 30 = 0$ **11.** $x^2 + x - 72 = 0$ **12.** $x^2 + 5x - 36 = 0$

13. $x^2 + 11 = 12x$ **14.** $x^2 + 9 = 8x$ **15.** $y^2 + 75 = -20y$

16. $y^2 + 29 = -30y$ **17.** $c^2 - 56 = c$ **18.** $z^2 - 4 = 3z$

19. $x^2 - 6x - 8 = 0$ **20.** $y^2 - 10y - 5 = 0$ **21.** $y^2 + 2y - 7 = 0$

22. $x^2 + 10x - 25 = 0$ **23.** $y^2 + 16y + 4 = 0$ **24.** $m^2 + 14m + 1 = 0$

25. $2x^2 - 3x + 1 = 0$ **26.** $2x^2 - 7x - 15 = 0$ **27.** $6x^2 + 13x - 8 = 0$

B **28.** $5x^2 + 8x + 1 = 0$ **29.** $4x^2 - 12x + 7 = 0$ **30.** $3x^2 - 4x - 1 = 0$

31. $2x^2 - 8x + 5 = 0$ **32.** $2y^2 - 3y - 1 = 0$ **33.** $(x + 4)^2 = 9x^2$

34. $(x + 1)(x - 4) = 50$ **35.** $(x + 2)(x + 3) = 42$ **36.** $(x + 3)(x + 5) = 24$

37. $\frac{x - 4}{x + 2} + \frac{x + 3}{x - 2} = \frac{9x + 2}{x^2 - 4}$ **38.** $\frac{x}{x - 3} + \frac{8}{x + 2} = 3$ **39.** $4x^2 = \frac{2x}{3} + \frac{1}{2}$

C **40.** $\frac{1}{y} + \frac{1}{2} = \frac{1}{y - 2}$ **41.** $\frac{1}{x} + \frac{1}{4} = \frac{1}{x - 8}$ **42.** $\frac{1}{a} + \frac{1}{3} = \frac{1}{a - 3}$

43. $\frac{2}{x} + \frac{x}{x + 1} = 5$ **44.** $3x^2 + 2x + 1 = 0$ **45.** $4x^2 + 3x + 2 = 0$

Solve for x by completing the square.

46. $4x^2 + 12x + c = 0$ **47.** $4x^2 + bx + c = 0$ **48.** $ax^2 + bx + c = 0$

13-4 SOLVING QUADRATIC EQUATIONS BY USING THE QUADRATIC FORMULA

Any quadratic equation may be written in the general form $ax^2 + bx + c = 0$ in which a, b, and c represent known numbers and $a \neq 0$. Now we shall solve $ax^2 + bx + c = 0$ for x to obtain a formula for finding all real-number solutions for any quadratic equation.

$$ax^2 + bx + c = 0$$
$$ax^2 + bx = -c$$

Divide by a to obtain 1 as the coefficient of the x^2 term. The coefficient of the middle term becomes $\frac{b}{a}$.

$$D_a \qquad x^2 + \frac{b}{a}x = -\frac{c}{a}$$

Complete the square.

$\left(\frac{1}{2} \cdot \frac{b}{a}\right)^2 = \frac{b^2}{4a^2}$. Add $\frac{b^2}{4a^2}$ to both members.

$$x^2 + \frac{b}{a}x + \frac{b^2}{4a^2} = \frac{b^2}{4a^2} - \frac{c}{a}$$
$$\left(x + \frac{b}{2a}\right)^2 = \frac{b^2 - 4ac}{4a^2}$$
$$x + \frac{b}{2a} = \pm\frac{\sqrt{b^2 - 4ac}}{2a}$$

Note that a is the coefficient of the x^2 term, b is the coefficient of the x term, and c is the constant term. Thus, the formula is developed in terms of known data for any quadratic equation.

$$x + \frac{b}{2a} = \frac{\sqrt{b^2 - 4ac}}{2a} \quad \text{or} \quad x + \frac{b}{2a} = -\frac{\sqrt{b^2 - 4ac}}{2a}$$
$$x = -\frac{b}{2a} + \frac{\sqrt{b^2 - 4ac}}{2a} \quad \Big| \quad x = -\frac{b}{2a} - \frac{\sqrt{b^2 - 4ac}}{2a}$$
$$x = \frac{-b + \sqrt{b^2 - 4ac}}{2a} \quad \Big| \quad x = \frac{-b - \sqrt{b^2 - 4ac}}{2a}$$

If each of these two numbers replaces x in the quadratic equation $ax^2 + bx + c = 0$, true sentences are obtained. Thus, these two numbers are the solutions of the equation. To help remember the two solutions, they are sometimes written as the **quadratic formula**.

$$x = \frac{-b \pm \sqrt{b^2 - 4ac}}{2a}$$

EXAMPLE 1 Solve $3x^2 - 5x = 2$ using the quadratic formula.

SOLUTION Write $3x^2 - 5x = 2$ to match the general form.

$$ax^2 + bx + c = 0$$
$$3x^2 + (-5x) + (-2) = 0$$
$$a = 3 \quad b = -5 \quad c = -2$$

Replace a, b, and c in the quadratic formula.

$$x = \frac{-(-5) \pm \sqrt{(-5)^2 - 4(3)(-2)}}{2 \cdot 3}$$
$$= \frac{5 \pm \sqrt{25 + 24}}{6}$$
$$= \frac{5 \pm \sqrt{49}}{6}$$
$$= \frac{5 \pm 7}{6}$$
$$x = 2 \quad \text{or} \quad x = -\frac{1}{3}.$$

CHECK

$$3x^2 - 5x = 2$$
$$3(2)^2 - 5(2) \stackrel{?}{=} 2$$
$$2 = 2 \checkmark$$

$$3x^2 - 5x = 2$$
$$3\left(-\frac{1}{3}\right)^2 - 5\left(-\frac{1}{3}\right) \stackrel{?}{=} 2$$
$$\frac{1}{3} + \frac{5}{3} \stackrel{?}{=} 2$$
$$2 = 2 \checkmark$$

EXAMPLE 2 Solve $9x^2 + 12x = 1$.

(M) SOLUTION

$$9x^2 + 12x = 1$$
$$9x^2 + 12x - 1 = 0$$

→ Use $a = 9$, $b = 12$, and $c = -1$ in $x = \dfrac{-b \pm \sqrt{b^2 - 4ac}}{2a}$.

$$x = \frac{-12 \pm \sqrt{12^2 - 4(9)(-1)}}{2 \cdot 9}$$
$$= \frac{-12 \pm \sqrt{180}}{18}$$
$$= \frac{-12 \pm 6\sqrt{5}}{18}$$
$$= \frac{-2 \pm \sqrt{5}}{3}$$
$$x = \frac{-2 + \sqrt{5}}{3} \quad \text{or} \quad x = \frac{-2 - \sqrt{5}}{3}$$

CHECK The check is left for the student.

SOLVING A QUADRATIC EQUATION BY USING THE QUADRATIC FORMULA

1. Write the equation in the form $ax^2 + bx + c = 0$.
2. Determine the values of a, b, and c.
3. Replace a, b, and c, in the quadratic formula.

$$x = \frac{-b \pm \sqrt{b^2 - 4ac}}{2a}$$

4. Simplify.
5. Check by replacing the variable in the original equation.

CLASSROOM EXERCISES

Solve using the quadratic formula. Check your results.

1. $2x^2 - x - 3 = 0$ **2.** $6x^2 - 10x = -3$

EXERCISES

A Solve using the quadratic formula. Check your results.

1. $x^2 - 3x - 10 = 0$ **2.** $x^2 - 4x - 21 = 0$ **3.** $x^2 + 6x - 16 = 0$

4. $x^2 + 12x - 45 = 0$ **5.** $6x^2 - 7x = -1$ **6.** $9x^2 - 15x = -4$

7. $3x^2 + 5x = 2$ **8.** $5x^2 + 9x = 2$ **9.** $4x^2 + 14x = 8$

10. $3x^2 + 13x = 10$ **11.** $k^2 - 3k = 1$ **12.** $x^2 - x = 1$

13. $m^2 - 3m = 5$ **14.** $x^2 - 6x = 11$ **15.** $4y^2 - 12y = -7$

16. $9x^2 + 12x = 1$ **17.** $3x^2 + 8x = 2$ **18.** $2x^2 + 5x = 4$

Solve by factoring. Check by using the quadratic formula.

B **19.** $2x^2 + 3x - 2 = 0$ **20.** $3x^2 + 2x - 5 = 0$

21. $x^2 + (x - 2)^2 = 10$ **22.** $(1 + x)^2 + (2x + 1)^2 = 34$

23. $\frac{3y}{2} - \frac{2}{y} - \frac{2y}{3} = 0$ **24.** $x + \frac{1}{x} = \frac{3}{x} + 3$ **25.** $\frac{x}{x + 3} + \frac{5}{x} = \frac{3}{2}$

C Solve using the quadratic formula. If no solution exists, explain why.

26. $\frac{x}{2x-2} = \frac{4}{x^2-1} + \frac{5}{x+1}$

27. $\frac{2y+3}{y^2+y} - \frac{y+5}{y^2-y} = \frac{21}{8y^2-8}$

28. $2x^2 = 3\left(x - \frac{4}{3}\right)$

29. $2\left(2x^2 - \frac{5}{2}x\right) = -2$

30. $2x^2 - 5kx + 2k^2 = 0$

31. $x^2 - 2rx - s = 0$

CHECKING YOUR UNDERSTANDING

WORDS

complete quadratic equation
completing the square
incomplete quadratic equation
perfect-square trinomial
quadratic equation
quadratic formula

CONCEPTS

- If $x^2 = a$, for $a > 0$, then $x = \pm\sqrt{a}$. [13-1]
- $x^2 + 2ax + a^2$ is a perfect-square trinomial. [13-2]
- Completing the square or using the quadratic formula will always provide the real-number solutions of any quadratic equation. [13-3, 13-4]

PROCESSES

- Complete a perfect-square trinomial. [13-2]

1. $x^2 + 6x + ?$

2. $x^2 - 10x + ?$

3. $x^2 + \frac{1}{4}x + ?$

- Solve a quadratic equation. [13-1, 13-3, 13-4]

4. $x^2 - 25 = 0$

5. $2x^2 - 14 = 0$

6. $x^2 - 2x - 15 = 0$

7. $x^2 - 2x = 2$

8. $2x^2 - 8x = 15$

9. $2x^2 + 2x - 5 = 0$

MIXTURES

One jar contains 100 mL of liquid bleach and another contains 100 mL of water. 1 mL of bleach is removed from the first jar and added to the second. The mixture is stirred and 1 mL of the mixture is returned to the bleach jar. Compare the quantity of bleach and water interchanged.

OBJECTIVE: Solve problems using quadratic equations.

13-5 PROBLEM SOLVING: USING QUADRATIC EQUATIONS

To solve problems, we often have to solve quadratic equations.

EXAMPLE 1 Twice the square of a number equals 40 more than twice the number. Find the number.

(M) SOLUTION Use n for the number.

$$2n^2 = 2n + 40$$
$$n^2 = n + 20$$
$$n^2 - n - 20 = 0$$
$$(n - 5)(n + 4) = 0$$
$$n - 5 = 0 \text{ or } n + 4 = 0$$
$$n = 5 \quad | \quad n = -4$$

CONCLUSION The number is 5 or -4.

CHECK $2(5)^2 \stackrel{?}{=} 2(5) + 40$, $50 = 50$ ✓ | $2(-4)^2 \stackrel{?}{=} 2(-4) + 40$, $32 = 32$ ✓

EXAMPLE 2 The sum of two numbers is 12. The sum of their squares is 80. Find the numbers.

(M) SOLUTION The sum of the squares of two numbers is 80.

Use x for one of the numbers.
$12 - x$ for the other number.

$$x^2 + (12 - x)^2 = 80$$
$$x^2 + 144 - 24x + x^2 = 80$$
$$2x^2 - 24x + 64 = 0$$
$$D_2 \qquad x^2 - 12x + 32 = 0$$
$$(x - 8)(x - 4) = 0$$
$$x - 8 = 0 \text{ or } x - 4 = 0$$
$$x = 8 \quad | \quad x = 4$$
Also, $12 - x = 4$. | Also, $12 - x = 8$.

CONCLUSION The two numbers are 8 and 4.

CHECK Is the sum of the squares of 8 and 4 equal to 80?

$$8^2 + 4^2 \stackrel{?}{=} 80$$
$$80 = 80 \checkmark$$

EXAMPLE 3 The length of a rectangular garden is 4 meters less than twice the width. Its area is 240 square meters. Find the length and width.

Ⓜ **SOLUTION** The area of the garden is 240.

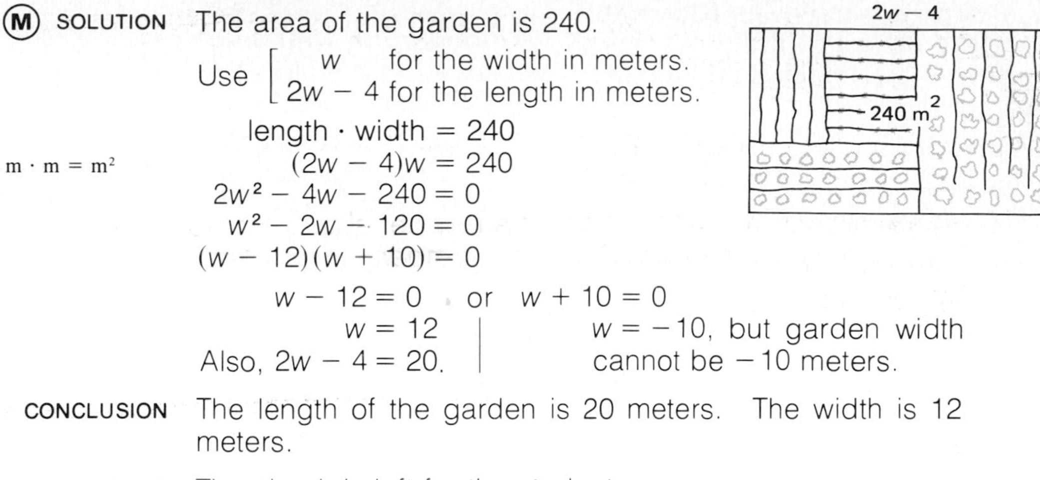

Use $\left[\begin{array}{ll} w & \text{for the width in meters.} \\ 2w - 4 & \text{for the length in meters.} \end{array}\right.$

$$\text{length} \cdot \text{width} = 240$$

$m \cdot m = m^2$

$$(2w - 4)w = 240$$
$$2w^2 - 4w - 240 = 0$$
$$w^2 - 2w - 120 = 0$$
$$(w - 12)(w + 10) = 0$$

$w - 12 = 0$ or $w + 10 = 0$

$w = 12$ | $w = -10$, but garden width cannot be -10 meters.

Also, $2w - 4 = 20$.

CONCLUSION The length of the garden is 20 meters. The width is 12 meters.

CHECK The check is left for the student.

CLASSROOM EXERCISES

Solve and check.

1. The square of a certain number is 60 more than 4 times the number. Find the number.
2. A garden is 2 meters longer than it is wide. Its area is 48 square meters. Find its length and width.
3. The sum of two numbers is 20. The sum of their squares is 208. Find the numbers.

EXERCISES

A Solve and check.

1. The square of a certain number is 30 more than the number. Find the number.
2. The square of a certain number is 4 more than 3 times the number. Find the number.
3. Twice the square of a certain number equals 40 increased by twice the number. Find the number.
4. Twice the square of a certain number equals 80 increased by 6 times the number. Find the number.
5. The difference of two numbers is 2. The sum of their squares is 52. Find the numbers.
6. The difference of two numbers is 4. The sum of their squares is 106. Find the numbers.
7. The sum of two numbers is 10. The sum of their squares is 58. Find the numbers.
8. The sum of two numbers is 17. The sum of their squares is 145. Find the numbers.

9. A rectangular lot is 22 meters longer than it is wide. Its area is 2280 square meters. Find its dimensions.

10. The area of a rectangular garden is 192 square meters. The length is 4 meters more than the width. Find the length and width.

11. The length of a rug is 2 times its width. Its area is 24.5 m^2. Find its dimensions.

12. The length of a corridor is 4 times its width. Its area is 144 m^2. Find its dimensions.

B **13.** The perimeter of a building is 56 meters. It covers an area of 195 square meters. Find the length of each side.

14. The perimeter of a picture frame is 80 cm. Its area is 396 cm^2. Find its length and width.

15. Robin rides 48 kilometers on her bicycle. The number of hours she travels is two less than her average speed in kilometers per hour. Find her average speed.

16. Tony drives 720 kilometers in one day. The number of hours he travels is one more than one-tenth his average speed in kilometers per hour. Find his average speed.

17. A rectangular flower bed is 5 meters long and 2 meters wide. It is surrounded by a grass border of uniform width whose area is $4\frac{2}{5}$ times that of the flower bed. Find the width of the border.

18. A photographic print is 14 cm long and 11 cm wide. A white border of uniform width is placed around the print. The area of the border is 116 cm^2. Find the width of the border.

C **19.** Mr. Lucas can paint a house in 2 days less than his son. When they work together they can do the job in $4\frac{4}{9}$ days. How long would it take each working alone to do the job?

20. A fish pond can be filled in 4 hours by two pipes when they are used at the same time. How many hours are needed for each pipe to fill the pond by itself if the smaller requires 3 more hours than the larger?

21. Mrs. Symancyk traveled 130 kilometers at a certain rate. By increasing the rate 13 kilometers per hour, the trip would have taken 30 minutes less time. What was the rate for the trip?

A SCHEDULING PROBLEM

The girls' camp director has eight staff members, Amy, Beth, Cathy, Doris, Evy, Flo, Gert, and Holly, who are to be assigned to two-member teams to do four jobs each of four days. The director wants to schedule the work so that each woman does a different job each day and does only one job with any other woman. Find a schedule that will meet these requirements.

13-6 PROBLEM SOLVING: THE PYTHAGOREAN THEOREM

A **right triangle** is one that has a right angle. The **hypotenuse** of a right triangle is the side *opposite* the right angle and is the longest side. The other two sides are the **legs** of the right triangle.

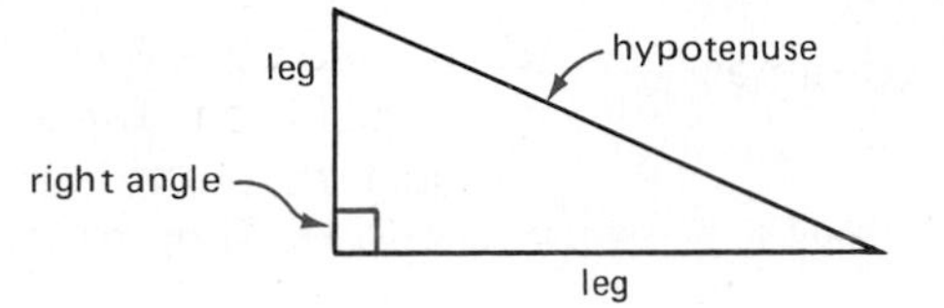

A very important theorem (a statement to be proved true) is stated sometimes as follows.

> For any right triangle, the square of the length of the hypotenuse equals the sum of the squares of the lengths of the legs.

This theorem, called the Pythagorean Theorem, is believed to have been proved first by the Greek scholar Pythagoras. It means that if c is the length of the hypotenuse and a and b are the lengths of the legs, then,

$$c^2 = a^2 + b^2$$

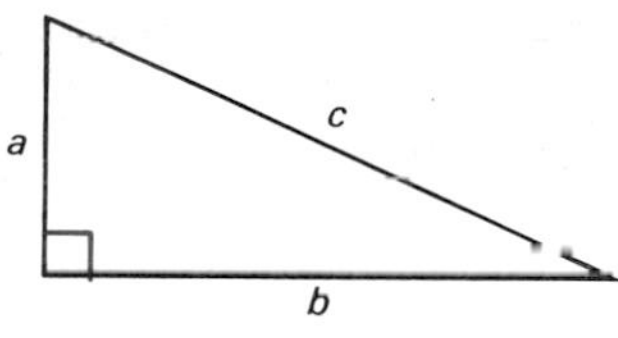

EXAMPLE 1 The lengths of the legs of a right triangle are 3 and 4. Find the length of the hypotenuse.

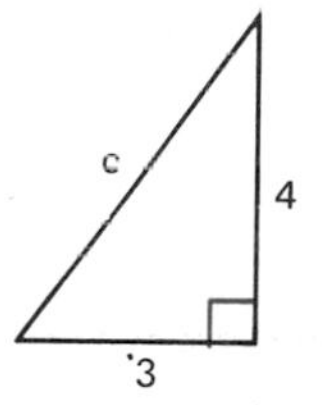

SOLUTION (M) The Pythagorean Theorem may be applied. Use c for the length of the hypotenuse.

$$c^2 = 3^2 + 4^2$$
$$c^2 = 9 + 16$$
$$c^2 = 25$$
$$c = \pm\sqrt{25}$$

Therefore, $c = 5$, or $c = -5$.
However, as a length, -5 has no meaning.

CONCLUSION The length of the hypotenuse is 5.

EXAMPLE 2 The distance across a TV screen as shown is 58 centimeters. The width of the screen is 46 centimeters. Find its height.

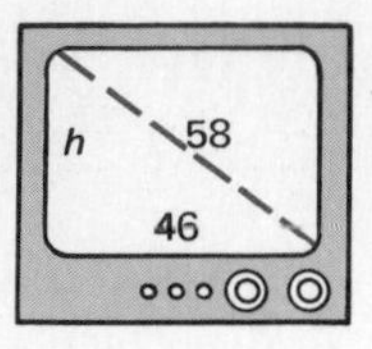

SOLUTION The Pythagorean Theorem may be applied.
(M) Use h for the height of the screen in centimeters.

$(\text{cm})^2 + (\text{cm})^2 = (\text{cm})^2$

$$h^2 + 46^2 = 58^2$$
$$h^2 + 2116 = 3364$$
$$h^2 = 1248$$
$$h = \sqrt{1248} \quad \text{or} \quad h = -\sqrt{1248}, \text{ but}$$
$$h = 4\sqrt{78}$$
$$h \doteq 35.3$$

negative height has no meaning for this situation.

CONCLUSION The height of the television screen is about 35.3 cm.

CHECK

$$(35.3)^2 + 46^2 \stackrel{?}{=} 58^2$$
$$1246.09 + 2116 \stackrel{?}{=} 3364$$
$$3362.09 \doteq 3364 \quad ✓$$

EXAMPLE 3 The length of the hypotenuse of a right triangle is 13. The length of one leg is 3 less than three times the length of the other leg. Find the length of each leg.

SOLUTION The Pythagorean Theorem may be applied.

(M) Use $\left[\begin{array}{l} x \text{ for the length of one leg.} \\ 3x - 3 \text{ for the length of the other leg.} \end{array}\right.$

$$x^2 + (3x - 3)^2 = 13^2$$
$$x^2 + 9x^2 - 18x + 9 = 169$$
$$10x^2 - 18x - 160 = 0$$
$$D_2 \qquad 5x^2 - 9x - 80 = 0$$
$$(x - 5)(5x + 16) = 0$$

The quadratic formula may be used here.

Therefore, $x - 5 = 0$ or $5x + 16 = 0$

$x = 5$ | $5x = -16$

Also, $3x - 3 = 12$. | $x = -\frac{16}{5}$, not possible

CONCLUSION The legs have lengths 5 and 12.

CHECK $5^2 + 12^2 \stackrel{?}{=} 13^2$

$169 = 169$ ✓

It has also been proved that if the sum of the squares of the lengths of two sides of a triangle equals the square of the length of the third side, then the triangle is a right triangle.

EXAMPLE 4 The lengths of two sides of a triangle are 6 and 8. How long must the third side be for the triangle to be a right triangle?

Ⓜ SOLUTION There are two cases.

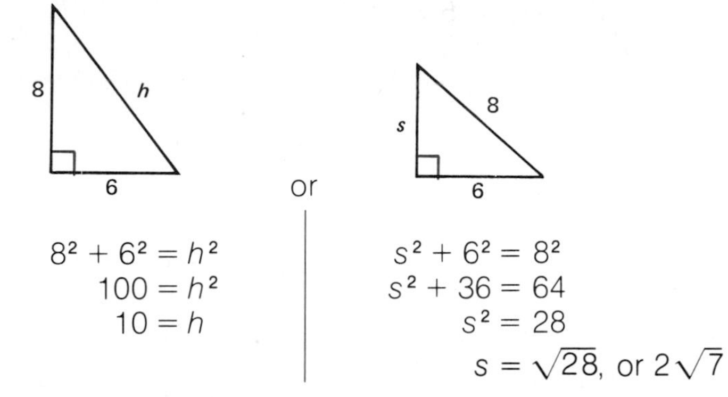

$$8^2 + 6^2 = h^2$$
$$100 = h^2$$
$$10 = h$$

$$s^2 + 6^2 = 8^2$$
$$s^2 + 36 = 64$$
$$s^2 = 28$$
$$s = \sqrt{28}, \text{ or } 2\sqrt{7}$$

We discard the negative square roots due to the nature of the problem.

CONCLUSION A triangle with sides 6, 8, and 10 is a right triangle. Also, a triangle with sides $2\sqrt{7}$, 6, and 8 is a right triangle.

CHECK Is the sum of the squares of the two sides equal to the square of the third side?

$$6^2 + 8^2 \stackrel{?}{=} 10^2$$
$$100 = 100 \quad \checkmark$$

$$(2\sqrt{7})^2 + 6^2 \stackrel{?}{=} 8^2$$
$$28 + 36 \stackrel{?}{=} 64$$
$$64 = 64 \quad \checkmark$$

CLASSROOM EXERCISES

Solve.

1. The lengths of the legs of a right triangle are 5 and 12. Find the length of the hypotenuse.
2. Find the length of a rectangle with width 12 cm and diagonal length 18 cm.
3. The length of the hypotenuse of a right triangle is 17. The length of one leg is one less than twice the length of the other leg. Find the length of each leg.
4. The lengths of two sides of a triangle are 9 and 12. How long must the third side be for the triangle to be a right triangle?

EXERCISES

A Use the Pythagorean Theorem to find the length of the hypotenuse for each right triangle. Simplify all radicals.

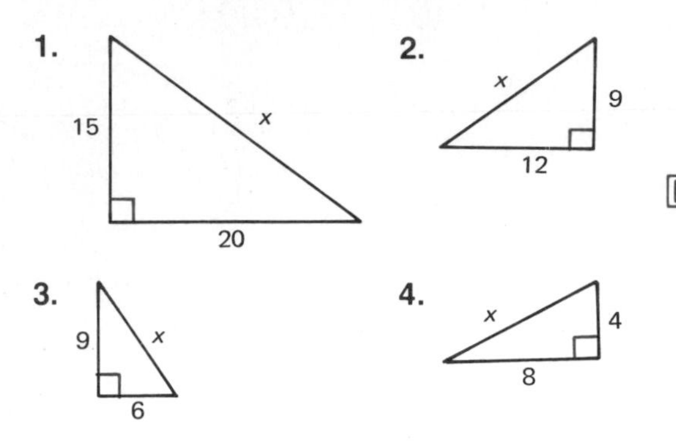

Copy and complete this chart.

	leg	leg	hypotenuse
5.	7	24	?
6.	16	30	?
7.	4	12	?
8.	6	10	?
9.	15	?	25
10.	?	80	100

Solve.

11. Find the length of a rectangular picture window whose width is 2 m and whose diagonal measures 3 m.

12. Find the width of a rectangular garden with length 15 m and diagonal length 20 m.

13. One leg of a right triangle has length 10 cm. Find the length of the hypotenuse when it is 2 cm longer than the other leg.

14. Find the lengths of the legs of a right triangle when their difference is 7 and the length of the hypotenuse is 13.

In each of the following, the lengths of two sides of a triangle are given. How long must the third side be for the triangle to be a right triangle?

15. 8 and 12 **16.** 10 and 15

17. 6 and 14 **18.** 9 and 18

B **19.** Find the length of the diagonal of a rectangular auditorium floor with area 480 m^2 and width one meter more than one-half its length.

20. Draw triangle *ABC* to be an equilateral triangle. Draw altitude *CD* to form right angles with side *AB* and separate side *AB* into two parts that are the same length. Each side of triangle *ABC* is 10 cm long. How long is the altitude?

Refer to the diagram for Exercise 20. Find the length of the altitude for the equilateral triangle whose sides have the following length.

21. 8 cm **22.** 6 cm **23.** $5\sqrt{3}$ cm

C The area of any triangle is given by the formula $A = \frac{1}{2}bh$.

Find the area of the equilateral triangle whose sides have the following length.

24. 6 cm **25.** 16 m **26.** $8\sqrt{3}$ mm

27. Derive a formula for the length of an altitude of an equilateral triangle.

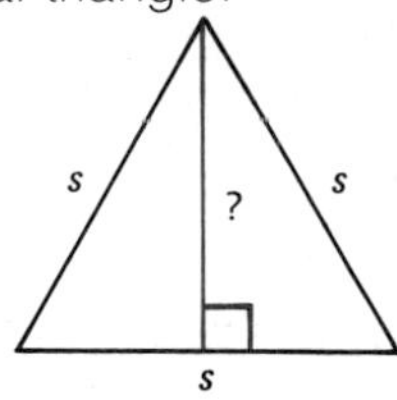

28. Derive a formula for the area of an equilateral triangle.

CHAPTER REVIEW

Solve. [13-1, 13-2]

1. $x^2 = 16$ **2.** $3x^2 = 27$ **3.** $4x^2 = 128$

4. $4x^2 - 1 = 0$ **5.** $16x^2 - 9 = 0$ **6.** $(2x - 3)^2 = 3(x^2 - 4x + 6)$

7. Square $x + 2$. **8.** $(2x - 3)^2 = ?$

Find k so that the trinomial is a perfect square.

9. $x^2 + 6x + k$ **10.** $x^2 - 10x + k$ **11.** $x^2 + \frac{1}{2}x + k$

Solve by completing the square. [13-3]

12. $x^2 + 8x + 12 = 0$ **13.** $x^2 + 4x - 12 = 0$ **14.** $x^2 - 7x + 12 = 0$

Solve by using the quadratic formula. [13-4]

15. $x^2 + 4x - 12 = 0$ **16.** $2x^2 + 5x + 2 = 0$ **17.** $5x^2 = 3x + 2$

Solve. [13-5]

18. The sum of two numbers is 10. The sum of their squares is 52. Find the numbers.

19. The areas of the square and the rectangle are equal. Find the dimensions of the rectangle.

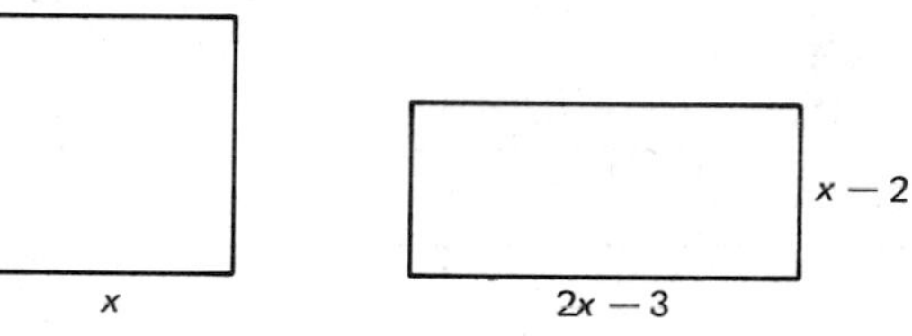

Find length x to the nearest one-tenth for each figure. [13-6]

20.

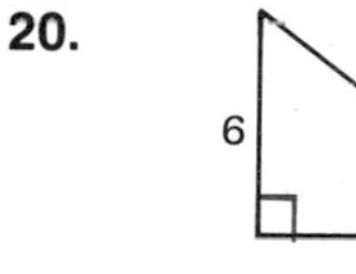

21.

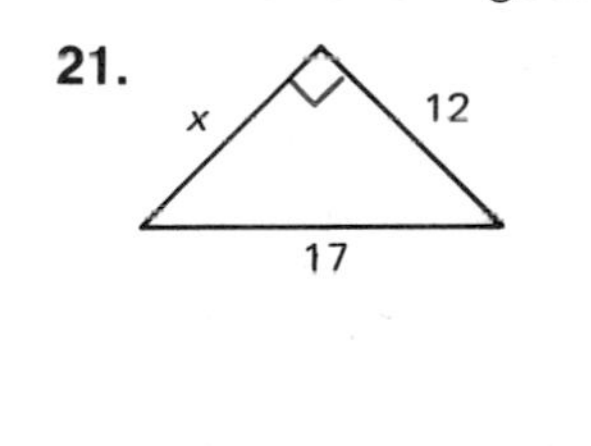

22.

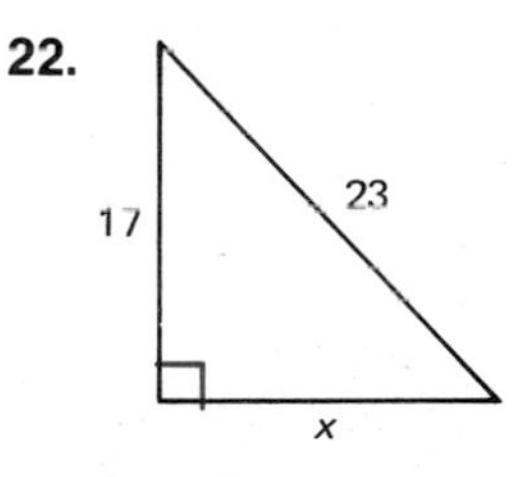

23. A rectangular field is 80 meters long and 30 meters wide. Find the length of a diagonal to the nearest meter.

24. The length of the diagonal of a square is $2\sqrt{3}$ meters. Find the length of a side in meters.

25. Find the length of each leg of this triangle.

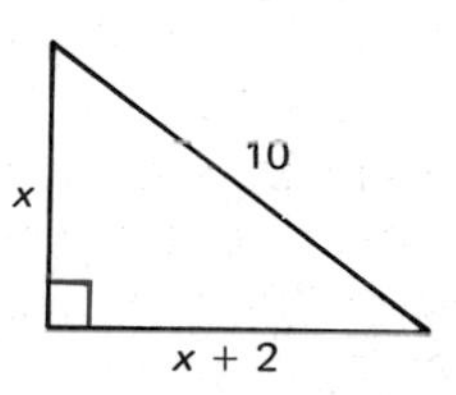

CAPSULE REVIEW

Write the letter of the best response.

1. The square of $x - 3$ is

a. $x^2 - 9$ **b.** $x^2 + 9$ **c.** $x^2 - 6x + 9$
d. $x^2 + 6x - 9$ **e.** $x^2 + 6x + 9$

2. The solution(s) for $x^2 = 16$ is (are)

a. 4 **b.** -4 **c.** 8
d. 8 and -8 **e.** 4 and -4

3. Which number for k makes $x^2 - 6x + k$ a perfect-square trinomial?

a. 9 **b.** -9 **c.** 36
d. -36 **e.** 6

4. When the lengths of the legs of a right triangle are x and $x + 1$, the length of the hypotenuse is

a. $\sqrt{x^2 + (x + 1)^2}$ **b.** $\sqrt{x^2 - (x + 1)^2}$ **c.** $\sqrt{(x + 1)^2 - x^2}$
d. $2x + 1$ **e.** $x(x + 1)$

5. When the length of the hypotenuse of an isosceles right triangle is $6\sqrt{2}$, the length of each leg is

a. $6\sqrt{2}$ **b.** $3\sqrt{2}$ **c.** 6
d. -6 **e.** $\sqrt{12}$

6. The length of each leg of the triangle is

a. $5\sqrt{2}$ **b.** $5\sqrt{2} + 2$
c. $5\sqrt{2} - 2$ **d.** 8 **e.** 12

7. The solutions for $x^2 - 7x = -12$ are

a. 1 and 6 **b.** -3 and -4 **c.** 3 and 4
d. -3 and 4 **e.** 3 and -4

8. Which are lengths of the legs of a right triangle?

a. 5 cm, 6 cm, 7 cm **b.** 3 km, 4 km, 7 km **c.** 4 m, 5 m, 7 m
d. 5 cm, 12 cm, 13 cm **e.** 2 cm, 2 cm, 3 cm

9. When the lengths of the legs of a right triangle are 3 and 5, the length of the hypotenuse is

a. $\sqrt{34}$ **b.** 34 **c.** $\sqrt{8}$
d. 8 **e.** 4

10. The solutions for $x^2 - 4x - 5 = 0$ are

a. 5 and -1 **b.** -5 and 1 **c.** 5 and 1
d. -5 and -1 **e.** 5 and 0.9

CHAPTER TEST

Solve.

1. $x^2 = 7$
2. $x^2 - 10 = 26$

Complete the perfect-square trinomial.

3. $x^2 - 8x + ?$
4. $x^2 + x + ?$

Solve by completing the square.

5. $x^2 + 6x = 16$
6. $x^2 + 2x - 15 = 0$

Solve by using the quadratic formula.

7. $2x^2 - x - 3 = 0$
8. $3x^2 - 5x - 2 = 0$

Solve.

9. The sum of two numbers is 15. The sum of their squares is 117. Find the numbers.
10. The width of a rectangle is 5 centimeters less than its length. The area is 84 square centimeters. Find the length and width in centimeters.
11. Find the length of the hypotenuse of a right triangle when the lengths of the legs are 5 centimeters and 12 centimeters.
12. The length of a diagonal of a rectangle is 26 meters. Find the width of the rectangle when its length is 24 meters.

Write the letter of the best response.

13. The solutions of $x^2 - 16 = 65$ are
    a. $\sqrt{65} \pm 4$ **b.** $4 \pm \sqrt{65}$ **c.** ± 7 **d.** $\pm\sqrt{61}$ **e.** ± 9
14. What number is needed to complete the perfect-square trinomial, $x^2 - 10x + ?$
    a. -100 **b.** -25 **c.** 20 **d.** 25 **e.** 100
15. What number would you add to both members of $x^2 + 6x = 91$ to solve by completing the square?
    a. 36 **b.** 9 **c.** -9 **d.** -10 **e.** -36
16. In using the quadratic formula for the equation $6x^2 - x - 2 = 0$, the expression $b^2 - 4ac =$
    a. 49 **b.** 28 **c.** 13 **d.** -47 **e.** -49
17. A number is 12 less than its square. Which equation will give the number?
    a. $x^2 = 12 - x$ **b.** $x^2 + 12 = x$ **c.** $x^2 - x = 12$
    d. $x - x^2 = 12$ **e.** $x - 12 = x^2$
18. What is the length of the hypotenuse of a right triangle for which the lengths of the legs are 6 meters and 9 meters?
    a. 10 m **b.** 10.2 m **c.** 10.4 m **d.** 10.6 m **e.** 10.8 m

CHAPTER 14
Trigonometric Ratios

Applying mathematics is a key to success in many areas of manufacturing. More importantly, however, applying mathematics is a key to the *degree* of success one may achieve. Applications can be as basic as making measurements or adding numbers. They can be as general as understanding and interpreting the functions and relationships upon which management decisions are based.

OBJECTIVES: Identify and find trigonometric ratios from information given for right triangles, and from tables.

14-1 ANGLES AND TRIANGLES

An **angle** is formed by two **rays** having a common endpoint. Three angles are determined by a triangle. These are the **angles of the triangle**. A **vertex** of a ray, an angle, or a triangle is a point as shown in the diagrams.

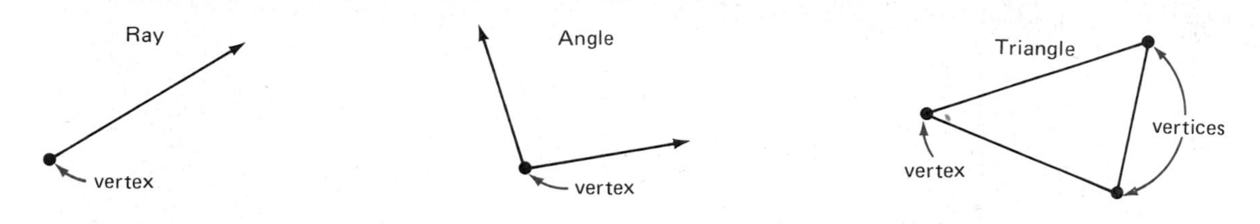

We *name* angles and triangles using the symbols ∠ and △ along with the names of the vertices. We *measure* angles with a **protractor**. The unit used on a protractor is a **degree**. Any angle has a measure in degrees between 0 and 180. We represent the *degree measure* of an angle, *A*, with the symbol $m\angle A$.

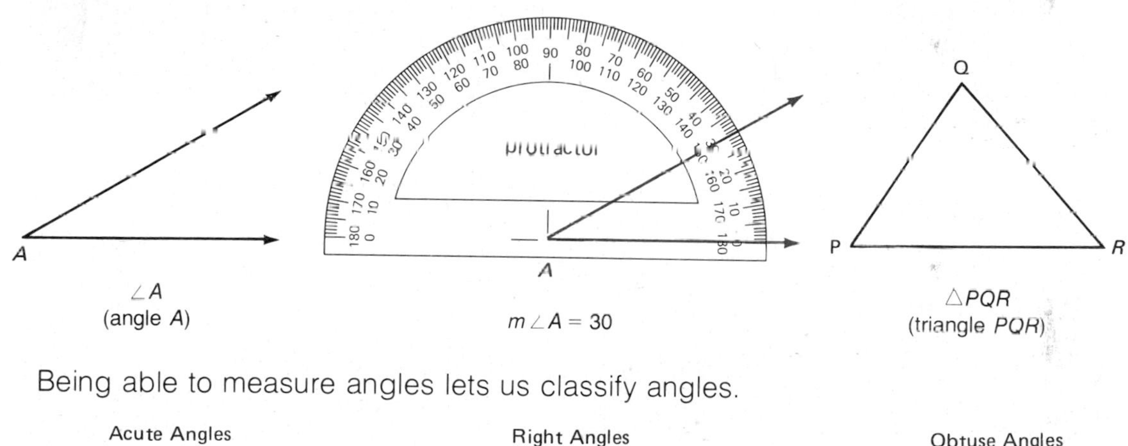

∠*A*
(angle *A*)

$m\angle A = 30$

△*PQR*
(triangle *PQR*)

Being able to measure angles lets us classify angles.

Acute Angles

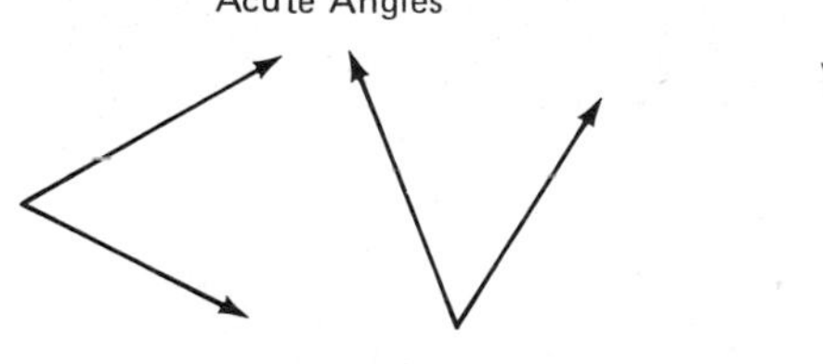

(less than 90°)

Right Angles

(equal to 90°)

Obtuse Angles

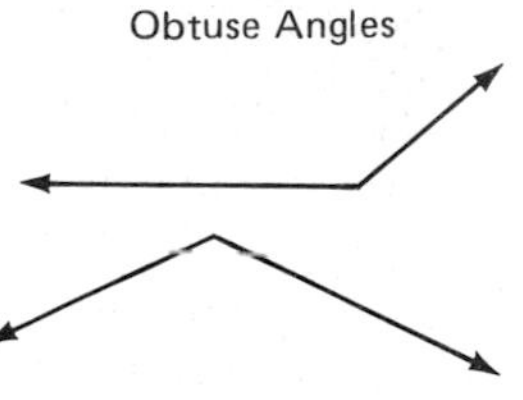

(between 90° and 180°)

Being able to measure angles lets us classify pairs of angles. It also lets us classify triangles.

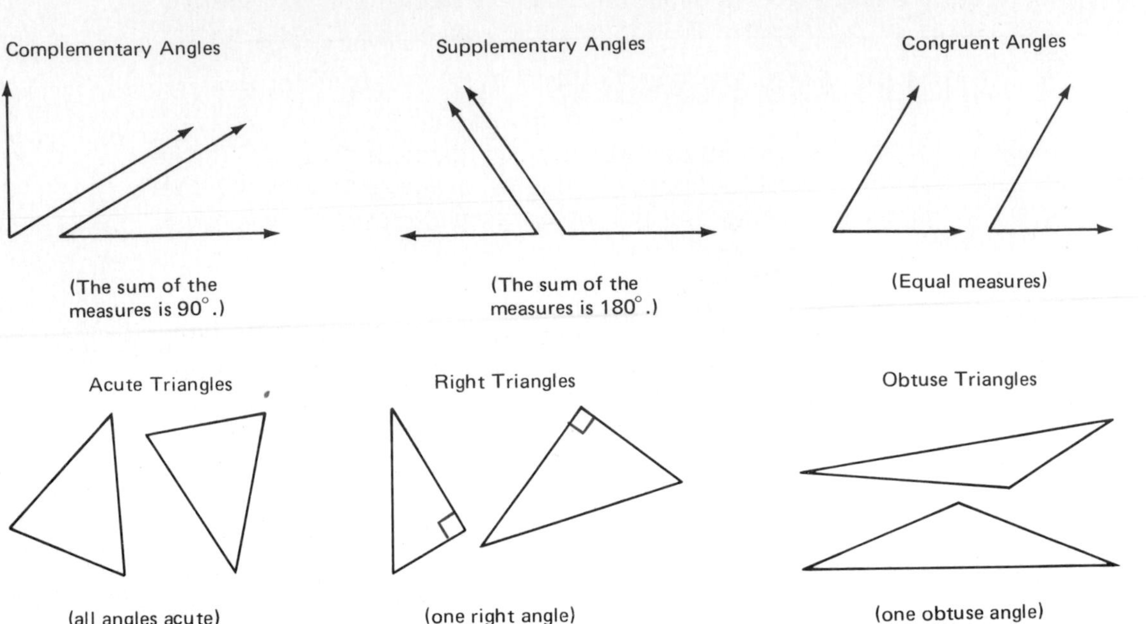

EXAMPLE 1 The measure of angle P in degrees is 40. Find the measure in degrees of a complementary angle; of a supplementary angle.

SOLUTION The sum of the measures in degrees of two complementary angles is 90.

Use c for the measure in degrees of an angle that is the complement of $\angle P$.

degrees + degrees = degrees

$$40 + c = 90$$
$$c = 50$$

The sum of the measures in degrees of two supplementary angles is 180.

Use s for the measure in degrees of an angle that is the supplement of $\angle P$.

degrees + degrees = degrees

$$40 + s = 180$$
$$s = 140$$

CONCLUSION For $\angle P$, the measure in degrees of a complementary angle is 50. The measure in degrees of a supplementary angle is 140.

In addition to its three angles, a triangle has three line segments that are the **sides of the triangle**. We represent a line segment by showing a bar over the names of its two endpoints. We represent the length of a line segment by showing the names of the two endpoints without the bar.

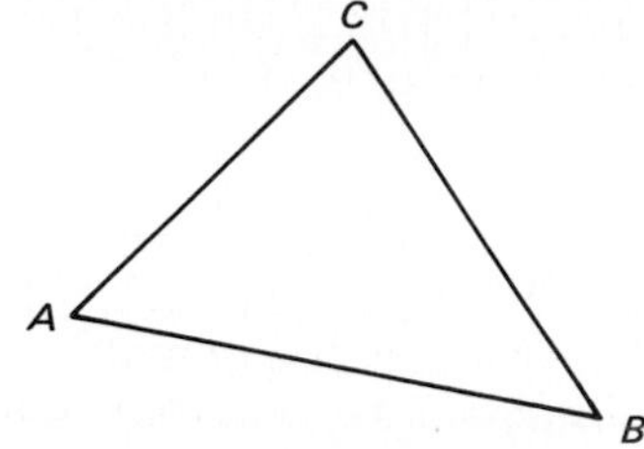

The sides of $\triangle ABC$ are $\overline{AB}$, $\overline{BC}$, and $\overline{CA}$.

Their lengths are AB, BC, and CA.

For the topics of this chapter, we shall want to relate angles and sides of a triangle. Thus, we say a side of a triangle is *adjacent* to an angle of the triangle if it is part of the angle. Otherwise, it is *opposite* the angle. In a right triangle, in particular, the hypotenuse is *opposite* the right angle. Each leg is *adjacent* to the right angle and to one of the acute angles.

Also, two sides of a triangle *include* the angle of the triangle that they determine. Two angles of a triangle *include* the side that they share.

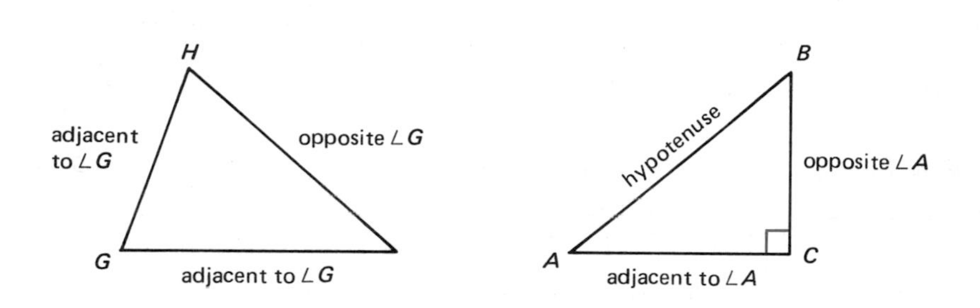

You also will need to recall the fact that the sum of the measures in degrees of the angles of a triangle is 180.

EXAMPLE 2 In triangle ABC, $m\angle A = 21$, $m\angle B = 86$. Find the measure in degrees of angle C.

Ⓜ **SOLUTION**

$$m\angle A + m\angle B + m\angle C = 180$$
$$21 + 86 + m\angle C = 180$$
$$m\angle C = 73$$

$^\circ + ^\circ + ^\circ = ^\circ$

CONCLUSION The measure of angle C in degrees is 73.

CHECK Is the sum of the degree measures of the angles equal to 180?

$$21 + 86 + 73 \stackrel{?}{=} 180$$
$$180 = 180 \checkmark$$

CLASSROOM EXERCISES

Use a protractor. Measure each angle.

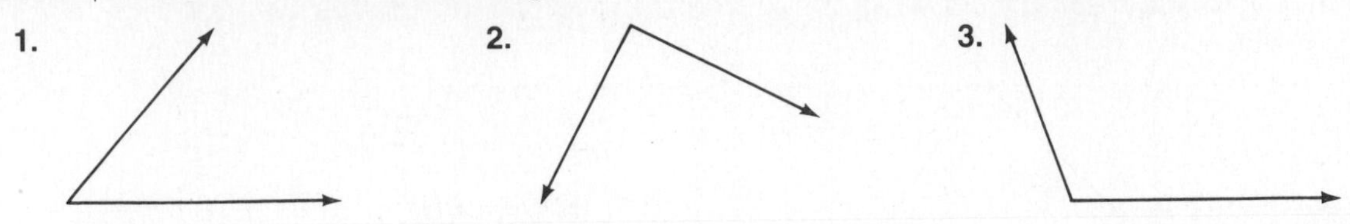

4. The measure of an angle in degrees is 60. Find the measure of a complementary angle and the measure of a supplementary angle.

EXERCISES

A Use a protractor. Measure each angle.

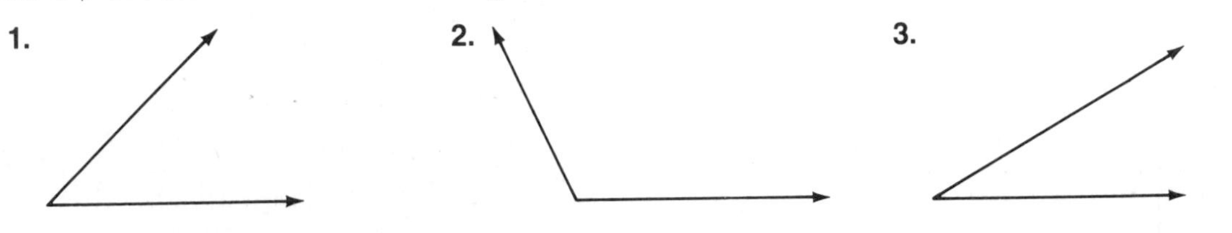

For an angle having the measure shown, find the measure of a complementary angle and the measure of a supplementary angle.

4. 20° **5.** 75° **6.** 30° **7.** 85° **8.** 53° **9.** 16°

For $\triangle DEF$, the measures of two angles are given. Find the measure of the third angle.

10. $m\angle D = 30$, $m\angle E = 100$ **11.** $m\angle D = 80$, $m\angle F = 40$ **12.** $m\angle E = 68$, $m\angle F = 36$

B **13.** Two angles are supplementary. The degree measure of one is 30 less than twice the degree measure of the other. Find the degree measure of each angle.

14. Two angles are complementary and the degree measure of one is 15 less than twice the degree measure of the other. Find the degree measure of each angle.

C **15.** One angle of a triangle has measure twice as large as the measure of one of the other angles. The measure of the third angle is equal to the sum of the measures of the other two. Find the measure of each angle.

16. How large is each angle of a triangle in which the second angle is 10° larger than the first angle and the third angle is 5° smaller than 3 times the first?

14-2 SIMILAR TRIANGLES

Two triangles that have the same size and shape are **congruent** ($\cong$). Two triangles that have the same shape are **similar** ($\sim$).

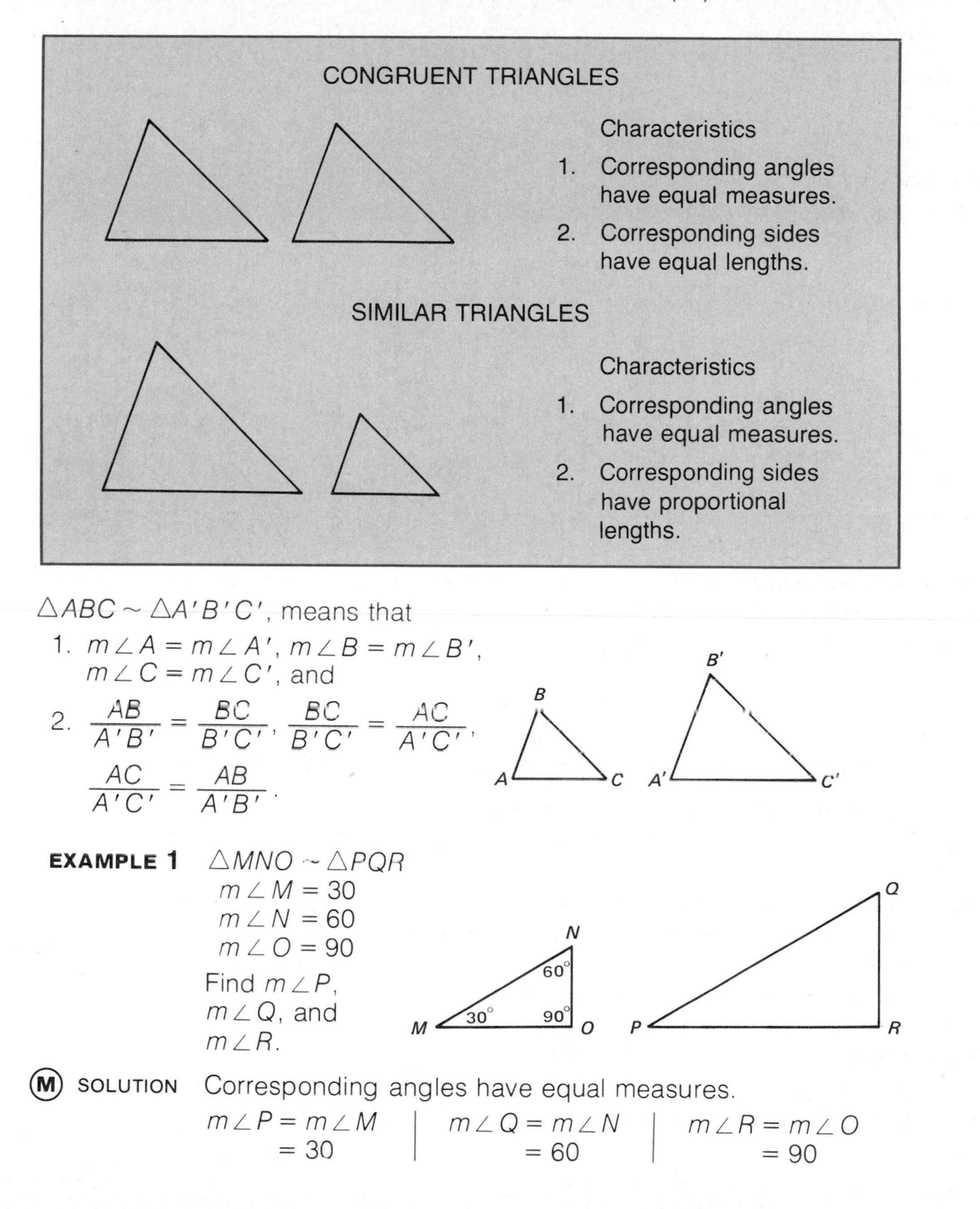

CONGRUENT TRIANGLES

Characteristics

1. Corresponding angles have equal measures.
2. Corresponding sides have equal lengths.

SIMILAR TRIANGLES

Characteristics

1. Corresponding angles have equal measures.
2. Corresponding sides have proportional lengths.

$\triangle ABC \sim \triangle A'B'C'$, means that

1. $m\angle A = m\angle A'$, $m\angle B = m\angle B'$, $m\angle C = m\angle C'$, and
2. $\frac{AB}{A'B'} = \frac{BC}{B'C'}$, $\frac{BC}{B'C'} = \frac{AC}{A'C'}$, $\frac{AC}{A'C'} = \frac{AB}{A'B'}$.

EXAMPLE 1 $\triangle MNO \sim \triangle PQR$

$m\angle M = 30$
$m\angle N = 60$
$m\angle O = 90$

Find $m\angle P$, $m\angle Q$, and $m\angle R$.

Ⓜ SOLUTION Corresponding angles have equal measures.

$m\angle P = m\angle M$	$m\angle Q = m\angle N$	$m\angle R = m\angle O$
$= 30$	$= 60$	$= 90$

EXAMPLE 2 $\triangle ABC \sim \triangle A'B'C'$
$AB = 5$, $BC = 3$, $AC = 6$, and $A'B' = 10$.
Find the length of side $B'C'$; of side $A'C'$.

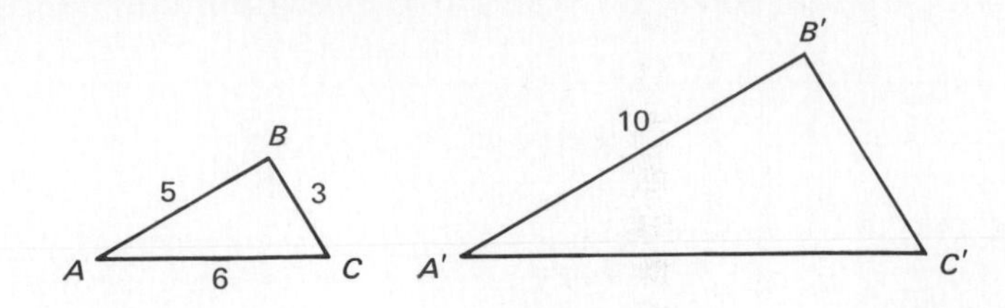

(M) SOLUTION The lengths of corresponding sides are proportional.

$$\frac{AB}{A'B'} = \frac{BC}{B'C'}$$
$$\frac{5}{10} = \frac{3}{B'C'}$$
$$5 \cdot B'C' = 30$$
$$B'C' = 6$$

$$\frac{AB}{A'B'} = \frac{AC}{A'C'}$$
$$\frac{5}{10} = \frac{6}{A'C'}$$
$$5 \cdot A'C' = 60$$
$$A'C' = 12$$

By definition, similar triangles have corresponding angles of equal measure *and* corresponding sides of proportional lengths. For two triangles to be similar, however, it is sufficient to show that *either* corresponding angles have equal measures, *or* corresponding sides have proportional lengths.

In particular, requiring only that corresponding angles have equal measures to prove two triangles similar, gives us the following useful fact about right triangles.

> If an acute angle of one right triangle has the same measure as an acute angle of another right triangle, the triangles are similar.

The importance of the fact should become clear in the next section when we demonstrate the particular interest that right triangles hold for us in our study of trigonometry.

EXAMPLE 3 In right triangles ABC and DEF, $\angle A$ has the same measure as $\angle D$. How long is side AC? side DF? side DE?

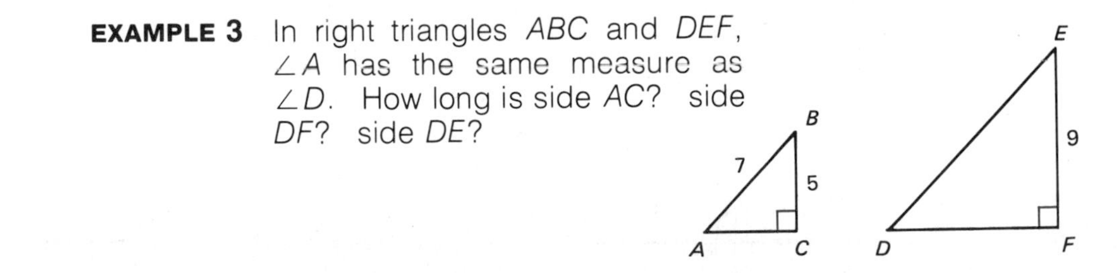

SOLUTION Since $\triangle ABC$ is a right triangle, the Pythagorean Theorem may be applied.

$$AC^2 + BC^2 = AB^2$$
$$AC^2 + 5^2 = 7^2$$
$$AC^2 + 25 = 49$$
$$AC^2 = 24$$
$$AC = 2\sqrt{6}$$

Since an acute angle of $\triangle ABC$ has the same measure as an acute angle of $\triangle DEF$, the triangles are similar. The lengths of their corresponding sides are proportional.

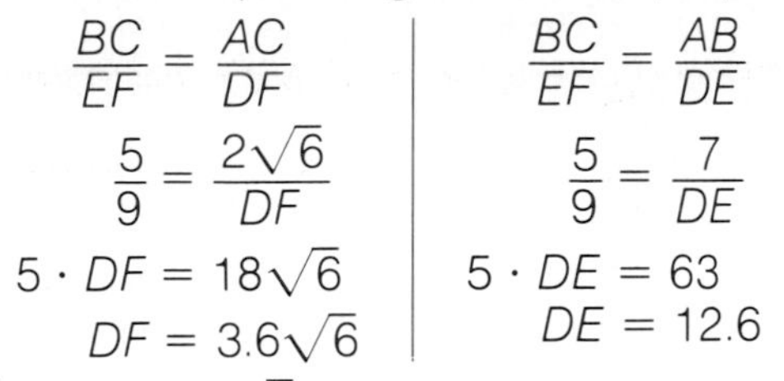

$$\frac{BC}{EF} = \frac{AC}{DF} \qquad \frac{BC}{EF} = \frac{AB}{DE}$$
$$\frac{5}{9} = \frac{2\sqrt{6}}{DF} \qquad \frac{5}{9} = \frac{7}{DE}$$
$$5 \cdot DF = 18\sqrt{6} \qquad 5 \cdot DE = 63$$
$$DF = 3.6\sqrt{6} \qquad DE = 12.6$$

CONCLUSION $AC = 2\sqrt{6}$, $DF = 3.6\sqrt{6}$, and $DE = 12.6$.

CHECK The check, using the Pythagorean Theorem, is left for the student.

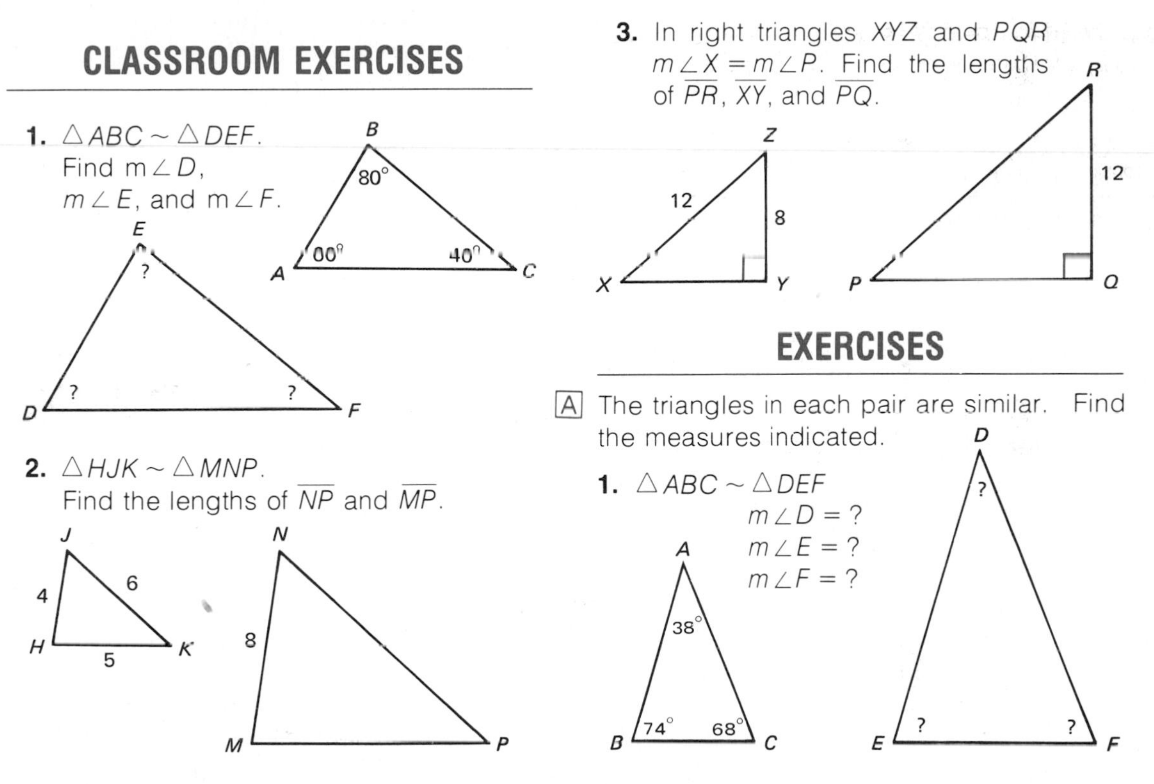

CLASSROOM EXERCISES

1. $\triangle ABC \sim \triangle DEF$. Find $m\angle D$, $m\angle E$, and $m\angle F$.

2. $\triangle HJK \sim \triangle MNP$. Find the lengths of $\overline{NP}$ and $\overline{MP}$.

3. In right triangles XYZ and PQR $m\angle X = m\angle P$. Find the lengths of $\overline{PR}$, $\overline{XY}$, and $\overline{PQ}$.

EXERCISES

A The triangles in each pair are similar. Find the measures indicated.

1. $\triangle ABC \sim \triangle DEF$
$m\angle D = ?$
$m\angle E = ?$
$m\angle F = ?$

2. $\triangle HJK \sim \triangle MNP$ $MN = ?$ $MP = ?$

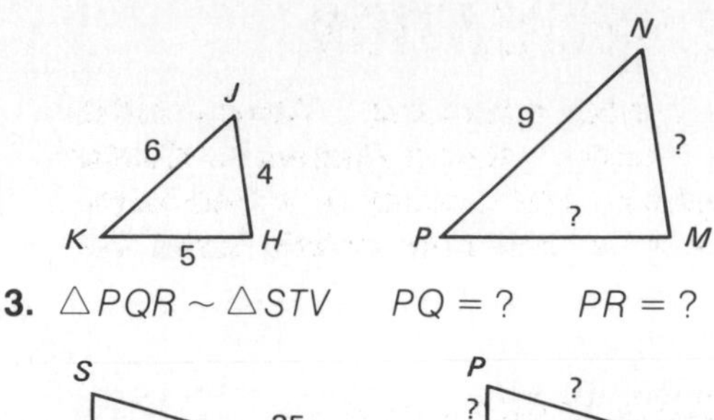

3. $\triangle PQR \sim \triangle STV$ $PQ = ?$ $PR = ?$

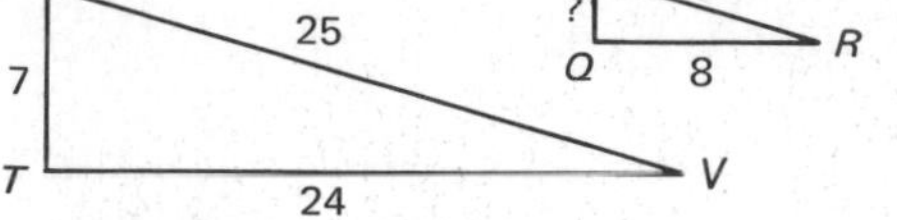

The triangles in each pair are right triangles with $m\angle X = m\angle P$. Find the measures indicated.

4. $PR = ?$ $YZ = ?$ $QR = ?$

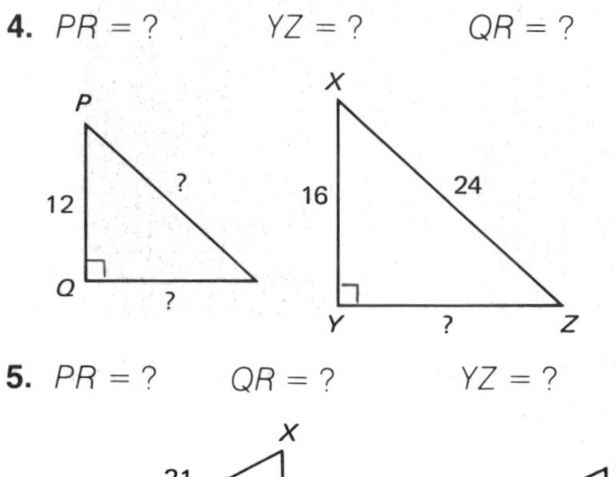

5. $PR = ?$ $QR = ?$ $YZ = ?$

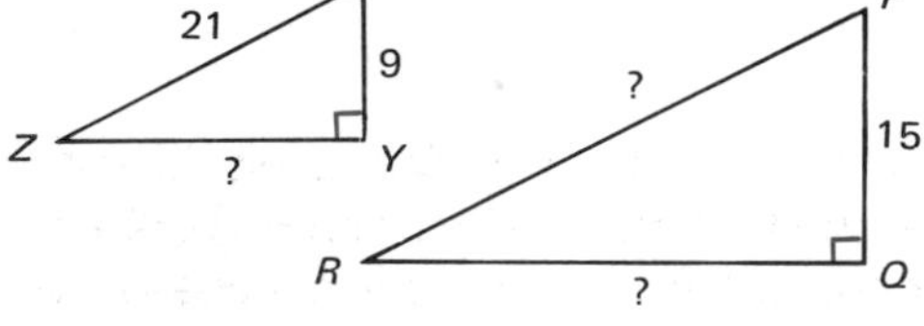

B **6.** When a tree in the Cortez's yard casts a shadow 20 meters long, Miguel's shadow is 1.8 meters long. Miguel is 1.2 meters tall. How tall is the tree?

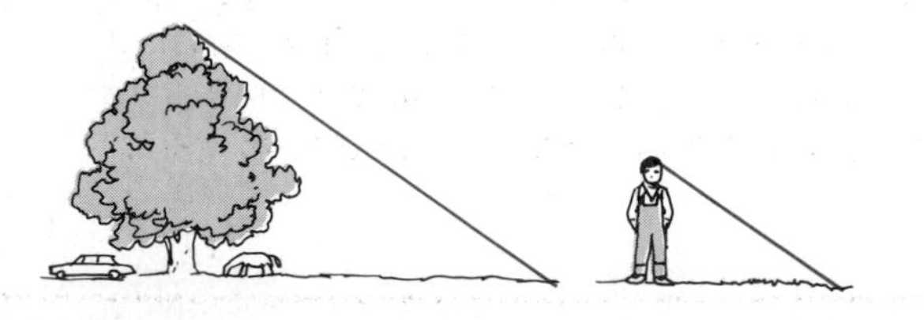

7. Use the information given before Example 3 in this section. Show that if an acute angle of a right triangle has the same measure as an acute angle of another right triangle, then the two triangles are similar.

8. A flagpole casts a shadow 13.2 meters long when a man 1.98 meters tall casts a shadow 5.94 meters long. How tall is the flagpole?

C **9.** Let MM' represent a mirror. When a ray of light from an object L strikes the mirror, it is reflected so that $m\angle MPL = m\angle M'PE$. An eye at E sees the image of the object L.

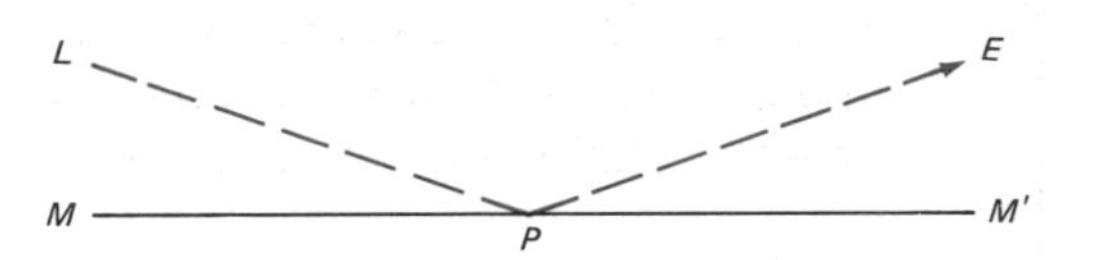

At camp last summer, Sara and Fran made use of this principle to find the height of a small tree. The girls placed a mirror horizontally on the ground at point B. Then Fran walked backward along the line AB keeping her eyes on the mirror until she saw the image of the top of the tree.

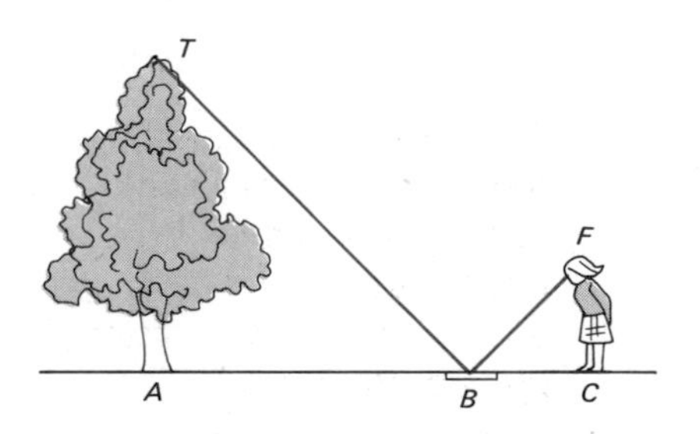

Sara then measured the distances BC and BA and found them to be 1.8 meters and 5.5 meters respectively. Fran's eyes were 1.8 meters from the ground. What did the girls find as the height of the tree, assuming that they made no error in computation?

HOSPITALITY AND RECREATION

Participation in organized recreation is rapidly expanding. Administrative occupations in recreation program services include that of a *Recreation Center Director* or a *Director of Parks and Recreation*. Many duties of a Recreation Center Director require basic mathematical skills and may include tasks like these.

- Prepare budgets.
- Schedule use of the Center, meeting budget and personnel requirements.
- Maintain records.

A Park Director is responsible for the administration of one or more parks, the overall park budgets, assignment of personnel, and park resource management. Duties may include these tasks.

- Schedule agricultural use and logging activities.
- Control camping and other recreational activities.
- Study and develop plans for soil conservation.

High school courses that help open career opportunities in recreation include algebra, geometry, sociology, botany, and biology.

MATHEMATICAL SAMPLER

1. As a Recreation Center Director you are running a five-day tennis tournament. You provided 15 dozen tennis balls when the tournament began. During the first two days of the tournament $6\frac{1}{2}$ dozen tennis balls have been used. How many more tennis balls, if any, should you order to ensure an ample supply? (Assume the same number of games are played each day.)
2. In a range of wilderness park land, the ratio of campground area to semi-developed area must not exceed 1 to 4. Also, the ratio of campground area to undeveloped area must not exceed 1 to 10. You wish to increase the amount of campground area. How many additional square kilometers of park land are needed for every additional square kilometer of campground?

14-3 TRIGONOMETRIC RATIOS

Ratios that compare the lengths of two sides of a right triangle are given special names, both as a group and individually. As a group the ratios are the *trigonometric ratios*. Individually, each ratio refers to lengths of line segments that form the triangle and each ratio name refers to an acute angle of the right triangle.

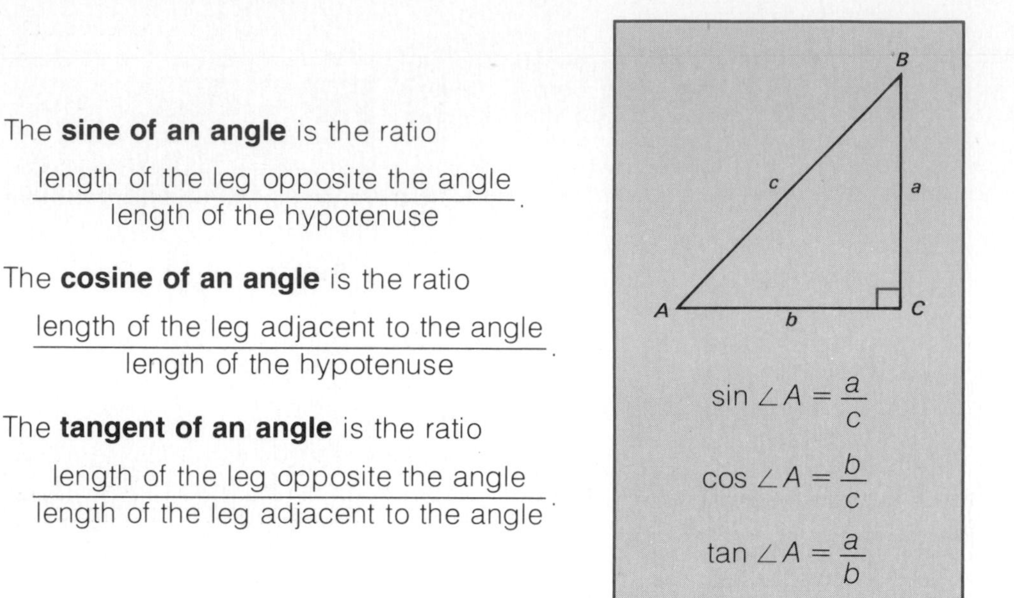

The **sine of an angle** is the ratio

$$\frac{\text{length of the leg opposite the angle}}{\text{length of the hypotenuse}}.$$

The **cosine of an angle** is the ratio

$$\frac{\text{length of the leg adjacent to the angle}}{\text{length of the hypotenuse}}.$$

The **tangent of an angle** is the ratio

$$\frac{\text{length of the leg opposite the angle}}{\text{length of the leg adjacent to the angle}}.$$

$$\sin \angle A = \frac{a}{c}$$

$$\cos \angle A = \frac{b}{c}$$

$$\tan \angle A = \frac{a}{b}$$

To simplify our work, when the angle is named angle A for example, we write *tan A* for "tangent of $\angle A$", *sin A* for "sine of $\angle A$", and *cos A* for "cosine of $\angle A$". Memorizing the following can help you in working with these ratios.

$$\sin A = \frac{\text{opposite}}{\text{hypotenuse}} \qquad \cos A = \frac{\text{adjacent}}{\text{hypotenuse}} \qquad \tan A = \frac{\text{opposite}}{\text{adjacent}}$$

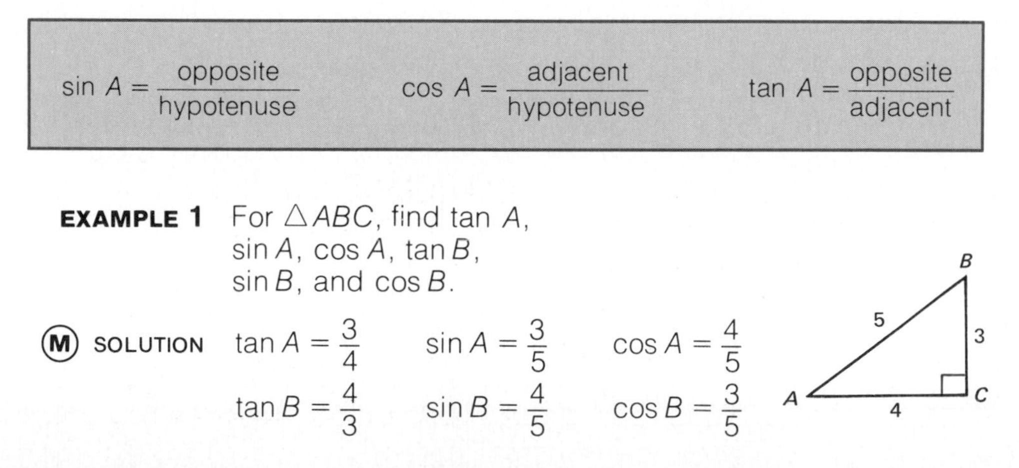

EXAMPLE 1 For $\triangle ABC$, find $\tan A$, $\sin A$, $\cos A$, $\tan B$, $\sin B$, and $\cos B$.

Ⓜ **SOLUTION**

$$\tan A = \frac{3}{4} \qquad \sin A = \frac{3}{5} \qquad \cos A = \frac{4}{5}$$

$$\tan B = \frac{4}{3} \qquad \sin B = \frac{4}{5} \qquad \cos B = \frac{3}{5}$$

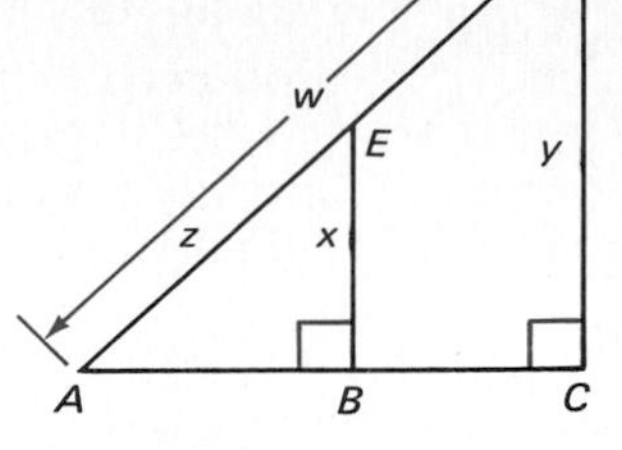

Notice in Example 1 that $\sin A = \cos B$, and $\cos A = \sin B$. Angles A and B are complements in right triangle ABC. The word *cosine* may be thought of as meaning the *sine* of the complement.

EXAMPLE 2 Find $\sin A$.

SOLUTION $\sin A = \dfrac{\text{opposite}}{\text{hypotenuse}}$

$= \dfrac{x}{z}$ or $\dfrac{y}{w}$

Either ratio is correct. Since right triangle ABE has an acute angle, $\angle A$, equal in measure to an acute angle, $\angle A$, of right triangle ACD, $\triangle ABE \sim \triangle ACD$. (See Section 14-2.) Therefore, corresponding sides of the two triangles have proportional lengths.

$$\frac{x}{y} = \frac{z}{w}$$

From this proportion, we find $xw = yz$ and

$$\frac{x}{z} = \frac{y}{w}.$$

CONCLUSION Even though an acute angle can help form more than one right triangle, there is just one number for the sine of the angle.

Similar conclusions can be made for the cosine and the tangent of an angle.

CLASSROOM EXERCISES

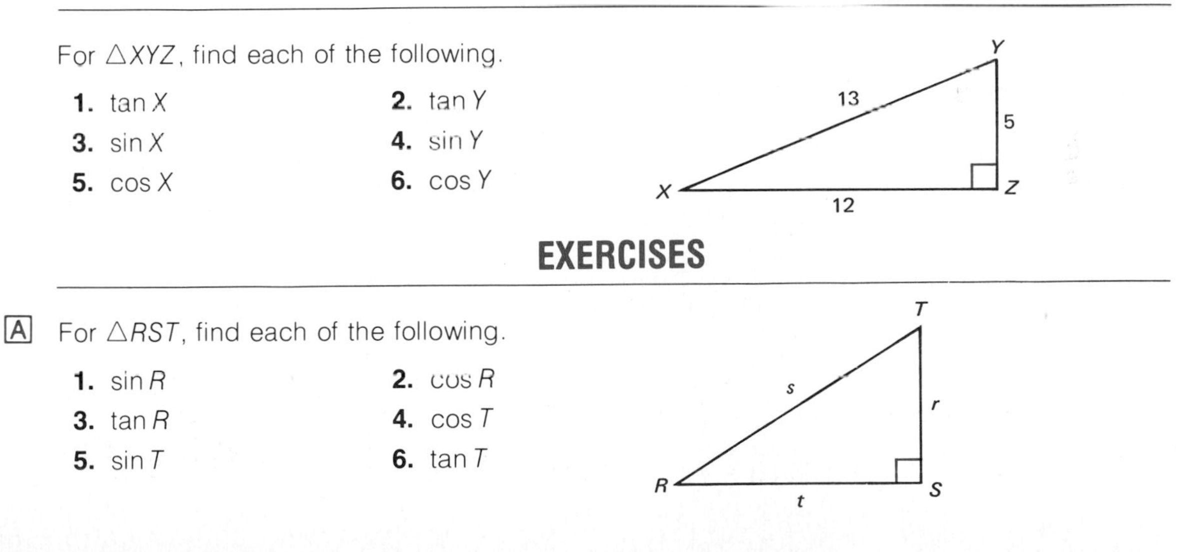

For $\triangle XYZ$, find each of the following.

1. $\tan X$ **2.** $\tan Y$
3. $\sin X$ **4.** $\sin Y$
5. $\cos X$ **6.** $\cos Y$

EXERCISES

A For $\triangle RST$, find each of the following.

1. $\sin R$ **2.** $\cos R$
3. $\tan R$ **4.** $\cos T$
5. $\sin T$ **6.** $\tan T$

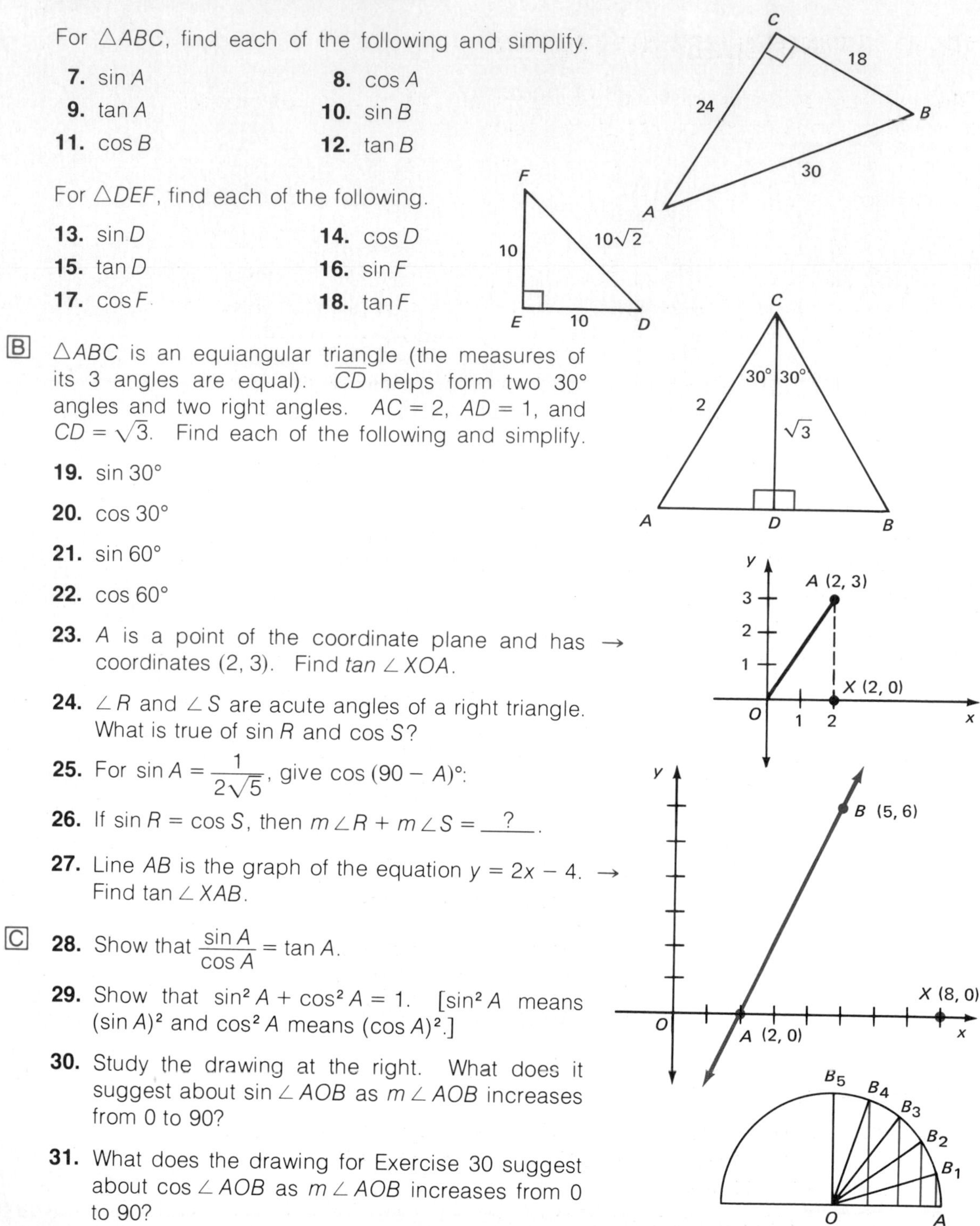

For $\triangle ABC$, find each of the following and simplify.

7. $\sin A$ **8.** $\cos A$

9. $\tan A$ **10.** $\sin B$

11. $\cos B$ **12.** $\tan B$

For $\triangle DEF$, find each of the following.

13. $\sin D$ **14.** $\cos D$

15. $\tan D$ **16.** $\sin F$

17. $\cos F$ **18.** $\tan F$

B $\triangle ABC$ is an equiangular triangle (the measures of its 3 angles are equal). $\overline{CD}$ helps form two 30° angles and two right angles. $AC = 2$, $AD = 1$, and $CD = \sqrt{3}$. Find each of the following and simplify.

19. $\sin 30°$

20. $\cos 30°$

21. $\sin 60°$

22. $\cos 60°$

23. A is a point of the coordinate plane and has coordinates (2, 3). Find *tan* $\angle XOA$. →

24. $\angle R$ and $\angle S$ are acute angles of a right triangle. What is true of $\sin R$ and $\cos S$?

25. For $\sin A = \dfrac{1}{2\sqrt{5}}$, give $\cos\,(90 - A)°$.

26. If $\sin R = \cos S$, then $m\angle R + m\angle S =$ __?__.

27. Line AB is the graph of the equation $y = 2x - 4$. → Find $\tan \angle XAB$.

C **28.** Show that $\dfrac{\sin A}{\cos A} = \tan A$.

29. Show that $\sin^2 A + \cos^2 A = 1$. [$\sin^2 A$ means $(\sin A)^2$ and $\cos^2 A$ means $(\cos A)^2$.]

30. Study the drawing at the right. What does it suggest about $\sin \angle AOB$ as $m\angle AOB$ increases from 0 to 90?

31. What does the drawing for Exercise 30 suggest about $\cos \angle AOB$ as $m\angle AOB$ increases from 0 to 90?

14-4 TRIGONOMETRIC TABLES

The sine, cosine, and tangent ratios for an angle depend only on the size of the angle and not on the size of any triangle.

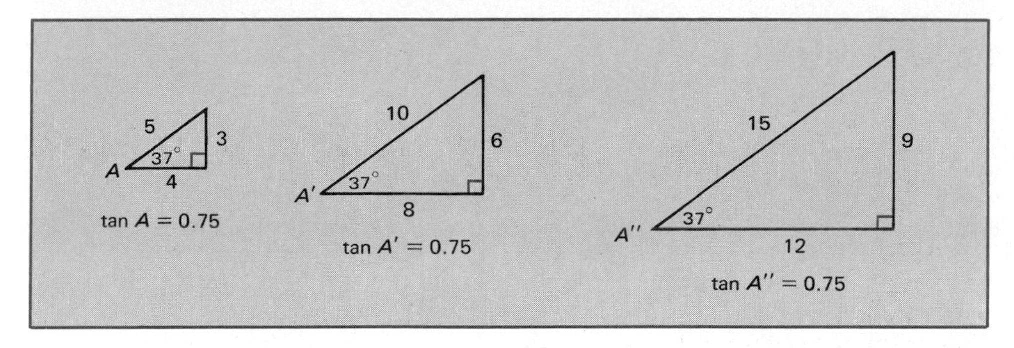

We can, therefore, put the sine, cosine, and tangent ratio quotients into a table such as that on the next page. The table entries are decimals, and most of them are approximations for the quotients.

Notice that the table lists angles according to their measures. For convenience we write *tan 37°* rather than "the tangent of an angle whose degree measure is 37."

EXAMPLE 1 Find tan 37°.

SOLUTION Use the table. Find 37° in the first column. Then move to the right in that row to the column headed "tan" (meaning tangent). To four decimal places, tan 37° = 0.7536. We may also write tan 37° ≐ 0.7536.

angle measure	sin	cos	tan
1°	0.0175	0.9998	0.0175
36°	0.5878	0.8090	0.7265
37°	0.6018	0.7986	0.7536
38°	0.6157	0.7880	0.7813
39°	0.6293	0.7771	0.8098

EXAMPLE 2 Find sin 50°.

SOLUTION Use the table. Find 50° in the "angle measure" column. Then move to the right in that row to the "sin" (meaning sine) column.

To four places, sin 50° = 0.7660.

Table of Trigonometric Ratios

angle measure	sin	cos	tan	angle measure	sin	cos	tan
				45°	0.7071	0.7071	1.0000
1°	0.0175	0.9998	0.0175	46°	0.7193	0.6947	1.0355
2°	0.0349	0.9994	0.0349	47°	0.7314	0.6820	1.0724
3°	0.0523	0.9986	0.0524	48°	0.7431	0.6691	1.1106
4°	0.0698	0.9976	0.0699	49°	0.7547	0.6561	1.1504
5°	0.0872	0.9962	0.0875	50°	0.7660	0.6428	1.1918
6°	0.1045	0.9945	0.1051	51°	0.7771	0.6293	1.2349
7°	0.1219	0.9925	0.1228	52°	0.7880	0.6157	1.2799
8°	0.1392	0.9903	0.1405	53°	0.7986	0.6018	1.3270
9°	0.1564	0.9877	0.1584	54°	0.8090	0.5878	1.3764
10°	0.1736	0.9848	0.1763	55°	0.8192	0.5736	1.4281
11°	0.1908	0.9816	0.1944	56°	0.8290	0.5592	1.4826
12°	0.2079	0.9781	0.2126	57°	0.8387	0.5446	1.5399
13°	0.2250	0.9744	0.2309	58°	0.8480	0.5299	1.6003
14°	0.2419	0.9703	0.2493	59°	0.8572	0.5150	1.6643
15°	0.2588	0.9659	0.2679	60°	0.8660	0.5000	1.7321
16°	0.2756	0.9613	0.2867	61°	0.8746	0.4848	1.8040
17°	0.2924	0.9563	0.3057	62°	0.8829	0.4695	1.8807
18°	0.3090	0.9511	0.3249	63°	0.8910	0.4540	1.9626
19°	0.3256	0.9455	0.3443	64°	0.8988	0.4384	2.0503
20°	0.3420	0.9397	0.3640	65°	0.9063	0.4226	2.1445
21°	0.3584	0.9336	0.3839	66°	0.9135	0.4067	2.2460
22°	0.3746	0.9272	0.4040	67°	0.9205	0.3907	2.3559
23°	0.3907	0.9205	0.4245	68°	0.9272	0.3746	2.4751
24°	0.4067	0.9135	0.4452	69°	0.9336	0.3584	2.6051
25°	0.4226	0.9063	0.4663	70°	0.9397	0.3420	2.7475
26°	0.4384	0.8988	0.4877	71°	0.9455	0.3256	2.9042
27°	0.4540	0.8910	0.5095	72°	0.9511	0.3090	3.0777
28°	0.4695	0.8829	0.5317	73°	0.9563	0.2924	3.2709
29°	0.4848	0.8746	0.5543	74°	0.9613	0.2756	3.4874
30°	0.5000	0.8660	0.5774	75°	0.9659	0.2588	3.7321
31°	0.5150	0.8572	0.6009	76°	0.9703	0.2419	4.0108
32°	0.5299	0.8480	0.6249	77°	0.9744	0.2250	4.3315
33°	0.5446	0.8387	0.6494	78°	0.9781	0.2079	4.7046
34°	0.5592	0.8290	0.6745	79°	0.9816	0.1908	5.1446
35°	0.5736	0.8192	0.7002	80°	0.9848	0.1736	5.6713
36°	0.5878	0.8090	0.7265	81°	0.9877	0.1564	6.3138
37°	0.6018	0.7986	0.7536	82°	0.9903	0.1392	7.1154
38°	0.6157	0.7880	0.7813	83°	0.9925	0.1219	8.1443
39°	0.6293	0.7771	0.8098	84°	0.9945	0.1045	9.5144
40°	0.6428	0.7660	0.8391	85°	0.9962	0.0872	11.4301
41°	0.6561	0.7547	0.8693	86°	0.9976	0.0698	14.3007
42°	0.6691	0.7431	0.9004	87°	0.9986	0.0523	19.0811
43°	0.6820	0.7314	0.9325	88°	0.9994	0.0349	28.6363
44°	0.6947	0.7193	0.9657	89°	0.9998	0.0175	57.2900

Reverse the steps in the previous examples to find the measure of the angle for a particular sine, cosine, or tangent ratio given in the table.

EXAMPLE 3 The cosine ratio is 0.4226. Find the measure of the angle.

SOLUTION Look down the "cos" column until you find 0.4226. Then move to the left in that row to the "angle measure" column. The angle measure is about 65°.

CLASSROOM EXERCISES

Use the Table of Trigonometric Ratios to find each of the following.

1. tan 16° **2.** sin 81° **3.** cos 37°

4. the measure of an angle whose tangent is 0.1051

5. the measure of an angle whose cosine is 0.6820

EXERCISES

A Use the table of Trigonometric Ratios to find each of the following ratios.

1. tan 60° **2.** tan 25° **3.** tan 89° **4.** tan 2° **5.** sin 24° **6.** sin 71°

7. sin 60° **8.** sin 5° **9.** cos 60° **10.** sin 1° **11.** cos 85° **12.** cos 30°

Use the table to find the measure of each angle.

13. $\tan \angle A = 1.3270$ **14.** $\tan \angle B = 7.1154$ **15.** $\cos \angle B = 0.2079$

16. $\cos \angle 1 = 0.9848$ **17.** $\sin \angle H = 0.9272$ **18.** $\sin \angle N = 0.2419$

19. $\tan \angle R = 0.9325$ **20.** $\tan \angle Q = 0.4040$ **21.** $\cos \angle B = 0.5446$

22. $\cos \angle 2 = 0.8387$ **23.** $\sin \angle X = 0.9994$ **24.** $\sin \angle Y = 0.5878$

B One degree (1°) of angle measure equals 60 *minutes* (60′). Use the table to help you find each of the following.

25. tan 56°30′ **26.** tan 20°40′ **27.** sin 40°30′

28. sin 85°12′ **29.** cos 14°30′ **30.** cos 65°45′

Find the measure of each angle in degrees and minutes.

31. $\tan \angle A = 0.3574$ **32.** $\tan \angle A = 2.1159$ **33.** $\sin \angle A = 0.2784$

34. $\sin \angle A = 0.9503$ **35.** $\cos \angle A = 0.2504$ **36.** $\cos \angle A = 0.9088$

C **37.** A hill has a slope of 8°. How far up the hill will a dam 18 meters high raise the water?

38. The Washington Monument is 169 meters high. What is the angle of elevation of its top when viewed from a point one kilometer away and on a level with the base of the monument?

39. $\triangle ABC$ is isosceles. Each of AC and BC is 24 centimeters and $m\angle B = 35$. Find the area of the triangle.

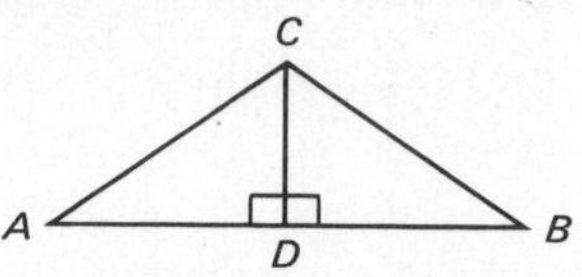

40. The base of an isosceles triangle is 20 centimeters long and each of the other sides is 18 centimeters long. Find the measures of its angles.

CHECKING YOUR UNDERSTANDING

WORDS AND SYMBOLS

side adjacent to an angle of a triangle
side opposite to an angle of a triangle
corresponding angles of two triangles
corresponding sides of two triangles
cosine ratio, cos A
sine ratio, sin A
tangent ratio, tan A
legs of a right triangle
sides of a triangle
similar triangles
degree measure of an angle, $m\angle A$, °
hypotenuse of a right triangle

CONCEPTS

- The sine, cosine, and tangent ratios for a certain angle may be found using *any* right triangle that includes an angle equal in measure to the given angle. [14-3]

PROCESSES

- Find the sine, cosine, and tangent ratios for the acute angles of a right triangle. [14-3]

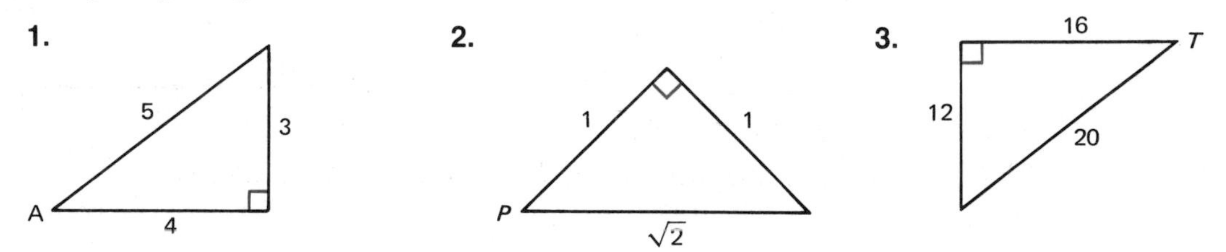

- Find a sine, cosine, or tangent ratio for any angle by using a table. Find an angle measure for a sine, cosine, or tangent ratio by using a table. [14-4]

4. $\tan 23° = ?$ **5.** $\cos 56° = ?$ **6.** $\sin ? = 0.6691$

OBJECTIVE: Solve problems using trigonometric ratios.

14-5 PROBLEM SOLVING: RIGHT-TRIANGLE PROBLEMS

Using the trigonometric ratios from a table, we can find the measurements for parts of a triangle indirectly.

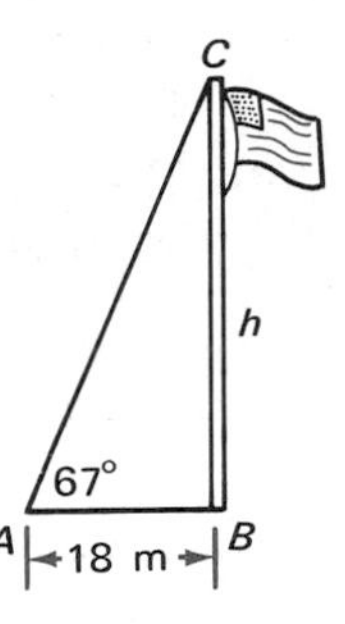

EXAMPLE 1 At a point 18 meters from the foot of a flagpole, $\angle A$ measures 67°. Find the height of the flagpole. Assume that $\angle B$ is a right angle.

Ⓜ SOLUTION

$$\frac{\text{length of leg opposite } \angle A}{\text{length of leg adjacent } \angle A} = \tan A$$

Use h for the height of the flagpole, or the length of the leg opposite $\angle A$, in meters.

$$\frac{h}{18} = \tan 67°.$$

$$h = 18(\tan 67°)$$

From the table, $\tan 67° \doteq 2.3559$.

$$h \doteq 18(2.3559)$$
$$h \doteq 42.41$$

tan 67° is a ratio, thus it is dimensionless.

$\frac{\text{m}}{\text{m}} = \text{(dimensionless)}$

$\text{m} = \text{m} \cdot \text{(dimensionless)}$

CONCLUSION The height of the flagpole is about 42 meters.

EXAMPLE 2 The two legs of a right triangle have measures 5.2 and 3.0. Find the measure of each acute angle.

Ⓜ SOLUTION

$$\tan D = \frac{\text{length of leg opposite } \angle D}{\text{length of leg adjacent } \angle D}$$

$$\tan D = \frac{3.0}{5.2}$$

$$\tan D \doteq 0.5769$$

From the table, $m\angle D \doteq 30$.

The sum of the degree measures of the acute angles is 90.

$$m\angle D + m\angle F = 90$$
$$30 + m\angle F \doteq 90$$
$$m\angle F \doteq 60$$

CONCLUSION The measures of the two acute angles are about 30° and 60°.

EXAMPLE 3 The radio station antenna is steadied by a set of cables that are attached to the antenna at B. Each cable is anchored in the ground and forms a 50° angle with the ground. B is 180 meters above the ground. How long are the cables? How far from the foot of the antenna are they anchored? Assume that $\angle C$ is a right angle.

Ⓜ SOLUTION $\sin A = \dfrac{\text{length of leg opposite } \angle A}{\text{length of hypotenuse}}$

Use l for the length in meters of a cable.

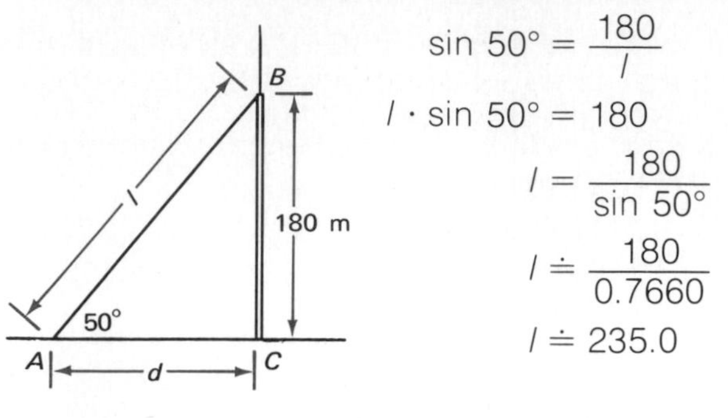

(dimensionless) $= \frac{\text{m}}{\text{m}}$

m · (dimensionless) = m

$$\sin 50° = \frac{180}{l}$$
$$l \cdot \sin 50° = 180$$
$$l = \frac{180}{\sin 50°}$$
$$l \doteq \frac{180}{0.7660}$$
$$l \doteq 235.0$$

CONCLUSION 1 The cables are about 235 meters long.

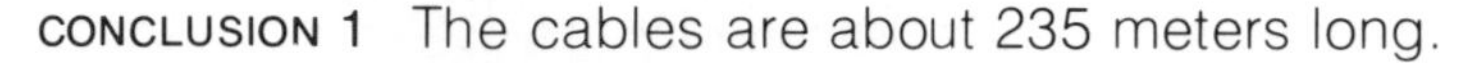

Use d for the distance in meters from the foot of the antenna to A.

(dimensionless) $= \frac{\text{m}}{\text{m}}$

m · (dimensionless) = m

$$\tan 50° = \frac{180}{d}$$
$$d \cdot \tan 50° = 180$$
$$d = \frac{180}{\tan 50°}$$
$$d \doteq \frac{180}{1.1918}$$
$$d \doteq 151.0$$

or

$$\cos 50° = \frac{d}{235}$$
$$d = 235 \cos 50°$$
$$d \doteq 235(0.6428)$$
$$d \doteq 151.1$$

CONCLUSION 2 The cables are anchored about 151 meters from the foot of the antenna.

CHECK By the Pythagorean Theorem,

$$d^2 + CB^2 = l^2$$
$$151^2 + 180^2 \stackrel{?}{=} 235^2$$
$$22\,801 + 32\,400 \stackrel{?}{=} 55\,225$$
$$55\,201 \doteq 55\,225 \quad ✓$$

EXAMPLE 4 How many meters long is the cable that supports the telephone pole shown in the diagram? How high above the ground is it connected to the pole?

Ⓜ **SOLUTION** Use l for the length in meters of the cable.

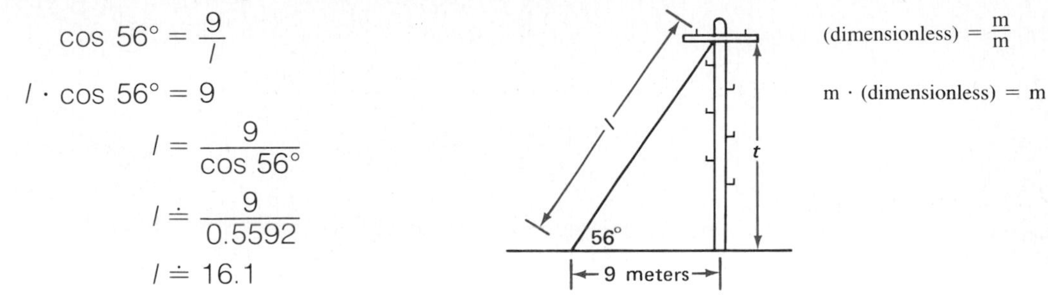

$$\cos 56° = \frac{9}{l} \qquad \text{(dimensionless)} = \frac{\text{m}}{\text{m}}$$

$$l \cdot \cos 56° = 9 \qquad \text{m} \cdot \text{(dimensionless)} = \text{m}$$

$$l = \frac{9}{\cos 56°}$$

$$l \doteq \frac{9}{0.5592}$$

$$l \doteq 16.1$$

CONCLUSION 1 The cable is about 16 meters long.

Use t for the distance in meters from the ground to the point of connection of the cable to the pole.

$$\sin 56° = \frac{t}{16.1} \quad \textit{or} \quad \tan 56° = \frac{t}{9} \qquad \text{(dimensionless)} = \frac{\text{m}}{\text{m}}$$

$$t = 16.1 \cdot \sin 56° \quad \Big| \quad t = 9 \cdot \tan 56° \qquad \text{m} = \text{m} \cdot \text{(dimensionless)}$$

$$t \doteq 16.1(0.8290) \quad \Big| \quad t \doteq 9(1.4826)$$

$$t \doteq 13.3 \quad \Big| \quad t \doteq 13.3$$

CONCLUSION 2 The cable is connected to the pole about 13 meters above the ground.

CHECK The check that $9^2 + t^2 \doteq l^2$ using 13.3 for t and 16.1 for l is left for the student.

CLASSROOM EXERCISES

1. The angle of elevation of the sun measured 50°. A flagpole cast a shadow 5 meters long. Find the height of the flagpole.
2. The two legs of a right triangle have measures 8 and 12. Find the measures of the two acute angles.
3. A supporting wire stretches from the ground to the top of a television transmitting tower 80 meters high. The degree measure of the angle that the wire forms with the ground is 75. Find the length of the wire.
4. An extension ladder is placed against a building so as to reach a window ledge 18 m above the ground. The angle the ladder forms with the ground measures 60°. How far from the building is the foot of the ladder?

EXERCISES

A Solve.

1. The angle of elevation of the sun measured 42°. The shadow from a chimney was 72 meters long. How tall is the chimney?

2. When the angle of elevation of the sun is 40°, a tree casts a shadow 80 meters long. How tall is the tree?
3. When an airplane was directly over a particular point, an observer 450 meters away found the angle of elevation of the airplane to measure 42°. The point of observation and the point below the airplane were on the same level. How high was the airplane?
4. From the information in Exercise 3, how high would the airplane be if the angle of elevation of the airplane measured 80° at an observation point 500 meters from the point below the airplane?
5. Two girl scouts standing 270 meters from the foot of a cliff and on a level with it find the angle of elevation of the top of the cliff to measure 34°. How high is the cliff?
6. Some tourists standing 150 meters from the base of a monument and on a level with it find the angle of elevation of the top of the monument to measure 40°. How tall is the monument?
7. A vertical pole 6 meters long casts a shadow 5 meters long in the sunlight. Find the measure of the angle of elevation of the sun.
8. A forest ranger at the top of a watchtower knows that the distance from eye level to the ground is 28 m. On the level plateau supporting the tower there is a rock known to be 170 m from the base of the tower. Find the measure of the angle formed at the top of the tower by the horizontal and the line of sight to the rock.
9. Two scouts wish to find the distance from point B to point A across a river. They set a stake at C making $m\angle BCA = 90$. They find that $m\angle B = 66$ and $\overline{BC}$ is 48 meters long. How long is $\overline{AB}$?

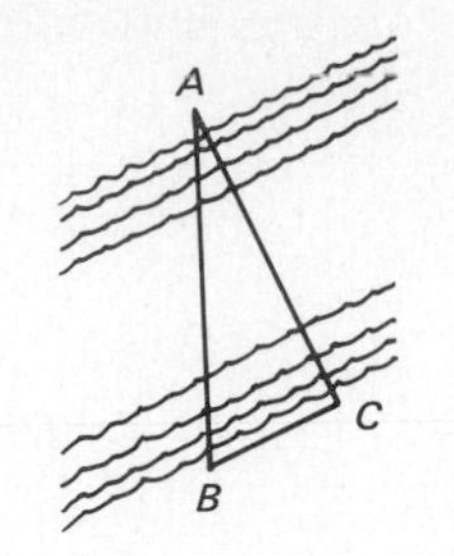

10. In Exercise 9, how long is $\overline{AB}$ if $m\angle B = 40$, and $\overline{BC}$ is 60 meters long?
11. An 8-meter pole leaning against the side of a house forms with the house an angle whose measure is 20°. How far from the house is the foot of the pole?
12. A 6-meter ladder is leaning against a stone wall. The ladder and the wall form an angle whose measure is 20°. How far is the foot of the ladder from the wall?
13. A smokestack is 50 meters tall. A guy wire is fastened to the stack 20 meters from its top. The wire and the ground form a 40°-angle. Find the length of the guy wire.
14. To brace a young tree she had just planted, a woman attached guy wires to the trunk of the tree 2 meters below the top. The wires and the ground formed 40° angles. The tree was 8 meters tall. How long were the guy wires?
15. A guy wire for a pole meets the ground 13 meters from the foot of the pole and forms a 45° angle with the ground. How long is the pole?
16. A guy wire for a pole meets the ground 10 meters from the foot of the pole and forms a 45° angle with the ground. How long is the pole?

B

17. $ABCD$ is a rectangle with diagonal $\overline{BD}$. $m\angle ABD = 40°$. $\overline{AB}$ is 34 centimeters long. Find the area of the rectangle.

18. $PQRS$ is a rectangle with diagonal $\overline{QS}$. $m\angle PQS = 30°$. $\overline{PS}$ is 20 centimeters long. Find the area of the rectangle.

19. $\triangle ABC$ is an equilateral triangle having $CB = 10$. $m\angle DCB = 30$, and $m\angle CDB = 90$. Find the length of $\overline{CD}$.

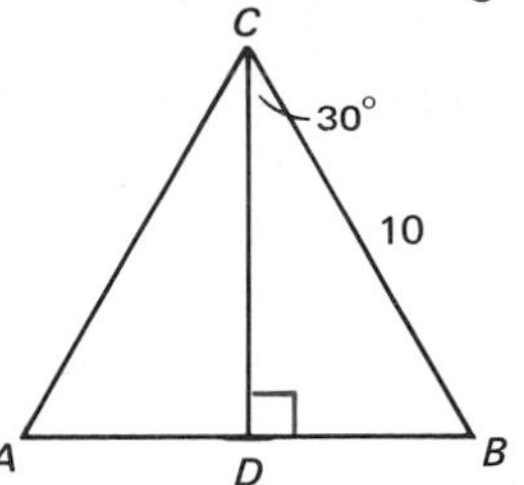

20. In isosceles triangle SQR, $QR = 16$, $m\angle SQR = 45$, and $m\angle QSR = 90$. Find the length of $\overline{SR}$.

21. One side of a rectangle has length 12 and forms with the diagonal of the rectangle an angle whose measure is 40°. Find the length of the diagonal.

22. One side of a rectangle has length 15 and forms with the diagonal an angle whose measure is 30°. How long is the diagonal?

23. A machinist wishes to drill 5 holes in a circular plate. These holes are to be equally distant from each other and 8 centimeters from the center of the plate. How far apart should the centers of the holes be placed?

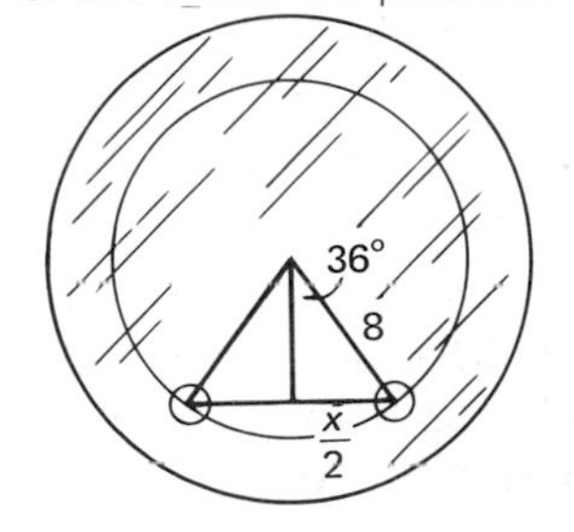

$\triangle ABC$ is a right triangle with hypotenuse $\overline{AB}$. $\overline{CD}$ and $\overline{AB}$ are perpendicular.

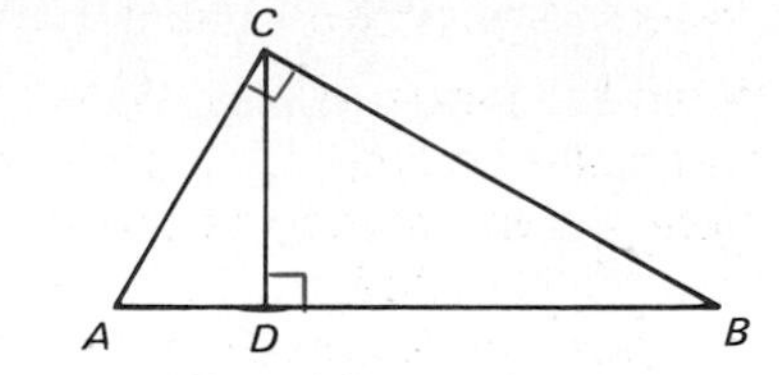

24. Show that $AD = AC \cos A$.

25. Show that $DB = BC \cos B$.

26. Show that $AB = \dfrac{AC}{\sin B}$.

C

27. The two metal plates A and B are placed together along line CD as shown in the figure. The angle parts fail to close by 0.002 centimeter. The plates are made so that they will fit exactly when a uniform width is ground off the horizontal part of plate A along $\overline{CD}$. What is this width? (Draw a right triangle showing the width to be found.)

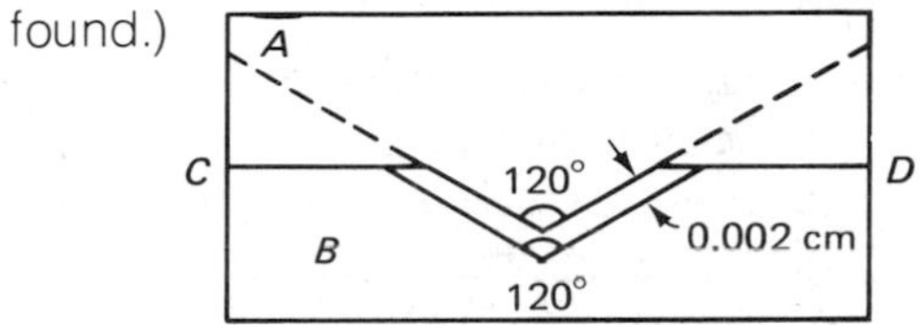

28. From the window of a room in a hotel overlooking a lake, the measure of the angle formed by the horizontal and the line of sight to a boat on the lake was 24°. The angle for a second boat in line with the first boat was 32°. The elevation of the window from the level of the lake was 200 meters. What was the distance between the boats?

29. Points A and B on the ground are in a line perpendicular to a tower at its base. From point A an observer found the angle of elevation of the top of the tower to measure 42°. An observer at point B found the angle of elevation of the top of the tower to measure 53°. Points A and B are 80 m apart. How tall is the tower?

CHAPTER REVIEW

1. Name the leg opposite $\angle A$. [14-1]

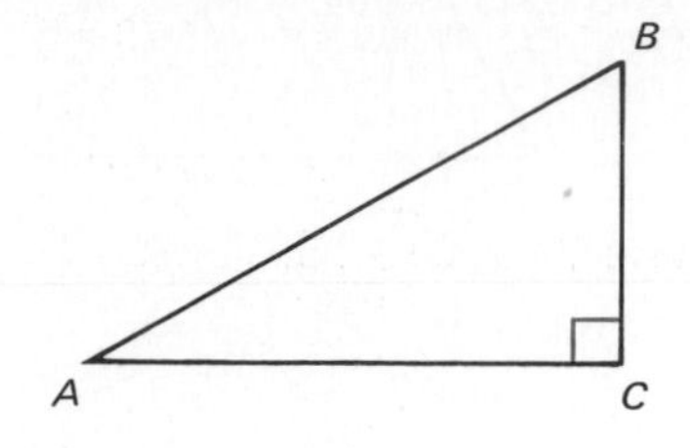

2. Name the leg adjacent to $\angle A$.

3. For the triangle shown above, $m\angle A + m\angle B + m\angle C = ?$

For $m\angle N = 30$, give the degree measure of each of these angles.

4. the complement of $\angle N$

5. the supplement of $\angle N$

6. The measure of an angle is 4 times that of its complement. Find the measure of each angle.

7. For $\triangle ABC$, $m\angle A = 47$ and $m\angle B = 50$. Find $m\angle C$.

8. The measures of the angles of a triangle are represented by x, $3x$ and $5x$. Find the degree measure of each angle.

$\triangle ABC \sim \triangle DEF$ [14-2]

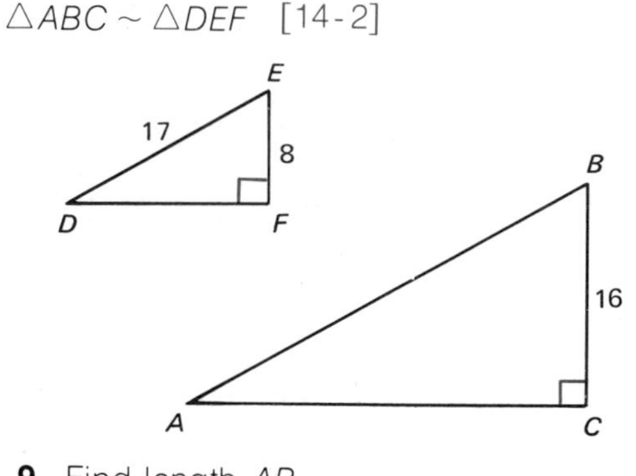

9. Find length AB.

10. Find length DF.

11. Find length AC.

$\triangle PQR \sim \triangle P'Q'R'$

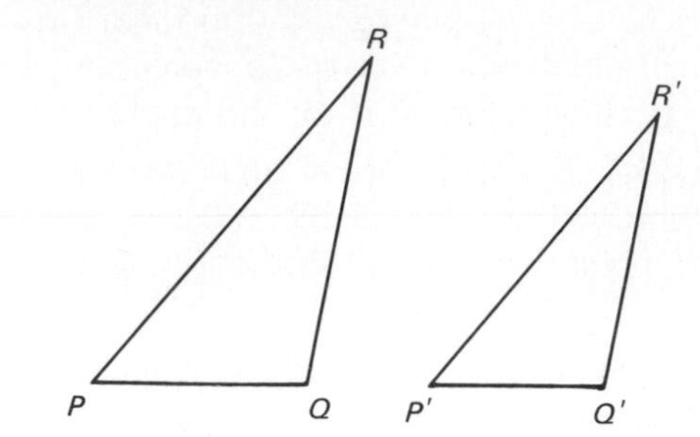

12. For $PQ = 15$, $PR = 9$, $P'Q' = 5$, find $P'R'$.

13. For $PQ = 10$, $QR = 10$, $P'Q' = 9$, find $Q'R'$.

14. For $m\angle P = 70$, find $m\angle P'$.

Give each ratio using the lengths m, n, and p. [14-3, 14-4]

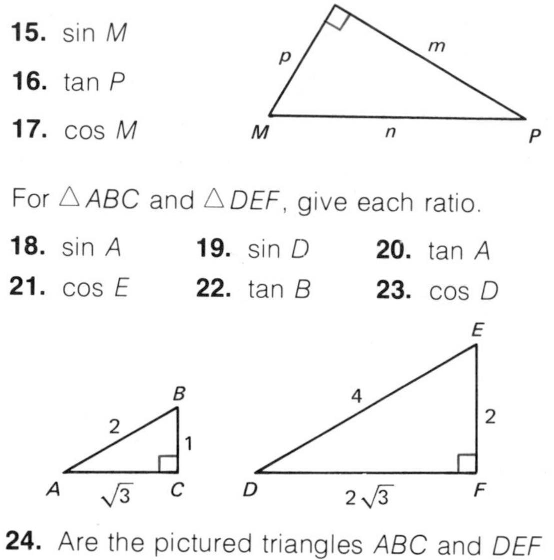

15. sin M

16. tan P

17. cos M

For $\triangle ABC$ and $\triangle DEF$, give each ratio.

18. sin A **19.** sin D **20.** tan A

21. cos E **22.** tan B **23.** cos D

24. Are the pictured triangles ABC and DEF similar?

25. $m\angle R = m\angle S$. $\sin R = \frac{2}{5}$. Find sin S.

26. $\angle D$ is a complement of $\angle E$. $\sin D = \frac{3}{5}$. Find cos E.

For $\triangle ABC$, approximate each ratio to 4 decimal places.

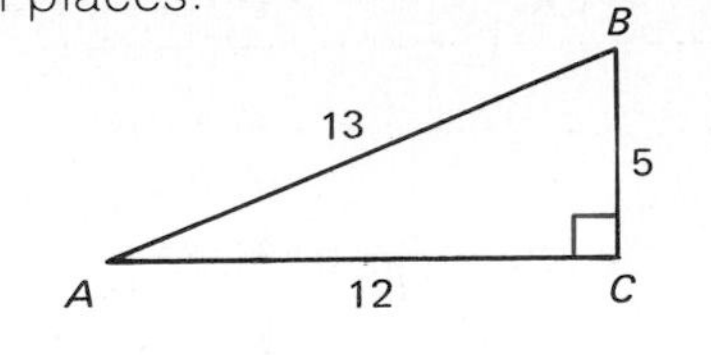

27. $\sin A$ **28.** $\cos A$ **29.** $\tan A$

Use the table on page 510 to approximate each ratio.

30. $\sin 67°$ **31.** $\cos 16°$
32. $\sin 89°$ **33.** $\cos 48°$
34. $\tan 45°$ **35.** $\tan 89°$

Use the table on page 510 to approximate the degree measure of each angle.

36. $\cos A = 0.9816$, $m\angle A \doteq ?$
37. $\sin X = 0.2756$, $m\angle X \doteq ?$
38. $\tan A = 0.4041$, $m\angle A \doteq ?$
39. $\cos S = 0.3256$, $m\angle S \doteq ?$
40. $\tan R = 2.9042$, $m\angle R \doteq ?$
41. $\sin B = 0.9998$, $m\angle B \doteq ?$

Solve. [14-5]

42. A road slopes upward from the horizontal to form a 10° angle. Find the amount of rise for the road over a horizontal distance of 1000 meters.

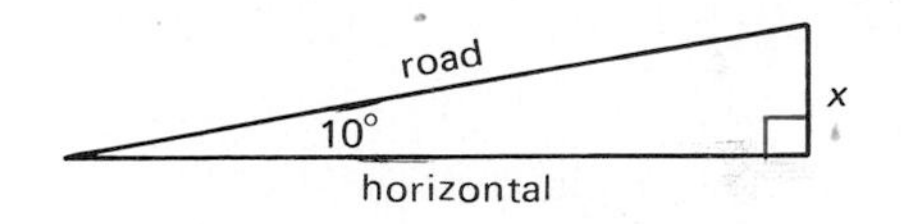

43. A ladder leaning against a wall forms a 70° angle with the ground. The ladder is 6 meters long. Find the distance from the ground to the top of the ladder in meters.

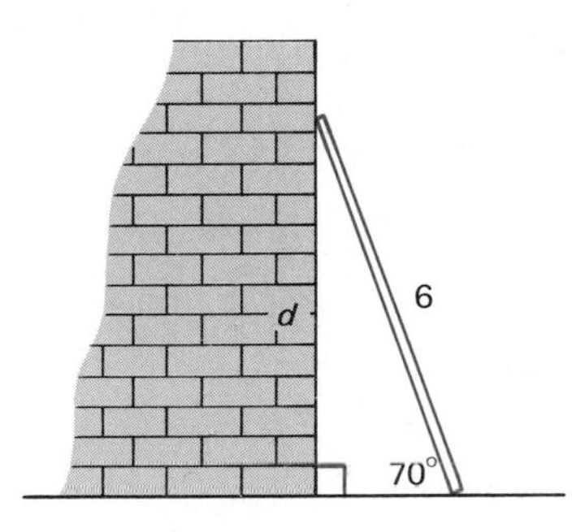

CAPSULE REVIEW

Write the letter of the best response.

1. Which pair of triangles shows non-similar triangles?

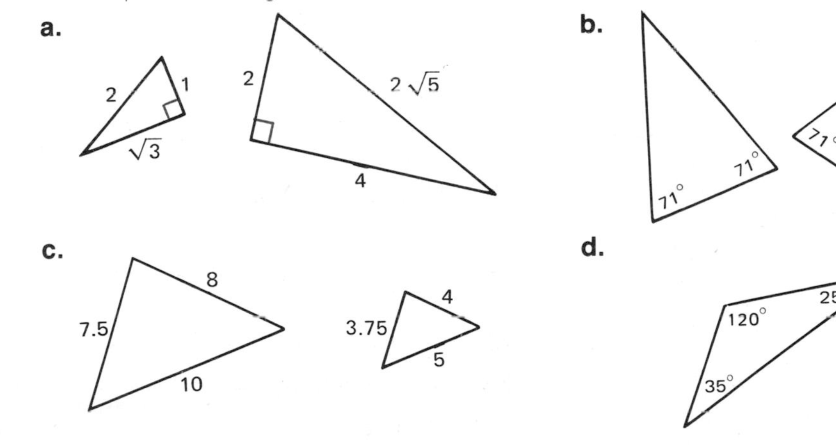

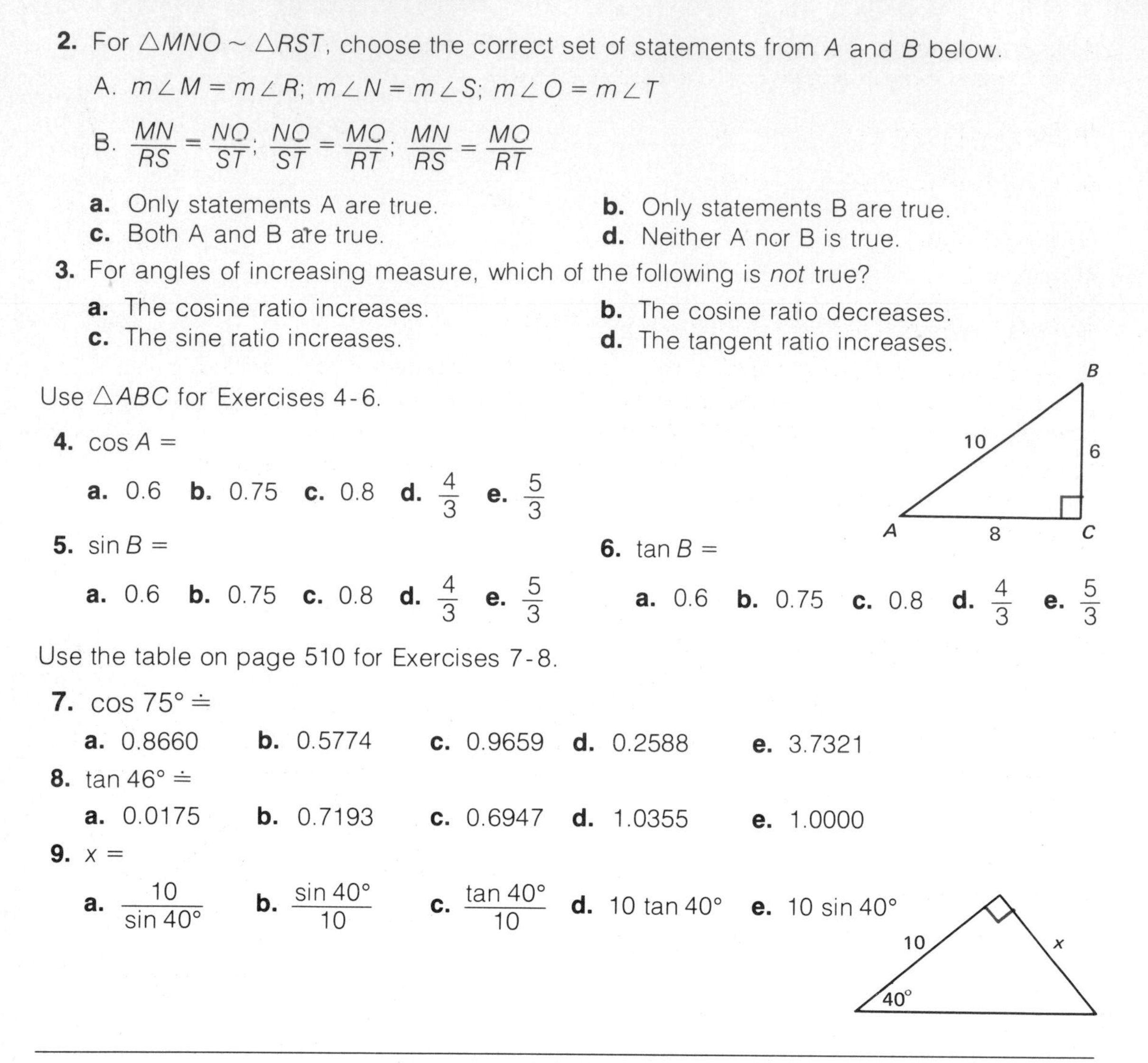

2. For $\triangle MNO \sim \triangle RST$, choose the correct set of statements from *A* and *B* below.

A. $m\angle M = m\angle R$; $m\angle N = m\angle S$; $m\angle O = m\angle T$

B. $\frac{MN}{RS} = \frac{NO}{ST}$; $\frac{NO}{ST} = \frac{MO}{RT}$; $\frac{MN}{RS} = \frac{MO}{RT}$

a. Only statements A are true. **b.** Only statements B are true.
c. Both A and B are true. **d.** Neither A nor B is true.

3. For angles of increasing measure, which of the following is *not* true?

a. The cosine ratio increases. **b.** The cosine ratio decreases.
c. The sine ratio increases. **d.** The tangent ratio increases.

Use $\triangle ABC$ for Exercises 4-6.

4. $\cos A =$

a. 0.6 **b.** 0.75 **c.** 0.8 **d.** $\frac{4}{3}$ **e.** $\frac{5}{3}$

5. $\sin B =$

a. 0.6 **b.** 0.75 **c.** 0.8 **d.** $\frac{4}{3}$ **e.** $\frac{5}{3}$

6. $\tan B =$

a. 0.6 **b.** 0.75 **c.** 0.8 **d.** $\frac{4}{3}$ **e.** $\frac{5}{3}$

Use the table on page 510 for Exercises 7-8.

7. $\cos 75° \doteq$

a. 0.8660 **b.** 0.5774 **c.** 0.9659 **d.** 0.2588 **e.** 3.7321

8. $\tan 46° \doteq$

a. 0.0175 **b.** 0.7193 **c.** 0.6947 **d.** 1.0355 **e.** 1.0000

9. $x =$

a. $\frac{10}{\sin 40°}$ **b.** $\frac{\sin 40°}{10}$ **c.** $\frac{\tan 40°}{10}$ **d.** $10 \tan 40°$ **e.** $10 \sin 40°$

CHAPTER TEST

1. Two angles are complementary. The measure of one angle is 40°. Give the measure of the other.

2. The length of one side of an equilateral triangle is 10 centimeters. Find the perimeter of the triangle in centimeters.

3. The two triangles are similar. Find *x*.

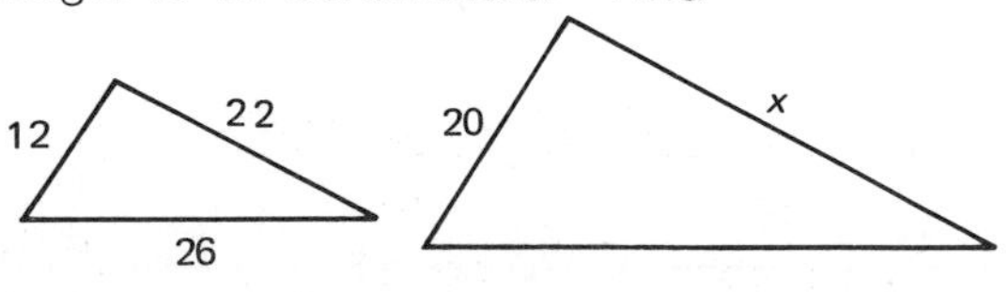

4. Two triangles are congruent. The perimeter of one triangle is 60 centimeters. Find the perimeter of the other triangle.

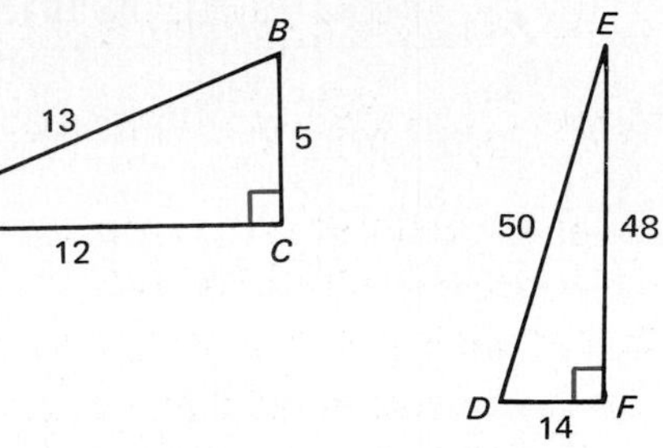

5. For $\triangle ABC$ pictured, find $\tan A$.

6. For $\triangle DEF$ pictured, find $\sin D$.

Use the table on page 510 for Exercises 7-10.

7. Find cos 42°.

8. Use a table and find $m\angle G$ when $\tan G = 2.0503$.

9. An airplane is directly above a radio tower. An observer who is on the ground 1000 meters from the tower sights the plane at an angle of 53° with the ground. Find the altitude of the airplane.

10. A 5-meter ladder is leaning against a wall. Its feet are 1.71 meters from the wall. Find the measure of the angle that the ladder forms with the ground.

Write the letter of the best response.

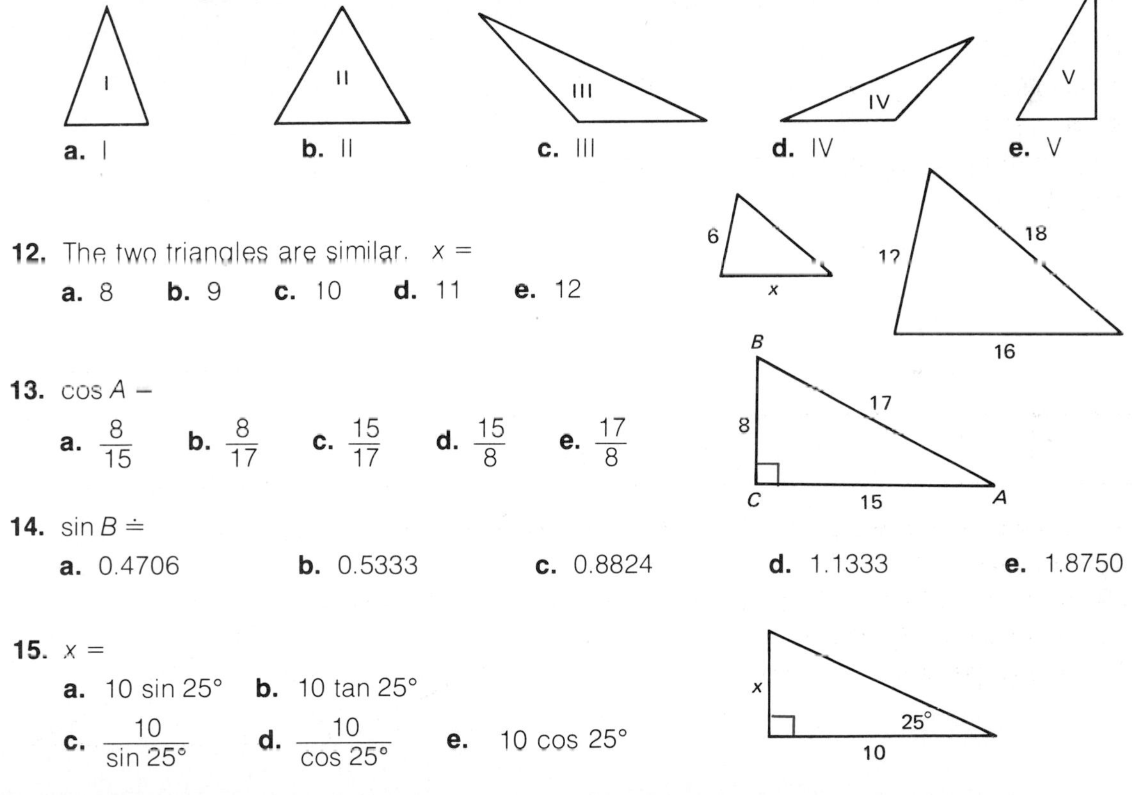

11. Which triangle appears to be both isosceles and obtuse?

a. I **b.** II **c.** III **d.** IV **e.** V

12. The two triangles are similar. $x =$

a. 8 **b.** 9 **c.** 10 **d.** 11 **e.** 12

13. $\cos A =$

a. $\frac{8}{15}$ **b.** $\frac{8}{17}$ **c.** $\frac{15}{17}$ **d.** $\frac{15}{8}$ **e.** $\frac{17}{8}$

14. $\sin B \doteq$

a. 0.4706 **b.** 0.5333 **c.** 0.8824 **d.** 1.1333 **e.** 1.8750

15. $x =$

a. 10 sin 25° **b.** 10 tan 25°

c. $\frac{10}{\sin 25°}$ **d.** $\frac{10}{\cos 25°}$ **e.** 10 cos 25°

CUMULATIVE REVIEW

Give the word(s) to complete each sentence.

1. $\sqrt{3}$ is an __?__ number.
2. The process of finding $\frac{\sqrt{3}}{3}$ as another name for $\frac{1}{\sqrt{3}}$ is called __?__.
3. $x = \frac{-b \pm \sqrt{b^2 - 4ac}}{2a}$ is called the __?__.
4. For any right triangle, the side opposite the right angle is the __?__.
5. __?__ angles are two angles for which the sum of the degree measures is 180.

Briefly answer each question. Refer to the concept suggested.

6. 1.414 is only an approximation for $\sqrt{2}$. Why?
7. $\sqrt{108}$ can be simplified to $6\sqrt{3}$. Why?
8. $\triangle ABC \sim \triangle DEF$. Why?

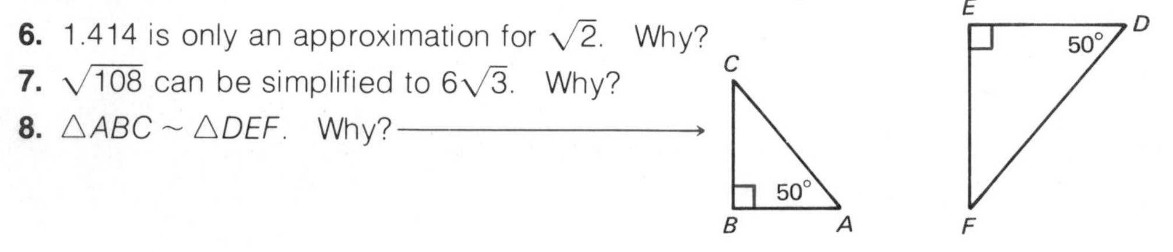

9. For any right triangle, if you know the lengths of two of the three sides, you can always find the length of the third side. Why?
10. $\sin 60° = \cos 30°$. Why?

Express each in decimal form.

11. $\frac{11}{16}$
12. $\frac{7}{11}$

Express each in $\frac{a}{b}$ form.

13. 5.625
14. $-0.\overline{8}$

15. Find a square root of 361.
16. Square $-9y$.
17. Find an approximation for $\sqrt{58}$ to one decimal place.

Simplify.

18. $\sqrt{128}$
19. $6\sqrt{75}$
20. $\sqrt{20} + \sqrt{45} - 2\sqrt{80}$
21. $9\sqrt{\frac{1}{3}} + 10\sqrt{\frac{1}{2}} - \frac{1}{2}\sqrt{32} + \frac{1}{2}\sqrt{12}$
22. $(8 + \sqrt{5})(8 - \sqrt{5})$

Rationalize the denominator for each.

23. $\frac{5\sqrt{6}}{\sqrt{12}}$
24. $\frac{6 + \sqrt{3}}{6 - \sqrt{3}}$

Factor.

25. $4h^2 + 12h + 9$ **26.** $x^2 - 9y^2$ **27.** $x^2 + 2x + \frac{3}{4}$

Solve.

28. $\frac{4}{x^2 - 5x + 6} + 3 = \frac{4}{x - 3} - \frac{1}{x - 2}$ **29.** $\sqrt{2x - 5} = 7$ **30.** $\frac{1}{3}\sqrt{x} + 3 = 7$

31. $2\sqrt{x} + 12 = 6$ **32.** $y^2 = 121$ **33.** $3x^2 - 54 = 0$

34. Simplify. $\sqrt{80x^5y^7z^{10}}$ **35.** Square. $(4y - 7)$

36. Write an equation for the line containing points $(1, 4)$ and $(-2, -17)$.

Solve by completing the square.

37. $4x^2 + 4x - 3 = 0$

Solve by factoring.

38. $2x^2 - 3x - 20 = 0$

Solve the system.

39. $5x + 6y = 0$
$x - 2y = -8$

40. Solve by using the quadratic formula. $y^2 + 3y - 4 = 0$

41. A wire is stretched from the top of a telephone pole with a height of 24 meters to a point on the ground 7 meters from the base of the pole. Find the length of the wire.

42. The measure of an angle is 110°. Find the measure of its supplement.

43. At a point 20 m from the base of a tree, the angle of elevation of the top of the tree measures 53°. Find, to the nearest meter, the height of the tree. Use the table on page 510.

Write the letter of the best response.

44. Which is an irrational number?

a. $0.1\overline{6}$ **b.** $\sqrt{81}$ **c.** $\sqrt{7}$ **d.** 0.0625

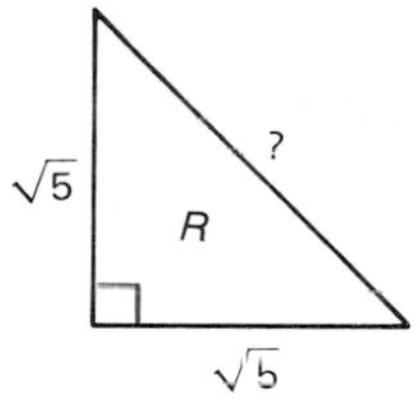

45. The hypotenuse of right triangle R has length

a. $\frac{\sqrt{5}}{5}$ **b.** $\sqrt{10}$ **c.** 5 **d.** $2\sqrt{5}$

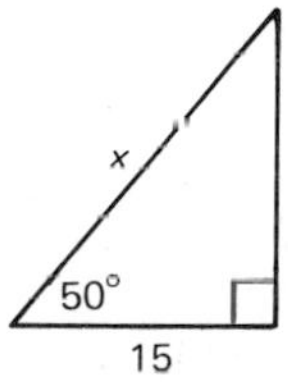

46. In the triangle pictured, $x =$

a. $15 \sin 50°$ **b.** $15 \cos 50°$ **c.** $\frac{15}{\sin 50°}$ **d.** $\frac{15}{\cos 50°}$

47. Which set is not a function?

a. $\{(1, 2), (2, 2), (3, 2), (4, 2)\}$ **b.** $\{(2, 1), (2, 2), (2, 3), (2, 4)\}$
c. $\{(1, 2), (2, 1), (3, 4), (4, 3)\}$ **d.** $\{(1, 1), (2, 2), (3, 3), (4, 4)\}$

48. Which trinomial is a perfect square?

a. $x^2 + 3x + 9$ **b.** $x^2 + 8x + 8$ **c.** $2x^2 - 4x + 4$ **d.** $x^2 + \frac{3}{2}x + \frac{9}{16}$

49. The solution(s) of $x + 2 = \sqrt{5x + 16}$ is (are)

a. 4 and -3 **b.** 4 **c.** -3 **d.** not given

50. Triangles P and Q are similar. Which proportion is correct?

a. $\frac{3}{y} \stackrel{?}{=} \frac{4}{x}$ **b.** $\frac{4}{y} \stackrel{?}{=} \frac{x}{3}$ **c.** $\frac{4}{y} \stackrel{?}{=} \frac{5}{\sqrt{x^2 + y^2}}$ **d.** $\frac{3}{\sqrt{x^2 + y^2}} \stackrel{?}{=} \frac{5}{x}$

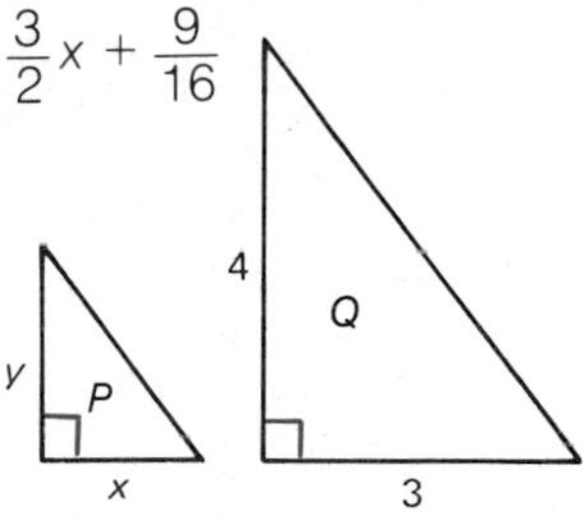

CHAPTER 15
Review by Topics

Roads are level, bridges span, and buildings stand because someone planned. It takes much work behind the scenes before the many ingredients of a construction project come together. When they do, the results, good or bad, often directly reflect the skills and abilities of the planners.

ARITHMETIC SKILLS I

Add.

1. $\begin{array}{r}125\\ \underline{647}\end{array}$ **2.** $\begin{array}{r}468\\ \underline{212}\end{array}$ **3.** $\begin{array}{r}172\\ \underline{291}\end{array}$ **4.** $\begin{array}{r}585\\ \underline{134}\end{array}$

5. $\begin{array}{r}476\\ \underline{154}\end{array}$ **6.** $\begin{array}{r}369\\ \underline{164}\end{array}$ **7.** $\begin{array}{r}487\\ \underline{638}\end{array}$ **8.** $\begin{array}{r}929\\ \underline{598}\end{array}$

Subtract.

9. $\begin{array}{r}582\\ \underline{219}\end{array}$ **10.** $\begin{array}{r}552\\ \underline{233}\end{array}$ **11.** $\begin{array}{r}757\\ \underline{163}\end{array}$ **12.** $\begin{array}{r}737\\ \underline{344}\end{array}$

13. $\begin{array}{r}662\\ \underline{488}\end{array}$ **14.** $\begin{array}{r}962\\ \underline{176}\end{array}$ **15.** $\begin{array}{r}604\\ \underline{546}\end{array}$ **16.** $\begin{array}{r}804\\ \underline{479}\end{array}$

Multiply.

17. $\begin{array}{r}236\\ \underline{2}\end{array}$ **18.** $\begin{array}{r}34\\ \underline{26}\end{array}$ **19.** $\begin{array}{r}27\\ \underline{55}\end{array}$ **20.** $\begin{array}{r}224\\ \underline{39}\end{array}$

Divide.

21. $8\overline{)424}$ **22.** $6\overline{)282}$ **23.** $7\overline{)1351}$ **24.** $24\overline{)4272}$

Find the sum.

25. $\frac{1}{2} + \frac{3}{5}$ **26.** $1\frac{3}{4} + 4\frac{1}{3}$ **27.** $2.8 + 0.43$ **28.** $0.01 + 5.4$

Find the difference.

29. $\frac{4}{7} - \frac{1}{3}$ **30.** $6\frac{1}{4} - 2\frac{1}{3}$ **31.** $4.2 - 0.14$ **32.** $2.56 - 0.79$

Find the product.

33. $\frac{5}{6} \times \frac{7}{8}$ **34.** $1\frac{1}{2} \times 1\frac{1}{4}$ **35.** $\frac{2}{3} \times \frac{9}{14} \times \frac{7}{12}$

36. 8.3×2.7 **37.** 2.7×0.16 **38.** 0.7×0.8

Find the quotient.

39. $\frac{4}{5} \div \frac{2}{3}$ **40.** $2\frac{1}{2} \div \frac{1}{4}$ **41.** $6\frac{3}{10} \div 1\frac{11}{25}$

42. $7.1 \div 0.2$ **43.** $6.5 \div 8$ **44.** $3 \div 0.05$

ARITHMETIC SKILLS II

Add.

1. 1728 and 846
2. 7.5 + 13.24
3. \$9 + \$1.87 + \$0.65

Subtract.

4. 129 from 896
5. 11.92 − 1.07
6. \$10 − \$1.87

Multply.

7. 147 by 64
8. 4.7×3.1
9. 11.4×0.003

Divide.

10. 13 056 by 32
11. $75 \div 2.5$
12. 107.164 by 1.46

Perform the indicated operation.

13. $\frac{2}{3} + \frac{5}{6}$
14. $\frac{7}{8} - \frac{1}{2}$
15. $\frac{3}{4} \times \frac{6}{7}$
16. $\frac{5}{16} \div \frac{3}{4}$
17. $3\frac{1}{5} \div \frac{4}{15}$
18. $7\frac{3}{4} \times \frac{3}{4}$
19. $7\frac{1}{2} - 5\frac{1}{3}$
20. $\frac{5}{12} + \frac{7}{36}$

SIMPLIFYING POLYNOMIALS

A Simplify by combining like terms.

1. $3a + 4b - 5a + 4c - 6b$
2. $x - y + z - 4x - 4y - 3z$
3. $3m - 4n + 4p - 6m - 8n - 4p$
4. $3h - 4 + 7h - 5h - 2 - h$
5. $2abc - 3b + 2c - 5a - abc - 2a - 2c$
6. $\frac{1}{2}x - \frac{1}{3}y + \frac{1}{6}x - \frac{1}{2}y$

B

7. $2.3a^2 + 1.7b - 4.5 - 4.4a^2 - 5.2b$
8. $2.3c + 4.1d + 5.2c - 8.6d + c$
9. $10x^3 + 5x^2 - 2x + 1 - x^3 - 10x^2 - 2x - 1$
10. $\frac{7}{9}c^2 + \frac{1}{3}c^2 + 0.4b - 0.15b + b$
11. $\frac{2}{5}x + \frac{6}{15}y - \frac{1}{10}x + \frac{11}{15}y + 0.6x$
12. $\frac{1}{2}x^2 + \frac{1}{3}y^3 - \frac{1}{3}x^2 + 0.5y^3$

ADDING POLYNOMIALS

A Add.

1. $2x - 3y + 4z$, $5x - y - z$, and $-x - y + z$
2. $3x^2 - 2x + 1$, $4x^2 - x - 9$, and $-6x^2 + 7x + 1$
3. $4a + 3b - c$, $5a - c + b$, and $4b - 6a$

4. $2x - 1$, $-3x + 2$, $4x - 5$, and $10x - 11$

5. $3ab - 4bc + 5cd$, $-bc + ab$, and $8ab - cd$

6. $x - y - z$, $5x - 3y - 7z$, and $2z - 3x + y$

B **7.** $ab^2 - a^2b + ab$ and $-ab^2 - 3a^2b + 4ab$

8. $x^3 - 2x^2y - xy^2 + 2y^3$ and $-x^3 - x^2y + 5xy^2 + y^3$

9. $st + st^2 - t^3$ and $3st^2 - ts - 3t^3$

10. $0.3x - 4.5y^2 + 3.1z$ and $-0.8x - 2.5y - 7.6z$

11. $4.9x^2 - 3.2x - 5$, $x^2 + 0.9$, and $4.4x - 5.7 - 3.9x^2$

12. $\frac{1}{2}x - \frac{1}{3}y + \frac{1}{5}z$ and $\frac{1}{3}x - \frac{1}{4}y - \frac{2}{3}z$

SUBTRACTING POLYNOMIALS

A Subtract.

1. $(7k + 6) - (2k + 4m - 8n)$

2. $(5x - 3y + 2z) - (x + y + z)$

3. $(-3a + 9b - 6c) - (2a + 3b - 7c)$

4. $(5a - 4b + 6c) - (6a - 7b - 3c)$

5. $(2a - b) - (a + 5b - 3)$

6. $(a + 2b - 5c) - (-a - b - 7c)$

B **7.** $7a^2 - (5a^2 - 4a + 8)$

8. $(0.3m - 1.49n - p) - (0.2m + 0.22n + 3p)$

9. $(5x^2 - 2x - 9) - (3x^3 - 2x^2 + 7)$

10. $(x^2 - 4xy + y^2) - (3x^2 - xy - y^2)$

11. $\left(\frac{1}{7}a - \frac{1}{4}b + \frac{1}{14}c\right) - \left(\frac{1}{14}a - \frac{3}{4}b - \frac{1}{2}c\right)$

12. $\left(\frac{1}{12}x - \frac{1}{5}y - \frac{1}{3}z\right) - \left(\frac{3}{5}x + \frac{3}{4}y - \frac{1}{2}z\right)$

REMOVING PARENTHESES

A Simplify.

1. $(3x - 4y + z) + (2x - y - z)$

2. $(4a - 2b + c) - (3a - 4b - c)$

3. $4 + (x - 1) - (3x + 1)$

4. $2k + (3k - 1) - (4k + 6)$

5. $(2x^3 - 3x^2 + x) - (x^2 - 1) + 4x^2$

6. $1 - x + (6x - 3) - (8 - 2x)$

7. $1 + 3(c - 1) - 4(2c - 4)$

8. $1 + 3(x - 4) - 5(2x - 5)$

9. $(3x - 1)4 - 5(6x + 7) + 3(x + 2)$

10. $x(x - 3) - (x^2 - 6) - (x^2 - 2x + 9)$

B **11.** $x - [-x - (x - 1)]$

12. $3b^2 - b[(-5 + 3b) - b]$

13. $2x^2 - [7x - 2(2x - 1)] + 5x$

14. $x^2 - [x(3 - x) - 3(x - 3)] - x^2$

15. $-9[a - (3x - 5a) - 4]$

16. $8x - 7[1 - 5(2x + 10 - 3x)]$

17. $3(x + 1) + 4[x - (3x + 2 + 9x)]$

18. $6y + 2[3 - (y + 4) - 3] + 5$

19. $(x - 1)(x - 2) - [x(x - 1) + 2] + 2$

20. $4(m + 3) - (m - 2)^2 + 4$

SOLVING LINEAR EQUATIONS

A Solve.

1. $3x - 6 = x + 10$
2. $x + 6 = -5x + 12$
3. $-2c + 8 = c - 4$
4. $x - 3 = 0$
5. $8 + x = -x + 5$
6. $10h + 1 = 8h + 2$
7. $4r - 10 = 7r + 5$
8. $x - 3(x + 4) = 2$
9. $7(m - 4) - (m - 4) = 0$
10. $3(x - 2) - 3 = 0$
11. $2(y - 6) = 3(y - 2)$
12. $4(x - 7) - 3x + 2 = 4$

B Solve for x.

13. $x^2 + 3 = (x + 5)(x + 9)$
14. $(x + 1)^2 - (x - 2)^2 = 21$
15. $4 - (x - 2)(x + 7) = 24 - x^2$
16. $\frac{x}{2} - \frac{x}{3} = 2$
17. $\frac{6a \cdot 22b}{x} = \frac{8a \cdot 10b}{4}$
18. $\frac{1}{4}(2x - 3y) - \frac{1}{6}\left(x - \frac{y}{2}\right) = \frac{y}{8}$
19. $x - 1 = 12 + \frac{3x - 4}{2}$
20. $\frac{2x - 7}{5} - \frac{5x + 3}{7} + 11 = 0$

SOLVING INEQUALITIES

A Solve. Graph each solution set.

1. $x - \frac{1}{5} > \frac{7}{15}$
2. $x - 8 > -3$
3. $3x > \frac{1}{4}$
4. $-3 < \frac{x}{-2}$
5. $6x - 2 > 3x - 4$
6. $x - 9 < x + 7 + x$
7. $\frac{-x + 2}{5} > 8$
8. $\frac{-x - 5}{3} < 4$
9. $\frac{-2x + 4}{8} < 6x$

B Solve for x. All other variables represent positive numbers.

10. $4x + 50 > 2x + 16$
11. $x - 3(-5) < 24$
12. $\frac{ax}{b} > c$
13. $-xy > 2$
14. $4(3x - 3) - 8(x + 5) > 2x$
15. $5(x - 4) < 8(x - 7)$
16. $\frac{r + s}{x} < t$
17. $\frac{m - nx}{kx} > h$
18. $\frac{-3x + 6}{9} < 5(x + 15)$
19. $r - p(x + 2) > q$

MULTIPLYING POLYNOMIALS

A Multiply as indicated.

1. $6(4x)$
2. $9(-3x^3)$
3. $\frac{3}{8}p(4p)$
4. a^4a^5
5. $(2a)(3a)(4)$
6. $-5(ax)(x)$
7. $(4x)^3$
8. $(4x)(-x)(y^2)^3$
9. $x(-2x^3)^5$
10. $(a+3)(a-2)$
11. $(c-3)(c+5)$
12. $(x-y)(x+y)$
13. $(7x-y)(2x+y)$
14. $(a-5)(a-7)$
15. $(3x-5y)(2x+3y)$
16. $4y(6y^2+3y+5)$
17. $-6x(-x^3+2x-1)$

B **18.** $-14\left(\frac{2}{7}a-\frac{1}{28}b-\frac{3}{21}c\right)$
19. $-12ab^2(2ab+5a^2-6b^3c)$
20. $(cd+1)(cd-3)$
21. $(a^2+b^2)(a+b)$
22. $(a+b)^3$
23. $(x^2+y^2)(x^2-y^2)$
24. $(c^2-c+3)(c+2)$
25. $(x^2-2x+1)(x-1)$
26. $(x-y+1)(x+y-1)$
27. $(x^2-xy+y^2)(x+y)$
28. $4(2x+5)(2x-4)$
29. $-4(x-3)(x+2)$
30. $(x+3)(x+3)(x+3)$
31. $(x-2)(x-2)(x+2)$

DIVIDING POLYNOMIALS

A Divide as indicated.

1. $9a^3 \div 3a$
2. $(-16x^6) \div (2x^3)$
3. $(15x^2y) \div (3y)$
4. $\frac{abc^3}{ac}$
5. $\frac{-36m^4}{9m^2}$
6. $\frac{10y^6}{2y^3}$
7. $\frac{4m^3-8m}{4m}$
8. $\frac{8x^2-12x}{-2x}$
9. $\frac{c^2-c}{-c}$
10. $\frac{6x^3-12x^2-30x}{-3x}$
11. $\frac{8x^3y^2-16x^2y^4}{4x^2y^2}$
12. $\frac{10x^3y-15x^2y^2}{-5x^2y}$
13. $(x^2+8x+12) \div (x+2)$
14. $(a^2-13a+12) \div (a-1)$
15. $(12x^3+20x^2+5x+3) \div (2x+3)$
16. $(12a^3-6a^2-12a-48) \div (a-2)$

B **17.** $(4.8x^4y^2+0.40x^3y^2z+x^5y) \div (0.04x^3y)$
18. $\left(\frac{3}{4}r^3s^2-\frac{5}{24}r^2s^3+18s\right) \div \left(-\frac{1}{6}s\right)$
19. $(x^2-2x-35) \div (x+5)$
20. $(4a^2+7ab-2b^2) \div (4a-b)$
21. $(x^3-3x^2+3x-1) \div (x-1)$
22. $(12a^3+34a^2-32) \div (3a+4)$
23. $(x^4-16) \div (x-2)$
24. $(x^5-32) \div (x-2)$
25. $(2c^3-5c+6-3c^2) \div (c^2+2-3c)$
26. $(8x^3-y^3) \div (2x-y)$

SOLVING FORMULAS

A Solve.

1. $C = 2\pi r$ for r

2. $PV = nRT$ for T

3. $g = \frac{6M}{R}$ for M

4. $V = \frac{x - y}{M}$ for x

5. $E = \frac{I}{R^2}$ for R

6. $V = \pi r^2 h$ for h

7. $s = \frac{1}{2}gt^2$. Find s for $t = 5$ and $g = 9.8$.

8. $V = \pi r^2 h$. Find V for $\pi = 3.14$, $r = 20$, and $h = 30$.

9. $F = \frac{m - 2}{r}$. Find F for $m = 52$ and $r = 12$.

B **10.** Solve $F = m\frac{v^2}{r}$ for v. Find v for $F = 50$, $r = 4$, *and* $m = 2$.

11. Solve $A = p + prt$ for t. Find t for $A = \$5500$, $r = 0.08$, and $p = \$5000$.

12. Solve $S = vt + \frac{1}{2}at^2$ for a. Find a for $S = 26$, $v = 4$, and $t = 2$.

13. Solve $\frac{1}{2}mv^2 = mgh$ for v. Find v for $m = 4$, $g = 9.8$, and $h = 32$.

SPECIAL PRODUCTS AND FACTORING

A Multiply as indicated.

1. $3m(a - b + c)$

2. $(3x + 5)^2$

3. $3a^2x(a^2 + ax + x^2)$

4. $(3x + 5)(4x - 5)$

5. $(3x - 2y)^2$

6. $(a - 5)(a - 7)$

7. $(7x - y)(2x + y)$

8. $(x^3 - y^2)(x^3 + y^2)$

9. $(a^2 - 3)(a^2 + 3)$

Factor.

10. $2x - 2y$

11. $x^4 - x^2$

12. $4xy - 8x^2y^2$

13. $P + Prt$

14. $x^2 - 16$

15. $a^4 - 81$

16. $a^2 - b^2$

17. $m^2 - 4n^2$

18. $1 + 4b + 4b^2$

19. $a^2 + ab - 20b^2$

20. $3a^2 - 4a - 4$

21. $x^2 - 6x - 7$

22. $2x^2 + x - 6$

23. $x^2 + x - 4x - 4$

B Multiply as indicated.

24. $(x^2y - 0.7)(x^2y + 2.5)$

25. $\left(3a^3 - \frac{2}{7}\right)\left(3a^3 + \frac{2}{7}\right)$

26. $(2x^4 - 3y^2)(x^4 + 4y^2)$

27. $\left(25a^2 + \frac{1}{4}\right)(1 - 2a)(1 + 2a)$

Factor.

28. $6x^5y - 36x^3y + 54xy$

29. $x^4 - y^4 + 2x^2y^2 - (x^2 + y^2)^2$

30. $x^3 - 4x$

31. $4a - 4ab^2$

32. $2b^2 + 12b + 18$

33. $6x^3 + x^2 - 5x$

34. $2c^3 - 10c^2 + 12c$

35. $3x^2 + 12xy - 135y^2$

36. $4n^2 - 16n - 20$

37. $a^4 + 2a^3 + a^2$

38. $20a - 8ax - ax^2$

39. $ab - 8cd + 2ad - 4bc$

40. $a^5 - a + 50a$

41. $9 - 13b^2 + 4b^4$

SOLVING QUADRATIC EQUATIONS

A Solve.

1. $2x^2 - 3x + 1 = 0$

2. $y^2 - 6y = 1$

3. $x^2 - 7x + 2 = 0$

4. $y^2 - 3y - 10 = 0$

5. $2x^2 - 7x + 3 = 0$

6. $m^2 - 2m + 1 = 0$

7. $y^2 + \frac{5}{2}y = 6$

8. $3x^2 + 2x = 8$

9. $2x^2 + 7x + 4 = 0$

B **10.** $(x + 1)^2 - 9 = 0$

11. $(2x + 3)^2 - (x + 2) = 16$

12. $\frac{x - 3}{2x} + 5 = \frac{9x + 7}{3x - 5}$

13. $\frac{x + 5}{x^2 - 3x} = \frac{4x}{x - 3}$

14. $\frac{1}{x} + \frac{2}{x - 3} = \frac{5}{6}$

15. $\frac{4(x^2 - 5)}{x^2 - 9} = \frac{9}{x - 3}$

LINEAR EQUATIONS IN TWO VARIABLES

A Graph each equation.

1. $x + 4y = 12$

2. $y = 3x + 2$

3. $x - 3y = 6$

4. $y = -4x + 1$

5. $2x - 3y = 8$

6. $y = -2x + 4$

B **7.** $\frac{9x + 6y}{\frac{1}{2}} = 54$

8. $\frac{2}{3}x - \frac{1}{4}y = 12$

9. $\frac{y + 15}{2} = -3x$

10. $y = -\frac{1}{2}x + 2$

SOLVING SYSTEMS OF LINEAR EQUATIONS

A Solve.

1. $2x + 3y = 7$
$4x - 5y = 3$

2. $5x - 3y = 23$
$x + y = 3$

3. $3x + y = 4$
$x + 3y = -4$

4. $4m - 5n = 8$
$2m + 3n = 10$

5. $3x = 5y + 22$
$5x - y = 0$

6. $c = d + 3$
$4d - c = 12$

7. $\frac{x}{4} - \frac{y}{5} = 0$
$x - y = -1$

8. $\frac{x}{3} + \frac{y}{5} = 11$
$\frac{x}{2} - \frac{y}{3} = 7$

9. $\frac{2}{3}x + \frac{y}{3} = 20$
$\frac{3}{4}x + \frac{2y}{5} = 2$

B

10. $\frac{7y-4}{5} + \frac{2x-3}{2} = \frac{3}{2}$
$\frac{5x-2}{3} + \frac{2y+1}{5} = 2$

11. $\frac{2x-y}{2} + \frac{x+y}{4} = 8$
$3(x+y) - (x-y) = 4$

12. $4(x+y) + 3(x+1) = -16$
$5(4x-2y) - (2x-4y) = 9$

13. $\frac{4}{x} + \frac{1}{y} = \frac{20}{xy}$
$\frac{2}{x} - \frac{3}{y} = \frac{30}{xy}$

FRACTIONS

A Simplify.

1. $\frac{4a}{6ab}$
2. $\frac{6xy}{9x^2y}$
3. $\frac{x+y}{x^2-y^2}$
4. $\frac{(x-y)^2}{x^2+xy-2y^2}$
5. $\frac{a^2-4a}{a^2-a-12}$
6. $\frac{bx+b^2}{x^2+2bx+b^2}$

Multiply.

7. $\frac{15a^6}{8y^2} \cdot \frac{16y^3}{5a^4}$
8. $\frac{3y}{7x} \cdot \frac{21x}{9y^3} \cdot \frac{2y^2}{5x}$
9. $\frac{(x^2-16)}{(x-4)^2} \cdot \frac{14x-56}{3x+12}$

Divide.

10. $\frac{4b}{5m} \div \frac{6abc}{m^3}$
11. $\frac{x^2-4}{x^2-1} \div \frac{x+2}{x-1}$
12. $\frac{x^2-2x-15}{x^2+6x+8} \div \frac{4x^2-16x}{6x^3+12x^2}$

Perform the indicated operations.

13. $\frac{x}{3} - \frac{2x}{7}$
14. $\frac{a}{b} + 1$
15. $\frac{c}{d} + \frac{d}{c}$
16. $\frac{2}{a} + \frac{3}{b} - \frac{4}{c}$
17. $\frac{x-1}{2} - \frac{x+3}{3}$
18. $\frac{a-1}{a+1} + \frac{a+1}{a-1}$

Simplify.

19. $\frac{1+\frac{1}{a}}{a-\frac{1}{a}}$
20. $\frac{\frac{a^2-1}{a}}{\frac{a-1}{a^2}}$
21. $\frac{\frac{x^2-y^2}{4}}{\frac{x+y}{32}}$
22. $\frac{x-\frac{36}{x}}{x+6}$

Write each as a polynomial or as an expression in mixed form.

23. $\frac{14c^2 - 6c - 3}{2c}$ **24.** $\frac{24x^3 - 40x^2 + 12x}{8x}$ **25.** $\frac{y^3 - 1}{y - 1}$

Solve.

26. $\frac{4}{5}x = 20$ **27.** $\frac{3}{8}x = 45$ **28.** $\frac{3x}{5} - \frac{x}{5} = 36$

29. $\frac{16}{x + 1} = 4$ **30.** $\frac{3}{a + 1} - \frac{1}{a + 1} = \frac{2}{3}$ **31.** $\frac{y + 3}{y - 2} = \frac{y - 1}{y + 3}$

B Simplify.

32. $\frac{5x^3 + 10x^2y - 40xy^2}{x^3 + 3x^2y - 4xy^2}$ **33.** $\frac{y^3 - 9y^2 + 18y}{y^2 + 4y - 21}$ **34.** $\frac{3a^2 + 15a - 18}{5a^3 - 15a^2 + 10a}$

Multiply.

35. $\frac{x^2 + 4x + 4}{x^2 - x - 6} \cdot \frac{x^2 - 6x + 9}{3x + 6}$ **36.** $\frac{7a - 14}{1 - x^2} \cdot \frac{2x + 2}{5a - 10}$

Divide.

37. $\frac{a^2 - 1}{a^2 - 4} \div \frac{3a - 3}{5a + 10}$ **38.** $\frac{a + 4}{a^2 + 2a - 3} \div \frac{3a + 12}{a^2 + 3a}$

39. $\frac{x^2 - 25}{x^2 + 10x + 25} \div \frac{x^2 + 5x}{x^2 + 2x - 15}$ **40.** $\frac{3x^3 + 9x^2 - 12x}{2x^2 - 2x - 12} \div \frac{6x^3 - 6x^2}{5x + 10}$

Perform the indicated operations.

41. $\frac{4x}{x^2 - 9} + \frac{5}{x + 3}$ **42.** $\frac{x^2 + 2x}{x^2 + 7x + 10} - \frac{x - 3}{x + 2}$

43. $\frac{5x}{x - 3} + \frac{x^2 - 2x}{x^2 - 5x + 6}$ **44.** $\frac{c - 1}{c^2} \frac{}{3c} + \frac{1}{c}$

45. $\frac{a + 2}{a + 3} + \frac{a - 3}{a + 1} - \frac{a^2 - 6}{a^2 + 4a + 3}$ **46.** $\frac{5b - 1}{b^2 + 3b} + \frac{6b}{b^2 + 8b + 15} - \frac{2b + 1}{b^2 + 5b}$

Write each as a polynomial or an expression in mixed form.

47. $\frac{4x^2 + 3xy - 27y^2 + 4}{x + 3y}$ **48.** $\frac{x^4 + 1}{x - 1}$ **49.** $\frac{a + b + \frac{b^2}{a}}{a + b + \frac{a^2}{b}}$

Solve.

50. $\frac{x - 4}{2} - \frac{3(2x + 1)}{9} + \frac{4(x - 2)}{6} = 0$ **51.** $\frac{2x - 2}{4} - \frac{x + 10}{5} = \frac{2x + 4}{10} + \frac{5x + 2}{2}$

52. $\frac{x + 6}{6} + \frac{x + 4}{2} + \frac{x + 2}{2} = 8$ **53.** $3y + \frac{1}{5}(2y - 3) + \frac{1}{3}(3y + 2) = 24$

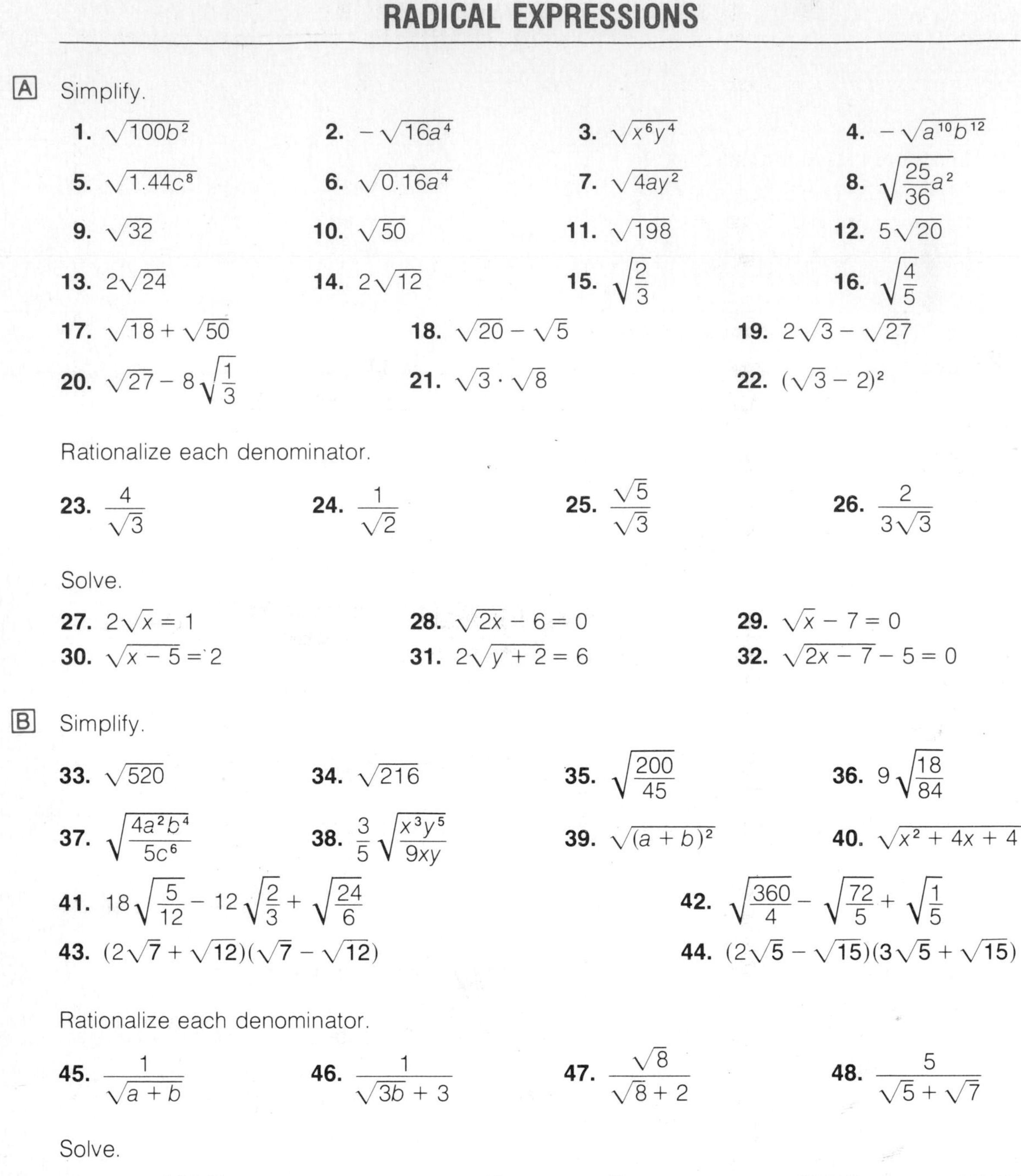

RADICAL EXPRESSIONS

A Simplify.

1. $\sqrt{100b^2}$ **2.** $-\sqrt{16a^4}$ **3.** $\sqrt{x^6y^4}$ **4.** $-\sqrt{a^{10}b^{12}}$

5. $\sqrt{1.44c^8}$ **6.** $\sqrt{0.16a^4}$ **7.** $\sqrt{4ay^2}$ **8.** $\sqrt{\frac{25}{36}a^2}$

9. $\sqrt{32}$ **10.** $\sqrt{50}$ **11.** $\sqrt{198}$ **12.** $5\sqrt{20}$

13. $2\sqrt{24}$ **14.** $2\sqrt{12}$ **15.** $\sqrt{\frac{2}{3}}$ **16.** $\sqrt{\frac{4}{5}}$

17. $\sqrt{18}+\sqrt{50}$ **18.** $\sqrt{20}-\sqrt{5}$ **19.** $2\sqrt{3}-\sqrt{27}$

20. $\sqrt{27}-8\sqrt{\frac{1}{3}}$ **21.** $\sqrt{3}\cdot\sqrt{8}$ **22.** $(\sqrt{3}-2)^2$

Rationalize each denominator.

23. $\frac{4}{\sqrt{3}}$ **24.** $\frac{1}{\sqrt{2}}$ **25.** $\frac{\sqrt{5}}{\sqrt{3}}$ **26.** $\frac{2}{3\sqrt{3}}$

Solve.

27. $2\sqrt{x}=1$ **28.** $\sqrt{2x}-6=0$ **29.** $\sqrt{x}-7=0$

30. $\sqrt{x-5}=2$ **31.** $2\sqrt{y+2}=6$ **32.** $\sqrt{2x-7}-5=0$

B Simplify.

33. $\sqrt{520}$ **34.** $\sqrt{216}$ **35.** $\sqrt{\frac{200}{45}}$ **36.** $9\sqrt{\frac{18}{84}}$

37. $\sqrt{\frac{4a^2b^4}{5c^6}}$ **38.** $\frac{3}{5}\sqrt{\frac{x^3y^5}{9xy}}$ **39.** $\sqrt{(a+b)^2}$ **40.** $\sqrt{x^2+4x+4}$

41. $18\sqrt{\frac{5}{12}}-12\sqrt{\frac{2}{3}}+\sqrt{\frac{24}{6}}$ **42.** $\sqrt{\frac{360}{4}}-\sqrt{\frac{72}{5}}+\sqrt{\frac{1}{5}}$

43. $(2\sqrt{7}+\sqrt{12})(\sqrt{7}-\sqrt{12})$ **44.** $(2\sqrt{5}-\sqrt{15})(3\sqrt{5}+\sqrt{15})$

Rationalize each denominator.

45. $\frac{1}{\sqrt{a+b}}$ **46.** $\frac{1}{\sqrt{3b}+3}$ **47.** $\frac{\sqrt{8}}{\sqrt{8}+2}$ **48.** $\frac{5}{\sqrt{5}+\sqrt{7}}$

Solve.

49. $4+\sqrt{x+1}=x-1$ **50.** $4\sqrt{x}-5=2\sqrt{x}$ **51.** $\sqrt{x+5}-4=6\sqrt{x+5}$

52. $\sqrt{x^2+5}+x=5$ **53.** $\sqrt{y^2-10}-2=y$ **54.** $10\sqrt{x}-1=17+2\sqrt{x}$

ALGEBRAIC REPRESENTATION

A Express algebraically. Use n to represent the unknown number.

1. Six times a number
2. Two more than 4 times a number
3. Three less than twice a number
4. The product of a number and 9
5. 5% of a number plus 4% of the same number

Write as an equation. Use the variable n only.

6. The sum of twice a number and one-half the number is 30.
7. Three times a number, decreased by 7, equals 25 decreased by 5 times the number.
8. Andy is 6 years older than Ricardo. The sum of their ages is 38.
9. One-third of a number, less 9, is 17.
10. There are 22 students in an algebra class. The number of girls exceeds 2 times the number of boys by 4.

B Express algebraically. Use n to represent the unknown number.

11. Four less than a number.
12. Twice the measure of an angle less the measure of its supplement.
13. Five more than twice another number.
14. Six times the measure of an angle less the measure of its complement.
15. One-half the difference between a number and 12.

Write as an equation. Use the variable n only.

16. The sum of three consecutive odd integers is 20 more than the smallest one.
17. The perimeter of a field is 450 meters. Its length is 50 meters more than twice its width.
18. The sum of two numbers is 164. The larger exceeds 3 times the smaller by 26.
19. The sum of three consecutive even integers is 42.
20. The sum of two numbers is 120. Four times the larger divided by twice the smaller is 34.

NUMBER PROBLEMS

A Solve.

1. The number of boys in a physical education class is one less than three times the number of girls. There are 39 students in the class. How many of them are girls?
2. The sum of a number and 6 is 19. Find the number.
3. 42 is equal to a number increased by 14. Find the number.
4. Four times a number equals 96 increased by the number. Find the number.
5. If 20 is added to three times a number, the sum is 101. Find the number.
6. The sum of two numbers is 620. The larger is 3 times the smaller. What are the numbers?
7. The sum of two numbers is 63. One number is 27 larger than the other. What are the numbers?
8. The sum of two numbers is 44. One number exceeds the other by 18. What are the numbers?
9. Four times a number, decreased by 5, equals 25 decreased by 6 times the number. What is the number?
10. One truck can carry 3600 kilograms of freight at a time. A larger truck can carry 5400 kilograms at a time. Together they haul 52 200 kilograms and the smaller truck makes two more trips than the larger truck. How many trips did each truck make?
11. The sum of two numbers is 45. If 3 times the larger is increased by 4 times the smaller, the result is 155. Find the numbers.
12. The sum of two numbers is 1200. One number is 800 less than three times the other. Find the numbers.
13. The sum of two numbers is 19. The sum of their squares is 185. Find the numbers.
14. The denominator of a fraction exceeds its numerator by 3. When each term of the fraction is increased by 7, the new fraction is equal to $\frac{3}{4}$. Find the original fraction.
15. The numerator of a fraction is 2 less than one-half the denominator. The value of the fraction is $\frac{1}{3}$. Find the fraction.
16. If twice the square of a number is decreased by 5 times the number, the difference is 3. Find the number.
17. When the square of a number is subtracted from 8 times the number, the difference is 12. Find the number.
18. The sum of the digits of a two-digit number is 14. The tens digit is 4 larger than the units digit. Find the number.
19. The sum of the digits of a two-digit number is 9. When the digits are reversed, the number is decreased by 27. Find the number.

B

20. The sum of two numbers is 108. When twice their difference is subtracted from the smaller number, the difference is 9. Find the numbers.
21. The sum of two numbers is 40. The difference of five times the larger and four times the smaller exceeds seven times the smaller by 8. Find the numbers.
22. The sum of two numbers is 62. Three times the smaller exceeds twice the larger by one. Find the numbers.
23. The difference of two numbers is 10. When twice the larger number is sub-

tracted from five times the smaller number, the difference is 22. Find the numbers.

24. The difference of two numbers is 2. The sum of their squares is 74. Find the numbers.

25. The number of B grades in a class was 4 times the number of A grades. The number of C grades was 6 times the number of A grades. The number of D grades equaled the number of B grades. The number of F grades equaled the number of A grades. There were 32 grades in all. How many of each kind were there?

26. The difference of the digits of a two-digit number is 6. The number is equal to three more than three times the sum of the digits. The number of units is greater than the number of tens. Find the number.

27. In a two-digit number, the number of units exceeds the number of tens by 5. The number itself exceeds five times the units digit by 4. Find the number.

PERCENT PROBLEMS

A Solve.

1. Mary spends 28% of her monthly salary for rent. Her rent is $350 a month. Find her salary for a month.

2. How much money must a person invest at 4% to produce an annual income of $600?

3. A number decreased by 10% of itself equals 405. Find the number.

4. A number increased by 16% of itself equals 185.6. Find the number.

5. 500% of a number is 75. Find the number.

6. A number less $12\frac{1}{2}$% of the number equals 567. Find the number.

7. On an exam, Laura answered 110 questions out of 125 correctly. Give her score as a percent.

8. A salesperson sold an automobile for $4550, which was 30% more than it cost. Find the cost of the car.

9. When the area of a rectangle is decreased by $8\frac{1}{2}$%, the remaining area is 30.5 square meters. Find the original area.

10. One number is three times another number. The larger number decreased by 15% of the smaller number equals 570. Find the numbers.

11. The population of a city has increased 15% in the last 10 years. The present population is 109 200. What was the population 10 years ago?

B 12. The measure of one of two complementary angles is 25% larger than the measure of the other. How large is each?

13. When wheat is ground into flour, 18% of the wheat becomes a by-product. How much wheat is needed to make 100 kilograms of flour?

14. Dick's mother sold the family's boat for $12 150. This was 10% less than the boat cost. Find the cost of the boat.

15. A shirt sold for $10.08 after discounts of 30% and 20%. Find the original selling price.

16. For how much should a merchant sell sneakers that cost $7.80 a pair to make a profit equal to 35% of the selling price?

17. A stereo receiver sold for $200 after discounts of 20% and 10%. Find the original selling price.

SPORTS PROBLEMS

A Solve.

1. A basketball team won 16 games and lost 9. What percent of its games did it win?
2. A baseball team with a winning average of .622 has won 28 games. How many games has it lost?
3. A baseball player was at bat 480 times and had a batting average of .275. How many hits did the player have?
4. At one hockey game, 2584 tickets were sold. The ticket prices were $1 for students and $1.50 for non-students. The total receipts for the game were $2995. How many tickets of each kind were sold?
5. Find a pitcher's ERA (earned run average) if 42 earned runs (ER) were given up in 198 innings pitched (IP). Use the formula $ERA = \frac{9(ER)}{(IP)}$

B

6. Becky can run 400 meters in 64 seconds. Grace can run the distance in 75 seconds. How many meters head start should Becky, who will run 400 meters, give Grace for the girls to finish the race at about the same time?
7. For a race, a sprinter who ran 5 meters a second, required 7.5 more seconds than the other sprinter, who ran 8 meters a second. Find the distance for the race.
8. The length of a basketball court is 4 meters less than twice its width. Its perimeter is 82 meters. Find the dimensions of the court.
9. Don's batting average is .333. If he gets two hits in his next two times at bat, his new batting average will be .375. Find the number of hits he has. Find the number of times he has been at bat.
10. The winning average for a junior baseball team was .381. If it had won 3 more games, then its winning average would have been .524. Find the number of games it won. Find the number of games it played.

RATIO AND PROPORTION

A Solve.

1. The ratio of two numbers is 2 to 5. Their sum is 42. Find the numbers.
2. The ratio of two numbers is 6:1. Their sum is 105. Find the numbers.
3. On a road map, 5 centimeters represent 75 kilometers. How many kilometers do 14.6 centimeters represent?
4. A ribbon 80 centimeters long is to be cut into two pieces whose lengths will have the ratio 3 to 2. How long should each piece be?
5. Two students are paid $18 for sorting apples. One student worked 3 hours. The other worked 2 hours. How much pay should each receive?

B

6. The regular quarterly dividend on 80 shares of stock is $22. What is the dividend on 150 shares of the stock for one year?
7. A tree casts a shadow 7 meters long. At the same time, a person who is 1.7 meters tall, casts a shadow 0.7 meter long. Find the height of the tree.
8. An electric current is directly proportional to the electromotive force (voltage). When a current is 4 amperes, the electromotive force is 24 volts. Find the current when the electromotive force is 96 volts.

9. A person does 102 joules of work by lifting a certain object to a height of 1.2 meters. The work done in lifting an object is directly proportional to the distance the object moves. How many joules of work does the person do by lifting the object to a height of 1.8 meters?

10. Which is the better buy: 475 mL of detergent at $1.59 or 950 mL of the same detergent at $2.89?

COIN PROBLEMS

A Solve.

1. Paul has two more nickels than dimes. The value of his nickels and dimes is $1.15. How many coins of each kind does he have?

2. Marci has twice as many nickels as dimes, and 5 more quarters than nickels. The value of her coins is $3.35. Find the number of each kind of coin that Marci has.

3. Joey has a total of 26 nickels and dimes in his toy bank. The coins are worth $2.45. How many coins of each kind does he have?

4. A purse contains 120 coins worth $10. The coins are nickels and dimes. How many of each kind are there?

5. Sarah has two more nickels than dimes, and five more quarters than nickels. Her coins are worth $7.85. How many coins of each kind are there?

6. The value of 92 coins is $14. The coins are dimes and quarters. How many are there of each?

7. The value of some nickels and quarters is $1.60. There are one-third as many nickels as quarters. How many nickels are there?

B 8. Karen gave the grocer quarters, dimes, and nickels worth $3.60. There were 3 times as many quarters as nickels, and 20 coins in all. How many coins of each kind were there?

9. Sergio's coins, consisting of nickels and dimes, have a value of $2.15. The number of dimes exceeds 3 times the number of nickels by 4. Find the number of each kind of coin.

10. A newspaper carrier has nickels, dimes, and quarters worth $2.65. The number of dimes exceeds the number of nickels by 1. The number of quarters is equal to the number of nickels decreased by 1. Find the number of each kind of coin.

AGE PROBLEMS

A Solve.

1. Dave is 5 years older than Rona. In 4 years, four times Dave's age will equal 6 times Rona's age. How old is each now?

2. Eric is 18 years old and his grandfather is 66 years old. How many years ago was the grandfather 9 times as old as Eric?

3. Ann is 7 years older than Jane. One year ago she was twice as old as Jane. How old is each now?

4. Frank is 5 times as old as Dick. Two years ago he was 7 times as old as Dick. How old is each now?

5. Marla is 3 times as old as Pam. In 8 years, she will be only twice as old as Pam. How old is each now?

6. Joyce is 5 years older than Joanne. The sum of their ages in six years will be 33 years. How old is each now?

7. Bernardo was 34 years old when his son was born. His age now exceeds 3 times his son's age by 8 years. How old is each?

8. Linda is 10 years old and her father is 3 times as old. In how many years will Linda be half as old as her father?

B

9. The sum of the ages of Valerie and her mother is 68 years. In 15 years, three times Valerie's age, increased by her mother's age then, will equal 168 years. How old is each?

10. The sum of the ages of a mother and her son is 54 years. Four years ago, the mother's age was two years more than 3 times the son's age. How old is each now?

11. Two years ago, Dorothy was 3 times as old as her niece was then. In 5 years, Dorothy will be only 2 times as old as her niece. How old is each?

12. John's age is 3 years more than twice Bill's age. Three years ago, John was 4 times as old as Bill was then. How old is each now?

GEOMETRY PROBLEMS

A Solve. Make a drawing for a problem whenever possible.

1. The perimeter of a rectangular wall in a room is 250 meters. The length of the wall exceeds 3 times the height by 5 meters. Find the area of the rectangular wall.

2. The length of a rectangular plot of land is 2 meters less than 3 times its width. The perimeter of the plot is 60 meters. Find the area of the rectangular plot.

3. The perimeter of a rectangle measures 156 centimeters. When the length is decreased by 13 centimeters and the width is increased by 13 centimeters, the resulting figure is a square. Find the dimensions of the rectangle.

4. A rectangle is four times as long as it is wide. Its perimeter is 300 centimeters. Find the width and length of the rectangle.

5. The perimeter of a triangular table is 284 cm. The length of the second side is $\frac{2}{3}$ the length of the first side. The third side is 16 cm longer than the first side. Find the length of each side of the triangular table.

6. The degree measure of one angle of a triangle exceeds the degree measure of another by 10. The degree measure of the third angle exceeds 3 times that of the smallest by 15. Find the measure of each angle.

7. Six times the degree measure of one of two complementary angles equals three times the degree measure of the other. Find the measure of each angle.

8. Two angles are supplementary. When 6 times the degree measure of the smaller is subtracted from 4 times the degree measure of the larger, the difference is 160. Find the measure of each angle.

9. The degree measure of the supplement of an angle is five times the degree measure of its complement. Find the measure of the angle.

10. The degree measure of the supplement of an angle is 12 larger than 5 times the degree measure of its complement. Find the measure of the angle.

11. A circle has a 20-centimeter radius. Find its circumference.

12. Find the radius of a circle whose circumference is 157 centimeters.

13. Find the length of an altitude of an equilateral triangle whose sides are each 12 centimeters long.

14. A tree 15 meters high casts a shadow 12 meters long at the same time that another tree casts a shadow 8 meters long. How high is the second tree?

B 15. The length of a rectangular garden exceeds twice its width by 8 meters. The area of the garden is 128 m^2 more than twice that of a square garden the length of whose side is the width of the rectangle. What are the dimensions of the rectangular garden?

16. How large a rectangular field, whose length is to exceed twice its width by 53 meters, can be enclosed by a one-kilometer fence?

17. The degree measure of one angle of a triangle exceeds the degree measure of another by 6. The sum of the degree measures of the two angles exceeds that of the third angle by 20. Find the measure of each angle.

18. In a triangle, the second angle is 10° larger than the first. The third angle is 5° smaller than 3 times the degree measure of the first. Find the measure of each angle.

19. The degree measure of one of two complementary angles exceeds the square of the degree measure of the other by 18. Find the measure of each angle.

20. The perimeter of a right triangle is 270 centimeters. The length of the hypotenuse is 117 centimeters. Find the length of each leg.

21. The lengths of the sides of a triangular emblem are 12, 13, and 15 centimeters. The longest side of a similar emblem is 105 centimeters. Find the lengths of the other sides.

MOTION PROBLEMS

A Solve.

1. Scott drives 80 kilometers an hour and Roberto drives 64 kilometers an hour starting at the same place but traveling in opposite directions. Scott starts 2 hours before Roberto. How many hours has Roberto been traveling when they are 376 kilometers apart?

2. Jane and Darcy are 228 kilometers apart. To meet, Jane drives 64 kilometers per hour and Darcy drives 56 kilometers an hour. Jane is delayed in a traffic jam for 45 minutes. How soon will they meet?

3. An hour after John left on a motorbike trip, his friend Jim started after him. John traveled 16 kilometers an hour. Jim traveled 22 kilometers an hour. How long did it take Jim to catch up with John?

4. Ellen travels 64 kilometers per hour. She leaves Philadelphia for Harrisburg at 8 o'clock. Gale leaves Harrisburg for Philadelphia at 9 o'clock and travels 80 kilometers per hour. The distance between the two cities is 160 kilometers. How long will Gale travel before meeting Ellen?

5. Two cross-country skiers started towards each other at the same time from places 24 kilometers apart. They met in $1\frac{2}{3}$ hours. One traveled twice as fast as the other. At what rates did they travel?

6. Two airplanes are traveling in opposite directions at the rates of 490 and 510 kilometers an hour. They started at the same time from the same place. How soon after the start will they be 1500 kilometers apart?

B

7. Two bicyclists start at the same time from towns 48 kilometers apart. They meet in $2\frac{1}{7}$ hours. The rate of one was 3.2 kilometers per hour less than the rate of the other. What was the rate of each?

8. A truck driver makes a daily run of 440 kilometers. One day the driver is $\frac{1}{2}$ hour late in starting and drives 8 kilometers per hour faster than usual to arrive on time. What is the usual rate of the truck?

9. An airplane can go 930 kilometers against the wind in the same time that it can go 999 kilometers with the wind. The rate of the wind is 15 kilometers an hour. What is the rate of the airplane in still air?

10. An automobile makes a trip of 530 km in 7 hours and 15 minutes. During the trip, it travels 50 km in stop-and-go traffic through towns. The rest is traveled non-stop on a highway. The average rate through the towns is half the rate on the highway. What is the average rate through the towns?

WORK PROBLEMS

A Solve.

1. Bruce can paint a house in 8 days and Rod can do it in 6 days. If they work together, how many days are needed?

2. One pipe can fill a tank in 12 hours and a smaller pipe can fill the tank in 15 hours. If both pipes are used, how many hours are needed to fill the tank?

3. Frank can hoe the garden in 7 hours and Bill can hoe it in 9 hours. If both work, how many hours are needed to hoe the garden?

4. One printing press can produce 4000 evening papers in an hour. A second press can produce 3000 papers in an hour. After the first press has been printing for $1\frac{1}{2}$ hours, it must be stopped for repairs. How much longer must the second press run to complete the daily edition of 15 000 papers?

5. Martha can do a piece of work in 5 days, Debby can do it in 7 days, and Carla can do it in 10 days. How long will it take them to do the work when working together?

B

6. Sally can wash the car in 15 minutes and Keith can wash it in 20 minutes. Suppose Sally works 5 minutes alone on the job and then Keith helps her. How long does Keith work?

7. Two backhoes working together can excavate a building foundation in 20 hours. If one backhoe can do the work $\frac{2}{3}$ as fast as the other, how long would it take each backhoe to do the work alone?

8. A construction crew can place a kilometer of oil pipe in 4 days. With the help of a second crew, the work can be done in $2\frac{1}{2}$ days. How long would it take the second crew to place a kilometer of oil pipe working alone?

MIXTURE PROBLEMS

A Solve.

1. Orange pekoe tea costs $5.20 a kilogram and green tea costs $4.00 a kilogram. How many kilograms of each kind should be used to make a mixture of 100 kilograms that can be sold for $4.72 a kilogram?

2. How many kilograms of nuts worth $3.80 a kilogram must be mixed with

60 kilograms of nuts worth $4.60 a kilogram to make a mixture worth $4.10 a kilogram?

3. How many kilograms of one kind of coffee worth $5.50 a kilogram and another kind worth $5.00 a kilogram should be used to make a 125-kilogram mixture that can be sold for $5.18 a kilogram?

4. How much milk testing 5% butterfat should be used with milk testing 25% butterfat to make 800 liters of milk testing 12% butterfat?

B **5.** How much water must be added to a liter of 90% alcohol solution to make a mixture that is 50% alcohol?

6. How much water must be added to 3 liters of acid that is 95% pure acid to make a mixture that is 25% acid?

7. A radiator contains 7.5 liters of a mixture of alcohol and water. The mixture is 70% alcohol. How much of the mixture must be drawn off and replaced by pure alcohol to get a mixture containing 80% alcohol?

8. A solution of 40 kilograms of salt and water is 6% salt. How much water must be evaporated so that the solution will be 15% salt?

BUSINESS AND INVESTMENT PROBLEMS

A Use these formulas to help you solve the business problems.

$$S = C + O + P$$

(Selling Price = Cost + Overhead + Profit)

$$M = O + P$$

(Margin = Overhead + Profit)

$$S = C + M$$

(Selling Price = Cost + Margin)

1. A suit is purchased by a retailer for $75. At what price must the retailer sell the suit so the margin will be 30% of the selling price?

2. At a 40%-discount sale, a sweater sold for $10.80. Find the original selling price.

3. A dealer paid $208 for a 35-mm camera. The overhead is 20% of the selling price and the profit is 15% of the selling price. At what price should the camera be sold?

4. A dealer's margin is to be 30% of the cost of an item. At what cost should an item be purchased so that it may be sold for $25?

5. Doris invested $30 000, part at 7% and the remainder at 6%. Her income from both investments was $2050. How much did she invest at each rate?

6. $10 000 is invested, part at 6% and the remainder at 5%. The yearly income from both investments is $566. Find the amount of each investment.

7. Part of $7000 was invested at 6% and the other part at 5%. The 6% investment yielded $90 more than the other investment. What was the amount of each investment.

8. A bank lends some money at 14% and an equal amount at 11%. The income from the 14% loan is $81 more than the income from the 11% loan. How much is loaned at each rate?

9. Sarah invested some money at 6%, and $500 more than this amount at 8%. The total income from these investments was $96.56. How much did Sarah invest at each rate?

B

10. The manager of a shoe store wishes to sell all goods at 35% more than cost. At what price must sandals be purchased by the lot so that the lot may be sold for $344.25?

11. A family bought a house for $42 000 and later sold it for $54 000. The expense for selling the house was $320. The profit was what percent of the cost?

12. From the data in Exercise 11, the profit was what percent of the selling price?

13. How much can a person afford to pay for eight $1000 7% bonds so that the annual rate of return on the investment will be $6\frac{1}{2}$%?

14. $2000 is invested at 8%, $3000 at 6%, and $1200 at 7%. What is the annual rate of interest on the three investments?

15. Howard has $4500 invested at 6% and a second amount invested at 7%. The income from the second investment exceeds that from the first by $80. Find the amount of the second investment.

16. Betty has some money invested at 5%, and $1500 more than the first amount, invested at 6%. Her total income from these investments is $200. How much has she invested at each rate?

VARIATION PROBLEMS

A Solve.

1. How do C and d vary in $C = \pi d$?

2. How do I and R vary in $I = \frac{E}{R}$?

3. How do E and R vary in $I = \frac{E}{R}$?

4. $S = vt - \frac{1}{2}gt^2$. Does S vary directly as t? Does it vary directly as the square of t?

5. A formula for the volume of a sphere is $V = \frac{\pi}{6}d^3$. How does V vary with respect to d?

6. Suppose c varies directly as n, and $c = 45$ when $n = 25$. Find c when $n = 36$.

7. Suppose x varies inversely as y, and $x = \frac{5}{3}$ when y equals 15. Find x when $y = \frac{5}{7}$.

8. The distance traveled at 80 kilometers per hour varies directly with the time spent traveling at that rate. Find the distance when the time is $2\frac{3}{4}$ hours.

B

9. Write a formula that relates x and y to match the entries in this table.

x	1	5	9	13	17
y	0	2	4	6	8

10. Suppose a varies inversely with b. How does a change when b is doubled?

11. Suppose $x + 1$ varies inversely with y, and $x = 3$ when $y = -5$. Find y when $x = 5$.

12. The formula $I = \frac{E}{R}$ shows the relationship between the amount of electric current, I, the electromotive force (voltage), E, and the resistance, R. For this formula, how do I and R vary? How do E and R vary?

APPENDIX 1
Sets

A **set** is a collection of elements. An **element** of a set is any member of the set. (Elements of a set need not be numbers.) We may use the region inside a closed curve to represent a set. Such a diagram is called a **Venn diagram**.

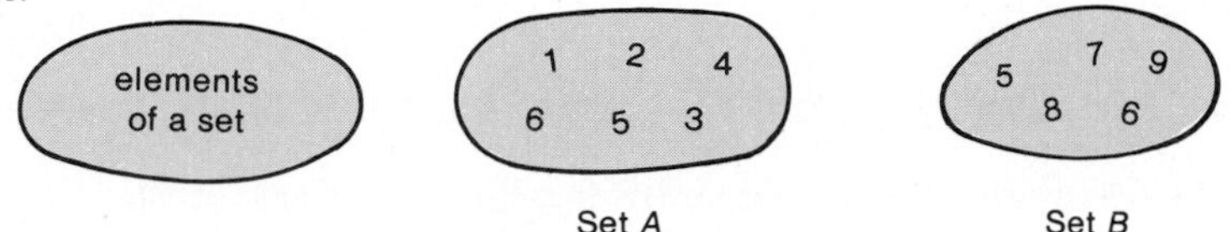

Set A Set B

A set also may be given in *roster notation,* $A = \{1, 2, 3, 4, 5, 6\}$. Given two sets, there are two operations that may be used to combine the sets. These operations are called *union* and *intersection*.

> The **union** of two sets is a set that consists of all elements belonging to at least one of the two sets. The union of two sets A and B is represented by $A \cup B$.

Read "A union B."

This definition may be extended to the "union of any number of sets."

Roster form | Venn form | Union

$A = \{1, 2, 3, 4, 5, 6\}$

$B = \{5, 6, 7, 8, 9\}$

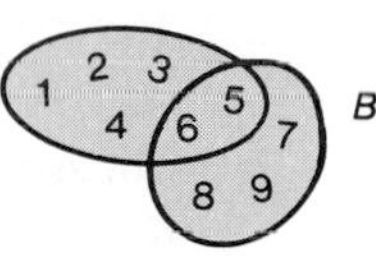

$A \cup B = \{1, 2, 3, 4, 5, 6, 7, 8, 9\}$

Two sets are **disjoint** when they have no common elements.

$C = \{-4, 0, 3\}$

$D = \{-1, 2, 7\}$

$C \cup D = \{-4, -1, 0, 2, 3, 7\}$

> The **intersection** of two sets is a set that consists of all elements common to the sets. The intersection of two sets A and B is represented by $A \cap B$.

Read "A intersection B."

This definition may be extended to the "intersection of any number of sets."

Roster form | Venn form | Intersection

$A = \{1, 2, 3, 4, 5, 6\}$

$B = \{5, 6, 7, 8, 9\}$

$A \cap B = \{5, 6\}$

The intersection of disjoint sets is the **empty set,** { }, or Ø. The empty set often is called the **null set**.

Roster form	Venn form	Intersection
$C = \{-4, 0, 3\}$	C: 3, 0, −4; D: −1, 7, 2	$C \cap D = \{\ \}$, or
$D = \{-1, 2, 7\}$		$C \cap D = \varnothing$

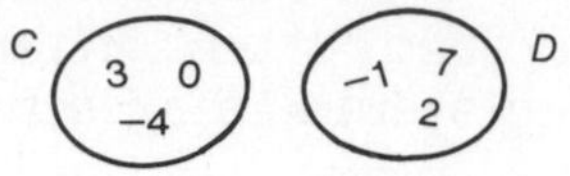

When all the elements of set A also are elements of set B, we call set A a **subset** of set B.

$E = \{6, 12\}$	E: 6, 12; F: 3, 15, 9	$E \cap F = \{6, 12\}$, or
$F = \{3, 6, 9, 12, 15\}$		$E \cap F = E$

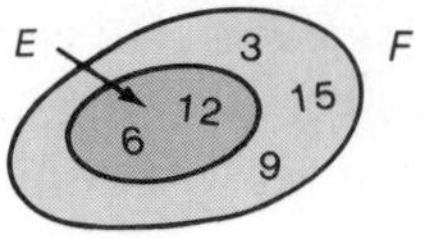

Every set is a subset of itself.

When we consider more than two sets, many patterns for using set operations are possible.

Roster form	Venn form	Typical Expressions
$G = \{1, 2, 3\}$	G: 1, 3, 2; H: 5, 4; J: 6	$(G \cup H) \cap J = \{2, 4\}$
$H = \{2, 3, 4, 5\}$		$G \cup (H \cap J) = \{1, 2, 3, 4\}$
$J = \{2, 4, 6\}$		

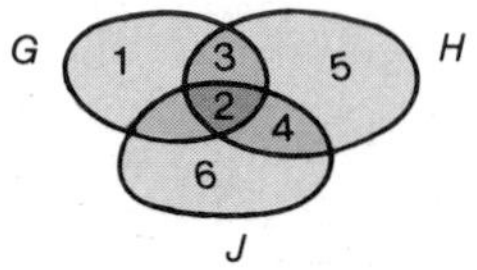

We can see that the commutative and associative properties are properties of operations with sets.

Commutative	Associative
$G \cup H = H \cup G$	$G \cup (H \cup J) = (G \cup H) \cup J = \{1, 2, 3, 4, 5, 6\}$
$G \cap H = H \cap G$	$G \cap (H \cap J) = (G \cap H) \cap J = \{2\}$

For sets, there are two distributive properties.

$$G \cup (H \cap J) = (G \cup H) \cap (G \cup J) = \{1, 2, 3, 4\}$$

$$G \cap (H \cup J) = (G \cap H) \cup (G \cap J) = \{2, 3\}$$

EXERCISES

1. Name the set that is the union of the set consisting of the element zero with the set consisting of the counting numbers.
2. Name the set that is the union of the set of integers with the set of rational numbers.
3. Describe the union of a given set with any subset of the given set.
4. Name the set that is the intersection of the set of integers with the set of even integers.
5. Name the set that is the intersection of the set of integers with the set of rational numbers.
6. Describe the set of points that is the intersection of two perpendicular lines.
7. Describe the set that is the intersection of two parallel lines.
8. Describe the intersection of a given set with any subset of the given set.
9. Give a meaning for the diagram.

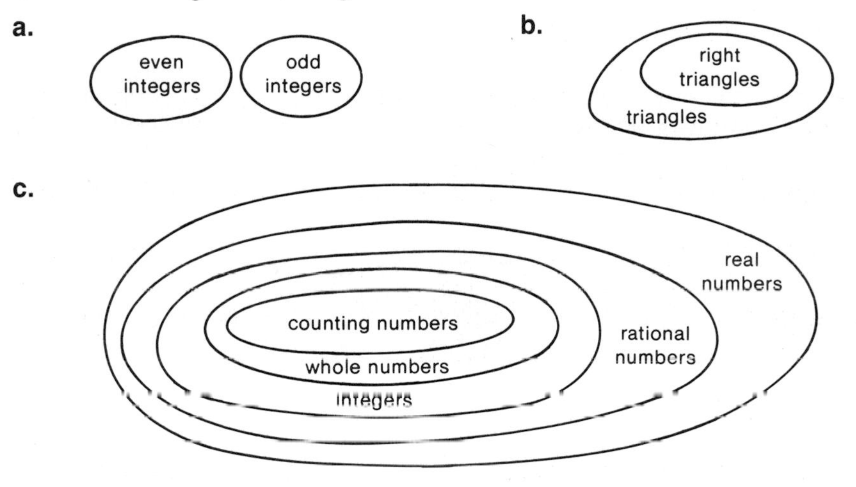

10. Use the diagram in Exercise 9c. Give an example of a number for each ring.
11. Without knowing a definition of complex numbers, what can you say about them by using this diagram?

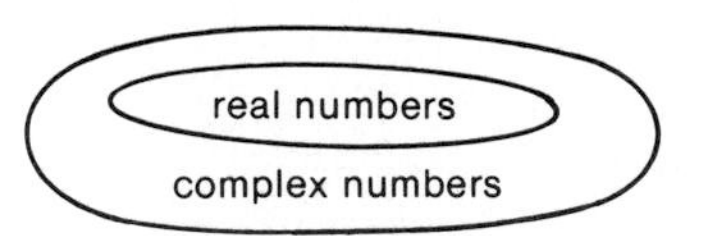

12. Make a Venn diagram that combines the information in the diagram for Exercise 9c with that in the diagram for Exercise 11.

APPENDIX 2
Scientific Notation

Reading and Writing Scientific Notation

A number given in scientific notation is expressed as the product of a factor between 0 and 10 and a factor that is an integral power of 10.

Standard form	Scientific notation
0.049	4.9×10^{-2}
7	7×10^{0}
70	7×10^{1}, or 7×10
1 234 000	1.234×10^{6}

To convert a number given in scientific notation to standard form, use the rules for multiplying by powers of 10.

EXAMPLE 1 Convert to standard form:

a. 1.776×10^{3} **b.** 4.06×10^{-4}

SOLUTION **a.** Move the decimal point 3 places to the right

$1.776 \times 10^{3} = 1.776.$
$= 1776$

b. Move the decimal point 4 places to the left.

$4.06 \times 10^{-4} = .0004.06$
$= 0.000406$

To convert a number from standard form to scientific notation, use the digits in the number to form a factor between 1 and 10. For the second factor, write 10 with a positive (negative) exponent that shows how many places to the right (left) the decimal point must be moved to give the number in standard form.

EXAMPLE 2 Convert to scientific notation:

a. 79 280.1 **b.** 0.00542

Ⓜ SOLUTION **a.** 7.92801×10^{4} **b.** 5.42×10^{-3}

Scientific models of electronic calculators usually give large and small numbers in exponential form (E-form).

Calculator display	Scientific notation	Standard form
1.51294 E−02 1.51294 E−2 1.51294 −2	1.51294×10^{-2}	0.0151294
1.624 E 10 1.624 10	1.624×10^{10}	16 240 000 00

Also, computer programming languages such as BASIC may disp large and small numbers in exponential form.

BASIC statement	PRINT .ØØ123	PRINT 93ØØØØØØØØ
Computer response	1.23 E−3	9.3E9

Computing with Numbers in Scientific Notation

To add or subtract numbers given in scientific notation, all addends must be given using the same power of 10.

EXAMPLE 3 Simplify. Use scientific notation.

$2.51 \times 10^3 + 1.05 \times 10^0 - 3.15 \times 10^2$

(M) SOLUTION 1 Write all addends using 10^3.

$$2.51 \times 10^3 + 0.00105 \times 10^3 - 0.315 \times 10^3$$
$$= (2.51 + 0.00105 - 0.315) \times 10^3$$
$$= 2.19605 \times 10^3$$

(M) SOLUTION 2 Write all addends using 10^2.

$$25.1 \times 10^2 + 0.0105 \times 10^2 - 3.15 \times 10^2$$
$$= (25.1 + 0.0105 - 3.15) \times 10^2$$
$$= 21.9605 \times 10^2, \text{ or } 2.19605 \times 10^3$$

(M) SOLUTION 3 Write all addends using 10^0.

$$2510 \times 10^0 + 1.05 \times 10^0 - 315 \times 10^0$$
$$= (2510 + 1.05 - 315) \times 10^0$$
$$= 2196.05, \text{ or } 2.19605 \times 10^3$$

Sometimes we wish to give a sum using a particular power of 10, such as 10^{-3}.

(M) SOLUTION 4 Write all addends using 10^{-3}.

$$2\,510\,000 \times 10^{-3} + 1\,050 \times 10^{-3} - 315\,000 \times 10^{-3}$$
$$= (2\,510\,000 + 1\,050 - 315\,000) \times 10$$
$$= 2\,196\,050 \times 10^{-3}$$

APPENDIX 3
Approximations And Precision

Approximations for Measurements

To help solve many problems, it is necessary to understand approximation and precision of measurement. Also, you should become familiar with techniques for computing with numbers that are approximations.

A number that gives the *count* of a finite set of items always is exact. A number that gives a *recorded measurement* for a quantity always is an approximation.

Numbers that give a count	Numbers used to give a recorded measurement
12 chairs	2 cm
1 dozen	35°
	4.5 seconds

The study of measurement is called *metrology*.

A measurement always is an approximation. How good the approximation is depends upon the *precision* (refinement) of the measurement. The precision of the measurement depends upon the unit of measurement available on the measuring instrument.

EXAMPLE 1 Approximate the measure of the line segment.

a. Use 1 cm for the scale unit.

b. Use 0.1 cm for the scale unit.

c. Use 1 mm for the scale unit.

SOLUTION **a.** Use a ruler with scale markings at 1-centimeter intervals only.

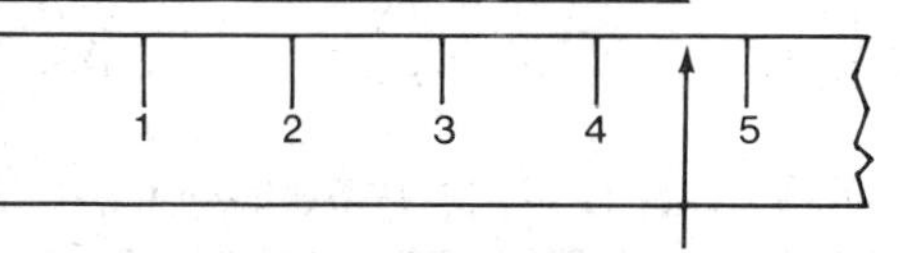

The measurement is 5 cm.

b. Use a ruler with scale markings at 1-millimeter intervals.

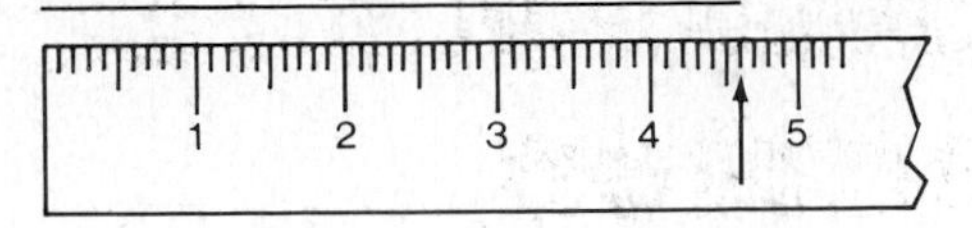

The measurement is 4.6 cm.

c. The measurement is 46 mm.

EXAMPLE 2 Give the measurement to the nearest one-tenth of a centimeter for the line segments. The line segments have one endpoint, *A*, at 0 and other endpoints at *B*, *C*, *D*, *E*, and *F*.

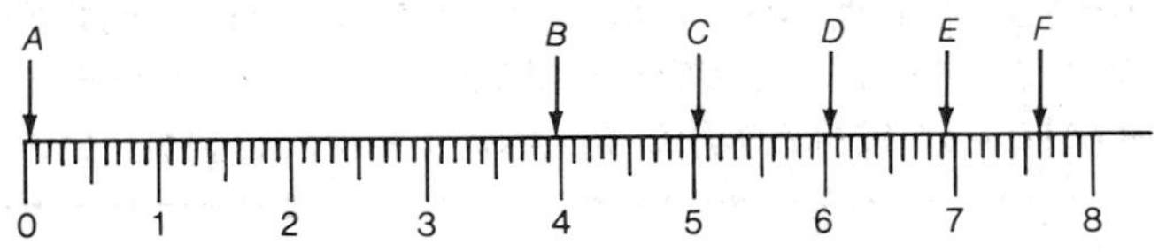

SOLUTION *AB* 4.0 cm; *AC* 5.0 cm; *AD* 6.1 cm; *AE* 6.9 cm; *AF* 7.6 cm.

The length of the vertical scale markings may contain clues for the use of the scale. Marks of the same length indicate the same unit of measurement.

0.5 cm marks

0.1 cm marks

1 cm marks

Often, it is possible to read a scale to one-half of the scale unit.

EXAMPLE 3 Use maximum precision. Give the measurements for the line segments having one endpoint, *A*, at 0 and other endpoints at *B*, *C*, *D*, *E*, *F*, *G*, *H*, *I*, and *J*.

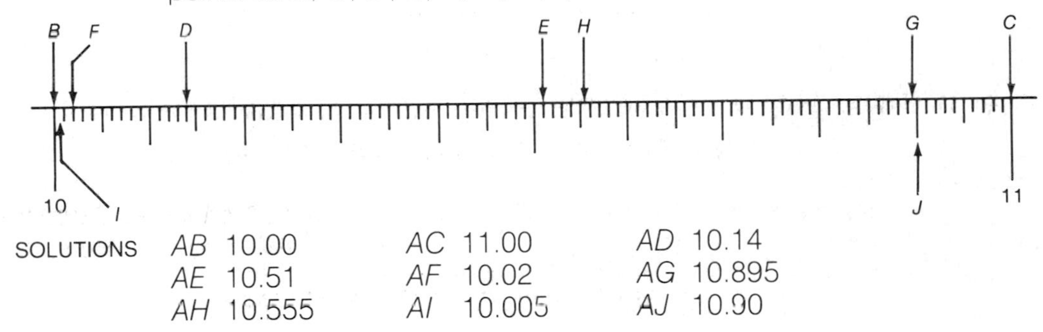

SOLUTIONS

AB 10.00	*AC* 11.00	*AD* 10.14
AE 10.51	*AF* 10.02	*AG* 10.895
AH 10.555	*AI* 10.005	*AJ* 10.90

In general, the smaller the unit of measurement, the greater is the precision with which measurements may be made.

Significant Digits in Measurement

A measurement recorded as 9 cm indicates that a length has been measured to the nearest centimeter. Such a measurement also indicates that the length is somewhere between 8.5 cm and 9.5 cm.

In this chart, refer to the middle column first, then to the side columns.

Lower limit	Recorded measurement	Upper limit
8.5 cm	9 cm	9.5 cm
8.95 cm	9.0 cm	9.05 cm
9.995 cm	10.00 cm	10.005 cm

In each recorded measurement in the chart above, all the digits are *significant* because they have real meaning. In general, all the digits in a recorded measurement are significant except zero, which may or may not be significant.

Zero is significant	Zero is not significant	Zero may be significant
2.0 mm	0.3 m	10 cm
3.00 cm	0.05 km	3000 km
70.04 cm		
1003.40 km		

We may use scientific notation to show when zeroes are significant.

Recorded measurement	Unit of measure	Scientific notation
1200 km	100 km	1.2×10^3 km
1200 km	10 km	1.20×10^3 km
1200 km	1 km	1.200×10^3 km

Although a measurement always is an approximation, all approximations are not necessarily measurements. We may use an approximation when it is not necessary to use all of the decimal places in a number.

Number	Infinite decimal expression	Approximations
$\frac{1}{3}$	$0.333 \cdots$	0.3, 0.33, 0.333, ...
$\frac{2}{3}$	$0.666 \cdots$	0.7, 0.67, 0.667, ...
π	$3.1415 \cdots$	3.14, 3.1416, 3.14159, ...
$\sqrt{2}$	$1.4142135 \cdots$	1.4, 1.414, 1.414214, ...

Rounding is a technique for writing approximations using a given number of significant digits or a given number of decimal places.

Number	Rounded to	Gives
12.060	4 significant digits	12.06
	3 significant digits	12.1
	2 significant digits	12
	1 significant digit	10
	1 decimal place	12.1
12.050	3 significant digits	12.1
	2 decimal places	12.05
	1 decimal place	12.1
12.0499	4 significant digits	12.05
	3 significant digits	12.0
	3 decimal places	12.050

Computing with Approximations

When we compute with approximations, the result also is an approximation. There are various rules for computing with approximations. In this book we follow rules that are easy to apply yet are sufficiently accurate.

Operation with approximations	Rule
$+$ $-$	Give the sum (difference) to the same number of *decimal places* as in the approximation having the least number of *decimal places*.
$\times$ $\div$	Give the product (quotient) to the same number of *significant digits* as in the approximation having the least number of *significant digits*.

A chain can be no stronger than its weakest link.

The following table shows the effect of using the rules.

Indicated computation	Result of computation
$3 + 4.03 + 5.7$	13
$1.305 \text{ cm} \times 2.1 \text{ cm}$	2.7 cm^2

When we use an electronic calculator or a computer for making computations with approximate numbers, we must be careful to give results that follow the rules.

Indicated computation with approximations	Result shown in calculator or computer display	Result using the rules
$1.0 + 2.00$	3	3.0
$(0.125)(40.0)$	5	5.00
$(0.2)(0.123)$	.0246	0.02
$623\,415 \div 3.14$	198539.8	199 000

When a constant coefficient in a formula is a number that gives a count, it is not affected by the rules for computing with approximations.

Coefficients are numbers that give a count	Coefficients are approximations
$P = 4s$	$A = 3.14r^2$
$s = \frac{1}{2}at^2$	$s = 4.9t^2$

We may estimate results by rounding off measurements to one significant digit.

$P = 4s \doteq 4(6) \doteq 24$ $\quad A = s^2 \doteq (6)^2 \doteq 36$

EXAMPLE 4 The recorded measurement for the side of a square is 6.43 cm. Find the perimeter and area of the square.

SOLUTION

$$P = 4s \doteq 4(6.43) \doteq 25.72 \text{ cm}$$

$$A = s^2 \doteq (6.43)^2 \doteq 41.3 \text{ cm}^2$$

$P = 2l + 2w \doteq 2(6) + 2(5) \doteq 12 + 10 \doteq 22$

EXAMPLE 5 The width and length of a room are recorded as 4.51 m and 5.8 m. Find the perimeter of the room.

SOLUTION

$$P = 2l + 2w \doteq 2(5.8) + 2(4.51) \doteq 11.6 + 9.02 \doteq 20.6 \text{ m}$$

Often it is necessary to use an approximation for π in computations with recorded measurements.

EXAMPLE 6 Find the volume of a sphere with measured radius 5.375 cm.

SOLUTION $V = \frac{4}{3}\pi r^3$

$\doteq \frac{4}{3}(3.142)(5.375)^3$

$\doteq 650.5 \text{ cm}^3$

$V = \frac{4}{3}\pi r^2$

$\doteq \frac{4}{3}(3)(5)^3$

$\doteq 4(125)$

$\doteq 500$

Here we use π to the same number of significant digits as given in the radius.

EXERCISES

A Give the measurements for the line segments having one endpoint, A, at 0 and other endpoints at B, C, D, F, G, H, I, and J.

G F C B H D I J

E_1 E_2

Note that this scale permits reading three significant digits.

1. for $E_1 = 1$, $E_2 = 2$ **2.** for $E_1 = 0.1$, $E_2 = 0.2$

Give the upper and lower limits for the recorded measurement.

3. 4.56 **4.** 8.30 **5.** 10 **6.** 7.00×10^3

Give the number of significant digits in the measurement.

7. 0.003 **8.** 10.003 **9.** 300.0 **10.** 300

Round off the number to

a. 3 significant digits. **b.** 3 decimal places. **c.** 2 significant digits.
d. 2 decimal places. **e.** 1 significant digit. **f.** 1 decimal place.

11. 1.0501 **12.** 200.49999

Use the table of square roots, page 454. Approximate to 3 significant digits.

13. $\sqrt{2}$ **14.** $\sqrt{20}$ **15.** $\sqrt{200}$ **16.** $\sqrt{600}$

Simplify. Assume that all given numbers are approximations. Give your result in the correct number of significant digits.

17. $(41.88)(0.025)$ **18.** $\frac{19.692}{547}$ **19.** $\frac{(4215.8)(0.15)}{316.185}$

20. $\frac{(1.25)(0.002)(4.4)(244.5)}{(1100)(0.00815)}$ **21.** $2(2.5 \times 10^2)^2$ **22.** $((3 \times 1.5)^2 \times 10)^3$

Solve.

23. The radius of a circular area watered by a field irrigation sprinkler measures 8.6 meters. Find the area that is watered.

24. Approximate the volume in cubic centimeters of a typical atom with diameter 10^{-8} cm.

The acceleration due to the earth's gravity is about 9.78 m/s^2.

Use $s = \frac{1}{2}at^2$. Compute free-fall distance, s, for the given elapsed time.

25. 0 to 4.67×10^{-1} seconds

26. 0 to 3.4×10^{-2} seconds

B Round the number to the nearest power of 10. The result is called the *order of magnitude* of the approximation.

27. 4.67×10^2

28. 6.023×10^{23}

29. 5.1×10^{-1}

30. 4.9×10^{-2}

31. A person is 1.75 meters tall. Give the person's height as an order of magnitude in

a. meters. **b.** centimeters. **c.** kilometers **d.** light-years.

32. Give the height in kilometers of a person 1.9 meters tall to

a. 3 decimal places. **b.** 2 significant digits. **c.** 3 significant digits.

33. Compute the volume in cubic centimeters of one sheet of paper from a ream (500 sheets) measuring 28 cm × 21.5 cm × 5.0 cm.

34. Design a scale that permits 3 decimal place precision for linear measurements.

C **35.** Use the diagram given for Exercise 1. Give the indicated approximations for $E_1 = 0$, $E_2 = 0.1$.

36. Measurements taken on a photograph made using a light that flashes at the rate 2500/s show that a projectile moved 0.1 m between flashes. Find the speed of the projectile in kilometers per hour.

APPENDIX 4
Unit Analysis and Conversion Factors

Many people, particularly those with some background in science, have found that it is useful to include an analysis of units of measure as an aid to solving problems. By analyzing the units of the constants and variables in an expression or equation we can determine three things:

1. the unit associated with the expression,
2. whether both members of an equation have the same units, and
3. something about the physical nature of an expression.
   $\left(\text{For example, from } \frac{\text{distance unit}}{\text{time unit}}, \text{ we may infer a rate.}\right)$

For each type of use, analysis of units can reveal errors in procedure. When the unit resulting from the analysis of an expression does not conform to the unit being sought, one can correctly conclude that an error has been made.

However, like so many techniques of checking one's work, analysis of units does not guarantee the correctness of a result. Even though analysis shows that a unit for an expression is the desired unit, the correctness of any numerical computations is another matter and may require further checking.

The following examples show how unit analysis may be used.

EXAMPLE 1 Find the time needed to travel 750 kilometers at a rate of 85 km/h.

SOLUTION This is a uniform rate problem.

1. Write the appropriate formula. $d = rt$
2. Solve the formula for the desired variable. $t = \frac{d}{r}$
3. Replace the appropriate variable(s) by the given value(s) *with their units of measure.* $t = \frac{750 \text{ km}}{85 \text{ km/h}}$
4. Work out the "arithmetic" of the units. $\frac{\text{km}}{\text{km/h}} = \text{km} \cdot \frac{\text{h}}{\text{km}} = \text{h}$
5. Verify that the unit found for the result conforms to a unit being sought. Time may be given in hour units. ✓
6. Carry out the numerical computations. $t \doteq 8.8$
7. State a conclusion. The time needed to travel 750 km at 85 km/h is about 8.8 h.

Unit Analysis and Conversion Factors

It is often necessary to change from one unit of measure to another. To do this, we multiply the given number of units by a fraction whose terms involve units that cancel undesired units and also introduce desired units. Such a fraction is called a *conversion factor*. It may be necessary to use more than one conversion factor to achieve a desired unit of measure.

EXAMPLE 2 Find the number of minutes elapsed in 1984 years.

SOLUTION Use t for the elapsed time in minutes.

$$t \doteq (1984 \cancel{\text{years}})\left(365 \frac{\cancel{\text{d}}}{\cancel{\text{year}}}\right)\left(24 \frac{\cancel{\text{h}}}{\cancel{\text{d}}}\right)\left(60 \frac{\text{min}}{\cancel{\text{h}}}\right)$$

$$t \doteq 1\,042\,790\,400, \text{ or about } 1.04 \times 10^9$$

There are about 1.04×10^9 minutes in 1984 years.

Note that the result is only slightly more than *one billion*.

EXAMPLE 3 A rocket booster travels 15 000 km/h. Find the time in seconds for the booster to travel one kilometer.

SOLUTION

$$d = rt$$

$$t = \frac{d}{r}$$

$$t = \frac{1 \cancel{\text{km}}}{15\,000 \frac{\cancel{\text{km}}}{\cancel{\text{h}}}\left(\frac{1 \cancel{\text{h}}}{60 \cancel{\text{min}}}\right)\left(\frac{1 \cancel{\text{min}}}{60 \text{ s}}\right)}$$

$$t = \frac{(60)(60)}{15\,000}$$

$$t = \frac{6}{25}$$

$$t = 0.24$$

The booster travels 1 km in 0.24 s.

A single conversion factor may be used: $\frac{1 \text{ h}}{3600 \text{ s}}$

EXAMPLE 4 The average thickness of sedimentary rock in the earth's crust is about 0.74 km. Assuming that 40 mm of rock are formed at a *uniform rate* ($d = rt$) every 50 000 years, how long did it take to form the sedimentary rock?

SOLUTION The completion of the solution is left for the student. The result is approximately 9.25×10^8 years, or 925 million years.

There are no exercises for this topic. Beginning with Section 1-7 in the text, unit derivations are given with all symbol assignments involving expressions. Unit equations are given with all appropriate worked examples. Students are encouraged to use unit analysis in their work.

Glossary

abscissa The first number in the ordered pair for a point in the coordinate plane.

absolute value The absolute value of a positive number or zero is the number itself. The absolute value of a negative number is its opposite.

acute angle An angle whose measure in degrees is greater than 0 and less than 90.

addend Any one of two or more numbers that are added.

Addition Property of Equality If a, b, and c are expressions for real numbers and $a = b$, then $a + c = b + c$.

Addition Property of Inequality If a, b, and c are expressions for real numbers and $a > b$, then $a + c > b + c$.

additive identity For any real number a, $a + 0 = a$. 0 is the additive identity.

additive inverse A number and its opposite are additive inverses of each other. The sum of a number and its additive inverse is zero.

adjacent side (to an angle) In a triangle, a side that is part of the angle.

angle A figure formed by two rays having a common endpoint.

Associative Property of Addition For all real numbers, a, b, and c, $(a + b) + c = a + (b + c)$.

Associative Property of Multiplication For all real numbers a, b, and c, $(a \cdot b) \cdot c = a \cdot (b \cdot c)$.

average The sum of the numbers in a set divided by the number of elements in the set.

base of a power One of the equal factors used to give the power.

binomial A binomial is a polynomial having two terms.

circumference Distance around a circle.

coefficient Any factor of a product is the coefficient of the other factor or factors.

common factor A factor that is common to all the terms in an expression.

Commutative Property of Addition For all real numbers a and b, $a + b = b + a$.

Commutative Property of Multiplication For all real numbers a and b, $a \cdot b = b \cdot a$.

Glossary

complementary angles Two angles which have 90 as the sum of their degree measures.

completing the square Forming a perfect square trinomial when two of its terms are given.

complex fraction A fraction that has a fraction in either the numerator or denominator or both.

conditional equation A number sentence which may be true for some, but not all, replacements for its variable(s).

consecutive even integers Numbers obtained by counting by two from any even integer.

consecutive integers Numbers obtained by counting by one from any integer.

consecutive odd integers Numbers obtained by counting by two from any odd integer.

coordinate(s) of a point The real number that corresponds to the point in the number line. The two real numbers that correspond to the point in the coordinate plane.

coordinate plane A plane for which a correspondence has been established between the points of the plane and ordered pairs of real numbers. The correspondence is established by referring to two perpendicular number lines in the plane.

cosine of an angle The ratio $\frac{\text{length of the leg adjacent to the angle}}{\text{length of the hypotenuse}}$, when the angle is an acute angle of a right triangle.

cross products For $\frac{a}{b}$ and $\frac{c}{d}$, $a \cdot d$ and $b \cdot c$ are the cross products.

degree A unit used for measuring angles.

degree of a polynomial The degree of the highest-degree term in the polynomial.

degree of a term The sum of the exponents of the variables in the term.

direct variation A relationship between two variables x and y that may be described by an equation of the form $y = kx$ in which k is a non-zero constant.

Distributive Property of Multiplication over Addition For real numbers a, b, and c, $a(b + c) = a \cdot b + a \cdot c$ and $(b + c)a = b \cdot a + c \cdot a$.

Division Property of Equality If a, b, and c are expressions for real numbers with $a = b$ and $c \neq 0$, then $\frac{a}{c} = \frac{b}{c}$.

Division Property of Inequality If a, b, and c are expressions for real numbers and $a > b$, then $\frac{a}{c} > \frac{b}{c}$ if c is positive, and $\frac{a}{c} < \frac{b}{c}$ if c is negative.

domain of a relation The set of first members of the ordered pairs of the relation.

domain of a variable The set of numbers that the variable may represent.

equation A number sentence showing that two expressions represent the same number.

equivalent equations Equations which have the same solution(s).

equivalent expressions Expressions that represent the same number.

evaluate an expression Find the standard name for the number obtained when each variable is replaced by a number.

exponent A number that tells how many times a factor, called the base, occurs in a product.

extremes *See* proportion.

factor Any one of two or more numbers that are multiplied. Also, the process of finding such numbers for a given product.

factored form Representation of a number or an expression as a product.

formula An equation which expresses a relationship in concise form, usually with a single variable as the left member.

Glossary

fractional equation An equation that has a variable in the denominator of one or more terms.
function A set of ordered pairs, no two of which have the same first member.

gram A unit for measuring mass.
graph The point in the coordinate plane associated with an ordered pair of numbers. The set of points in the coordinate plane associated with a set of ordered pairs of numbers. Also, the process or result of representing such a point.
graph of an equation The graph of the solution set of the equation.
greatest common factor The greatest counting number that is a factor of each of two or more counting numbers.

hypotenuse The side opposite the right angle in a right triangle.

identity A number sentence that is true for all meaningful replacements for its variable(s).
inequality A number sentence showing that two expressions represent different numbers.
intercept The point which the graph of an equation in two variables has in common with a coordinate axis.
inverse variation A relationship between two variables, x and y, that may be described by an equation of the form $xy = k$, in which k is a non-zero constant.
irrational number A real number that cannot be expressed in the form $\frac{a}{b}$ in which a and b represent integers and $b \neq 0$.

least common multiple The smallest counting number that is a multiple of each of two or more counting numbers.
leg of a right triangle Either of the two sides which form the right angle.
like terms Monomials that contain the same powers of the same variables.
linear equation A first-degree equation in two variables. The standard form is $ax + by = c$, where a, b, and c represent known real numbers and x and y are the variables.
linear function A function defined by a linear equation. The ordered pairs that are solutions of $ax + by = c$.
liter A unit for measuring volume or capacity.
literal equation An equation in several variables all but one of which are treated as constants when solving for the remaining variable.
lowest terms A fraction for which the numerator and the denominator have no common factor involving a variable and no common integral factor, except 1 or -1.

means *See* proportion.
meter A unit for measuring length.
mixed expression An expression in which one term is a fraction and others are not.
monomial A term which is a constant, a variable, or an indicated product involving constants and variables.
Multiplication Property of Equality If a, b and c are expressions for real numbers and $a = b$, then $a \cdot c = b \cdot c$.
Multiplication Property of Inequality If a, b, and c are expressions for real numbers and $a > b$, then $ac > bc$ if c is positive, and $ac < bc$ if c is negative.
Multiplication Property of Negative One For any real number a, $(-1)a = -a$.
Multiplication Property of One For any real number a, $1 \cdot a = a$.
Multiplication Property of Zero For any real number a, $0 \cdot a = 0$.

obtuse angle An angle whose measure in degrees is greater than 90 and less than 180.

opposite side (to an angle) In a triangle, the side that is not part of the angle.

ordinate The second number in the ordered pair for a point in the coordinate plane.

origin The point common to the two perpendicular number lines in the coordinate plane.

parallel lines Lines that are contained in the same plane but have no point in common.

percent A ratio having denominator 100.

perimeter The sum of the lengths of the sides of a polygon.

plot The process of drawing a picture in a number line or in the coordinate plane to represent a number or an ordered pair of numbers, respectively.

polynomial A monomial or an indicated sum or difference of monomials.

power of a number The number represented by a base and exponent.

prime number A whole number greater than one having no whole number factors other than itself and one.

principal square root The positive square root.

product of powers When two factors are powers of the same base, their product is given by the base and an exponent that is the sum of the exponents of the factors.

proportion An equation in which each member is a ratio. For the proportion $\frac{a}{b} = \frac{c}{d}$, a and d are the *extremes* and b and c are the *means*.

protractor An instrument for measuring angles.

Pythagorean Theorem For any right triangle, the square of the length of the hypotenuse equals the sum of the squares of the lengths of the legs.

quadrant One of the four regions into which the axes separate the coordinate plane.

quadratic equation A second-degree equation in one variable.

radical The radical sign and the radicand.

radical equation An equation having a variable in a radicand.

radical sign The symbol $\sqrt{}$.

radicand The number or expression under a radical sign.

range of a relation The set of second members of the ordered pairs of the relation.

rate A comparison of one quantity to another quantity.

ratio A comparison of numbers, given in the form $\frac{a}{b}$ or $a : b$.

rational number A number that may be expressed in the form $\frac{a}{b}$ in which a and b are integers and $b \neq 0$.

rationalize the denominator Simplify a fraction whose denominator includes a radical so that there are no radicals in the denominator.

real numbers The set of numbers each of which matches one point of the number line.

reciprocals Two numbers for which the product is 1. A reciprocal also is called a *multiplicative inverse*. For a real number, a, the reciprocal is $\frac{1}{a}$.

repeating decimal A numeral in which the decimal digits follow an endless repeating pattern.

right angle An angle whose measure in degrees is 90.

right triangle A triangle with a right angle.

similar Two shapes with corresponding angles having equal measure and corresponding sides having proportional lengths.

Glossary

sine of an angle The ratio $\frac{\text{length of the leg opposite the angle}}{\text{length of the hypotenuse}}$, when the angle is an acute angle of a right triangle.

slope of a line For two points in the line, the ratio of the difference of the two ordinates to the difference of the two abscissas.

slope-intercept form for a linear equation $y = mx + b$, where m is the slope of the line represented by the equation and b is its y-intercept.

solution of an equation The number(s) that gives a true sentence when used in place of the variable(s).

solution of a system of equations An ordered pair of numbers that is a common solution for the equations in the system.

solution set of an equation The set of all solutions of the equation.

square of a number The product of the number and itself.

square root of a given number A number which when multiplied by itself produces the given number.

substitution method A method for solving a system of equations. Using one equation, one variable is expressed in terms of the other. Then the variable is replaced by this expression in the other equation.

Subtraction Property of Equality If a, b, and c are expressions for real numbers and $a = b$, then $a - c = b - c$.

Subtraction Property of Inequality If a, b, and c are expressions for real numbers and $a > b$, then $a - c > b - c$.

supplementary angles Two angles which have 180 as the sum of their degree measures.

system of equations A set of two or more equations in two or more variables.

tangent of an angle The ratio $\frac{\text{length of the leg opposite the angle}}{\text{length of the leg adjacent to the angle}}$, when the angle is an acute angle of a right triangle.

trigonometric ratio Any one of the six ratios that can be formed using the three sides of a triangle two at a time. Of these, only the sine, cosine, and tangent ratios are used in this book.

uniform motion Motion in which an object moves at a constant rate.

variable A symbol for a number, usually a letter from the English or Greek alphabet.

whole number Any of the numbers 0, 1, 2, 3, and so on.

x-axis The horizontal number line in the coordinate plane.

x-coordinate The first number in the ordered pair that corresponds to a point in the coordinate plane.

x-intercept The x-coordinate of the point that a line shares with the x-axis.

y-axis The vertical number line in the coordinate plane.

y-coordinate The second number in the ordered pair that corresponds to a point in the coordinate plane.

y-intercept The y-coordinate of the point that a line shares with the y-axis.

ANSWERS
Selected Exercises

Chapter 1 Introduction to Algebra

Page 6, Exercises 1. 64 **3.** 12 **5.** 48 **7.** 1 **9.** 4 **11.** 12 **13.** $2\frac{1}{2}$ **15.** 3 **17.** 7.68 **19.** $2\frac{1}{4}$ **21.** 3 **23.** 12 **25.** 10 **27.** 54 **29.** 72 **31.** $\frac{8}{9}$ **33.** $\frac{18}{5}$ **35.** $\frac{7}{6}$ **37.** 48 **39.** 15 **41.** $\frac{1}{18}$ **43.** 0 **45.** $\frac{9}{14}$ **Pages 8-9, Exercises 1.** 2 **3.** $\frac{1}{4}$ **5.** z^3 **7.** 4^3a^2 **9.** $\left(\frac{1}{3}\right)^2y^3$ **11.** $(s+3)^3$ **13.** $a \cdot a$ **15.** $(3y)(3y)(3y)$ **17.** $m \cdot m \cdot n$ **19.** 9 **21.** 162 **23.** $\frac{4}{9}$ **25.** 9, $\frac{1}{4}$, 0.49 **27.** 216, 1, 2.744 **29.** 54, $\frac{3}{2}$, 2.94 **31.** 16 **33.** 0 **35.** 36 **37.** x^3y^3 **39.** $\left(\frac{1}{2}\right)^5c^5$ **41.** 3^5z^4 **43.** $\frac{4}{25}$ **45.** 11.19744 **47.** $\frac{675}{4096}$ **49.** $\frac{9}{10}$ **51.** $\frac{9}{400}$ or (0.0225) **53.** $\frac{32}{675}$ **55.** $\frac{9}{4}$ **57.** 49 **59.** $\frac{3}{8}$ **61.** $\frac{8}{27}a^{12}b^6$ **63.** $625h^{12}k^{24}$ **65.** no **67.** no **69.** no **71.** yes **73.** yes **75.** Answers will vary. **Pages 11-12, Exercises 1.** 5 **3.** 3 **5.** 84 **7.** 200 **9.** 72 **11.** 9 **13.** 58 **15.** 48 **17.** $\frac{5}{4}$ **19.** 20 **21.** 126 **23.** 100 **25.** 0.486 **27.** 128 **29.** 144 **31.** 0 **33.** 520 **35.** 20.5 **37.** 66 **39.** 96 **41.** 240 **43.** 9 **45.** 7 **47.** 0 **49.** 4 **51.** 0 **53.** $\frac{1}{54}$ **55.** $\frac{11}{64}$ **57.** $\frac{13}{30}$ **59.** $\frac{29}{30}$ **Page 16, Exercises 1.** $6+m$ **3.** $3y+5x$ **5.** $4k+6h$ **7.** $w \cdot 12$ **9.** $(9d)\cdot(7c)$ **11.** $(10y)\cdot(4x)$ **13.** $a+(b+6)$ **15.** $(4m+6n)+8p$ **17.** $5a+(10b+15c)$ **19.** $8\cdot(a\cdot b)$ **21.** $(4c\cdot 8d)\cdot 12f$ **23.** $9p\cdot(18q\cdot 27r)$ **25.** $3a+3b$ **27.** $8p+8q$ **29.** $12d-cd$ **31.** $(7+18)h$ **33.** $7(c+d)$ **35.** 25 **37.** 32 **39.** 15 **41.** h **43.** $(0+1)x$ **45.** No. $9-3 \neq 3-9$, $9 \div 3 \neq 3 \div 9$ **Pages 18-19, Exercises 1.** $23z$ **3.** $\frac{13}{15}b$ **5.** $18k$ **7.** $40x^2$ **9.** $86r^2$ **11.** $2.7z^2$ **13.** $18c+14d$ **15.** $63k+38h$ **17.** $26p+18q$ **19.** $15x+4x^2$ **21.** $38y^2+29y$ **23.** $20m^2+25m$ **25.** $26b$ **27.** $54h$ **29.** $14z$ **31.** 60a **33.** $36m$ **35.** $26p+20q+18$ **37.** $40x+38y+50$ **39.** $20c+18d-30$ **41.** $10x^2+11x+11$ **43.** $6c^2+3c+9$ **45.** $6h^3+14hk+3k^3$ **Page 19, Checking Your Understanding 1.** $x+(7+3)$ **2.** $4\cdot 5x$ **3.** $5x+5\cdot 3$ **4.** $(5+1)y$ **5.** $9a$ **6.** $2x+5x^2$ **7.** $13a-5b+2$ **Page 22, Exercises 1.** $5n$, $0.05n$ **3.** $h-1$ **5.** $s-4$ **7.** $z+24$ **9.** $60m$ **11.** $3z-5$ **13.** Use y for number of yellow marbles, $3y+5$ for number of green marbles, $4y-1$ for number of red marbles and $3(4y-1)$ for number of blue marbles.

Chapter 2 Positive and Negative Numbers

Page 29, Exercises 1. 4 m west **3.** A.D. 34 **5.** $7\frac{1}{3}$ **7.** 80° west longitude **9.** 8 mm below average **11.** 5 **13.** 4.3 **15.** $8\frac{1}{4}$ **17.** -12 **19.** 10 **21.** -9.9 **23.** 12 **25.** 13 **27.** 13 **29.** false **31.** true **33.** true **Page 32, Exercises 1.** -2 **3.** 11 **5.** 4 **7.** -10 **9.** 0 **11.** 8 **13.** 6 **15.** 5.5 **17.** $-10\frac{2}{7}$ **19.** $-5\frac{2}{5}$ **21.** $-9\frac{1}{2}$ **23.** $-2\frac{1}{2}$ **25.** $-\frac{5}{6}$ **27.** $-4\frac{1}{2}$ **29.** -8 **Page 35, Exercises 1.** -5 **3.** 2 **5.** -2 **7.** -2 **9.** -11 **11.** -9 **13.** $\frac{1}{12}$ **15.** $-\frac{1}{12}$ **17.** -16.8 **19.** 16.8 **21.** -4.77 **23.** 0 **25.** -12.9 **27.** -1 **29.** -39 **31.** -5 **33.** -17 **35.** -847 **37.** -25 **39.** 0.715 **41.** 11.65 **43.** 9.35 **45.** 2.35 **47.** 14.65 **Pages 38-39, Exercises 1.** -4 **3.** 12 **5.** 12 **7.** 16 **9.** -20 **11.** 20 **13.** -27 **15.** $-\frac{1}{2}$ **17.** 10 **19.** -23.16 **21.** 29 **23.** -3 **25.** 5 **27.** 0 **29.** -1 **31.** -5 **33.** $\frac{7}{5}$ **35.** -3.19 **Page 39, Checking Your Understanding 1.** 3 and 3 **2.** -7.1 and 7.1 **3.** $\frac{4}{5}$ and $\frac{4}{5}$ **4.** -8 **5.** -2 **6.** 5 **7.** -5 **8.** 11 **9.** -15 **Page 42, Exercises 1.** -15 **3.** -9 **5.** -80 **7.** 2 **9.** -5 **11.** 16 **13.** 1 **15.** -100 **17.** 2 **19.** $-\frac{1}{28}$ **21.** $\frac{9}{2}$ **23.** $\frac{1}{2}$ **25.** $-\frac{2}{9}$ **27.** -293.04 **29.** -18.3 **31.** -1 **33.** 1 **35.** 9 **37.** 1 **39.** 5 **41.** 11 **43.** 0.3 **45.** 35.2 **Pages 44-45, Exercises 1.** $7x$ **3.** $-3a$ **5.** $-7a$ **7.** $7x$ **9.** y **11.** b **13.** $4a+b$ **15.** $4a-b$ **17.** $2x-2x^2$ **19.** $9a-11b$ **21.** a^2-b^2 **23.** $-6b^2$,

25. $18r + 2t$ **27.** $19x^2 + 12x + 6$ **29.** $29b + 21$ **31.** $11x^2 - x$ **33.** $2a - 5b - c$ **35.** $5p + 5q - 3r$ **37.** $11a^2 - 7a + 6b$ **39.** $-5x - 2y + 4z$ **41.** $18x^2 + 28$ **43.** $-8x - 12$ **45.** $6x + 32$ **47.** $44x + 40$ **49.** $4a + 19b + 38$ **51.** $17a + 13b$ **53.** $11a + 27$ **55.** $80a^2 + 48a + 6$ **57.** $175a + 78b + 954$ **Page 48, Exercises** **1.** -2 **3.** -6 **5.** -2 **7.** -4 **9.** 7 **11.** 0 **13.** -0.5 **15.** -5 **17.** -9 **19.** -3 **21.** -6 **23.** -4 **25.** -8 **27.** -81 **29.** 70 **31.** -20 **33.** -27 **35.** $5\frac{1}{3}$ **37.** -12 **39.** $\frac{1}{3}$ **41.** -4 **43.** -22 **45.** $\frac{120}{13}$ **Pages 50-51, Exercises** **1.** -5 **3.** 12 **5.** 6 **7.** 13 **9.** -5 **11.** 10 **13.** 0 **15.** 64 **17.** 64 **19.** -34 **21.** 20 **23.** 49 **25.** -15 **27.** 132 **29.** -1 **31.** 1 **33.** 0 **35.** $\frac{42}{13}$ **37.** 0.171 **Page 51, Checking Your Understanding** **1.** -15 **2.** 56 **3.** -3 **4.** 6 **5.** $-9x$ **6.** $4x - 3y$ **7.** $-13x^2 + x$ **8.** 126 **9.** -29 **Pages 55-56, Exercises** **1.** $30x$ **3.** $-4by$ **5.** $4rs$ **7.** $-12ab$ **9.** $4ghk$ **11.** $6h^2$ **13.** $\frac{1}{3}c^2$ **15.** x^2 **17.** $0.1p^2$ **19.** $-28a^3$ **21.** $-80m$ **23.** x^{10} **25.** $25a^2b^4$ **27.** $-42b^7$ **29.** $-10x^4$ **31.** $9c^4dx$ **33.** $0.8x^9$ **35.** 10^7 **37.** 5^5 **39.** 9^3 **41.** $-27x^6y^6z^3$ **43.** $-a^4b^2c^2$ **45.** $0.6x^4y^2z^3$ **47.** $0.6x^2y^2z^3$ **49.** $7a^6$ **51.** $-12a^3b^4c$ **53.** $-16x^5y^4$ **55.** $\frac{x^2}{9}$ **57.** x^{2n+1} **59.** y^{n+3} **61.** x^{10n} **63.** x^9 **65.** $x^{2n}y^2$ **67.** x^ny^n **69.** x^{mn} **71.** no simplifying possible. **Page 59, Exercises** **1.** $\frac{1}{5a^2}$ **3.** $\frac{a}{b}$ **5.** $\frac{12x}{yz}$ **7.** $\frac{20a^2}{21b^2}$ **9.** $\frac{4}{7}$ **11.** $\frac{-21}{5}m$ **13.** $\frac{b^3}{a}$ **15.** $\frac{-3c}{4d}$ **17.** 4 **19.** $4x$ **21.** $33x$ **23.** $\frac{z^4}{15}$ **25.** $\frac{19x^3}{4}$ **27.** $\frac{ab^2z}{9}$ **29.** $8ax$ **31.** $\frac{4m^4}{15n}$ **33.** $\frac{3}{40x}$ **Page 62, Exercises** **1.** c^2 **3.** $-2m^2$ **5.** $2x$ **7.** -1 **9.** $\frac{1}{5x^2}$ **11.** $2a^3b^2$ **13.** $-10cd^2$ **15.** $\frac{2c}{b}$ **17.** $\frac{1}{4x^2}$ **19.** $7m^3$ **21.** $4m^4$ **23.** 8 **25.** $-x^3$ **27.** -1 **29.** $\frac{2x^2}{y}$ **31.** $\frac{-9a^3}{2b^3}$ **33.** $5x$ **35.** $-8a^2b$ **Page 65, Exercises** **1.** 48 **3.** $\frac{3}{4}$ **5.** $\frac{4}{5}$ **7.** xy **9.** $\frac{2a}{3}$ **11.** $\frac{y}{x}$ **13.** $-\frac{a^2}{bc}$ **15.** $\frac{a^2}{b^2}$ **17.** $\frac{xy^2}{a^2}$ **19.** $\frac{722x}{3}$ **21.** $\frac{64}{63}$ **23.** $\frac{7}{9}$ **25.** $\frac{3}{2}$ **27.** $\frac{1}{24a^3b}$ **29.** $\frac{9x^2z^4}{40y^6}$ **Pages 68-69, Exercises** **1.** 1 **3.** $\frac{2a}{3}$ **5.** $\frac{a+b}{c}$ **7.** $\frac{2}{c}$ **9.** $\frac{1}{xy}$ **11.** $\frac{11}{20}$ **13.** $\frac{13t}{21}$ **15.** $-\frac{7b}{20}$ **17.** $\frac{27c + 8d}{36}$ **19.** $\frac{12x - 10y}{15}$ **21.** $\frac{3a + 3b}{a + b}$ or 3 **23.** $\frac{6x - 11}{3x}$ **25.** $\frac{-b + 12c}{36}$ **27.** $\frac{x^2 - 8x + 1}{6x^2}$ **Page 69, Checking Your Understanding** **1.** $-6x^5$ **2.** $20ab$ **3.** -8 **4.** $-4x^2$ **5.** $\frac{1}{3x}$ **6.** $6x$ **7.** $\frac{5x^2}{9}$ **8.** x **9.** $-\frac{7x}{12}$ **10.** $\frac{19x^2}{6}$

Chapter 3 Equations and Inequalities

Page 77, Exercises **1.** $=$ **3.** $\neq$ **5.** $=$ **7.** $=$ **9.** $<$ **11.** $>$ **13.** $=$ **15.** $=$ **17.** no **19.** no **21.** $=$ **23.** $>$ **25.** $>$ **27.** $<$ **29.** Varies with x and y values. **31.** no **Page 83, Exercises** **1.** -25 **3.** $\frac{17}{12}$ **5.** $\frac{1}{3}$ **7.** 20 **9.** $-\frac{1}{2}$ **11.** $-\frac{13}{10}$ **13.** 0.5 **15.** -5.16 **17.** -100 **19.** 19 **21.** -47 **23.** 50 **25.** -11 **27.** $-\frac{5}{6}$ **29.** $\frac{7}{6}$ **31.** -1.15 **33.** 1.68 **35.** 11.64 **37.** 11.08 **39.** 2.54 **41.** -24 **43.** $-\frac{55}{12}$ **45.** -39 **47.** -25 **49.** 7 **51.** 28 **53.** 185 **55.** $c - b$ **57.** $c + b$ **59.** $d - b - c$ **61.** $d - b - c$ **63.** $d - c + b$ **Page 87, Exercises** **1.** 6 **3.** -8 **5.** 0.7 **7.** -0.8 **9.** $\frac{1}{15}$ **11.** $-\frac{2}{17}$ **13.** 16 **15.** -55 **17.** 48 **19.** -51 **21.** 90 **23.** -50 **25.** 2 **27.** $-\frac{2}{3}$ **29.** 20 **31.** -8.4 **33.** $\frac{3}{4}$ **35.** -5 **37.** 1 **39.** $-\frac{1}{18}$ **41.** -177 **43.** $\frac{cb}{da}$ **45.** $-\frac{ba}{dc}$ **47.** $\frac{ac}{bd}$ **Page 89, Exercises** **1.** 4 **3.** -6 **5.** -2 **7.** 4 **9.** 6 **11.** -10 **13.** 16 **15.** -8 **17.** 80 **19.** 600 **21.** -24 **23.** 16 **25.** 612 **27.** $\frac{p}{rg + sk}$ **Pages 92-93, Exercises** **1.** 3 **3.** -8 **5.** -7 **7.** 7 **9.** 70 **11.** -48 **13.** -64 **15.** 56 **17.** -8 **19.** 4 **21.** -2 **23.** 12 **25.** 144 **27.** -36 **29.** -14 **31.** $\frac{480}{7}$ **33.** 49 **35.** -27 **37.** -120 **39.** 90 **41.** 29 **43.** -38 **45.** -57 **47.** 84 **49.** 5 **51.** -9 **53.** -7 **55.** 20 **57.** $-\frac{5}{8}$ **59.** 2.8 **61.** -14 **63.** $\frac{c - b}{a}$ **65.** $\frac{adf - bde}{bcf}$ **Page 95, Exercises** **1.** 4 **3.** 4 **5.** -2.5 **7.** -15 **9.** -5 **11.** 2 **13.** 18 **15.** $\frac{20}{13}$ **17.** -5 **19.** 6 **21.** -108 **23.** $\frac{12}{5}$ **25.** 12 **27.** -18 **29.** $\frac{-252}{97}$ **31.** 20 **33.** -0.5 **35.** 11 **37.** 1 **39.** -3 **41.** $\frac{df + bc}{c - a}$ **Page 96, Checking Your Understanding** **1.** $=$ **2.** $<$ or $\neq$ **3.** $>$ or $\neq$ **4.** no **5.** yes **6.** 6 **7.** $\frac{2}{3}$ **8.** -5 **Page 99, Exercises**

1. $8n = 48$ **3.** $n + 43 = 74$ **5.** $n - \frac{2}{3} = \frac{1}{2}$ **7.** $6 = 2n - 10$ **9.** $n + (n + 1) = 43$
11. $n + (n + 15) = 85$ **13.** $2[n + (n + 5)] = n(n + 5) + 4$ **15.** $n + \frac{1}{2}n = 8$
17. $n - \frac{1}{3}n = 48$ **19.** $(a + b)^2 = a^2 + b^2 + 2ab$ **Pages 102-103, Exercises 1.** 54
3. 127 **5.** -9 **7.** 8 **9.** $-15, -16$ **11.** 18, 45 **13.** 9, 45 **15.** 8, 64
17. $l = 22, w = 7$ **19.** 36 **21.** 1 **23.** $-40, -39, -38$ **25.** 22, 24, 26
27. 575, 1150, 1725 **Page 103, Checking Your Understanding 1.** $2t + 3 = 9$
2. $n + (n + 2) = 56$ **3.** 14 **4.** $2(l - 4) + 2l = 68, l = 19, w = 15$ **Page 107, Exercises 1.** $x > 4$ **3.** $r < 3$ **5.** $x > -4$ **7.** $w < -12$ **9.** $f > 7$ **11.** $m < 23$
13. $x > 5$ **15.** $h > -5$ **17.** $r > -3\frac{1}{2}$ **19.** $x < 5\frac{1}{4}$ **21.** $y > 1.9$ **23.** $t < 8$
25. $g < -2$ **27.** $x > 13$ **29.** $m > -25$ **31.** $g > -35$ **33.** $x > b - a$
35. $x < n + 2c$ **37.** $x < -p - q$ **Page 110, Exercises 1.** $x < 2$ **3.** $r > -3$
5. $m > 4$ **7.** $h > -28$ **9.** $s > 60$ **11.** $b > -10$ **13.** $x < -35$ **15.** $p < 50$
17. $b > -6$ **19.** $a < -14$ **21.** $a > \frac{20}{3}$ **23.** $x > -12$ **25.** $t > 1\frac{1}{8}$ **27.** $v < 4$
29. $x < -\frac{bc}{a}$ **31.** $x > -\frac{d^2e}{c}$ **Page 112, Exercises 1.** $x > 10$ **3.** $d > -8$
5. $r > -4$ **7.** $n < -6$ **9.** $q > 2$ **11.** $y < 4$ **13.** $d < 2$ **15.** $k > -16$ **17.** $a < -20$
19. $z > 80$ **21.** $y < -\frac{1}{6}$ **23.** $s > \frac{66}{25}$ **25.** $x > \frac{c - b}{a}, a > 0; x < \frac{c - b}{a}, a < 0$
Page 116, Checking Your Understanding 1. $x > 8$ **2.** $x > -\frac{21}{4}$ **3.** $x > -\frac{1}{3}$
4. $x > -1$ **Page 119, Exercises 1.** $n < 7$ **3.** $5n \leq 32$ **5.** $n + (n + 1) \geq 21$
7. $n \geq -2$ **9.** Tom is less than 14 years. Sam is less than 19 years.
11. less than \$88.25 **13.** less than 235.5 hectares **15.** at least 80 children's tickets; at least 280 adult's tickets. **17.** $n > 1\,000\,000$ or $n < 0$

Chapter 4 Special Equations Called Formulas

Page 127, Exercises 1. $p = 3, 6, 15, 24, 45$ **3.** $A = 1, 4, 9, 25, 121$
5. $c = 3.14, 6.28, 9.42, 18.84, 28.26$ **7.** $B = 11, 19, 35, 54$
9. 4.9, 19.6, 44.1, 122.5, 490 **11.** Formula is the average of n numbers. Find the sum of the numbers, then divide by the number of addends. **Pages 129-130, Exercises 1.** 22 **3.** 78.4 **5.** 1950 km **7.** 140 **9.** 441 **11.** Normal mass, over or under: 61.7 kg, +3.5 kg; 74.5 kg, −5.0 kg; 79.4 kg, 0 kg
13. 2 h 46 min 40 s (10 000s) **Page 134, Exercises 1.** 80 **3.** 48 **5.** 200.96
7. 18.3 cm **9.** 16.8 m **11.** 31.4 **13.** 64 cm^3 **15.** 314 cm^3 **17.** 113.04 cm^3
19. no **21.** 15 072 km **23.** 8478 **25.** 1 000 000 **Pages 137-138, Exercises**
1. $p = 3b + 2$ **3.** $p = 2s + 2l + w$ **5.** $A = ac$ **7.** $A = a^2 - b^2$ **9.** $V = 8e^3$
11. $V = b^2d - \pi r^2 d$ **13.** $p = 2l + 2w$ **15.** $c = \frac{V}{1000}$ **17.** $C = 1400 + 4n$
19. $C = 0.85 + 0.15(n - 3)$ **21.** $P = 2a + 2b + 2c$ **23.** $A = \pi m^2 - \pi \frac{m^2}{4}$
25. \$22.00 **Pages 140-141, Exercises 1.** $P = 3s$; 12, 18, 30 **3.** $S = C + 8.5$; 13.5, 18.5, 28.5 **5.** $A = \frac{5l}{2}$; 12.5, 25, 42.5 **7.** $I = \frac{110}{R}$; 22, 4.4, 1
9. $A = s^2$; 16, 144, 225 **11.** decreases **Page 141, Checking Your Understanding 1.** 2.25 **2.** $3\frac{1}{3}$ **3.** 210 km **4.** 32 cm **5.** $\frac{p + q + r}{3}$ **6.** $4x^2 - \pi r^2$
7. $j = 2h + 1, h = \frac{j - 1}{2}$ **Page 146, Exercises 1.** $p = A - i$ **3.** $G = S - C - M$
5. $m = \frac{F}{a}$ **7.** $a = 3A - b - c$ **9.** $V = \frac{M}{D}$ **11.** $a = \frac{2s}{t^2}$ **13.** $b = \frac{P - 2s}{2}$ **15.** $p = \frac{i}{rt}$
17. $w = \frac{R - S}{2}$ **19.** $r = \frac{Wv^2}{Fa}$ **21.** $W = \frac{Far}{v^2}$ **23.** $n = \frac{D + 360}{180}$ **25.** $T = \frac{W + Vt}{V}$
27. $W = \frac{6S}{S - 1}$

Chapter 5 Problem Solving: Using Equations

Page 155, Exercises 1. $2n, 2n + 2, 2n + 4$ **3.** Flo m, $40m$; Joe, $3m$, $3(40m)$
5. t – number of hours; $100t$ – distance in km
7. Use s for 2d angle, $2s$ for 1st angle, $3s$ for 3d angle. $s + 2s + 3s = 180$
9. Use l for length, $\frac{l}{3}$ for width. $l\left(\frac{l}{3}\right) = 100$ **11.** $62.5n$ **Pages 157-158, Exercises**
1. 7.2 **3.** 25% **5.** 20% **7.** 21 **9.** 75% **11.** 40% **13.** approx. 18% **15.** 0.005

17. 2400 **19.** 80% **21.** 4.5% **23.** 500 **Pages 160-161, Exercises 1.** 28 **3.** 135 **5.** 50% **7.** 150% **9.** 8 **11.** \$82.50 **13.** 5% **15.** 5% **17.** \$179.40 **19.** \$6.36 **21.** \$450. **23.** $8\frac{1}{3}$% **Pages 163-164, Exercises**
1. Alpers \$1000; Betta \$500; Gamoff \$500. **3.** 280 **5.** 9, 3
7. mud/snow \$41.91; regular \$38.10 **9.** 229 customers **Page 168, Exercises**
1. 17.4 km **3.** Bernardo \$10/h; Maki \$5/h. **5.** 2.5 **7.** 3 h **9.** 40 km/h
11. 200 km/h; 180 km/h; **13.** approx. 1.1 h
15. winter, approx. 0.015; summer, approx. 0.016 **Page 171, Exercises**
1. $7m - 7n$ **3.** $4b - 5a$ **5.** 1 **7.** $\frac{10}{3}$ **9.** 13 **11.** -9 **13.** 7 **15.** 8
17. $-2a^3b + ab^3 - 4a^2b^2$ **19.** -2 **21.** 3 **23.** x **25.** 8 **27.** 4 **Pages 174-175, Exercises 1.** $12(n - 1)$ **3.** $3.5(n - 3)$ **5.** $35(t + 1)$ **7.** $\frac{2.5k - 1}{4}$ **9.** $5(10 - n)$
11. $0.06(200) + 0.05(m - 200)$ **13.** $2.25 + 0.38(2n - 3)$
15. $25 + 0.01(2000n - 1000)$ **17.** $4(s - 5)$ **19.** $100(26 + n) + 80(2 + m)$
21. $0.08d + 0.07(1000 - d)$ **23.** $0.02r(800 - d)$ **25.** $\frac{101(2n - 3)}{10}$ **Page 175, Checking Your Understanding 1.** h, $5h(5.75)$ **2.** $10x - 5(x - 3)$ **3.** 468.75
4. Abby \$6 Cass \$21 **5.** 24 minutes **6.** 3 **7.** 4 **Page 177, Exercises 1.** 43
3. 162, 158 **5.** 16, 30 **7.** 11, 5 **9.** 384, 416 **11.** $33\frac{1}{3}, 41\frac{1}{3}, 44\frac{1}{3}$ **13.** $4x + 2$
Page 180, Exercises 1. 4 quarters, 7 dimes **3.** 6 nickels, 13 dimes
5. 4 half-dollars, 12 nickels, 10 dimes **7.** 9 nickels, 12 dimes
9. 14 nickels, 24 quarters, 40 dimes **11.** 3 nickels, no dimes. **Page 182, Exercises 1.** Roberta 15, Ricky 5 **3.** Doris 16, Jennifer 13 **5.** Frank 20, Carla 5
7. Otto 22, Yusef 12 **9.** 8 **11.** father 42, son 12 **13.** Sol 45, Troy 25
15. Elsie 15, Herman 23 **Page 185, Exercises 1.** 7 cm, 9 cm, 9 cm.
3. $w = 24$ cm, $l = 27$ cm **5.** $l = 58.75$ m, $w = 14.75$ m.
7. 8.06 cm, 6.06 cm, 6.06 cm, 9.06 cm, 9.06 cm **9.** $l = 12$ m, $w = 6$ m
11. 81 m, 9 m, 27 m

Chapter 6 Operations With Polynomials

Pages 192-193, Exercises 1. $k - 11$ **3.** $-2k^2 - 11k - 5$ **5.** $2x^2 + 3xy - 9y^2$
7. $11x^2 - x - 1$ **9.** $-2x^3 - 4x^2 - 11$ **11.** $5a - b$ **13.** $12a^2 + a - 4$
15. $7a - b - 2c$ **17.** $22x - 9y - 18$ **19.** $-3x^2 + 6xy - 5y^2 + 6z^2$ **21.** $a + b + c$
23. $\frac{5}{8}a - \frac{1}{8}b - c$ **25.** $\frac{9}{4}x^2 - \frac{37}{10}x + 9$ **27.** $-1.9a - 5.6b + 0.05c + 6.55$
29. $-9.7a^2 + 5.33a - 1.95$ **31.** $5a - 14 + 2x$ **33.** $8a - 10$ **35.** $10x - 15y$
37. $8a + 8b - 4c$ **39.** $(a + p)x^2 + (b - q)x + c + r$
41. $5x^3 - 9xy + 5xz - 24z + 18$ **Pages 195-196, Exercises 1.** $2x + 4y + 4z$
3. $-3r - 5s + 2t$ **5.** $-3x^2 - 2x - 3$ **7.** $\frac{9}{2}a^2 - \frac{7}{2}a + 8$ **9.** $-0.7x^2 - 0.8x - 0.28$
11. $a - 4b - 4c$ **13.** $17m + 15$ **15.** $\frac{3}{10}a + \frac{9}{20}b$ **17.** $6.7x + 0.2y - 3z$
19. $8a^2 + 0.5a - 4.97$ **21.** $c^3 - 4c^2 + 4c - 1$ **23.** $-a + 4b + 2$
25. $12m^4n^2 - 3m^2n + 21$ **27.** $-4x^2 + 6x + 4$ **29.** $2xy$ **31.** $-x$ **33.** $8x - 13$
35. $21x^2 - 31x - 37$ **Pages 198-199, Exercises 1.** $8xyw$ **3.** $42kmn$ **5.** x^3
7. $3x^3$ **9.** $-24h^4$ **11.** $-0.01r^2$ **13.** $64x^3y^3$ **15.** $-64x^6$ **17.** $4a^6b^2$ **19.** $4096y^8$
21. $16x^6y^2$ **23.** $a^2b^2c^2$ **25.** $12x^3y^2$ **27.** $-18a^4y^3$ **29.** $\frac{1}{4}x^2$ **31.** $-2700a^7b^4$
33. $\frac{4}{125}x^7$ **35.** $262\,144x^{18}$ **37.** $16x^{40}$ **39.** a^{bcd} **41.** x^{2a+2} **43.** x^ny^{n+2} **45.** $-x^{5m}y^{5n}$
Page 201, Exercises 1. $12x - 32y - 20$ **3.** $18b - 6c$ **5.** $4ax^2 - 5ay$
7. $8a^3 + 14a^2 - 20a$ **9.** $10a^2 + 35$ **11.** $4ax^3 - 7a^2x$ **13.** $3a^3 + 2a$
15. $2a^2y^2 - 10ay$ **17.** $7c^2 - 14c - 21$ **19.** $2x^3 + 2x^2 + 2x$ **21.** $-5a^2 + 25a - 35$
23. $3a^5 + 6a^4 - 18a^3$ **25.** $21m^3 + 28m^2 - 49m$ **27.** $-3a^6 + 6a^5 - 15a^4$
29. $-2a^4 + 6a^3$ **31.** $-68b^5d^4 - 187b^6d^5 - 85b^4d^6$ **33.** $0.8m^2 + n + 1.6$
35. $6y^5 + 8y^4 - 14y^3$ **37.** $(14n^2 - 2nd)$ cents **39.** Use the Distributive Property.
41. $-\frac{3}{5}x^3y^3z^3 + \frac{2}{3}x^5y^2z^5 - \frac{9}{13}x^5y^5z^4$ **Page 204, Exercises 1.** $12a$ **3.** ab^2c
5. $3y$ **7.** $2b^3c^3d$ **9.** $15x^2y^4$ **11.** $-2m^4$ **13.** $-18a^2$ **15.** $-5x$ **17.** $4a^2$
19. $-7abc^3$ **21.** $22mn^2$ **23.** $-25p^3q$ **25.** $\frac{a^3b}{3c}$ **27.** $0.5ab$ **29.** $9x^3$ **31.** 12 **33.** $\frac{3x}{2}$

35. $2m^2$ **37.** $3c$ **39.** $16x^4$ **41.** $-20x^2y$ **43.** $\frac{r}{7s}$ **45.** $\frac{100x^6y^4z^6}{9}$ **47.** $\frac{1}{96}a^8b^7$
Pages 206-207, Exercises **1.** $x - 3$ **3.** $-8a^3 - 2a^2$ **5.** $-x^2 + 3x$
7. $5x^3 - 8x^2 + 4x$ **9.** $x + 1$ **11.** $2a^3 - 8a^2 + 5a$ **13.** $8x^2 - 10x + 1$
15. $-2a^2 + a - 1$ **17.** $-7b^4 + 8b^2 - 4$ **19.** $15 - 11x + 6x^2$ **21.** $4x^2 - 6x + 5$
23. $7x^4 - 8x^2 + 2$ **25.** $4x^3 - 5x^2 + 6x$ **27.** $b - c$ **29.** $r - h$ **31.** $4x + 2x^2y - 1$
33. $-3a^6b + 2a^4b^2 - 4a^2b^3$ **35.** $20x^4y - 16x^3y^2 + 8x^2y$
37. $3a^3b - 7a^2b^2 + 4ab^3$ **39.** $3mn + 5n^2$ **41.** $7x^2y^3 - \frac{64}{5}x^3y^2 + \frac{21}{5}x^4y$ **43.** (an) days
45. $100x + 5y$ **Page 207, Checking Your Understanding** **1.** $-x^2 + 2x + 3$
2. $-7x^2 - 7x + 7$ **3.** $-6x^3$ **4.** $16r^8$ **5.** $-5xy$ **6.** $-\frac{a^3}{2b^2}$ **7.** $-14c^4 + 63c^3 - 105c^2$
8. $4x^2 - 2x - 1$ **Page 209, Exercises** **1.** $x^2 + 4x + 4$ **3.** $a^2 + 5a + 6$
5. $r^2 - 3r + 2$ **7.** $c^2 - 3c - 40$ **9.** $r^2 - 36$ **11.** $2x^2 - 5xy - 3y^2$
13. $6x^2 - 13xy + 6y^2$ **15.** $4m^2 - 3mn - n^2$ **17.** $a^3 - 7a^2 + 15a - 9$
19. $-4x^3 + 4x^2 + 11x - 6$ **21.** $x^3 + 4x^2 + x - 2$ **23.** $2x^3 + 5x^2 + 7x - 5$
25. $16a^2 + 8a + 1$ **27.** $27x^3 - 54x^2y + 36xy^2 - 8y^3$ **29.** $a^3 - 3a^2b + 3ab^2 - b^3$
31. $5x^2 + 4x + 4$ **33.** $-2a^2 + 9ab - 2b^2$ **35.** $-x^2 + 2x + 3$ **37.** $x^2 - 4y^2$
39. $x^4 + x^3 + 7x - 3$ **41.** $a^{3n} + 9a^{2n} + 27a^n + 27$
43. $8 - 12b^n + 6b^{2n} - b^{3n}$ **Page 211, Exercises** **1.** 3 **3.** $\frac{3}{2}$ **5.** $-\frac{17}{2}$ **7.** 5 **9.** -1
11. $\frac{9}{2}$ **13.** 4 **15.** 3 **17.** -1 **19.** -7 **21.** 1 **23.** $-\frac{1}{3}$ **25.** $\frac{17}{9}$ **27.** 2 **29.** -4 **31.** m
33. $\frac{3b}{2ac}$ **Pages 216-217, Exercises** **1.** $6\frac{3}{7}$ **3.** 10 : 24 **5.** 5h **7.** $3\frac{3}{4}$h **9.** 5 h
11. 5 P.M.; Mary 148 km, Bob 120 km **13.** $\frac{3}{4}$h, $\frac{3}{5}$h **15.** 6 km **17.** 2016 km/h
19. $\frac{2}{5}$h **Page 220, Exercises** **1.** $1\frac{1}{5}$h **3.** $5\frac{1}{2}$h **5.** $\frac{1}{2}$h **7.** $2\frac{1}{10}$h **9.** 4h
11. 1.2 days **13.** 3 : 1 **15.** 9.6 h **Pages 223-224, Exercises** **1.** 28
3. 10 kg licorice, 20 kg peppermint **5.** 6.25, 18.75 **7.** 1.875 **9.** 25 **11.** 20
13. 10, 15 **15.** 30 kg **17.** 16 **19.** 12 mL of the 8% solution, 4 mL of the 24%
solution **Pages 226-227, Exercises** **1.** $m + 6$ **3.** $x - 5$ **5.** $y - 7 + \frac{1}{y - 2}$
7. $2x + 9 + \frac{135}{x - 7}$ **9.** $x - 2$ **11.** $x + y$ **13.** $h + 4y - \frac{48y^2}{h - 4y}$ **15.** $4x + 9 + \frac{15}{x - 2}$
17. $4a + 4b$ **19.** $r - 11s$ **21.** $x^2 - 3x + 1$ **23.** $6x^2 + 6x - 12$ **25.** $a^2 - a + 1$
27. $x^2 + 3x + 9$ **29.** $9x^2 - 6x + 4$ **31.** $a^2 + ab + b^2$ **33.** $2x^2 + x + 3 + \frac{16x}{3x^2 - 5x + 7}$
35. -21 **Page 227, Checking Your Understanding** **1.** $6x^3 - 2x^2 + 2x + 10$
2. $2x - 3$ **3.** 12 **4.** -2 **5.** 700 km/h, 800 km/h **6.** $2\frac{1}{2}$h

Chapter 7 Special Products and Factoring

Pages 235-236, Exercises **1.** 9 **3.** $2c$ **5.** $7c^2d$ **7.** $3(a + b)$ **9.** $5(x^2 + 3)$
11. $3(x + 2y^2)$ **13.** $5(x + 5yz^2)$ **15.** $5(a^2 + 4b)$ **17.** $s^2(sr + t^2)$ **19.** $6a + 6b$
21. $0.2x + 0.2y$ **23.** $r^4 + r^2s$ **25.** $9b + 27$ **27.** $80s + 5r$ **29.** $x^6 + x^2y^2$
31. $(a + b)$ **33.** $(x - y)$ **35.** 2 **37.** $x + 8$ **39.** x^2 **41.** $5(x^2 - x - 2)$
43. not factorable **45.** $x(x^2 - x - 42)$ **47.** $5k(k^2 + k - 12)$ **49.** $180(n - 2)$
51. $2\pi r(r + h)$ **53.** $x(x^3 - x^2 + x - 1)$ **55.** $7x^2y^3(6 - 5xy - 2x^3y^3)$
57. $9a^2b^2(3b - 2a + b)$ **59.** $4(3x^3 + 15x^2 - 16y)$ **61.** $\frac{1}{8}x^2(4x^2 - x + 2)$
63. $A = r^2(4 - \pi)$ **65.** $A = \pi(R^2 - r^2)$ **67.** $S = \frac{n}{2}(a + l)$ **69. a.** $A = \frac{1}{2}bh$,
b. $A = \frac{1}{2}b'h$, **c.** $A = \frac{1}{2}bh + \frac{1}{2}b'h$, **d.** $A = \frac{1}{2}h(b + b')$ **Pages 238-239,
Exercises** **1.** 36 **3.** $9r^2$ **5.** $64m^2$ **7.** $16x^6$ **9.** $4r^4s^2$ **11.** $\frac{1}{4}g^2t^2$ **13.** $0.16x^4$
15. $100x^{10}$ **17.** 7 **19.** $\frac{1}{5}$ **21.** 9 **23.** 12 **25.** ab **27.** $11p^2$ **29.** $3mx^2$ **31.** $10x^5$
33. $a + b$ **35.** $5ab^2c^3$ **37.** $156.25x^6y^8$ **39.** $\frac{1}{169}x^8y^{10}$ **41.** $10\,201x^{28}$ **43.** $0.81a^2$
45. $\frac{2x}{3y}$ **47.** $\frac{7a}{8b^2}$ **49.** $0.7x^4y^6$ **51.** $\frac{x + y}{z^2}$ **53.** $36y^{10}$ **Page 239, Checking Your
Understanding** **1.** $9(x + y)$ **2.** $x^2y(x + y)$ **3.** $2x(2x^3 + x^2 + 3x + 5)$ **4.** $9x^6$ **5.** 9
6. $6p^3r^4$ **Pages 241-242, Exercises** **1.** $x^2 + 5x + 4$ **3.** $a^2 + 2a - 3$ **5.** $a^2 - 4$
7. $c^2 - 6c + 9$ **9.** $1 + 3x + 2x^2$ **11.** $14 - 5x - x^2$ **13.** $-x^2 - 7x - 10$
15. $a^2 - 21a + 20$ **17.** $y^2 + 2y - 80$ **19.** $49c^2 + 28c - 5$ **21.** $20c^2 - 11c - 4$

23. $64 - z^2$ **25.** $3z^2 - 10z + 3$ **27.** $a^2 + a - 2$ **29.** $24x^2 - 10x - 4$
31. $x^2 - 6x - 40$ **33.** $2x^2 - 3x - 2$ **35.** $12 + 7b - 12b^2$ **37.** $60c^2 + 83c - 45$
39. $8x^2 + 6x - 20$ **41.** $a^2 + 2ab + b^2$ **43.** $x^4 + x^2y - 12y^2$ **45.** $a^4 - 5a^2 + 4$
47. $x^2y^2 + 6xy + 9$ **49.** $4y^2 - 25$ **51.** $9a^2 - 16b^2$ **53.** $x^2 + 0.7x + 0.12$
55. $b^2 + \frac{1}{12}b - \frac{1}{12}$ **57.** $81a^2 - \frac{1}{4}b^2$ **59.** $4c^2 - 0.09$ **61.** $a^6 - \frac{1}{25}$
63. $m^2 - 0.5mn + 0.04n^2$ **65.** $\frac{5}{4}x^2 - 3xy + \frac{17}{4}y^2$ **67.** $x^2 - 8x + 16$
Pages 245-246, Exercises **1.** $(c + 1)(c + 4)$ **3.** $(z + 2)(z + 5)$ **5.** $(y + 6)^2$
7. $(m + 6)(m + 2)$ **9.** $(x + 1)(x + 2)$ **11.** $\left(y + \frac{1}{3}\right)\left(y + \frac{2}{3}\right)$ **13.** $(m + 6)(m - 5)$
15. $(c - 5)(c + 4)$ **17.** $(m + 9)(m - 2)$ **19.** $(y - 10)(y + 4)$ **21.** $(1 - p)(4 + p)$
23. $(z - 4.8)(z + 0.2)$ **25.** $(x - 1)(x - 4)$ **27.** $(y - 9)(y - 2)$ **29.** $(y - 5)^2$
31. $(x - 5)(x - 8)$ **33.** $(3 - c)(4 - c)$ **35.** not factorable **37.** $(x + y)(x + 2y)$
39. $(m + 2n)(m + 6n)$ **41.** $(m - 2n)(m + 4n)$ **43.** $(h - 6k)(h - 3k)$
45. $(a - 8b)(a - b)$ **47.** not factorable **49.** $(5y + 7)(y + 2)$ **51.** $(3c + 5)(c + 1)$
53. $(6p + 5)(p - 5)$ **55.** $(5x - 7)(x - 2)$ **57.** $(2 - 3c)(1 - 4c)$ **59.** not factorable
61. $(3a - 5b)(a + b)$ **63.** $(5m + n)(3m - 5n)$ **65.** $(7c - 5d)(6c - 7d)$
67. $(2x - y)(x + 3y)$ **69.** $(k^3 - 7)(k^3 + 2)$ **71.** $(xy - 6)(xy + 4)$
73. $(4ab^2 - 3)(2ab^2 + 5)$ **75.** $(2a)(x - 3)(x + 2)$ **77.** $2(q + 4)(2q - 1)$
79. $2x - 19, x + 10$ **81.** $(4x^2 + 7y^2)(2x^2 - 3y^2)$ **Page 248, Exercises**
1. $x^2 + 4x + 4$ **3.** $c^2 - 2cd + d^2$ **5.** $36 - 12x + x^2$ **7.** $4a^2 + 16a + 16$
9. $16a^2 - 8a + 1$ **11.** $4x^2 - 12x + 9$ **13.** $16x^2 - 56x + 49$ **15.** $9x^2 - 36x + 36$
17. $x^2 - 18xy + 81y^2$ **19.** $9a^2 + 12ab + 4b^2$ **21.** $9x^2 + 42x + 49$ **23.** $x^2 - x + \frac{1}{4}$
25. $x^2 - x + 0.25$ **27.** $x^2 + 0.6x + 0.09$ **29.** $9x^2 - 78x + 169$
31. $4y^2 + 124y + 961$ **33.** $36a^2 + 48ab + 16b^2$ **35.** $-2a^2 + 24ab - 72b^2$
37. $2m^2 + \frac{1}{2}m + \frac{13}{16}$ **39.** $2n^2 + 4.2n + 5.85$ **Page 251, Exercises** **1.** $x + 3$ **3.** $x - 7$ **5.** $2 - x$ **7.** not a perfect square **9.** $6x - 1$
11. $a + 8$ **13.** $8y - z$ **15.** $3u + v$ **17.** $a - \frac{1}{2}$ **19.** $5k^4 - 3$ **21.** $2x^4 + 5$
23. $x - \frac{2}{3}$ **25.** 25 **27.** 4 **29.** 1 **31.** $\frac{36x^2 - 12x + 1}{9}$ **Pages 253-254, Exercises**
1. $c^2 - 9$ **3.** $x^2 - 49$ **5.** $4 - k^2$ **7.** $a^2b^2 - 1$ **9.** $m^2 - n^2$ **11.** $p^2 - q^2$ **13.** $9c^2 - 1$
15. $100x^2 - 81$ **17.** $4x^2 - n^2$ **19.** $9k^2 - 25h^2$ **21.** $r^2 - 0.25$ **23.** $\frac{9}{16}x^2 - \frac{1}{4}y^2$
25. $0.09a^2 - 0.25b^2$ **27.** $a^2b^2c^2 - \frac{1}{9}$ **29.** $x^4 - 64$ **31.** $x^4 - 81$ **33.** $r^6 - 4s^8$
35. $m^4 - n^4$ **37.** $h^8 - k^8$ **39.** $9x^4y^8 - 64z^6$ **41. a.** $y + 9$, **b.** $y^2 - 81$
43. $a^2 + 2ab + b^2 - c^2$ **45.** $81x^4 - 100x^3y + 100x^2y^2 - 40xy^3 + 10y^4 - 81$
47. $V = 81x^4 - 625y^4$ **Page 256, Exercises** **1.** $(x - m)(x + m)$ **3.** $(x - 1)(x + 1)$
5. $(2 - c)(2 + c)$ **7.** $(x - 3)(x + 3)$ **9.** $(a - 5)(a + 5)$ **11.** $(a - 7)(a + 7)$
13. not factorable **15.** $(2x - 1)(2x + 1)$ **17.** $(6h - 5)(6h + 5)$ **19.** $(5r - 1)(5r + 1)$
21. $\left(m - \frac{1}{3}\right)\left(m + \frac{1}{3}\right)$ **23.** $(1 - 3a)(1 + 3a)$ **25.** $(7 - m^2)(7 + m^2)$
27. $(8x - 7y)(8x + 7y)$ **29.** $(3p - 9q^2)(3p + 9q^2)$ **31.** $(cd - ab)(cd + ab)$
33. $(a^3b^4 - 11)(a^3b^4 + 11)$ **35.** $(1.3x^4 - 0.9y^2)(1.3x^4 + 0.9y^2)$
37. $\left(3r - \frac{1}{2}\right)\left(3r + \frac{1}{2}\right)$ **39.** $(0.3x - 0.4y)(0.3x + 0.4y)$ **41.** $8(x + 2)$ **Page 258, Exercises** **1.** $5(x + 2)$ **3.** prime **5.** $2x(x - 3)$ **7.** $a(bx + 1)$ **9.** prime
11. $(m - 5)(m + 5)$ **13.** $(c + 1)^2$ **15.** $(a - 7)(a + 6)$ **17.** $(h - 4)(h - 2)$
19. $(r - 12)(r + 5)$ **21.** $3x^2(2x^2 - 3)$ **23.** $(y - 2)^2$ **25.** $(p - 8)(p + 7)$
27. $-2a(a^2 - 2b^2 + 3c^2)$ **29.** $(a - 8b)(a + 8b)$ **31.** $(x - 4)(x + 3)$
33. $(x + 2)(x + 6)$ **35.** $(4x + y)^2$ **37.** prime **39.** $(5x - 1)(5x + 1)$ **41.** prime
43. $(xy^2 - w)(xy^2 + w)$ **45.** $(2x - 5)^2$ **47.** $(3y - 7)(2y + 2)$ **49.** $(k^5 + 1)^2$
51. $(ab - 3c)^2$ **53.** $(x^2 + 0.5)(x^2 + 8)$ **55.** $(a + b - 1)(a + b - 3)$
57. $(x + 5)(x - 5)$ **59.** $4y(x + z)$ **61.** $(x + 3)(x - 3)(x - 1)$ **Page 260, Exercises**
1. $6(a + 1)$ **3.** $4(c - 1)(c + 1)$ **5.** $x^2(x + 3)(x + 4)$ **7.** $4a(4a - b^2)$ **9.** $c(4c - 9)$
11. $b(x + 3)(x - 3)$ **13.** $c(3x + 1)(x + 2)$ **15.** $a(a - 25)$ **17.** $\pi(R + r)(R - r)$
19. $2\pi r(r + h)$ **21.** $a(a^3 - 16)$ **23.** $x(x - 1)(x + 1)$ **25.** $x^3(x - 1)(x + 1)$
27. prime **29.** $a(x - 2y)(x + 2y)$ **31.** $(a^2 - 3)(a + 1)(a - 1)$

33. $a(3a + 5)(a + 1)$ **35.** $8(a + 1)^2$ **37.** $(m - 7)(m - 5)$ **39.** $4(x + 4)(x - 3)$ **41.** $p(1 + qt)$ **43.** $y^2(3a - 2)(2a + 3)$ **45.** $6(c - 7d)(c - 2d)$ **47.** $9x(x + 3y)(x - 3y)$ **49.** $B^2(A - 2B)(A - 3B)$ **51.** $(x - 11)^2$ **53.** $(3ab - 4c)(3ab + 4c)$ **55.** $(7s - r - 5)(7s - r + 5)$ **57.** $8a(a - b)$ **59.** $-2x(y - 2z)$ **61.** $-36x(x - 1)(x - 9)$ **Page 261, Checking Your Understanding 1.** $8y^2 - 8y - 6$ **2.** $4x^2 - 4x + 1$ **3.** $9a^2 - 4$ **4.** $(x - 4)(x - 1)$ **5.** $(2x - 1)^2$ **6.** $3(x - 5)(x - 3)$ **7.** $(x + 10)(x - 10)$ **8.** $(2x + y)(2x - y)$ **9.** $(5x + 6y)(5x - 6y)$ **10.** $2(x + 2)(x - 2)$ **11.** $5x(x - 3)(x + 1)$ **12.** $2(x - y)^2$ **13.** $9x^2 - 6x + 1$ **14.** $(5x - 1)^2$ **Pages 263-264, Exercises 1.** -5 or 3 **3.** ± 2 **5.** 0 or 3 **7.** -3 **9.** 2 **11.** 0 or 6 **13.** 8 or 4 **15.** ± 1 **17.** 2 or 1 **19.** ± 3 **21.** $\frac{3}{2}$ or 3 **23.** -5 or 3 **25.** 0 or 16 **27.** 0 or 4 **29.** 5 or -3 **31.** $-\frac{3}{2}$ or 2 **33.** 11 or -6 **35.** $-\frac{5}{2}$ or 1 **37.** -6 or -4 **39.** -3 or -9 **41.** 4 or 5 **43.** $\pm a$ **45.** $\frac{y}{2}$ or $-2y$ **47.** $-10y$ or $2y$ **49.** $-\frac{8}{3}$ or 2 **Pages 266-267, Exercises 1.** 9, 15 **3.** 10, 11 **5.** 16 cm, 11 cm **7.** 9, 81 **9.** 1 or 5 **11.** $-\frac{3}{2}$ or 2 **13.** 11 **15.** 2m **17.** 16m, 8m **19.** 1.5 cm **21.** $\frac{s-d}{2}$ and $\frac{s+d}{2}$

Chapter 8 More Problem Solving

Page 275, Exercises 1. 96 **3.** -360 **5.** 6 **7.** $-\frac{140}{9}$ **9.** $\frac{2}{5}$ **11.** $-\frac{17}{7}$ **13.** $-\frac{7}{18}$ **15.** $\frac{11}{9}$ **17.** 138 **19.** -747 **21.** $-\frac{108}{7}$ **23.** $\frac{258}{5}$ **25.** -72 **27.** -8 **29.** $\frac{9}{2}$ **31.** -2 **33.** 50 **35.** $-\frac{312}{11}$ **Page 279, Exercises 1.** 40 **3.** 2 **5.** 18 **7.** 2 **9.** 0.75 **11.** -7 **13.** 9 **15.** 1.95m **17.** 2 **19.** 3.625 **21.** 7.84375 **23.** approximately 0.83 m **25.** $\frac{100p + 10hk - mn}{10h + m}$ **Pages 281-282, Exercises 1.** 16 **3.** height 14 cm, base 12 cm **5.** 56 **7.** 21 **9.** 10 years **11.** 35 cm, 25 cm, 25 cm **13.** 18, 30 **15.** 4, 12 **17.** 6 dimes, 18 nickels, 12 quarters **Pages 284-285, Exercises 1.** \$300 **3.** \$120 **5.** \$195 **7.** \$200 **9.** \$160 **11.** \$2449 **13.** approximately 9.2% **15.** \$3200 **Page 288, Exercises 1.** \$73.50 **3.** \$8400 **5.** \$15 200 **7.** \$216 **9.** \$6153.85 **11.** 3.9 years **13.** $t = \frac{1}{r}$ **Page 291, Exercises 1.** 0.245 **3.** approximately 213 **5.** approximately 86% **7.** 79% **9.** approximately 11.1 **11.** Barry 1 m/s, Mark $1\frac{1}{4}$ m/s **13.** 2.45 **15.** 12 hits, 45 times at bat **17.** 7 hits, 20 times at bat **Pages 294-295, Exercises 1.** \$54 **3.** $63\frac{1}{4}$ **5.** 12% **7.** \$1150 @ 6%, \$1700 @ 7% **9.** \$3692.31@ 7%, \$4307.69 @ 6% **11.** \$2000 **13.** \$4000 at 7%, \$2000 at 4% **Page 295, Checking Your Understanding 1.** $-\frac{1}{10}$ **2.** 19 **3.** 40 **4.** 2.5 m **5.** 48 **Pages 298-299, Exercises 1.** 2 : 5 **3.** 3 : 8 **5.** 1 : 5 **7.** 1 : 2 **9.** 3 : 2 **11.** yes. **13.** no. **15.** yes. **17.** no. **19.** $2\frac{1}{2}$ **21.** $\frac{1}{2}$ **23.** 3 : 7 **25.** 1 : 12 **27.** ± 4 **29.** *A* 4 : 3, *B* 7 : 1, *C* 5 : 4, *D* 10 427 : 750 approx. 14 : 1, *E* 218 107 : 41 152 approx. 11 : 2 **31.** 18 **33.** $3m$ **35.** Answers will vary. **Pages 301-302, Exercises 1.** 120 min, or 2 hours **3.** \$1320 **5.** \$42.25 **7.** 88 **9.** 300 **11.** 450 mm (or 45 cm, or 0.45 m) **13.** 30 amperes **15.** 13 **17.** 32, 48 **Page 305, Exercises 1.** yes, $\frac{9}{15} = \frac{12}{20}$. **3.** 18 cm, 22.5 cm **5.** 9.6 m **7.** 10 m **9.** 7200 km **11.** 16 m

Chapter 9 Graphs, Linear Equations and Functions

Page 315, Exercises 1. $A(4, 4)$, $B(-5, -2)$, $C(-2, 3)$, $D(0, 5)$ y-axis, $E(-3, 0)$ x-axis, $F\left(5, -2\frac{1}{2}\right)$, $G(0, -4)$ y-axis **3.** fourth **Page 318, Exercises** Numbers **1** through **21**, answers will vary. **23.** $\left(-3, \frac{5}{8}\right)$ **Page 321, Exercises** Answers will vary. **Page 325, Exercises 1.** 3 **3.** -4 **5.** $\frac{1}{3}$ **7.** $-\frac{1}{4}$ **9.** 0 **11.** no slope **13.** 1 **15.** $-\frac{1}{3}$ **17.** 5 **19.** -6 **21.** $\frac{5}{3}$ **23.** $-\frac{4}{3}$ **25.** 15 **27.** 0 **29.** no **Pages 328-329, Exercises 1.** 7, 0 **3.** $-2, 4$ **5.** $\frac{2}{3}, -10$ **7.** $-4, 0$ **9.** $-\frac{1}{2}, 0$ **11.** $3, -4$ **13.** $0, -4$ **15.** 2, 10 **17.** 5, 6 **19.** $\frac{1}{2}, -3$ **21.** $-8, -2$ **23.** $\frac{1}{2}, -2$

25. $\frac{5}{3}, -4$ **27.** 1, 6 **37.** The two lines are perpendicular. **39.** $-\frac{2}{9}, \frac{2}{3}$
Pages 331-332, Exercises 1. $y = -2x + 5$ **3.** $y = -\frac{5}{12}x - 4$ **5.** $y = 6x + 16$
7. $y = -x - 8$ **9.** $y = -\frac{1}{3}x - 3$ **11.** $y = -2x - 13$ **13.** $y = 4x - 7$
15. $y = -\frac{1}{3}x - 6$ **17.** $y = -\frac{2}{3}x + \frac{7}{3}$ **19.** $y = \frac{1}{2}x + 2$ **21.** $y = x - \frac{2}{5}$ **23.** $y = 2x + 5$
25. $y = 3$ **27.** $y = -x + 2 + b$ **29.** $y = \frac{(b + 5)x - 3b - 5a}{a - 3}$ **Page 332, Checking Your Understanding 1.** $(1, -4)$ **2.** $(3, 4)$ **3.** *A* **4.** *E*
5. $-\frac{6}{5}$, *x*-intercept $-\frac{7}{3}$, *y*-intercept $-\frac{14}{5}$, $y = -\frac{6}{5}x - \frac{14}{5}$
6. Has slope $\frac{2}{3}$ and *y*-intercept $-\frac{5}{3}$. **Page 336, Exercises 1.** $M = 6n$
3. $C = 0.18n$ **5.** 31 **7.** 20 **9.** 27 **11.** 12.8 **13.** 135.4 km **15.** approx. 3
Pages 339, Exercises 1. $l = 0.05s + 180$ **5.** $y = 10x + 2$
7. $l = \frac{1}{4}w + 45$, 59 cm **9.** $C = 0.1k + 0.65$, \$6.65 **Page 343, Exercises**
1. $\{-4, 0, 1, 5\}$ **3.** $(-4, -9)(0, -2)(1, 3)(5, 7)$ **5.** $11, -1, -13$
7. $(1, 9)(2, 18)(3, 27)(4, 36)(5, 45)$ **9.** $(-5, 13)(-4, 11)(-3, 9)(-2, 7)(-1, 5)$
11. $(-2, 6)(-1, 5)(0, 4)(1, 3)(2, 2)$ **13.** $(-1, 8)(-\frac{1}{3}, 6)(0, 5)(\frac{1}{3}, 4)(1, 2)$
15. 81, 25, 9, 49 **17.** 221, 13, −59, −995 **Page 352, Exercises**
1. $(-4, -9)(0, 3)(0, 10)(6, -5)(6, 0)$ **3.** Has ordered pairs like (2, 3)(2, 4)(2, 5).
5. Has ordered pairs like (4, −2)(4, 2)(9, −3)(9, 3). **Page 353, Checking Your Understanding 1.** 20 **2.** 14 **3.** $(0, -2)(2, -1)(4, 0)$

Chapter 10 Systems of Linear Equations

Page 361, Exercises 1. (7, 1) **3.** (−6, 2) **5.** (parallel lines) no solution **7.** (2, 2)
9. (same line) infinitely many solutions **11.** (−2, 3) **13.** (−1, 3)
15. (same line) infinitely many solutions **17.** (−1, −3) **19.** $(-\frac{7}{8}, -4\frac{1}{4})$
21. $(3\frac{2}{3}, 12\frac{1}{2})$ **Page 364, Exercises 1.** (−2, 0) **3.** (3, −1) **5.** (0, 1) **7.** (−1, 1)
9. (−4, −4) **11.** (2, −2) **13.** (−3, −8) **15.** (200,300) **17.** $(-k, \frac{1}{2}k)$
19. $\left(\frac{r + s}{2p}, \frac{r - s}{2q}\right)$ **Page 368, Exercises 1.** (5, 3) **3.** (3, 6) **5.** (3, −2)
7. (same line) infinitely many solutions **9.** (−3, 3) **11.** (same line) infinitely many solutions **13.** (120,480) **15.** $(\frac{1}{3}, \frac{1}{2})$ **17.** $\left(\frac{c}{3a}, \frac{c}{3b}\right)$ **19.** (same line) infinitely many solutions if $kd = ja$, otherwise no solution **Pages 370-371, Exercises 1.** (5, −4)
3. $(\frac{5}{6}, -4)$ **5.** (4, −6) **7.** (3, 4) **9.** (4, 3) **11.** (−1, −3) **13.** (0, 4) **15.** $(\frac{27}{8}, \frac{107}{48})$
17. (same line) infinitely many solutions **Page 374, Checking Your Understanding 1.** (−1, −6) **2.** (parallel lines) no solution **3.** (4, 2) **4.** (−4, 6)
5. (−2, −6) **6.** (−2, −5) **Pages 376-377, Exercises 1.** 14 and 36 **3.** 9 and 25
5. 8 and 12 **7.** 112 cm by 312 cm **9.** orange 13¢, grapefruit 35¢ **11.** 6 and 18
13. 7 and 23 **15.** length 9 m, width 6 m **17.** 3 and 8 **19.** 5 and 8 or $\frac{41}{19}$ and $\frac{188}{19}$
Pages 379-380, Exercises 1. $r_b = 15$ km/h, $r_c = 3$ km/h
3. $r_w = 38$ km/h, $r_p = 152$ km/h **5.** $r_b = 24$ km/h, $r_c = 4$ km/h **7.** 50
9. $r_h = 160$ km/h, $r_w = 26$ km/h **11.** 5 km/h uphill, 10 km/h downhill
Pages 384-385, Exercises 1. 47 **3.** 49 **5.** 12 **7.** 27 **9.** 32 **11.** 57 **13.** 75
15. 86

Chapter 11 Fractions and Fractional Equation

Page 393, Exercises 1. 54 **3.** 2 **5.** $12a$ **7.** 15 **9.** 14 **11.** $(x + 4)(x + 2)$
13. $3b^2 - 4b - 15$ **15.** $\frac{2}{5}$ **17.** $\frac{1}{2}$ **19.** $\frac{b}{c}$ **21.** $\frac{1}{x^2y^2}$ **23.** $\frac{3x^2y^4}{4}$ **25.** $-\frac{1}{r}$ **27.** $\frac{5}{6}$ **29.** $\frac{2}{3}$
31. $x + 1$ **33.** $\frac{x + 1}{2}$ **35.** 4 **37.** $2x$ **39.** $\frac{a - 1}{a + 1}$ **41.** $\frac{2x + 1}{2x - 3}$ **43.** $a + b$
45. Is in lowest terms. **47.** $a + b + x + y$ **Pages 395-396, Exercises 1.** $\frac{ab^7}{4}$
3. $\frac{y^2}{m^3x}$ **5.** $\frac{7}{3n}$ **7.** $\frac{a^4}{b^3c}$ **9.** $\frac{4c^4}{15d^5}$ **11.** $\frac{5a^5}{6c^5}$ **13.** $\frac{5}{4x - 4y}$ **15.** $\frac{2}{3}$ **17.** $\frac{1}{3}$ **19.** $\frac{3x - 3}{4x}$
21. $-\frac{3}{2x - 2b}$ **23.** $\frac{7}{3}$ **25.** $\frac{2}{x - y}$ **27.** $\frac{3}{4}$ **29.** $a - 1$ **31.** $\frac{8m + 64}{m - 7}$ **33.** $\frac{1 + c}{b - bc}$

35. $\frac{4b+12}{3}$ **37.** $\frac{7y}{2}$ **39.** $2x-5$ **41.** $\frac{x-4}{x+5}$ **43.** $\frac{9a^2-33a-12}{2a^3+22a^2+60a}$ **45.** 1 **Page 398, Exercises** **1.** x **3.** $9x-18$ **5.** $\frac{m-1}{4}$ **7.** $\frac{xy}{x-y}$ **9.** $\frac{ab}{a-b}$ **11.** $\frac{3+y}{3}$ **13.** 1 **15.** $\frac{x}{a+x}$ **17.** 1 **19.** $\frac{1}{x}$ **21.** $\frac{4x-8}{x^2-4x}$ **23.** x **25.** -1 **27.** $\frac{c^2}{3-7c+2c^2}$ **29.** $\frac{3(a+2b)^2}{4(a-b)(a-2b)}$ **31.** $2a-c$ **Page 402, Exercises** **1.** $\frac{7}{x}$ **3.** $\frac{11a}{12}$ **5.** $\frac{y}{5}$ **7.** $\frac{5}{y+2}$ **9.** $\frac{1+2a+3a^2}{a^3}$ **11.** $\frac{-c+19}{6}$ **13.** $\frac{-11x+3b}{20}$ **15.** $\frac{a^2-ab}{40}$ **17.** $\frac{b^2-2b+7}{2b-2}$ **19.** $\frac{-x-8}{x^2+x-6}$ **21.** $\frac{-x^2-y^2}{x^2-y^2}$ **23.** $\frac{3a^2-2a}{a^2+a-12}$ **25.** $\frac{4x-2y}{x^2-y^2}$ **27.** $\frac{7a+8}{a^2-4}$ **29.** $\frac{-23}{6a-12}$ **31.** $\frac{3b-3}{2a}$ **33.** $\frac{23a^2-20a-5}{14a^2}$ **35.** $\frac{2a^2-a}{a^2-1}$ **37.** $\frac{2x^2}{(1-x)(1+x)}$ **39.** $\frac{-11m-8}{18m^2-18m}$ **41.** $\frac{6x}{(x+4)(x-4)(x-2)}$ **43.** $\frac{2x-24}{(x+4)(x-4)^2}$ **Page 406, Exercises** **1.** $\frac{-y-3}{y+2}$ **3.** $-\frac{1}{x+1}$ **5.** $\frac{y}{y-5}$ **7.** $\frac{2z}{z-3}$ **9.** $\frac{7}{2x-3}$ **11.** $\frac{-2}{2x-3}$ **13.** $\frac{6x-3y}{4x-2}$ **15.** $y-x$ **17.** -4 **19.** $-a^2-b^2$ **21.** $-\frac{x+3}{12x+1}$ **23.** $\frac{m-n}{m+3n}$ **25.** $\frac{3-x}{3+x}$ **27.** $\frac{-aby}{x+y}$ **Page 409, Exercises** **1.** $\frac{y^2+5}{y}$ **3.** $\frac{a^2+a+2}{a+1}$ **5.** $\frac{7x-5y}{x-y}$ **7.** $\frac{10+3x}{x+2}$ **9.** $\frac{x^2-3}{x+2}$ **11.** $\frac{14x^3+6x^2+8x-1}{2x}$ **13.** $\frac{4}{x}-1$ **15.** $x+1+\frac{1}{x}$ **17.** $b+c+\frac{2}{a}$ **19.** $3x-4+\frac{2}{5x}$ **21.** $2x-1+\frac{4}{3x-2}$ **23.** $y-5-\frac{9}{y-3}$ **25.** $\frac{2x^2+xy}{x+y}$ **27.** $\frac{n^2}{n-2}$ **29.** $\frac{x^2-2x-8}{x-2}$ **31.** $2x-1+\frac{4}{x+2}$ **33.** $4x^2+6x+9$ **35.** $3x-2y+\frac{2}{x+2y}$ **Page 412, Exercises** **1.** $\frac{10}{3}$ **3.** $\frac{a+b}{a-b}$ **5.** $\frac{a^2}{a-1}$ **7.** $\frac{5x^2+5y^2}{3x+3y}$ **9.** $\frac{4}{a^2-b^2}$ **11.** $\frac{2xy+6y^2}{2x-y}$ **13.** x **15.** $\frac{x+3}{3}$ **17.** mn **19.** $\frac{(m+n)^2}{(m-n)^2}$ **21.** $\frac{b-6}{b}$ **23.** $\frac{c-3}{c}$ **25.** $\frac{x+6}{x-1}$ **27.** $\frac{2c}{a+b+c}$ **Page 413, Checking Your Understanding** **1.** $\frac{2y^2}{7x}$ **2.** $\frac{2}{3+b}$ **3.** $\frac{x}{5y+1}$ **4.** -1 **5.** $\frac{x+4}{-4}$ **6.** $\frac{4x-3y}{6a}$ **7.** $\frac{13x}{12}$ **8.** $\frac{4a+10b}{a^2-b^2}$ **9.** $\frac{x^2+xy+2y+3}{x^2-4}$ **10.** $\frac{2a^2}{3}$ **11.** $\frac{1}{2bx-2by}$ **12.** $\frac{9rt^2}{s^3}$ **13.** $\frac{2m-3n}{x-3}$ **14.** $\frac{a}{c-b}$ **15.** x^2-1 **16.** $\frac{4-c}{-d-6}$ or $\frac{-4+c}{d+6}$ **17.** $\frac{x^2+3}{x}$ **18.** $\frac{x^2+x-11}{x+4}$ **19.** $4x+\frac{5}{2x^2}$ **20.** $\frac{y}{x}$ **21.** $\frac{2x+3}{3}$ **22.** $\frac{2a-2}{3}$ **Page 416, Exercises** **1.** 9 **3.** 21 **5.** $\frac{5}{3}$ **7.** $\frac{1}{4}$ **9.** $-\frac{75}{2}$ **11.** $\frac{5}{8}$ **13.** $\frac{5}{6}$ **15.** $\frac{3}{8}$ **17.** no solution **19.** 3 **21.** $-\frac{2}{7}$ **23.** $-\frac{11}{2}$ **25.** $-\frac{20}{9}$ **27.** $-\frac{4}{9}$ **29.** $-\frac{23}{5}$ **31.** $-\frac{9}{2}$ **33.** $-\frac{19}{3}$ **35.** -1 **37.** 6 **Pages 419-420, Exercises** **1.** $\frac{9}{4}$ **3.** 2 **5.** -4 **7.** $6, -5$ **9.** no solution **11.** 2 **13.** -2 **15.** $-\frac{1}{2}, -\frac{4}{3}$ **17.** -1 **19.** $\frac{3}{2}$ **21.** $4, -\frac{10}{9}$ **23.** 14 **25.** $15, -12$ **27.** no solution **29.** $\frac{1}{2}, -22$ **31.** 4, 1 **Page 423, Exercises** **1.** $\frac{e-d}{c}$ **3.** 2 **5.** $\frac{3cd-2c}{d}$ **7.** $\frac{rq}{p}$ **9.** $\frac{p-q}{kt}$ **11.** $a+2$ **13.** 2 **15.** $\frac{ab}{c}$ **17.** $\frac{3V}{\pi r^2}$ **19.** $\frac{1}{T-t}$ **21.** $Mg-Mb$ **23.** $\frac{2cd-2c^2}{2c-5d}$ **25.** $2a$ **27.** $a+b$ **29.** $\frac{2s-an}{n}$ **31.** $a-2b$ **33.** $\frac{yz}{yzw-z-y}$ **Pages 425-426, Exercises** **1.** (4, 5) **3.** (2, 3) **5.** (1, 1) **7.** (2, −2) **9.** no solution **11.** $a=\frac{1}{2}, b=-1$ **13.** (3, 7) **15.** (−2, 5) **17.** (5, −2) **19.** $(b-a, b-a)$ **Page 426, Checking Your Understanding** **1.** $\frac{14}{3}$ **2.** $\frac{1}{2}$ **3.** no solution **4.** $\frac{a}{b-a}$ **5.** $\frac{S-a}{S}$ **6.** (2, −1) **7.** no solution **Pages 429-430, Exercises** **1.** $-\frac{1}{4}$ or 4 **3.** $\frac{12}{9}$ **5.** $\frac{8}{11}$ **7.** 18, 37 **9.** $4\frac{2}{3}$ hours **11.** 24, 30 **13.** $\frac{2}{3}$ **15.** $\frac{3}{4}$ **17.** 8 h, 12 h **19.** going 6 km/h; returning 4 km/h **21.** 12 **Page 434, Exercises** **1.** 6 km/h **3.** 15 km/h **5.** 4.9 km/h, 2.1 km/h **7.** $\frac{1}{2}$ km/h **9.** 540 km/h **11.** 2 km/h **Pages 437-438, Exercises** **1.** 1 **3.** 8 **5.** 55 **7.** 6 **9.** $\frac{1}{6}$ **11.** \$14.25 **13.** approx. 4.27 h **15.** 4 m **17.** 60 km/h, 45 km/h **19.** 25 **21.** 121.875 m

Chapter 12 Radical Expressions

Page 448, Exercises **1.** $81c^2$ **3.** $36h^2$ **5.** $64m^2$ **7.** $\frac{9c^2}{25d^4}$ **9.** $\frac{49h^2}{144k^4}$ **11.** $\frac{16x^2}{81y^4}$ **13.** $49z^6$ **15.** $441x^8$ **17.** $196h^4$ **19.** ± 9 **21.** ± 16 **23.** ± 22 **25.** $x^4y^6z^2$ **27.** $0.01m^6n^4$ **29.** $\frac{49a^{10}b^{12}}{64y^6}$ **31.** $\frac{16m^2n^4}{121s^8t^{10}}$ **33.** x **35.** $-a^2$ **37.** $17m^5n^6$

39. $-1.2a^5b^8$ **41.** $3a + 3b$ **43.** $x + 3$ **45.** $2x + 1$ **47.** $3x + 3$ **49.** $ax + b$
Page 452, Exercises **1.** 0.75 **3.** 0.6875 **5.** $-0.8\overline{3}$ **7.** $0.\overline{3}$ **9.** $0.\overline{72}$ **11.** $0.\overline{54}$
13. $0.1\overline{36}$ **15.** $\frac{19}{20}$ **17.** $\frac{1}{5}$ **19.** $-\frac{45}{8}$ **21.** $\frac{2}{9}$ **23.** $\frac{5}{9}$ **25.** $\frac{51}{11}$ **27.** $-\frac{19}{45}$ **29.** $\frac{7}{18}$ **31.** $\frac{76}{99}$
33. $\frac{1}{3}$, $0.\overline{3}$ **35.** $\frac{1}{15}$, $0.0\overline{6}$ **37.** $\frac{1}{33}$ **39.** $0.\overline{9} \rightarrow \frac{9}{9} = 1$, Explanations will vary.
41. false For example: $1 + \sqrt{2}$ and $1 - \sqrt{2}$, or 0.101100111000... and 0.010011000111... **43.** false For example: $\sqrt{2}$ and $\sqrt{2}$ **Pages 453-455, Exercises** **1.** 1.7 **3.** 9.5 **5.** 6.9 **7.** 10.4 **9.** 3.162 **11.** 4.359 **13.** 4.123
15. 8.775 **17.** 9.434 **19.** 17 **21.** 2.785 **23.** true **25.** false **27.** 16.852
29. 0.806 **Page 455, Checking Your Understanding** **1.** $100x^2$ **2.** 15 **3.** $-7r^3$
4. 3.873 **5.** 5.657 **6.** 25.298 **7.** 0.875 **8.** $0.1\overline{6}$ **9.** $\frac{19}{8}$ **10.** $\frac{4}{11}$ **Page 458, Exercises** **1.** 9 **3.** 8 **5.** $10\sqrt{3}$ **7.** $27\sqrt{5}$ **9.** $5z\sqrt{2z}$ **11.** $4k^2\sqrt{3k}$ **13.** $\frac{6}{7}$
15. $\frac{\sqrt{30}}{6}$ **17.** $\frac{\sqrt{51}}{17}$ **19.** $\frac{3\sqrt{10}}{10}$ **21.** $\frac{4\sqrt{21}}{21}$ **23.** $16\sqrt{10}$ **25.** $75\sqrt{3}$ **27.** $5a^3\sqrt{5a}$
29. $6y^5\sqrt{5y}$ **31.** $\frac{\sqrt{x}}{x^2}$ **33.** $\frac{\sqrt{a}}{a^6}$ **35.** $\frac{\sqrt{m}}{m^5}$ **37.** $2x^3y^2\sqrt{10}$ **39.** $2h^2k^2\sqrt{15h}$
41. $2y^2z^3\sqrt{70y}$ **43.** $10x^3y^4\sqrt{5xy}$ **45.** $\frac{x^2z^2\sqrt{x}}{6y}$ **47.** $\frac{v\sqrt{5}}{2}$ **49.** $0.3x^2y^3$ **51.** $0.02h$
Page 460, Exercises **1.** $11\sqrt{3}$ **3.** $-2\sqrt{6}$ **5.** $2\sqrt{11}$ **7.** $7\sqrt{7} - \sqrt{2}$
9. $-3\sqrt{5} + 4\sqrt{13}$ **11.** $-4\sqrt{6} + 6\sqrt{10}$ **13.** $19\sqrt{3}$ **15.** $24\sqrt{2}$ **17.** $7\sqrt{6}$
19. $2\sqrt{5} - \frac{8}{3}\sqrt{3}$ **21.** $\frac{24}{5}\sqrt{5} - 2\sqrt{2}$ **23.** $3\sqrt{5} - \frac{17}{6}\sqrt{6}$ **25.** $\frac{7}{5}\sqrt{5}$ **27.** $\frac{17}{6}\sqrt{6}$
29. $\frac{7}{3}\sqrt{6}$ **31.** $2\sqrt{5} + \sqrt{10}$ **33.** $11\sqrt{x} - 9\sqrt{y}$ **35.** $12a\sqrt{a} - b$
37. $7\sqrt{3y} - 19\sqrt{3x}$ **39.** $9a\sqrt{3a}$ **41.** $\frac{b}{3}\sqrt{3a}$ **Page 462, Exercises** **1.** $\sqrt{35}$
3. $\sqrt{39}$ **5.** $\sqrt{190}$ **7.** $70\sqrt{3}$ **9.** $48\sqrt{10}$ **11.** $126\sqrt{2}$ **13.** $9\sqrt{5} - 5$ **15.** $3\sqrt{2} + 2$
17. $8\sqrt{14} - 14$ **19.** $3 + \sqrt{3}$ **21.** $52 + 3\sqrt{2}$ **23.** $-59 + 16\sqrt{11}$ **25.** $\frac{\sqrt{30}}{9}$
27. $8\sqrt{15}$ **29.** $\frac{\sqrt{2}}{4}$ **31.** $\sqrt{42} + 6\sqrt{3}$ **33.** $4\sqrt{14} - 14\sqrt{3}$ **35.** $22 - 4\sqrt{10}$
37. $37 + 12\sqrt{7}$ **39.** $4x - 12\sqrt{xy} + 9y$ **41.** $-10y\sqrt{14}$ **43.** $-6a^3b$ **45.** $10m^3n^2$
47. $9a^4b + 6a^2\sqrt{bc} + c$ **49.** $a\sqrt{a} + 3a\sqrt{b} + 3b\sqrt{a} + b\sqrt{b}$
51. $(4x + 1)\sqrt{x + 1} - (4x + 3)\sqrt{x}$ **53.** $160x^2$ **Page 465, Exercises**
1. $\frac{4\sqrt{7}}{7}$ **3.** $\frac{3\sqrt{10}}{10}$ **5.** $\sqrt{14}$/[illegible] **7.** $\sqrt{30}$/[illegible] **9.** $\frac{9\sqrt{2}}{4}$ **11.** $\sqrt{14}$ **13.** $\frac{2y\sqrt{10y}}{5}$ **15.** $z\sqrt{6z}$/[illegible]
17. $k^2\sqrt{2k}$ **19.** $5 - 3\sqrt{3}$ **21.** $-9 - 4\sqrt{5}$ **23.** $\frac{17 - 8\sqrt{2}}{7}$ **25.** $\frac{x\sqrt{y}}{y}$
27. $\sqrt{3}$ **29.** $\frac{\sqrt{3a}}{2b}$ **31.** $\frac{\sqrt{30r}}{2s}$ **33.** $\frac{(x - 4)\sqrt{x} - 2x + 8}{x - 4}$ **35.** $\frac{3x + 1 - 4\sqrt{x}}{x - 1}$ **37.** $\sqrt{3}$
39. $7\sqrt{5}$ **41.** $\frac{42 + 13\sqrt{6}}{25}$ **43.** $\frac{6 + 15\sqrt{3} + 15\sqrt{6} + 3\sqrt{2}}{-73}$ **45.** $\frac{30 + 16\sqrt{14}}{61}$
Pages 467-468, Exercises **1.** 4 **3.** 225 **5.** 576 **7.** 9 **9.** 196 **11.** 248
13. no solution **15.** 144 **17.** 23 **19.** $\frac{7}{9}$ **21.** $\frac{9}{4}$ **23.** $\frac{133}{5}$ **25.** 144 **27.** $\frac{1}{36}$ **29.** $\frac{73}{8}$
31. 2 **33.** -2 **Page 468, Checking Your Understanding** **1.** $2\sqrt{13}$ **2.** $15\sqrt{2}$
3. $10x\sqrt{2x}$ **4.** $\frac{3\sqrt{10a}}{10a^2}$ **5.** $\frac{5\sqrt{3}}{3}$ **6.** $3\sqrt{3}$ **7.** $3 + 7\sqrt{2}$ **8.** $6\sqrt{3} - \frac{15}{2}\sqrt{2}$
9. $6\sqrt{2}$ **10.** $-\sqrt{2}$ **11.** $\frac{3 - \sqrt{3}}{2}$ **12.** 9 **13.** no solution **14.** -8

Chapter 13 Quadratic Equations
Page 474, Exercises **1.** ± 7 **3.** ± 9 **5.** $\pm 4\sqrt{2}$ **7.** $\pm 10\sqrt{5}$ **9.** ± 5 **11.** ± 6
13. $\pm 2\sqrt{3}$ **15.** $\pm \frac{2}{3}$ **17.** $\pm \sqrt{5}$ **19.** $\pm 2\sqrt{3}$ **21.** $\pm 2\sqrt{2}$ **23.** ± 3 **25.** $\pm \sqrt{2}$
27. $\pm \frac{\sqrt{2}}{2}$ **29.** $\pm \sqrt{c}$ **31.** $\pm \sqrt{a + b}$ **Pages 476-477, Exercises** **1.** $x^2 - 16x + 64$
3. $x^2 + 18x + 81$ **5.** $x^2 + \frac{4}{5}x + \frac{4}{25}$ **7.** $x^2 + 2hx + h^2$ **9.** $m - 5$ **11.** $k + 7$
13. $x + \frac{1}{3}$ **15.** 100 **17.** 81 **19.** $\frac{25}{4}$ **21.** $\frac{169}{4}$ **23.** $\frac{1}{36}$ **25.** $\frac{25}{36}$ **27.** n^2 **29.** 4 **31.** $\frac{b^2}{4}$
33. $\frac{1}{9}c^2$ **35.** $(a + b)^2$ **37.** 9 **39.** $(b + c)^4$ **41.** $\frac{3}{64}$ **43.** 1 **Page 481, Exercises**

1. $-5, 1$ **3.** $9, -3$ **5.** $-4, 24$ **7.** $4, 7$ **9.** $8, -5$ **11.** $8, -9$ **13.** $11, 1$ **15.** $-5, -15$ **17.** $8, -7$ **19.** $3 \pm \sqrt{17}$ **21.** $-1 \pm 2\sqrt{2}$ **23.** $-8 \pm 2\sqrt{15}$ **25.** $\frac{1}{2}, 1$ **27.** $\frac{1}{2}, -\frac{8}{3}$ **29.** $\frac{3 \pm \sqrt{2}}{2}$ **31.** $2 \pm \frac{\sqrt{6}}{2}$ **33.** $2, -1$ **35.** $4, -9$ **37.** 3, (2 is not a solution) **39.** $\frac{1 \pm \sqrt{19}}{12}$ **41.** $4 \pm 4\sqrt{3}$ **43.** $\frac{-3 \pm \sqrt{41}}{8}$ **45.** no answer in set of real numbers **47.** $\frac{-b \pm \sqrt{b^2 - 16c}}{8}$ **Pages 484-485, Exercises 1.** $5, -2$ **3.** $-8, 2$ **5.** $1, \frac{1}{6}$ **7.** $-2, \frac{1}{3}$ **9.** $\frac{1}{2}, -4$ **11.** $\frac{3 \pm \sqrt{13}}{2}$ **13.** $\frac{3 \pm \sqrt{29}}{2}$ **15.** $\frac{3 \pm \sqrt{2}}{2}$ **17.** $\frac{-4 \pm \sqrt{22}}{3}$ **19.** $-2, \frac{1}{2}$ **21.** $3, -1$ **23.** $\frac{\pm 2\sqrt{15}}{5}$ **25.** $6, -5$ **27.** $\frac{61 \pm 3\sqrt{641}}{16}$ **29.** no solution in set of real numbers **31.** $r \pm \sqrt{r^2 + s}$ **Page 485, Checking Your Understanding 1.** 9 **2.** 25 **3.** $\frac{1}{64}$ **4.** ± 5 **5.** $\pm\sqrt{7}$ **6.** $5, -3$ **7.** $1 \pm \sqrt{3}$ **8.** $2 \pm \frac{1}{2}\sqrt{46}$ **9.** $-\frac{1}{2} \pm \frac{1}{2}\sqrt{11}$ **Pages 487-488, Exercises 1.** 6 or -5 **3.** 5 or -4 **5.** 6, 4 **7.** 7, 3 **9.** $l = 60$ m, $w = 38$ m **11.** 7 m, 3.5 m **13.** 15 m, 13 m **15.** 8 km/h **17.** 2 m **19.** Mr. Lucas 8 days, son 10 days **21.** 52 km/h **Page 492, Exercises 1.** 25 **3.** $3\sqrt{13}$ **5.** 25 **7.** $4\sqrt{10}$ **9.** 20 **11.** $\sqrt{5}$ m, approx. 2.24 m **13.** 26 cm **15.** $4\sqrt{13}$ or $4\sqrt{5}$ **17.** $2\sqrt{58}$ or $4\sqrt{10}$ **19.** 34 m **21.** $4\sqrt{3}$ cm, approx. 6.93 cm **23.** 7.5 cm **25.** $64\sqrt{3}$ m², approx. 110.85 m² **27.** $a^2 = s^2 - \left(\frac{1}{2}s\right)^2 \rightarrow s^2 - \frac{1}{4}s^2 \rightarrow \frac{3}{4}s^2,\ a = \frac{\sqrt{3}}{2}s$

Chapter 14 Trigonometric Ratios

Page 500, Exercises 1. 45° **3.** 30° **5.** 15°, 105° **7.** 5°, 95° **9.** 74°, 164° **11.** $m\angle E = 60$ **13.** 110, 70 **15.** 30°, 60°, 90° **Pages 503-504, Exercises 1.** 38, 74, 68 **3.** $2\frac{1}{3}, 8\frac{1}{3}$ **5.** $35, 10\sqrt{10}, 6\sqrt{10}$ **7.** Corresponding angles of the first triangle can be proven congruent to the corresponding angles of the second triangle. **9.** 5.5 m **Pages 507-508, Exercises 1.** $\frac{r}{s}$ **3.** $\frac{r}{t}$ **5.** $\frac{t}{s}$ **7.** $\frac{3}{5}$ **9.** $\frac{3}{4}$ **11.** $\frac{3}{5}$ **13.** $\frac{\sqrt{2}}{2}$ **15.** 1 **17.** $\frac{\sqrt{2}}{2}$ **19.** $\frac{1}{2}$ **21.** $\frac{\sqrt{3}}{2}$ **23.** $\frac{3}{2}$ **25.** $\frac{\sqrt{5}}{10}$ **27.** 2 **29.** substitute $\frac{a^2}{c^2}$ for $\sin^2 A$ and $\frac{b^2}{c^2}$ for $\text{Cos}^2 A$, then multiply both sides by c^2. This gives $a^2 + b^2 = c^2$ **31.** decreases from 1 to 0 **Pages 511-512, Exercises 1.** 1.7321 **3.** 57.2900 **5.** 0.4067 **7.** 0.8660 **9.** 0.5000 **11.** 0.0872 **13.** 53° **15.** 78° **17.** 68° **19.** 43° **21.** 57° **23.** 88° **25.** 1.5112 **27.** 0.6494 **29.** 0.9681 **31.** 19°40′ **33.** 16°10′ **35.** 75°30′ **37.** 129.3 m, not 128.1 m **39.** approx. 271 cm² **Page 512, Checking Your Understanding**
1. $\sin A = 0.6000$, $\cos A = 0.8000$, $\tan A = 0.7500$
2. $\sin P = 0.7070$, $\cos P = 0.7070$, $\tan P = 1.000$
3. $\sin T = 0.6000$, $\cos T = 0.8000$, $\tan T = 0.7500$ **4.** 0.4245 **5.** 0.5592 **6.** 42° **Pages 515-517, Exercises 1.** approx. 64.8 m **3.** approx. 405.2 m **5.** approx. 182.1 m **7.** approx. 50° **9.** approx. 118 m **11.** approx. 2.7 m **13.** approx. 46.7 m **15.** approx. 13 m **17.** approx. 970 cm² **19.** approx. 8.66 **21.** approx. 15.7 **23.** approx. 9.4 cm **25.** Use $\cos B = \frac{DB}{BC}$, then multiply both sides by BC. **27.** approx. 0.0023 cm **29.** approx. 224.1 m

Index

Index

Index

BCDEFGH 0876543
Printed in the United States of America

Index